COMPARATIVE PSYCHOLOGY
Research in Animal Behavior

COMPARATIVE PSYCHOLOGY

Research in Animal Behavior

BY

STANLEY C. RATNER, Ph.D.
Professor of Psychology

and

M. RAY DENNY, Ph.D.
Professor of Psychology

Both of Michigan State University

1964 • THE DORSEY PRESS

HOMEWOOD, ILLINOIS

First Printing, August, 1964

Library of Congress Catalog Card No. 64–22112

To Our Wives

PREFACE

This book is addressed to both psychologists and zoologists. It was prepared mainly for students of comparative psychology and animal behavior and for research workers in these areas. An effort was made to achieve the following goals: (1) to present a detailed and unified account of animal behavior; (2) to illustrate research methods for a variety of animal forms and a variety of behavior processes; (3) to select reports from a wide variety of journals; and (4) to provide abundant bibliographic material for each topic covered.

Each goal was before us as we worked. Topics and chapters were included only if they bore directly on the theme of the behavior of organisms. For example, the analysis of sensory processes was made in terms of the behavioral consequences of inheriting special sensory structures. Theoretical themes were de-emphasized, but a general stimulus-response orientation was maintained. This orientation was blended with the ethological approach whenever appropriate.

Each selected research report was chosen to illustrate a research method and a behavior process and to cover many species and many problems of behavioral analysis. Considerable attention was given the behavior of invertebrates and nonlaboratory species.

The bibliographic material has been presented in four main ways: (1) the references within the text which cite documentation or suggest sources for further study; (2) the references within the text that are marked by a single asterisk (*) and refer to studies that are summarized within the text; (3) the references that are marked by double asterisks (**) and refer to the complete experimental reports (selected studies) that come at the end of each chapter; and (4) the references at the end of each selected study which supplement the other material.

We are pleased to have had the opportunity to present in Chapter 12 certain fragments of the experimental work of John F. Shepard, professor emeritus of the University of Michigan. This work is largely unpublished; the present account is mainly based on MRD's lecture notes of 1942–43 while a student of Shepard.

In nearly every way the work on the book was equally divided between the two authors. Ratner had the primary responsibility for chapters 2, 4, 5, 6, 7, and 8. Denny had the primary responsibility for chapters 3, 9, 10, 11, 12, and 13.

Quite frankly, the project on which we embarked was a difficult one. We were assisted and encouraged by colleagues and students with whom many of our ideas were first revealed and reviewed. However, errors, insofar as they exist, are ours, not theirs. Particular thanks are due Eugene Eisman, Ronald Weisman and Howard Farris for a critical reading of certain chapters.

The authors gratefully acknowledge permission to quote and use materials from the following sources:

American Association for the Advancement of Science (*Science*); American Ornithologists Union (*Auk*); American Philosophical Society (*Proceedings of the American Philosophical Society*); American Physiological Society (*Journal of Neurophysiology*); American Psychological Association (*Journal of Comparative and Physiological Psychology, Journal of Experimental Psychology*); Appleton-Century Co. (*Behavior of Organisms,* Skinner); Bailliere, Tindall, and Cox (*Animal Behaviour*); Cambridge University Press (*Current Problems in Animal Behaviour,* Thorpe and Zangwill); Duke University (*Ecology*); E. J. Brill, Ltd. (*Behaviour*); Journal Press (*Journal of Genetic Psychology*); Macmillan Co., (*Nature*); McGraw-Hill Co. (*Physiological Psychology,* 2d ed., Morgan and Stellar; *Principles of Animal Psychology,* Maier and Schnierla; *Principles of Zoology,* Storer); Principia Press (*Psychological Record*); Society for the Experimental Analysis of Behavior (*Journal of Experimental Analysis of Behavior*); University of Chicago Press (*Physiological Zoology*); University of Kansas (*Evolution*); University of Toronto Press (*Canadian Journal of Psychology*); Wilson Ornithological Society (*Wilson Bulletin*).

July 8, 1964

S.C.R.

M.R.D.

TABLE OF CONTENTS

CHAPTER

PAGE

1. INTRODUCTION TO COMPARATIVE PSYCHOLOGY.............. 1

2. GENETICS, EVOLUTION, AND BEHAVIOR..................... 17
   Genetics of Hoarding: II. Hoarding Behavior of Hybrid and Backcrossed
   Strains of Rats—JOHN S. STAMM................................ 37
   Studies in Experimental Behavior Genetics: I. The Heritability of Photo-
   taxis in a Population of *Drosophila Melanogaster*—JERRY HIRSCH and
   JAMES C. BOUDREAU.. 44
   On Locomotory Movements in Birds and the Intention Movements De-
   rived from Them—A. DAANJE................................. 52
   Morphological and Ethological Notes on a Hybrid between a Domestic
   Duck and a Domestic Goose—HOLGER POULSEN..................... 75
   The Evolution of Nest-Building Behavior in *Apicotermes* (Isoptera)—
   ROBERT S. SCHMIDT... 81

3. THE BEHAVIORAL CONSEQUENCES OF INHERITING SPECIAL SENSORY
   STRUCTURES 98

   Auditory Scanning in the Dolphin—W. N. KELLOGG.................... 108
   Color Vision in the Marmoset—RAYMOND C. MILES.................... 112
   The Discrimination by the Nose of the Dog of Individual Human Odours
   and in Particular of the Odours of Twins—H. KALMUS................. 116
   The "Language" and Orientation of the Bees—KARL VON FRISCH........ 129
   The Echolocation of Flying Insects by Bats—DONALD R. GRIFFIN, FREDERIC
   A. WEBSTER and CHARLES R. MICHAEL............................ 138

4. THE INNATE BEHAVIOR OF INVERTEBRATES................... 163

   Effect of Pressure on the Behavior of Decapod Larvae (Crustacea)—A. C.
   HARDY and R. BAINBRIDGE.................................... 177
   Experimental Studies on the Mating Reaction of Male *Habrobracon*—
   DANIEL S. GROSCH.. 180
   The Stimuli Releasing the Stinging Response of Honeybees—J. B. FREE.. 190
   Analyses of the Behaviour of Commensals in Host-Factor. 1. A Hesioned
   Polychaete and a Pinnotherid Crab—DEMOREST DAVENPORT, GEORGE
   CAMOUGIS and JOHN F. HICKOK.. 198

ix

5. THE INNATE BEHAVIOR OF VERTEBRATES.................... 216

    Pecking of Laughing Gull Chicks at Models of the Parental Head—JACK
    P. HAILMAN 233
    An Ethological Analysis of the Reproductive Behavior of the Bitterling
    (*Rhodeus Amarus* Bloch)—P. R. WIEPKEMA........................... 243
    A Study of the Behaviour of the Chacma Baboon, Papio Ursinus—NIELS
    BOLWIG 261

6. INTERNAL FACTORS AND INNATE BEHAVIOR.................. 277

    Stridulation and Associated Behaviour in Certain Orthoptera. 3. The Influ-
    ence of the Gonads—P. T. HASKELL................................ 299
    Effects of Gonadectomy and Hypophysectomy on Prespawning Behavior
    in Males of the Gobiid Fish, *Bathygobius Soporator*—WILLIAM N.
    TAVOLGA 309
    The Effect of Oestrogen and Progesterone on the Nest-Building of Domes-
    ticated Canaries—ROSLYN P. WARREN and R. A. HINDE................ 330
    Hormonal Regulation of the Micturition Behavior of the Dog—THALES
    MARTINS and J. R. VALLE.. 339

7. BEHAVIORAL CONSEQUENCES OF EARLY BEHAVIOR: EARLY EX-
    PERIENCE 351

    The Effects of Restricting Early Experience on the Problem-Solving Ca-
    pacity of Dogs—WILLIAM R. THOMPSON and WOODBURN HERON......... 369
    The Effect of Prolonged Exposure to Visually Presented Patterns on Learn-
    ing to Discriminate Them—ELEANOR J. GIBSON and RICHARD D. WALK.. 385
    A Laboratory Approach to the Study of Imprinting—A. OGDEN RAMSAY and
    ECKHARD H. HESS... 392
    Escape and Avoidance Learning as a Function of Emotionality Level in
    the Wyoming Ground Squirrel—ROLLIN H. DENNISTON, II............ 404
    Effects of Early Handling upon Adult Behavior in Two Subspecies of
    Deermice, *Peromyscus Maniculatus*—JOHN A. KING and BASIL E. ELEF-
    THERIOU 410

8. BEHAVIOR OF ANIMALS IN GROUPS........................ 422

    Effect of Learning to Be Submissive on Status in the Peck Order of Domes-
    tic Fowl—STANLEY C. RATNER...................................... 438
    Territorial Rank in Starlings—DAVID E. DAVIS..................... 445
    The Development of Schooling Behavior in Fishes—EVELYN SHAW....... 458
    The Occurrence of Fighting Behavior in the Grain Beetle *Tenebrio Moli-
    tor* with the Possible Formation of a Dominance Hierarchy—ROBERT
    STEARNS HOWARD 470

9. CONSUMMATORY ACTIVITY: MOTIVATION VIEWED AS BEHAVIOR.. 479

    The Effect of Restraint upon Copulatory Behavior in the Rat—KNUT
    LARSSON 490
    The Development of Social Facilitation of Eating in Puppies—W. T.
    JAMES 494
    The Effect of Frustration on the Nonnutritive Sucking of the Infant Rhesus
    Monkey—LORNA SMITH BENJAMIN 499
    Effects of Hunger and Male Sex Hormone on Self-Stimulation of the Brain
    —JAMES OLDS.. 506
    Competition between Feeding and Investigation in the Rat—M. R. A.
    CHANCE and A. P. MEAD.. 511
    Effect of Post Partum Separation of Mother and Kid on Maternal Care

in the Domestic Goat—LEONARD HERSER, A. ULRIC MOORE, and JULIUS B. RICHMOND 519

10. GENERALITY OF CONDITIONING............................ 523

Forward Conditioning, Backward Conditioning, and Pseudo-Conditioning in the Goldfish—H. F. HARLOW...................................... 534
Classical Conditioning in Earthworms, *Lumbricus Terrestris*—STANLEY C. RATNER and KLIEM R. MILLER...................................... 544
Nictitating Membrane: Classical Conditioning and Extinction in the Albino Rabbit—I. GORMEZANO, NEIL SCHNEIDERMAN, EDWARD DEUX, and ISRAEL FUENTES 551
Formaton of Conditioned Responses in Infant Monkeys—W. A. MASON and H. F. HARLOW.. 555
Intrasubject Conditioning as a Function of the Intensity of the Unconditioned Stimulus—K. W. SPENCE, D. F. HAGGARD, and L. E. ROSS......... 561

11. GENERALITY OF INSTRUMENTAL LEARNING.................. 566

Effect of Magnitude of Reinforcement on Acquisition and Extinction of a Running Response—HARVARD L. ARMUS........................... 583
One Bar-Press per Day: Acquisition and Extinction—M. RAY DENNY...... 587
Some Observations on an Operant in the Octopus—P. B. DEWS............ 594
The Learning Curve of a Land Snail—THOMAS R. GARTH and MARY PICKNEY MITCHELL 602
Apparent Learning of the Paramecium—MILTON S. KATZ and WILLIAM A. DETERLINE 611

12. LEARNING WITH COMPLEX CUES........................... 619

Maze Learning of a Turtle—O. L. TINKLEPAUGH...................... 640
Double Alternation by Racoons—JOHN I. JOHNSON, JR................... 645
The Question of Insight and Delayed Reaction in Fish—NORMAN L. MUNN 651
Learning Sets in Marmosets—RAYMOND C. MILES and DONALD R. MEYER.. 661
Concept Formation in Chimpanzees—ROGER T. KELLEHER.............. 667
Raphael's "Idealess" Behavior—GREGORY RAZRAN...................... 671

13. NEURAL TISSUE IN RELATION TO COMPLEXITY OF LEARNED BEHAVIOR 674

Multiple Discrimination and Patterned String Performance of Normal and Temporal-Lobectomized Monkeys—A. J. RIOPELLE, R. A. ALPER, P. N. STRONG, and H. W. ADES... 686
Conditioned Reflexes and Leão's Spreading Cortical Depression—J. BUREŠ, O. BUREŠOVÁ, and A. ZÁHOROVÁ...................................... 694
Corpus Callosum and the Interhemispheric Transmission of Tactual Learning—FORD F. EBNER and RONALD E. MYERS..................... 705
Successive and Maintained Conditioning in Spinal Carnivores—ROSCOE A. DYKMAN and PHIL S. SHURRAGER.................................. 719
Analysis of the Effects of Frontal Lesions in Monkey:
II. Variations of Delayel Response—MORTIMER MISHKIN and KARL H. PRIBAM 732
REFERENCES 741
INDEX 765

CHAPTER 1

INTRODUCTION TO COMPARATIVE PSYCHOLOGY

The field of comparative psychology includes a wide array of facts, theories, and methods that are oriented around the general topic of the behavior of organisms (general psychology) and the specific topic of comparative analysis. Briefly stated, comparative psychology involves comparing the behaviors of different species of animals. One of the most conspicuous aspects of comparative psychology is that animals other than humans are the objects of study. This is so apparent that comparative psychology is sometimes considered to involve the exclusive study of infrahuman species. However, man is not excluded in principle from comparative psychology; rather, he is considered as one of a number of species whose behaviors are of interest. Thus, research and theory regarding man have a place in this book, but his behavior is de-emphasized for several reasons. One reason is that the behavior of human organisms is considered in detail in other places; another is that the number and kinds of infrahuman behaviors are so extensive that they occupy most of our attention.

Reasons for the Study of Animal Behavior

A perennial question that is asked of psychologists, particularly comparative psychologists, is why study the behavior of animals. The answer to this question is somewhat complex because it involves a number of different ideas and assumptions. However, an answer is necessary in order to give some perspective to the diversity of data, and to the methods and theories that are included in the present text. Four general reasons for the study of animal behavior will be discussed. They are: (1) for information about *the animal itself;* (2) for information about this animal form as an important *economical element;* (3) to use one animal form *as a model* for understanding other animal forms; and (4) for purposes of *comparative analysis.*

The Animal Itself. This orientation to the study of animal behavior is rather unfamiliar to the student of psychology but is well

1

known to the student of zoology. Zoology has a long tradition of investigations by and contributions from naturalists, both amateur and professional. These contributions are ordinarily oriented around a general interest in animals and their behavior. An outstanding example of this orientation is seen in the work of E. A. Armstrong, an English Vicar, who has studied the behavior of birds for many years and has published a number of highly regarded works summarizing his observations and analyses (Armstrong, 1942 and 1955). Some of this work was conducted in the garden of the vicarage. Informal interest in behavior of animals is characteristic of many people as judged from the widespread acceptance of zoos and the widespread use of stories and pictures of animals such as are featured in newspapers and magazines.

Animal behavior is of interest for its own sake. In this case, the animal itself is of interest to the scientist. The data so obtained can make many concrete contributions to the general understanding of animal behavior and comparative psychology.

The Animal as an Economic Element.   While it is self-evident that many animal forms are important economic elements, the relevance of behavior study may not be immediately apparent. One economically important group of animals are those raised for commercial purposes, primarily the domestic animals including horses, cattle, sheep, dogs, cats, and poultry. A number of these animals such as horses, dogs, and cats are assiduously maintained because of their behaviors—their working behavior and/or their affectional behavior. Thus, information and theory regarding the behavior of horses, dogs, and cats have direct relevance to their value (Hafez, 1962).

The relationship between the behavior study of other domesticated animals and their economical value is less direct but no less relevant. Specifically, such behaviors as reproduction, care of the young, and eating, that are of concern to the student of behavior, are also of concern to people who deal with these animals commercially. For example, a number of complex behavioral problems are involved in the artificial breeding of such animals as cattle and swine.

On the other hand, a number of species are important because they are *not desirable.* Once again, it is typically the behavior of the species or a by-product of the behavior that is important. The most conspicuous examples involve insects that spread disease or consume things that are meant for other purposes. Furthermore, the control of some insects has been achieved by the control of their behavior. A simple example is the use of a yellow light rather than a white light for outdoor illumination. A more complex example is seen in the control and prediction of the behavior of locusts in the Near East, as a result of years of research by locust research centers which are jointly supported by a number of European and African countries.

Breland and Breland (1961) have called attention to another economic value of animals that arises from their behavior. This is the trained animal that is used in advertising, as the hero in movies, and as the performer in fairs and circuses. These last examples represent high points for the application of principles of learning and comparative psychology.

The Animal as a Model. Much of the research dealing with the behavior of animals is conceived around the general idea that the behavior of the species that is studied is a model of the behavior of other, usually higher, species. While this point is not often acknowledged explicitly, it seems to provide the rationale for much of the animal research that psychologists do. The animal that is the most common model is the laboratory rat. Surveys indicate that as much as 60 percent of the research on infrahumans is done with varieties of the rat (Beech, 1950; Bitterman, 1960). Other species used in a similar way are the dog, cat, and monkey.

Models are used in a number of places in scientific work. For example, in some instances the model is a model of the process or event being studied (the rat as a mammal); model of the relationship between samples of events and population of these events (statistical models); models of the theoretical characteristics of the events being studied (mathematical probability systems as a model for a process). As indicated, one animal form is often studied as a model of a process that is assumed to appear in other forms. Thus, the conclusions from research with one species are used for application to other species. Obviously, verification of the validity of the model is required. A well-known example occurs in pharmacological research where progressively higher species are used in the development of products that are ultimately useful with humans.

Comparative Study with Animals

The study of animal behavior through comparative analysis is the most complex of the various approaches to the topic of animal behavior. Its complexity comes from the breadth of the subject matter and the diverse objectives of comparative analysis. Comparative psychology includes the majority of behaviors of concern to the general psychologist with particular emphasis on the many species that may exhibit these behaviors. A brief statement of the objectives of comparative analysis as applied to psychology is necessary in order to appreciate the approach.

Five related objectives of comparative analysis can be identified: (1) to identify, characterize, and classify behavior processes of animals; (2) to understand the characteristics of behaviors sufficiently well to identify the animal form that shows the behavior most clearly or to its best advantage; (3) to establish and conceptualize relations between behaviors of similar species and different species; (4) to identify the origins of behavior processes and trace their development both within and between species; and (5) to develop general theories that summarize, relate and predict specific facts and relationships.

These objectives provide the "big picture" of the study of behavior. As applied within this text they include consideration of physiological, genetic, and evolutionary variables in addition to the typical psychological variables. The objectives are presented above in an ordered list so as to suggest the levels or the sequence of steps which are involved in the comparative analysis of behavior. The rationale for the levels might be put simply as follows: Scientific activity involves a sequence of activities that lead to general theory. Although each level is based on prior levels, refining the prior levels by retracing them is necessary.

The Objectives of Comparative Psychology and Some Criticism of It

The progress of comparative psychologists toward each of the objectives of the field will be suggested and some critical comments regarding research and theory relevant to each objective will be mentioned. The critical comments are introduced as precautions to the student who is entering the field.

Identification and characterization of behavior classes of different species is the first level of comparative research. Research oriented around this objective requires that the experimenter be well informed about the behavior and biological characteristics of the species he has chosen to study. The typical error is to treat all species as if they were higher vertebrates and then to design experiments and draw conclusions as if this were true. For example, some early studies of behavior of invertebrates that were interpreted in terms of learning have been shown to be in error (Dethier and Stellar, 1961). In one case several arms of a starfish were restrained by pegs and the animal worked its way free with its unrestrained arms. On test trials without pegs the animal did not move the arms that had previously been restrained. This was interpreted as learning but later research indicated that the restrained arms had become fatigued or habituated and were not used for that reason. Breland and Breland (1961) point out their surprise at discovering that learning is sharply limited for a number of vertebrate species that have strong innate tendencies that compete with the learned ones. For example, raccoons persisted in holding and rubbing together discs (token rewards) that they had previously learned to put in a slot to get food. These innate responses persisted even though they interfered with obtaining reward. The tendency for innate responses to appear in the course of learning and to interfere with the learned response is called "instinctive drift" (Breland and Breland, 1961). Another example of the error of viewing all animals as higher vertebrates is seen in a study of worms. A recent study of cerebral dominance in the behavior of worms overlooked the fact that the neural tissue in these species regenerates. This means that tests for effects of removed tissue must be conducted very soon after the tissue is removed.

The second level and objective of comparative psychology deals with specifying animals (species) whose behavior has the properties that are relevant for a particular study. This objective is also noted by Rogers (1938, p. 5) and Prosser (1959) as it relates to comparative physiology. Prosser states: "The comparative approach seeks to provide unique, possibly simple, but specialized preparations for the study of specific functions which may be difficult to study in most species." (1959, p. 31). Problems regarding research arising from this objective come primarily from the overenthusiastic use of a single species for the analysis of all behavioral processes. As Bitterman (1960) and Beach (1950) have noted, more than half of the animal research done in psychology has been done with the rat, and the laboratory rat at that. While the animal is obviously useful, its limitations are particularly apparent if behaviors are to be studied that involve acute vision, rich innate behavior patterns, or a highly differentiated brain.

The third level and objective of comparative analysis emphasizes establishing relationships between behavior classes and between species. This level specifically implies comparison. One approach to this objective is to investigate similar behaviors in similar species and in different species; the other is to investigate different behaviors in the same species. One problem associated with this research is that the comparisons that are made are often *capricious comparisons*. Such comparison leads to conceptualizing relationships between species or behavior processes that have little meaning. In other words, the danger is that the comparisons involve comparisons of only formal properties of the species or behaviors. The results of these formal comparisons often leave the experimenter with very little to say after his data are collected. For example, vast numbers of species of vertebrates and invertebrates have been tested in mazes. Relationships between intelligence of some of these species has presumably been established in this way (Fink, 1954), but the problems of comparing a turtle, a bird, and a rat in a maze and drawing conclusions about the intelligent behavior of these animals are enormous. Such research often has the characteristic of "I wonder what will happen research." While such research may have its place in the early development of a field of study, it does not provide a solid basis for establishing relationships between behavior processes. In other words, a lot of research that passes as theoretically based comparison is actually capricious comparison.

Progress is still relatively slow with respect to the two objectives of establishing origins of behavior and establishing a general theory with which to relate the data and concepts of comparative psychology. An analysis of the work at these levels is particularly difficult without the reader having an acquaintance with the general body of information of comparative psychology. However, one comment about the fifth objective, that of establishing a general theory of comparative behavior, seems appropriate: This theory need not be the theory of evolution. Obviously, evolution must be considered since species constitute an important variable for comparative psychology but the theory of evolution need not constitute the general theory of psychology. This view contrasts with the view of Konrad Lorenz, a distinguished zoologist. He has said that "An American journal masquerades under the title of 'Comparative Psychology' although . . . no really comparative paper has ever really been published in it." (Lorenz, 1950, p. 240). Lorenz seems to mean that no research has ever been published that flows directly from the evolutionary model of comparative biology. We are suggesting that while the zoologist's commitment in comparative analysis is necessary to evolutionary theory, comparative psychology has a number of unfulfilled objectives, and the final one is constructing and testing a general theory.

Methods for Comparative Research

Two general methods for collection of data are commonly used in comparative psychology. These are the *field method* (sometimes called the naturalistic method) and the *laboratory method* (sometimes called the experimental method). The field method, more common in zoology than in psychology, involves studying the behavior of organisms in their natural surroundings. The laboratory method involves studying the behavior of organisms in the controlled laboratory situation.

Each of these methods has particular advantages and limitations. The field method allows description of the behavioral repertoire of an animal and identification of the kinds of stimuli to which the animal ordinarily responds. Field studies also suggest what behaviors and which of their parameters might be most profitably studied in the lab. The principal limitation of the field method arises from the difficulty in controlling or specifying what things are happening or have happened to the animal under study. Long-term observation of the same species in the same place circumvents this limitation to some extent, but opportunity for changing or controlling the environment or specific stimulus conditions are still limited. Tinbergen presents a detailed and highly readable account of the field method in his book *The Curious Naturalist* (1958), and examples of field research are presented in Chapter 8 which deals with social behavior of animals.

The laboratory method provides an excellent complement to the field method. The lack of control associated with the field method is overcome in the laboratory where control is the principal characteristic. On the other hand, opportunities to understand and identify the behavioral repertoire of an animal are seriously limited in the laboratory. The artificial and less-than-optimal conditions under which the animals frequently live and are studied limits the range or forms of behaviors that can be observed. For example, laboratory conditions rarely allow study of the full range of behaviors associated with such processes as reproduction and reactions to predators. After extensive field work, these behaviors may be more rigorously studied in the laboratory. The majority of the studies reported in remaining chapters of the book illustrate the laboratory method as applied in comparative research.

The S–R Approach to Behavior Analysis

A definite attempt is made in this book to present material in a unified fashion. No special theory has been stringently followed, although several portions of the book represent an elaboration of a theoretical framework with which the second author is mainly identified (Denny and Adelman, 1955). In general, however, we can say that the book is organized around a stimulus-response (S–R) approach, which can be briefly characterized as systematic, objective common sense. This approach, together with certain broad comparative principles, provides the thread that ties the topics and chapters together. By a stimulus-response approach we mean not only traditional American psychology, but a bit more. We mean rejecting elaborate theoretical concepts which are often called intervening variables or hypothetical constructs. Instead, we emphasize that detailed specification and analysis of the stimulus and response variables provide the main clues to understanding behavior. The more you know about stimulus and response the more you can understand and control behavior.

We define stimulus in the way in which it is *actually* used in practice, both in theory and in setting up an experiment. When this is done, stimulus becomes quite abstract or complicated. Stimulus is not just an object or a form of physical energy. There are at least three other defining characteristics: (1) It is potentially capable of eliciting a response. Specifically, this means that we have clear information that it has *previously* elicited a response. (2) It is relative to a particular class of organisms. For example, a tone of 50,000 cycles elicits a response in a bat but not in most other organisms. (3) The stimulus involves a particular set of receptor organs or at least the afferent nervous system for organisms for which this applies. For lower undifferentiated species, this last distinction is not appropriate, for in this instance the entire organism is involved. Because of this third qualification direct activation of a muscle or motor-neuron is called innervation, most often electrical innervation, and is not considered a stimulus. In other words, sound waves are not a stimulus when an organism's auditory mechanism is eliminated; and a wall, for a totally blind but otherwise intact individual, is not a stimulus unless the wall is capable of being touched or until sound waves are bounced from it.

The concept of stimulus is used in two ways: In the theoretical way just described where it enters into lawful statements with the concept of response and, secondly, in the description of ongoing behavior where a specific response is said to be elicited in a particular organism by a particular stimulus. Much of comparative psychology is concerned with using the stimulus in its second sense—namely, for describing ongoing behavior in terms of the stimuli that elicit the responses for different species of animals. Such description is *then* used for the construction of lawful statements about behavior. Another way of stating this is to say that the functions of the stimuli are then established. A familiar example of study of stimulus functions is seen in the work of B. F. Skinner who analyzed stimulus-response relationships in the lever-pressing situation. He postulated a number of different functions for stimuli including discriminative, secondary rewarding, and primary rewarding. For instance, the sound of the feeding mechanism in the lever-pressing apparatus (Skinner box) has both discriminative and secondary reward functions. Stimulus functions for innate responses have been intensively studied by investigators of animal behavior. Tinbergen (1951, p. 15) labels the study of stimulus functions as the study of "casual factors" in behavior and suggests: "First we want to know what stimuli the sense organs of a given animal can receive. Second, the actual effective stimuli, those responsible for the release of each reaction, have to be determined."

As indicated above, the concept of response is also used in different ways. At one level the concept refers to the actual movements or actions of an organism. This usage is particularly common in descriptions or analyses of innate behaviors in which one task for the experimenter involves the precise specification of the movements or actions of the organism. The second usage is more abstract. In this case the concept refers to an entire class of movements which are coordinated with some object or event (stimulus), all of which have the same function with regard to this stimulus. Bar-pressing in the Skinner box is an example of such a functional group. In this instance many of a large number of different movements, any of which leads to a depressed bar, are defined as an instance of a bar-press. When response is used in this second sense, the response class is inferred in part from the stimulus situation in which the specific response occurs. For instance, if a rat is running *toward a place* where it has previously found food, then the response is classified as approach. If the same sort of running behavior is observed when the rat is running *from a place* where there is an electrified shock grid, then running is classified as escape response. Examples of response used in the second, functional sense include approaching, avoiding, eating, mating, brooding, aggression, bar-pressing, head-scratching, and so forth. Note that these response classes vary with respect to how well they can be quantified or identified.

When a response class is sufficiently abstract, though readily identifiable as illustrated by rate of bar-pressing, it is usually highly predictable. Whereas, with the exception of some innate behavior, prediction of response is extremely difficult if it involves predicting the specific movements of a particular organism at a particular moment in time. On the other hand, if the classification of responses is too broad or abstract too many aspects of behavior may be left unspecified and prediction becomes trivial. For example, a response class, called movement, that includes all small and large actions of an organism would be too broad to be useful for prediction.

The fact that response classes are defined in terms of the stimulus with which they are coordinated does not mean that the definitions of stimulus and response need to be circular. Statements of lawful relations between stimulus and response involve a stimulus concept whose definition does not depend on the response in question. Similarly, the definition of the response class is not inferred from the stimulus in question. When rate of conditioning of the eyelid reflex is related to the intensity of the unconditioned stimulus (the intensity of the air puff), the conditioning rate (response class) is not dependent at all for its measurement or identification on the unconditioned stimulus.

The approach that we will be following in the comparative analysis of behavior is that the stimulus is always an independent variable, "cause," and must be fully considered in any analysis of behavior. The dependent variable, "effect," is always a response; but response, since it leads to stimulus changes (response-produced stimuli), can be either an independent or dependent variable. In this context, all behavior can be objectively viewed and lawfully described, without special regard for a particular theoretical position.

The Ethological Approach to Behavior Analysis

The word *ethology* means the study of habits or behavior. The name seems to be as appropriate for the subject matter of psychology as for any particular approach to psychology, but in practice the word ethology refers to a particular approach to the study and analysis of animal behavior. Ethology has been developed mainly by zoologists and is strongly influenced by the theories and methods of zoology as they apply to behavior. Specifically, the ethologists are concerned with taxonomy or classification of behavior, evolutionary theory, and the study of the animal in its natural surrounds (the field method). Ethologists pay close attention to what the animal is doing and try to state why it is doing it. The emphasis on evolutionary theory has meant that ethology is a comparative discipline, much like comparative anatomy and comparative physiology. Detailed discussion of the theory, methods, and data of ethology are presented by Tinbergen (1951), Lorenz (1950), Thorpe (1956), Hinde (1959), and Hess (1962). Professors Tinbergen and Lorenz are both associated with the early theoretical aspects of ethology; and portions of their work are discussed in Chapters 4, 5, 6, and 8.

The basic concepts of ethology are discussed in these chapters but they will be identified briefly at this point. The concept of *fixed action pattern* was formalized by Lorenz based on his work and the work of Heinroth and Whitman who were the first to describe the fixed action pattern. These patterns are sequences of actions performed by an animal without specific prior learning or experience. Fixed action patterns are assumed to be *species-specific*. That is, the particular responses that are identified as fixed action patterns are assumed to occur for all members of a species and to occur differentially for other species, although the differences may be rather subtle. In some respects the concept is similar to the concept of unconditioned response as used in the analysis of conditioning. The similarity is based upon the view that both are unlearned responses.

The companion concept to fixed action patterns is *sign stimulus* or *releaser,* also formalized by Lorenz. Defined briefly, the sign stimulus is usually some component of a stimulus situation, such as an odor or a movement, that reliably elicits (releases) a particular unlearned response. Sign stimuli are also assumed to be *species-specific* which means that they are relevant for a particular species and function without prior training of the animal. The concept of sign stimulus is similar in some respects to the concept of unconditioned stimulus as used in conditioning.

It is important to note several things about the relationship between the S–R and the ethological approaches. The ethological approach is *not* inconsistent with the S–R approach nor does it subsume in entirety the S–R approach. The ethological approach is used primarily in analyses of innate behaviors, especially instincts, and the S–R approach is used primarily in analyses of behavior modification, especially conditioning and learning. As will be discussed in detail in later chapters, we will see an intimate relationship between innate and learned behaviors, although the theoretical positions associated with each are not explicitly merged.

Historical Considerations

The general orientation of the history of comparative psychology taken in the present chapter is based on the work of Kantor (1963).

The Naturalism of the Greeks. The first general treatise in comparative psychology was written by Aristotle. His analysis of behavior is summarized in two books *De Anima* and *Parva Naturala* (Ross, 1942). *De Anima,* the more comparative of the two, is oriented around several of the objectives of comparative analysis that were noted above,

including identification and classification of behavior, postulation of
relationships between behavior classes, and consideration of the development and origins of behavior between and within species.
Aristotle anticipated in detail a number of major ideas regarding
behavior which fell into oblivion and were then rediscovered many
centuries later. For example, he postulated phylogenetic development
and continuity between species; he postulated a doctrine of five senses;
he noted and described basic behavior and functions that arise from
biological organization, such as nutrition, sensation, discrimination,
appetite, and locomotion; and he postulated a doctrine of behavior
modification (an elementary S–R theory).

The Rise of Dualism. The insights and formulations regarding
behavior that culminated in Aristotle's work were set aside and
virtually lost for many centuries. During these centuries another
philosophical model dictated much of the thinking of the scholars.
This model, called *dualism,* was based on an assumption of two worlds
—the psychic world and the physical world. During this period more
attention was paid to defining the nature of the soul, the psychic
world, than to exploring the natural characteristics of the physical
world, the body.

Eventually the idea of two worlds (dualism) became thoroughly
established as a basic fact, although it is more properly considered
as an assumption. This trend toward dualism followed naturally from
the domination by theology of most of the practical and scholarly
aspects of life. In short, comparative psychology was not a "going
concern" during this time, nor were any of the biological sciences.

Dualism in Disguise. The seventeenth century saw a shift in the
style of thinking that had important implications for all biological
and psychological inquiry. The shift is characterized as follows: "In
the first place, there is an intensification of the sensitivity *to events*
on the part of the thinkers of the period; in the second, these thinkers
take definite account of the mechanical and other technological advancements evolved at the time" (Kantor, 1963, p. 360). Some of
the outstanding figures involved in this shift were Hobbes, Descartes,
Spinoza, and Leibnitz.

These men were dualists but they began to attempt to *naturalize
the soul* and make it a topic for scientific inquiry. They did not
seriously question or reject the assumption of dualism but they worked
within its framework. The transcendental soul became disguised in
naturalistic, quantitative or quasi-experimental theorizing. The talk
shifted from the soul to the mind; and Descartes' separation of animals

from men in terms of two principles of functioning, mechanical and rational, further facilitated the advance in biological inquiry with animals. About this time, Harvey was demonstrating the principles of circulation of blood in animals, and human anatomy was being studied from the examination of a person's body that had become snagged in a river. The "dissection" was made by the action of the river's currents over the body.

Dualism in Retreat. The scientific advances from the seventeenth to the twentieth centuries are almost breath-taking. The advances came in observation and analysis and in methods and technology. For example, a classification, taxonomy, of animal forms was available for Darwin's incisive theory of the mechanism associated with the origins and development of animal forms. Available surgical and recording techniques permitted the study of neural and muscular tissue in animals as shown in the work of Hall (1790–1857) and Flourens (1794–1867). These advances in the spirit of philosophical materialism furthered reformulations of dualism. Emphases on the mind gave way to emphases on the central nervous system and to organic theories of motivation, such as hormonal theories.

During this period many of the properties of the transcendental soul were simply attributed to organs and structures such as the hormonal or nervous systems. Following Darwin there was general espousal of the idea of *continuity of process* across all animal forms. The naturalization of the soul and the theory of evolution are specific forerunners of contemporary comparative psychology. Excerpts from the writings of several important figures of the time are included below to give the flavor of this work.

Charles Darwin (1809–1882) attempted a comprehensive review of behavior following the evolutionary model. This is described in his book, *Expression of the Emotions in Man and Animals*. Darwin states, "I will begin by giving the three principles, which appear to me to account for most of the expressions and gestures involuntarily used by man and the lower animals, under the influence of various emotions and sensations" (1920, p. 27). Darwin then proceeds to describe specific movements, postures, and facial characteristics of a variety of species and to relate these movements, etc. to the "states of mind of the animal."

C. Lloyd Morgan, author of the famous canon of parsimony, dealt explicitly with animal behavior in a comparative way in terms of behavioral categories. Among these categories of behavior were: organic, conscious, instinctive, intelligent, social, and emotional.

Morgan made use of the abundant data that had been collected with regard to a number of animal forms and like Aristotle he even included material on behavior of plants. In tune with the retreat from dualism, Morgan dealt with consciousness in only one chapter in which he said: "It is possible that all organic behavior is accompanied by consciousness. But there is no direct means of ascertaining whether it is so or not" (1908, p. 42). Morgan's further analysis of the concept of consciousness provides a particularly clear example of the type of thinking that was associated with the naturalization of the soul into a process of consciousness and into an equivalence with the central nervous system. He states, "We seem to be led to the conclusion both from *a priori* considerations and from the results of observation, that effective consciousness is associated with the nervous system" (1908, p. 43). In order to prevent rampant misuse of concepts dealing with consciousness as they were applied to a variety of animal forms, the so-called canon of parsimony was stated by Morgan in his text *Introduction to Comparative Psychology* (1894). Morgan's canon reads as follows: "In no case may we interpret an action as the outcome of the exercise of a higher psychical faculty, if it can be interpreted as the outcome of the exercise of one that stands lower in the psychological scale" (1894, p. 53). While this statement has continued to receive a great deal of attention in the construction of theories about animal behavior, one caution need be noted in particular. It should be noted that the rules for judging the level of concept to be applied depends on knowing the *psychological scale of animals;* and as a matter of fact this scale is not yet known, unless it be taken as a simple equivalent of the evolutionary scale which is not a simple linear scale.

George J. Romanes (1848–1894) is often described in a negative way because of his apparent devotion to the *anecdotal method.* But his text on comparative psychology entitled *Animal Intelligence* is a serious inquiry into animal behavior. Romanes organized the text by animal groups (phyla) and he used all of the data he could obtain, much of this from popular sources, to inquire into the phenomena of "mind throughout the animal kingdom" (1912, p. 1). Romanes struggled in the introductory chapter with the problem of dualism, the body and mind of animals, but it was particularly difficult since he included the behavior of lower invertebrates. He came to the kind of conclusion that is not unfamilar in recent work, he made a rough equivalent between mental and neural. Romanes' error seems to be one of attempting to deal with complex behavioral episodes with molar concepts. For example, he notes a report of the death of a snake that had been separated from its original owners and then suggests that: ". . . the probability rather points to the death of the animal having been accelerated by emotional shock. But then of course the question is an open one" (1912, p. 261). This incident was used by Romanes as an example of the development of associations (learned responses) on the part of reptiles. It was not, as his critics imply, that he was assuming the emotional life of reptiles to be the same as men's. However, the example illustrates Romanes' use of the anecdotal method.

At about the same time that the work of Morgan and Romanes was receiving attention in comparative psychology, a number of other outstanding scientists were observing and reporting the behavior of animals. Their contributions are still affecting current research and theory and some of their work is noted in later chapters. Among these scientists were: Pavlov, studies of conditioning; Watson, behavioristic theory in S–R terms; Yerkes, comparative studies of learning; Jennings, theory and study of behavior of invertebrates; Loeb, theory and study of behavior of invertebrates; Thorndike, theory and study of instrumental learning; and Lashley, neurology of learning.

We should like to suggest that this chapter might acquire added meaning if it were read again at the completion of the book.

Summary

Five aims or levels of comparative psychology are identified. They are: (1) identifying and classifying behavior, (2) specifying animals and situations that are appropriate for special study, (3) conceptualizing relationships between behavior classes, (4) establishing origins and development of behavior within and between species, and (5) postulating general processes and mechanisms for behavior and behavior change.

Comparative psychology is associated with the study of animal behavior including man. Other reasons for the study of animal behavior exclusive of man are: (1) scientific and general interest in animals themselves, (2) animals are important economic elements, and (3) understanding one species provides a model for understanding others. Field and laboratory methods are used to gather data about animal behavior for any of the reasons that are noted.

Stimulus-response (S–R) and ethological approach to the analysis of animal behavior are presented. It is concluded that both approaches are useful to achieve the aims of comparative psychology. The S–R approach emphasizes behavior change while the ethological approach emphasizes innate or species-specific behaviors.

The history of comparative psychology, a portion of the history of the entire field of psychology, is characterized in terms of the rise, fall and rise of objective analysis of behavior. Aristotle's naturalistic approach to comparative psychology gave way to dualism that precluded comparative psychology. Dualism retreated in the disguise of neural and hormonal theories that are only gradually being tied to objective study of behavior and theory construction.

CHAPTER 2

GENETICS, EVOLUTION, AND BEHAVIOR

The fact of individual differences in behavior is a truism in psychology. In general, it is assumed that individual differences in behavior arise from the interaction of genetic (hereditary) and environmental factors, where environmental includes both nongenetic biological changes and learning. In the present chapter some of the effects of genetic factors will be described and discussed, as well as the major methods that are used in studying them. Then, long-term genetic changes that are present in the evolutionary process will be considered, as these changes are related to behavior.

Genetics and Behavior

Investigation of the details of the relationship between genetics and behavior is a difficult task that has been attempted by only a small number of psychologists. Calvin Hall pointed out in a review of genetics and behavior (Hall, 1951) that the topic was inadequately investigated, although he saw it as an important area of study. Similar statements have been made more recently (Hirsch, 1958). However, it is accurate to state that research and theory regarding genetics, evolution, and behavior have moved forward since 1950 and that a full understanding of behavior requires a great deal of knowledge about both genetics and evolution.

Methods for Investigating Genetics and Behavior. We indicated above that research on genetics and behavior is a difficult task. This is true because such research typically involves several steps, and the steps may be long and somewhat tedious. The first step is the identification and measurement of a particular behavior that occurs in a population and seems to have a genetic component. The second step involves the assessment and analysis of the genetic factor or factors that are associated with this behavior. The identification and precise measurement of the behavior from a population of animals requires drawing a sample from the appropriate population, measuring the behavior,

17

and establishing the validity and reliability of the measuring procedure. While such procedures are common in psychological testing, as it is applied to humans (Anastasi, 1961), they are not commonly applied to the standard measures which are used to assess the behavior of infrahumans. For example, before Calvin Hall could investigate genetics and emotionality he had to conduct a series of experiments to identify and measure emotionality of rats in a valid and reliable way (Hall, 1934). Similar steps are required prior to the investigation of the genetic basis of any behavior, as seen in the studies by Hirsch (1958 **) and Stamm (1956 **). Some general reference texts that deal with topics of genetics that are beyond the consideration of the present text are Lerner (1950), Snyder and David (1957), and Srb and Owen (1952).

Genetic effects on behavior are established by a number of methods. These are identified as the *method of selective breeding, comparisons between strains,* and *analysis for effects of single genes* (pleiotropic effects).

Selective Breeding. The method of selective breeding is probably the most familiar method for assessing genetic effects. In its simplest form, selective breeding involves mating animals that show a particular behavior pattern, then mating the offspring of those showing the pattern, and so forth for a number of generations. If the behavior is genetically controlled, continued selection and mating of such animals for a number of generations will result in a generation of individuals that show the behavior in predictable ways (breeding true for the behavior under consideration). The method of selective breeding was used in the familiar Tryon experiment on genetics of "Intelligence in rats" and some of Tryon's data are reproduced by Hall (1951). The study by Hirsch (1958 **) also illustrates the method and will be described in greater detail later in this chapter.

Once the general contribution of genetics to a behavior pattern has been identified, variations of the selective breeding method are frequently used. For example, *back breeding* and *crossbreeding* are used to evaluate in greater detail the specific contribution of genetic factors to the variation in the behavior pattern among the individuals from the population. Back breeding involves mating individuals of one generation with those of earlier generations. The breeding is then followed by testing the behavior of the back-bred offspring. This method allows evaluation of the extent to which the genetic factors are behaving in accord with the Mendelian ratio law of inheritance. Crossbreeding involves mating individuals that show the behavior pattern in question in markedly different degrees and then examining the behavior of the offspring of these crossbred individuals. This method also allows us to refine our statements about the specific genetic factors that may be operating when a genetic contribution to behavior has already been identified. The study by Stamm (1956 **) illustrates the use of the methods of back breeding and crossbreeding in investigating the genetic factors in the hoarding behavior of rats. The study by Paulsen (1951 **) illustrates another version of crossbreeding. Paulsen studied the behavior of a hybrid that can be considered a crossbreed. In this case the hybrid was a very unusual one, namely, a cross between a duck and a goose. (Call it what you wish, a doose or a guck.)

Strain Comparisons. The second general method for establishing and evaluating genetic factors in behavior involves the comparison of the behaviors of different strains of the same species. This method differs from selective breeding in that the strains are already available and the original breeding was very likely based on selection for structural characteristics. The problem becomes one of identifying any behavior differences among the strains. A strain is considered to be a group of animals that have common genetic lineage that arose from natural or artificial inbreeding. The genetic purity of the strain is a function of the degree of inbreeding that has taken place. For example, a high degree of inbreeding from the mating of brothers and sisters, for a number of generations, produces a relatively pure strain of individuals. Such individuals are called homozygous. This means that their reproductive cells, zygotes, were derived from the union of gametes identical in respect to quality, quantity and arrangements of their genes or certain of their genes. Lesser degrees of inbreeding produce less pure (less homozygous) strains. It follows from the definition of strains, especially pure strains, that differences in behavior of individuals of different strains are due to differences in genetic characteristics, assuming the individuals are raised in identical environments.

The results of studies which compare the behavior of different strains provide material for genetic analysis and comparative psychology. That is, the method is a patently comparative one that has been used a great deal in the recent work on comparative analyses of behavior. Several of the summarized studies illustrate the data from comparisons among strains, such as strains of mice (Thompson, 1953 *; King and Mavromatis, 1956 *), strains of rats (Carr and Williams, 1957 *), and breeds (strains) of purebred dogs (Fuller, 1955 *).

CARR, R. M., AND WILLIAMS, C. D.   Exploratory behavior of three strains of rats. *J. comp. physiol. Psychol.*, 1957, **50**, 621–23.

Three highly inbred strains of rats were tested for exploratory behavior as measured by the number of sections of a Y-maze that each animal traversed. Twenty albino rats, 20 black (nonagouti selfed) rats, and 18 black-hooded (nonagouti piebald) rats were raised under very similar conditions and then tested when mature. The black-hooded rats were significantly more active than either the blacks or albinos, although these two groups did not differ from each other. It was concluded that different strains of rats have different levels of activity that are at least determined in part by genetic factors.

FULLER, J. L.   Hereditary differences in trainability of purebred dogs. *J. Genet. Psychol.*, 1955, **87**, 229–38.

Males and females of four pure breeds of dogs were tested to determine if the breeds differed in rate of learning to walk under control of a leash. All of the dogs were raised under identical conditions and then trained at 19 weeks of age for two five-day periods. The performances of each animal was scored in terms both of errors, such as balking, and degree of cooperativeness, an index that reflects differences in temperament. Highly significant differences in performance scores were obtained for the various breeds. The rankings of the breeds from most trainable to least were: Wirehaired Fox Terrier, Cocker Spaniel, Beagle, hybrid Basenji-Cocker Spaniel, Shetland Sheep Dog, and Basenji. Males and females differed significantly only for several breeds.

Unit Characters.   The observation of the action of single pairs of genes provides striking evidence for the effects of genetics on behavior. These effects are called unit characters and can be considered as instances of pleiotropic effects in which single pairs of genes affect a variety of structures and/or behaviors. A unit character is assumed to exist if selective matings of individuals yield simple Mendelian ratios in their offspring, for the trait in question. Some of the details of the method and the rationale for inferences about unit characters are discussed by Hall (1951, p. 316) and Caspari (1958). Several studies of unit characters associated with behavior have been undertaken. Among these are susceptibility to audiogenic seizures in strains of mice (Frings and Frings, 1953 *), and mating pattern of strains of fruit flys (Bastock, 1957 *).

BASTOCK, M. A.   A gene mutation which changes a behavior pattern. *Evolution*, 1957, **10**, 421–39.

The mating behavior of two strains of fruit fly, *Drosophila melanogaster*, were compared. One strain was wild; the other a yellow mutant. The mating behaviors of the males of the two strains were found to differ. Control experiments indicated the differences were not due to differences in responses of the females. The yellow mutant males courted with less vigor and for briefer periods of time than the wild males. It was concluded that the differences in mating were due to specific behaviors of the males and the implications of such differences in behavior are noted in terms of evolutionary consequences such as establishing isolated populations from the larger population.

FRINGS, H. AND FRINGS, M. The production of stocks of albino mice with predictable susceptibilities to audiogenic seizures. *Behav.,* 1953, 5, 305–19.

Selective breeding was carried out with a large number of hybrid mice in order to determine if groups of animals could be bred for high susceptibility and low susceptibility to audiogenic seizures. An audiogenic seizure is a convulsive seizure, like epilepsy, that occurs to brief and intense sounds. Seven generations of breeding of susceptible animals produced increasingly susceptible offspring, one subgroup of which showed clonic seizures, the other showed tonic-clonic seizures. Breeding of nonsusceptible animals led to a generation with very low susceptibility. It was concluded that susceptibility to audiogenic seizures is determined by genetic factors to some extent but the action is not a unit gene factor since both groups had some offspring that were not typical and latencies of responses differed within the groups.

Genetics and Behavior of Invertebrates

The study of genetic factors in behavior of invertebrates has been confined largely to the phylum Arthropoda and, within this phylum, to the insects. In view of the importance of innate behaviors among insects and the importance of biological organization in innate behavior, positive findings regarding genetic control of innate behaviors are expected. Three series of investigations of genetic factors and innate behavior will be discussed. They are investigations of genetic factors and taxis (orientation to specific classes of stimuli) of the fruit fly *Drosophila,* mating behavior of several species of *Drosophila,* and care of the young by several strains of bees.

The study by Hirsch (1958 **) illustrates the traditional approach to the investigation of genetic factors in behavior. In this study the phototactic response of individuals of a strain of fruit fly, *Drosophila melanogaster,* was reliably measured, then the method of selective breeding was used to assess the effects of genetic factors. The results of a number of generations of this selective breeding showed that the behavior responded to such breeding. That is, by the ninth generation the offspring of flys that showed a strong approach to light showed this response to a greater extent and with less variability than unselected flys, while progressive generations of flys that showed a weak approach to light became successively weaker in their response to light. Hirsch (1959) has also investigated the geotactic response of these flys. Geotaxis is the respose of orientating to a gravitational field. Negative geotaxis refers to the response of moving upward or away from the earth's field, positive geotaxis refers to the response of moving downward or toward the stronger gravitational field. Such responses are discussed in detail in Chapter 4. It was found that the geotactic response, like the phototatic response, is affected by selective breeding and that specific populations of *Drosophila* could be bred with predetermined response strengths to the gravitational stimulus.

Genetic factors have been found to affect aspects of mating behavior of *Drosophila*. Bastock (1957*) found the gene for body color that led to a yellow fruit fly has pleiotropic effects with regard to mating. The vigor of the mating response by males was directly associated with the yellow mutant. An even more specific effect on mating occurred for the "ebony fly" that was less vigorous than the normal control males when mating in the light, but was not different in mating when tested in the dark.

Genetic factors have been found to affect mating of insects in other ways (Caspari, 1958). Male moths were bred that were particularly responsive to some females but not to others, and the larva of the moth *Ephestia* were found to spin different types of cocoon in response to selective breeding. Such findings regarding the effects of genetic factors on reproductive behavior and particularly on mating are felt to have important implications for evolution. This is due to the fact that such behavior patterns may isolate a group of animals from the general population and lead to the development of a sub-species or special strain. However, general consideration of the relationships between genetics and the evolution of behavior will be discussed in a later section.

Research with bees has shown that different strains have different susceptibilities to bacterial diseases that attack the larva in the hives. Careful observation of the bees in the hives revealed that the different susceptibilities were associated with different behavior patterns of the workers that took care of the larva (Rothenbuhler, 1958). Specifically, the workers of the susceptible strains did not check and remove the diseased larva, while the workers of the "healthy strains" did. Matings of the members of the two strains revealed that the sequence of behaviors associated with keeping a "healthy strain" was genetically controlled. It was found that two separate behavior patterns were necessary. The workers had to check the larva and also had to remove the sick ones. The results of selective breeding studies suggested that each pattern was independently controlled by a single pair of genes, the healthy strains had both pairs of genes and showed both behaviors, while the other strains had only the genes for the first behavior component.

As suggested by this brief review, studies of genetic factors in behavior of invertebrates have concentrated on the highest invertebrates, namely Arthropods. This does not mean that genetic factors may not operate among other invertebrates; rather it means that the analysis of the behavior of other phyla of invertebrates is less complete.

Genetics and Behavior of Vertebrates

The comments that follow apply equally to invertebrates and vertebrates. However, the variety and number of behaviors that have been studied in relation to genetic factors is greater for vertebrates than invertebrates. Thus, general comments have been held for this section.

In principle it is expected that genetic factors are involved to some extent in accounting for individual differences in all behaviors of all organisms. This is expected since these factors affect structures (sensory, motor, neural, and hormonal), the development of these structures and their functional organization. However, a number of other factors are involved in accounting for individual differences within a species with regard to any particular behavior. Among these are environmental factors, both prenatal and postnatal, learning and short-term biological changes such as drug states. Thus, the contribution of genetic factors to the behavior of some particular species may extend from almost complete absence of effect to almost complete determination as is true in some forms of color blindness.

The effects of genetic factors will be considered for the following classes of behavior of vertebrates: reproduction, learning, and temperment. All three methods or types of analyses for effects of genetic factors have been applied to these investigations with vertebrates. However, the amount of time required for the reproduction and development of a vertebrate has limited the method of selective breeding to work with a relatively small number of generations.

Genetics and Reproductive Behavior. The analysis and measurement of reproductive behavior is a very complex matter that is discussed in detail in Chapters 5, 6, and 8, but for the present purposes only several general points need to be made. The first point is that for most vertebrates reproductive behavior consists of a number of components including courtship, copulation, nest building, and care of the young. These components are considered to consist largely of innate or unlearned response sequences that occur in the presence of appropriate stimuli. However, individual differences exist in the frequency, vigor, and precise form of the responses within and between groups of animals. That is, reproductive behaviors are characterized by both stereotypy and individual differences. These characteristics suggest that genetic factors may affect components of reproductive behavior. The specific behavioral mechanisms that are associated with the genetic effects are not yet known, so the present section will discuss some findings regarding the effects of genetics on behavior without attempting to relate the findings to a broader theory of behavior.

The courting responses of males of a number of species have been shown to be affected by genetic factors. Specifically, the form and sequence of some of these responses are intermingled in hybrids of two related species as compared to the responses of the parent species. The study by Paulsen (1951 **) describes some of the behaviors of a hybrid of a duck and a goose and identifies some behaviors of each parent that survived in the hybrid. Similar observations have been made with crosses of species of fish (Clark, *et al.*, 1954) and birds (Hinde, 1958 *). The behaviors of such hybrids are generally intermediate in form or strength between the behaviors of the parents. However, these intermediate forms cannot be predicted from simple Mendelian ratios.

HINDE, R. A. The behavior of certain cardueline F_1 interspecies hybrids. *Behav.*, 1956, 9, 201–13.

Since the behavior patterns, especially display reactions, of a number of species of birds are well known and used to assess phylogenetic relations, the behaviors of hybrids of such species are of interest. In this study the behaviors of hybrids of Greenfinch (*Chloris chloris*), Goldfinch (*Carduelis carduelis*), and the Canary were studied. Reactions to predators (mobbing), fighting, courtship, and calls were studied in each hybrid group. Some of the behavior patterns of the different species are different in form, such as the calls; others are similar in form but differ in the intensity of some aspect of the total pattern, such as the reaction to predators. It was found that all behavior patterns that are identical in both parents (species) are shown in identical form in their offspring, patterns that are different in the parents appear in forms intermediate between the forms shown by the parents, patterns that are common in one parent and rare in the other also occur in intermediate forms in the offspring. Thus, it was concluded that the organization of the response patterns observed with these hybrids is dependent in a large measure on genetic factors.

McGILL, T. E. Sexual behavior in three inbred strains of mice. *Behav.*, 1962, 19, 341–50.

The sexual behavior of the males of the strains of mice C57BL, DBA/2, and BALD/c were intensively studied. The animals were maintained under similar conditions, were studied from two months until eight months of age, and were tested with females of their own strain. Sixteen behavior measures relating to the mating of the males were taken: among these were frequency of mounting, frequency of intromission, duration of intromission, and latency of ejaculation. The three strains differed significantly from each other on twelve of the measures. In general, it was found that the C57BL strain was characterized by speed (short time before first intromission, and less time between intromissions). The DBA/2 were slower than the C57BL but faster than the BALD/c males which took the longest time to gain intromission (more than one hour) and to ejaculate.

The contribution of genetic factors to the frequency and form of copulation has been studied in mice (McGill, 1962 *), guinea pigs (Valenstein, *et al.*, 1955), and domestic fowl (Wood-Gush and Oliver, 1956). These studies indicate that these aspects of reproductive behavior are also influenced by genetics. Indirect evidence from the study of domestic fowl suggests that the genetic effect may be mediated by the hormonal systems that are involved in mating behavior. The effects of genetic factors are also intimately tied to other aspects of the animals' lives. For example, frequency and form of copulation of the guinea pigs was found to be modified by the specific early experiences of the males (Valenstein, 1955). It has also been found that the manner in which female rats cared for their young was affected both by strain differences and the characteristics of the pups that they were caring for.

Genetics and Learning. The existence of a relationship between learning and genetic factors has been well recognized since Robert Tryon's research on selective breeding of rats for maze learning. Genetic factors have been found to operate in almost all learning situations in all vertebrates in which this effect has been investigated. Fuller (1955 *) reports differences in trainability for different pure breeds of dogs. This is a fact that is generally believed but not specifically tested by most dog raisers. The bases for Fuller's conclusions are more sound than those of dog raisers, since Fuller's breeds were all raised in an identical environment and tested with standardized learning tests. Strain differences have also been obtained with rats in learning a maze (McGaugh, et al, 1961 *) and with mice in learning to avoid electric shock (King and Mavromatis, 1956 *). Thus, it seems clear that reliable differences in learning are found for genetically different groups within the same species of animals.

KING, J. A. AND MAVROMATIS, A.   The effect of a conflict situation on learning ability of two strains of inbred mice. *J. comp. physiol. Psychol.*, 1956, 49, 465–68.

   This study illustrates some of the complexities in the relationships between genetic factors and learned behaviors. Mice from two genetically different pure strains (C57 BL/10 and BALD/c) were conditioned to jump a hurdle to avoid an electric shock. The mice of each strain were then divided into two groups. One group of each strain received 35 days of exposure to an approach-avoidance conflict situation (shock at the water bottle); the other group of each strain was maintained under normal conditions as control animals. All mice were then tested for relearning of the original avoidance response. It was found that the BALD/c strain learned the original avoidance response significantly more slowly. This seemed to be due to the fact that these mice "froze" rather than ran after presentation of the electric shock. The

C57BL/10 mice subjected to conflict lost more weight than the others during the conflict trials. Relearning scores showed a reversal from original learning. The BALD/c strain relearned significantly faster than the other strain and the treatment produced greater differences between the treated and control animals for the BALD/c mice. In general, treated animals relearned more slowly than control animals.

McGAUGH, J. L., WESTBROOK, W. AND BURT, G.   Strain differences in the facilitative effects of 5–7 diphenyl–1–3–diazadamantan–6–ol (1757 I.S.) on maze learning. *J. comp. physiol. Psychol.,* 1961, 54, 502–5.

The control groups in this study consisted of rats from Tryon's "bright strain" (B), his "dull strain" (D), and the first generation crosses of Bs and Ds (Fl). The experimental groups consisted of Bs, Ds, and Fls that received interperitoneal injections of 1757 I.S. on each day ten minutes before learning trials started. A Lashley III maze with four units, eight culs, and food in the goal box was used for learning. The control groups differed significantly in learning the maze. Group B made the least errors, group D the most, and group Fl an intermediate number. The drug, 1757 I.S., had differential effects on the experimental groups. Group B performed as well as group B of the control group, but groups D and Fl also performed as well as group B of the control group. The results for the control groups showed differences that were expected for these strains of rats. The results for the experimental groups were interpreted in terms of differential effects of the drug. This drug is assumed to produce neural change, consolidation of neural effects, between learning trials.

The implications of these findings regarding genetic factors in learning are less clear or definite than might be supposed. Careful testing of the different genetic groups such as Tryon's "maze-bright" and "maze-dull" rats suggests that such groups differ in specific behaviors that are correlated with specific features of the learning situation. For example, Searles (1949 *) found that Tryon's so-called "maze-bright" rats showed less fear in the learning situation than the "maze-dull" rats. Thus, greater fear in the maze may account for poorer learning. Amount of spontaneous activity is another specific behavior pattern that is responsive to selective breeding. Brody (1941 *) found that the selective breeding of inactive rats led to progressively more inactive individuals through 25 generations. The findings regarding genetic differences in spontaneous activity and fear have obvious implications for studies of learning which use a runway or a maze in which activity or fearfulness may be important components.

SEARLES, L. V.   The organization of hereditary maze brightness and maze dullness. *Genet. Psychol. Mono.,* 1949, 39, 279–375.

Rats that had been bred by Tryon for learning a maze quickly, (maze-bright), or slowly, (maze-dull), were tested on nine separate behavior tests to determine the specific respects in which the groups differed. Among the test situations were the open-field test of emotionality, complex maze, and water escape. The maze-brights had slightly higher total scores than the maze-dulls but they were not superior on all tests. For example, the maze-dulls had better scores on the test for escaping from water and lower emotionality scores on the open-field test. It was concluded that the differences between the groups in maze learning were related to a complex of specific behavior patterns and not a "general intelligence" factor.

BRODY, E. G. Genetic basis of spontaneous activity in the albino rat. *Comp. Psychol. Mono.*, 1941, **17**, 1–23.

Selective breeding was carried out with a large number of hybrid albino rats in order to investigate the contribution of genetic factors to activity of the rats. Activity was measured in activity wheels in which the animals lived for a period of 21 days after they were sexually mature. The rats that were most active were interbred as were those that were least active. Selective breeding of active rats for 25 generations did not change the mean or variability of the activity scores. Selective breeding of inactive rats for 25 generations produced progressively less active offspring and eventually led to a sterile line. It was concluded that activity is affected by selective breeding but it is not a unit character.

Genetic factors in learning also interact with the variable of early experience. This has been shown in several ways with strains of mice. For example, learning differences were found among strains before the mice were 30 days of age but not after that age (King and Shea, 1959). Another line of evidence is the finding that specific early experiences affect learning, swimming behavior, and reaction to shock, in one strain of mice more than another (King and Mavromatis, 1956 *; King, 1961).

Genetics and Temperament. A relationship between genetics and temperament in higher vertebrates has also been assumed. That is, specific breeds or strains of animals are thought to be more aggressive than others, more emotional than others, and so forth. For example, terriers that were bred for fighting are considered to be more aggressive than Beagles that were bred for working in groups. In the case of temperament, as in the case of trainability, the research findings agree in general with these views that have been put forward by people who train animals. However, as was found in studies of the effects of genetic factors on learning, the effects of genetic factors on temperament may be modified by specific early experiences. Such alterations in temperament were found by Scott and Charles (1954) in a study of a number of breeds of dogs. Specifically, they found that early training tended to magnify differences in temperament between breeds. The possibility of confusing genetic effects with effects of early experience was studied by Broadhurst (1961 *). An extended discussion of the relationship between temperament and early experience for a variety of species is included in Chapter 7.

BROADHURST, P. L. Analysis of maternal effects in the inheritance of behavior. *Anim. Behav.*, 1961, **9**, 129–41.

This study was designed to investigate the effects of two conditions that could imitate or confound effects of genetic factors. Specifically, prenatal and postnatal environments were studied in relation to their effects on emotionality of laboratory rats *(Rattus norvegicus)*. Emotional rats and nonemotional rats, as measured by the open-field test (counting defecation and exploration) were bred in reciprocal crosses. That is, to assess the effect of prenatal environment emotional animals bred with nonemotional ones and then the offspring bred back to the parents. The behavior of the offspring and the young of the offspring with parent breedings could be used on an indirect measure of effects of prenatal environment. No such effects were found. The effect of postnatal environment was investigated more directly by placing offspring of emotional rats with nonemotional mothers and visa versa. The behavior of the cross-fostered young was then measured. No effect of postnatal maternal environment was found in terms of emotionality of the young.

HALL, C. S.   The inheritance of emotionality. *Amer. Scientist,* 1938, 26, 17–27.

A total of 165 rats of the strain *Rattus norvegicus* were tested for emotionality using the Hall Open Field test. Frequency of urination and defecation and time before the animal would eat were used as indexes of emotionality. Seven males and seven females which showed the most emotionality were bred, as were seven pairs that showed the least emotionality. There were 40 young of emotional pairs and 35 young of nonemotional pairs. The offspring of these pairs (F_1 generation) were then tested for emotionality when they were 90 days of age. The offspring of the emotional rats were significantly more emotional than the offspring of the others by a factor about 8 to 1. It was concluded that emotionality was responsive to selective breeding and therefore affected by genetic factors.

Behaviors classified as emotionality, wildness, and aggressiveness are aspects of temperament that have been commonly investigated in relation to genetic factors. Each of these characteristics has been measured in a different way, and the extent to which the measures may all be measuring a single process is not clear. Emotionality, as noted in the paper by Hall (1938 *), is usually measured in terms of the frequency of occurrence of urination and defecation in an "open-field" test. The assumption underlying the measure is that the more frequently urination and defecation occur in the open-field test situation, the greater the degree of emotionality. For example, Hall placed rats in unfamiliar, brightly lighted circular enclosures for two minutes a day for 12 consecutive days and then noted the number of days when urination or defecation occurred. Using this measure, Hall found that emotionality was affected by selective breeding so that by the 12th generation the scores of emotional groups were four times higher than those of nonemotional groups (Hall, 1951).

Measurement of wildness and analyses of genetic effects on wildness have been undertaken primarily with strains of rats. Degree of wildness is measured in terms of attacks on objects placed in the cage, attempts to bite the handler, and the time required to get the animal to remain quietly in the hand of the handler. Wild and domesticated strains of rats differ reliably and markedly in degree of wildness and breed true for this characteristic. Differences in temperment are also found among strains of mice and species of birds (Thompson, 1953 *; Stokes, 1962 *).

THOMPSON, W. R.   The inheritance of behavior: Behavioral differences of 15 mouse strains. *Canad. J. Psychol.,* 1953, **7**, 145–55.

Food drive, emotionality, and exploratory behavior of 14 highly inbred strains and one hybrid strain of laboratory mice were tested. Ten males and ten females all between the ages of 70–90 days (sexually mature) were tested after having been raised under identical conditions. The measure of food drive was the amount the individual ate in a ten-minute test period. The Hall Open Field test that involves placing the animal in an open and un-familiar area was used to measure emotionality and exploration. Amount of defecation was the index of emotionality and amount of the area of the open field that was traversed was the index of exploration. Both of these are common indexes. Significant differences were found among a number of the strains on each of the three behavioral measures. The differences were attributed to genetic differences since the animals were raised under identical conditions.

STOKES, A. W.   The comparative ethology of Great, Blue, Marsh, and Coal Tits at a winter feeding station. *Behav.,* 1962, **19**, 208–18.

The behavior of four different but closely related species of birds of the genus *Parus* (commonly called titmice) was studied to determine the specific respects in which these species were similar and different. The birds were studied in a natural setting but all of them have a similar habitat. Thus, differences in behavior could be ascribed to genetic or species differences. It was found that all four species had similar display patterns (innate re-actions to the approach of another bird) but the frequencies of the responses differed among the species. It was found that the particular display re-actions that occurred, such as ones associated with fighting, staying, or escap-ing, differed among the species as a function of the distance from the ap-proaching bird and the total number of birds in the immediate area. In other words, some species seemed more timid than others. For example, Blue Tits were less timid than Great Tits as measured by the distance they would tolerate between each other. It was suggested that some general characteristic such as timidity may be a genetic factor.

The temperamental characteristic of aggressiveness, closely related at the conceptual level to the characteristic of wildness, has also been studied. Aggressiveness is defined and measured in terms of fighting with members of the same species. The principal experimental ani-mals used for studies of genetic factors in aggressiveness have been purebred mice and rats. As noted by Scott (1958), the evidence from these experimental studies clearly indicate that genetic factors affect degree of aggressiveness for these species. The scores from rating scales of aggressiveness, such as those presented by Hall (1951), were the principal measures of aggressiveness that were used with these rodents.

Aspects of temperament can be measured in a number of ways. For example, heart rate and electro-dermal response (galvanic skin response of humans) are potential measures of emotionality for a variety of animal forms. Activity cages with recorders are available for measuring activity of birds (Ratner and Ringer, 1959). Such a device lends itself to research on genetic factors because pure strains of domestic fowl are available.

Other specific behavior patterns such as hoarding, audiogenic seizures (Frings and Frings, 1958 *), and food drive (Thompson, 1953 *) have been investigated with vertebrates to assess the effects of genetic factors. In general, such effects have been found.

Behavior and Evolution

Evolution can be defined briefly as the cumulative changes in characteristics of populations of organisms. These cumulative changes occur through successive generations of organisms that are related by descent, that is, genetically. In general, a two-way relationship exists between behavior and evolution. On one hand, the comparative study of behavior assists in the understanding of evolution, particularly taxonomic relationships. On the other hand, evolutionary change can be considered as a process that is associated with changes in behavior.

Lorenz (1957) describes in considerable detail the logic and use of behaviors as characteristics for classification of animals (taxonomy). He points out that some innate behaviors are as useful as structural characteristics in the classification of species and the assessment of their evolutionary origins. One striking example of the use of behavior as a taxonomic character involves the classification of pigeons. Classification cannot be reliably done using structural characteristics such as feathers or shape of the wings but can be done in terms of characteristics of nesting behaviors. Specifically, pigeons of the group *Columbae* are characterized by the fact that during brooding season the male sits on the eggs from early morning till late afternoon; the female sits on the eggs the rest of the time (Lorenz, 1957, p. 150). This is not true of other species.

Simpson (1961, p. 76) also considers the use of behavior for assessing evolutionary relationships and the origin of species. Simpson and Lorenz both acknowledge that this is a complex task but agree that by the selection of appropriate behaviors such interpretations can be made. Simpson points out that gross behaviors, such as the form of locomotion, are too general to be useful but specific innate behavioral patterns, such as the courtship sequence, may be relevant.

Basic Concepts regarding Evolution and Behavior

Before considering some of the specific relationships between behavior and evolution, some basic concepts regarding evolution will be discussed. The probable course of evolutionary development is shown in Figure 2–1. This figure shows the main branches of evolutionary development that terminate at one branch with the social insects and at the other with social primates. The major phyla, some identifying characteristics of each phylum, and examples of species in each phylum are shown. It is important to note that the animals, such as primates, dogs, cats, and rats that are most frequently used in psychological research, even comparative psychological research, are all quite highly evolved and therefore not representative of the range of animal forms. The range of forms comprising the animal kingdom is so broad that caution is necessary in generalizing interpretations of behavior from one species to the behavior of organisms in general.

One of the main sources of data used to establish the course of evolutionary development is the presence of similarities among species. Considerable attention has been given to analysis of these similarities. One principle to emerge from these analyses is that a number of different sources or kinds of similarities must be recognized. In other words, animals can be similar for a variety of reasons.

The major classes of similarities are: *homologous* similarities and *homoplastic* similarities (Simpson, 1961, p. 78). By homologous similarity or homology is meant a resemblance in structure or behavior due to inheritance from a common ancestor. In general, those animals with a great number of homologues are more closely related than those with only a few. Thus, the horseshoe crab (*Timulus*) is more closely related to spiders than to other crabs, such as *Cancer*. In general appearance, Timulus seems more like a crab than a spider. However, it shares at least one more critical homologous feature with spiders than with other crabs, namely the composition of its blood. By homoplastic similarity or homoplasy is meant a resemblance due to factors other than common ancestory.

Several types of homoplastic similarity are identified: *parellelism, convergence, analogy, mimicry,* and *chance similarity. Parallelism* refers to the occurrence of similar characteristics from two independent hereditary lines through independent causes bearing on both lines. Parallel similarities usually develop in related animal forms that have been isolated from each other but have remained in similar environ-

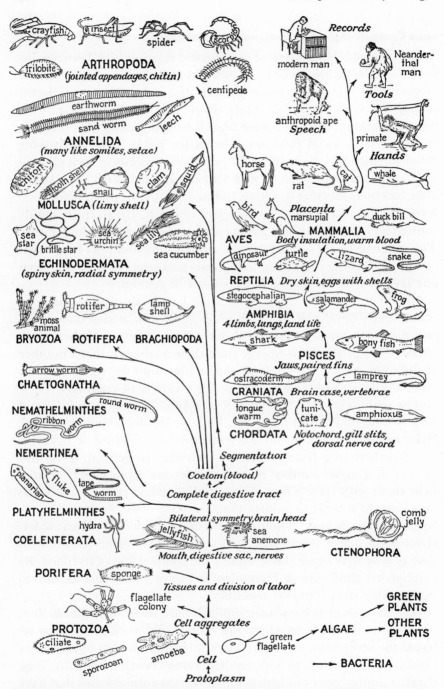

Fig. 2–1. The Animal Kingdom. A "genealogical tree" to indicate the probable relationships and relative position of the major groups (named in boldfaced type). All groups above a given characteristic (named in italics) possess that character. Figures not to same scale.

ments. For example, the Australian marsupial animals are considered to represent examples of similarity through parallel evolution. *Convergence* refers to the occurrence of similar characteristics from two independent hereditary lines through the animal's adapting to similar ecological (environmental) states. Similarities through convergence are sometimes difficult to separate from similarities through parallelism. An example of a convergent characteristic are spines on the backs of animals. These have evolved independently among a number of orders of animals, including the porcupine, a rodent, and the hedgehog, an insectivore. The spines of these animals resemble each other and function similarly but the species have evolved from different ancestors. *Analogy* refers to characteristics of two independent hereditary lines that are similar in *function*. The wings of insects and birds are considered to be analogous structures. They are used for flight in both animal forms but they evolved in different ways. The wings of insects evolved as derivatives of the body wall; those of birds evolved as modifications of limbs. *Mimicry* refers to occurrences of similarity in characteristics of two independent hereditary lines in the same general environment that arise from one line taking on characteristics of another because of the adaptive advantage that arises from this. Examples of mimicry are most common among insects. In one form of mimicry, Batesian mimicry, one species evolves to look like another species that is protected from predators by being poisonous or distasteful. Homoplasy associated with *chance similarity* refers to occurrences of similar characteristics in independent hereditary lines from independent causes that happen to be similar.

These classes of similarities are theoretical concepts that are useful for analysis of evolutionary relationships. However, the processes that are suggested by the names, such as parallel development, are not considered to be the reasons for this similarity. The reasons are usually established from detailed analyses of data from studies of comparative anatomy, embryology, morphology, and paleontology. Observation of similarities and differences in structures of animals usually provides the data for evolutionary hypotheses, but behavioral data has sometimes been used for these hypotheses. One of the shortcomings of behavioral data, like physiological data, is that it does not exist in anything but presently living forms. That is, data regarding behavior and physiology must be inferred indirectly, for fossil forms.

Research regarding Evolution and Behavior

Three approaches to the study of evolution and behavior will be considered.

Evolution of Structures and Behavior Change. The fact that structures have changed in the course of evolutionary development means that behaviors must also have changed. That is, the occurrence of different sensory, neural, and motor systems among different groups of animals means that the behaviors of these groups of animals are also different. For example, the evolution of food-getting, a fundamental behavior function, obviously differs from one phylum to another as the sensitivities and locomotor systems of the animals differ. Thus, the broad course of evolution of these behaviors can be inferred from the data on structures of the fossil forms and from the probable relations of species to each other. For example, some of the similarities and particularly the differences in behavior in present-day cats (felids) as compared with dogs (canids) can be traced from the divergence of two evolutionary lines from the original land-living carnivores called *Miacids.* These early carnivores had teeth and limb development appropriate for hunting as predators. Following the separation into two groups, the canids evolved as swift runners with great endurance and, in some species, were gregarious hunters. The felids continued as solitary hunters with an emphasis on ambush and a sudden rush at great speed. The fossil remains of early felids and the structures of present-day ones suggest the evolutionary development to specialization in pouncing upon the prey and stabbing and shearing meat from it. It should be noted that even the temperamental characteristics of cats as opposed to dogs (solitary animals versus gregarious animals) seem to follow these evolutionary adaptations. A number of other examples of inferences regarding the evolution of behavior based on the evolution of structure are described by Colberts (1958).

Behavioral Homologies. A somewhat different approach to the problem of the evolution of behavior has been to consider *behaviors as structural units,* much like teeth or limbs, and to examine the behaviors of different species for the presence of *homologous features.* The behaviors that are used for this type of analysis are innate behaviors, described in detail in subsequent chapters. Innate behaviors can be briefly defined as being characteristic for entire species and typically involve such activities as food-getting, reproduction (including courting, copulation, nesting, and care of the young), and fighting. Examples of such evolutionary analyses are presented by Tinbergen (1951, p. 189), Mayr (1942) and Daanje (1955 *).

Mayr has suggested that under some conditions evolutionary theory deduced from structural features is sometimes ambiguous and misleading while behavioral features provide important suggestive information. For example, nesting behavior of a number of species of birds was considered by Tinbergen to determine the similarities and differences among the species for this behavior pattern. Tinbergen concluded that setting within the nest while building it and scraping with the feet were homologous characteristics in that they appeared in all of the species that were examined. However, the manner of making the walls of the nest were quite different from one species to another. Some species weave the nest material into the walls; others work the nest material into the walls by quivering movements of the head which persist until the material that is held in the bill catches in the wall of the nest. Thus, it is not appropriate to conclude that nest building is homologous, rather certain components of the total pattern are homologous; others are not.

A highly speculative example of homologous behavior among higher vertebrates involves responses such as scratching and rubbing the head, associated with care of the body surface. This behavior is also observed when the animal is stopped during behavior that is directed toward a goal. It can be observed that cats "wash their faces" under these conditions, birds preen, rats "wash their faces," and humans and other primates scratch their heads, stroke their faces, or adjust already adjusted hair. It is suggested that such responses are homologous.

Comparisons among Behaviors of Closely Related Species. A third approach to the analysis of the evolution of behavior involves the study of behavior of closely related species. Evolutionary development in this case is established from analysis of structures and analysis of the behavior patterns. In general, it is assumed that for a particular type of behavior, the more primitive the species, as judged from structural characteristics, the more primitive the form of behavior. The study by Schmidt (1955 **) on evolution of termite behavior illustrates this type of research and the theoretical position associated with it. A similar approach has been made by Davis (1942) in a study of the evolutionary development of four species of a subfamily of cuckoo (Crotophaginae). Based on evidence from morphological characteristics, the species *Guira guira* was judged to be the most primitive, the species *Crotophaga major* was judged to be more highly evolved, and the two species *Crotophaga ani* and *Crotophaga sulcirostris* were judged to be the most highly evolved and specialized. The nesting behavior of these species was then evaluated along a dimension of communality. Communality is a behavioral characteristic of this subfamily of cuckoo. The most primitive species, *Guira guira,* showed the lowest level of communal nesting. They nested and defended the nest in pairs. The intermediate evolutionary group, *Crotophaga major,* had an intermediate level of communality in nesting. Pairs built nests but the members of a number of pairs united in the defense of the nesting area. The most highly evolved species, as inferred from structural features, showed the most highly evolved forms of communal nesting. *Crotophaga ani* and *Crotophaga sulcirostris* made communal nests, engaged in communal mating and defended the nesting area as a large group. Thus, the data from the analysis of behavior supported the hypothesis about phylogenetic levels as they were deduced from the morphological data. Similar methods have been used with primates (Andrew, 1963 *).

ANDREW, R. J.   The origin and evolution of the calls and facial expressions of the primates. *Behav.,* 1963, **20,** 1–109.
   The vocalizations and facial expressions of more than ten species of primates are described in detail. Some of the characteristics of the vocalizations are: twitters, clicks, grunts, wails, and shreiks. The twitter is identified as the most primitive vocalization. These vocalizations are found to be associated with specific facial expressions that are coordinated with sound production and the overall movement patterns with which they occur; specifically, threat and fear. It is hypothesized that vocalizations and facial expressions are "protective responses" associated with the total patterns of threat and fear. In addition, it is suggested that "protective responses" are elicited by novel or noxious stimuli and the greater their novelty or noxiousness, the greater the intensity of the vocal and facial response.

   In summary three related approaches to the study of evolution of behavior have been considered. In one the broad course of evolution of behavior is assessed on the basis of gross structural changes associated with evolutionary development. These data can be used to understand differences and similarities in the behaviors of living animal groups. A second approach involves the search for homologous behaviors among species of a particular class or order. The third approach involves a refinement of the first in which the evolution of behavior is examined in closely related species in terms of specific items of behavioral evolution. Such data also provide supplementary information to support inferences about evolution based on structural features. In general, innate behavior patterns, involving specific stimulus-response elements or larger functional units, such as nesting, are used for these analyses. Tinbergen (1951) points out that the response elements, the movements associated with these behavioral units, are more conservative indexes of evolutionary change and are, therefore, more useful as indexes of evolutionary development than the stimulus elements that elicit these movements.

GENETICS OF HOARDING: II. HOARDING BEHAVIOR

OF HYBRID AND BACKCROSSED STRAINS OF RATS

JOHN S. STAMM
California Institute of Technology

In the previous investigation (3) simultaneous hoarding tests were conducted with groups of rats from homozygous strains. Rats from a nonagouti black-hooded strain hoarded significantly more than the group of agouti Irish rats. The results suggested that hoarding behavior of rats is influenced by heredity. The genetic basis of hoarding was further explored in the present experiments by conducting tests with progenies from the two groups of rats.

Hoarding tests were first conducted with the F1 generation, from crosses between Ss from the high-hoarding and low-hoarding strains. According to procedures of genetic experimentation (2), the genetic characteristics might then be established from the hoarding scores of the F1 Ss and their offspring in the F2 and backcrossed generations to the high-hoarding and low-hoarding parental groups. However, it was practically not possible to conduct simultaneous tests with three relatively large groups of rats, because each hoarding experiment requires a considerable amount of equipment and lasts for several weeks. Since the hoarding performance of the F1 Ss was found to be strikingly similar to that of their high-hoarding parents, the F1 rats were mated with rats from the low-hoarding Irish strain, and the hoarding activity of the offspring, the Fb Ss, was determined. The genetic influences on hoarding behavior might then be clarified by comparisons of hoarding scores among four strains of rats—the F1 and Fb Ss and the two parental groups.

METHOD

Animals

The F1 Ss were the progeny of crosses between the black-hooded and Irish rats used in the previous investigation (3). This group consisted of six litters from black-hooded females and one litter from an Irish mother. At birth the mean litter size was 7.4. The young remained in breeding cages until they were approximately five weeks old, when they were weaned, marked, and placed in group cages of four to seven rats of the same sex. They were transferred in individual experimental cages when 155 to 190 days old. At that time the median weight for the females was 190 gm. and for the males 275 gm. Hoarding tests were conducted with 23 female and 17 male rats from the Fl generation.

The Fb Ss were the backcross generation between Fl and Irish rats. This group consisted of 12 litters from Fl and two litters from Irish females, because fewer Irish females were available. According to this breeding procedure one would not expect to obtain many hoarding differences resulting from sex-linked factors. At birth the mean litter size was 6.1. The young were raised according to the procedure used for the Ss in the Fl group. The Fb rats were placed in experimental cages when 128 to 162 days old. At that time the median weights were 170 gm. for the females and 237 gm. for the males. The experimental group consisted of 31 females and 20 male rats from the Fb generation.

Procedure

The apparatus and experimental procedure were similar to those described previously (3), except that the hoarding alleys were only 30 in. long. Because only 28 hoarding alleys and cages were available, it was necessary to run groups of Ss consecutively. Twelve Ss in the Fl group had hoarding trials after 28 Ss in this group had completed the experiment. The hoarding trials of the Fb group began with 28 Ss, and subsequently four groups, consisting of 5 to 9 Ss each, were placed in the apparatus as it became available.

The Ss were placed in the experimental cages 4 to 6 days before the first hoarding trial. Each daily 20-min. hoarding trial was preceded by a 40-min. feeding period when Ss was permitted to consume two pellets of Purina Laboratory Chow. An S was removed from the hoarding apparatus after it had hoarded consistently for 12 consecutive days. The range of daily room temperature was 68° to 76° F. during the hoarding experiment with the Fl group and 72° to 78° F. during the experiment with the Fb group.

Hoarding Scores

The mean hoarding score for each S was derived from its hoarding activity during the 12-day test period. This period began when the hoarding curve for S no longer showed systematic changes, but only fluctuated from its mean value. The consistency of hoarding during this period was verified by comparing the S's mean score for the first six days with the mean score for the last six days. The two mean scores did not differ significantly for any S. The 12-day test period started several days after the onset of hoarding; the median interval was 2.6 days for the Fl and 2.7 days for the Fb group.

In order to compare the hoarding behavior of the two experimental groups, which did not have simultaneous hoarding tests, it was important to select an appropriate hoarding scale. Hoarding scales which have been generally employed are the "number of pellets collected per trial," or a logarithmic function of this measure, as proposed by Morgan (1). The latter scale results in a more normal distribution of scores and minimizes variabilities of scores for high-hoarding rats. However, Morgan's scale gives undue weight to differences between low-hoarding scores, i.e., when no or only a few pellets are collected. For the present analysis Morgan's scale was therefore modified by assigning scores of 0 or 1 to pellet collections of 0 or 1, respectively. For collections of 2 pellets or more, logarithmic scores (H scores) were obtained according to the equation $H = 10 \log (\text{no. of pellets} + 1) - 3$. The resulting H scale, which ranged from 0 to 16, seemed suitable for evaluating the present data. Each S's mean H score for the 12-day test period was then computed.

RESULTS

The main findings of the present investigation are summarized in Table 1, which includes the hoarding scores for the original parent strains. For comparisons of hoarding activity between groups of *Ss*, the H scale was divided into four categories. The upper limits of these categories correspond to collections of 4, 13, 34, and 88 pellets, respectively. The proportion of *Ss* in each experimental group with mean H scores in each of these categories is also shown in Table 1. (The lowest mean H score obtained was 1.7 for a Fb *S*; the highest was 15.8 for a *S* in the F1 group).

TABLE 1
MEAN HOARDING SCORES FOR FOUR STRAINS OF RATS

Strain	N	H Score for Group		Proportion of S's in Hoarding Category (H Scale)			
		Mean	σ	1–4	5–8	9–12	13–16
Irish	10	5.8	2.05	.40	.50	.100	.00
Black-hooded	10	12.5	3.26	.10	.00	.10	.80
F1	40	13.2	2.46	.025	.075	.125	.775
Fb	51	8.2	3.97	.234	.273	.293	.196

It may be seen from Table 1 that the hoarding performance of the F1 group was similar to that of its high-hoarding parent strain. The mean hoarding score for the Fb group was between the scores for the two parent groups. Moreover, the Fb group had about the same number of *Ss* in each of the four hoarding categories.

The significance of the differences of hoarding activity between groups of *Ss* was determined by computing chi-square coefficients for scores above and below 8.5. These coefficients, as shown in Table 2, indicate that there were no significant differences between the F1 and

TABLE 2
CHI-SQUARE COEFFICIENTS BETWEEN GROUPS OF SUBJECTS *

Groups compared	Chi Square	Probability
Irish vs. black-hooded	16.2	$< .01$
F1 vs. Irish	23.8	$< .01$
F1 vs. black-hooded	0.0	$> .10$
F1 vs. Fb	15.3	$< .01$
Fb vs. Irish	3.8	.05
Fb vs. black-hooded	4.1	$< .05$

* For criterion of H score $= 8.5$; using Yates's corrections for continuity.

the black-hooded groups, whereas both these groups hoarded significantly more than did either the Irish or the Fb group. The difference
between the Fb and Irish groups did not appear significant according
to the present criterion.

For further comparisons between the F1 and Fb groups, their distributions of individual hoarding scores were obtained and are shown
in Figure 1. These curves are constructed from the 12 daily scores for

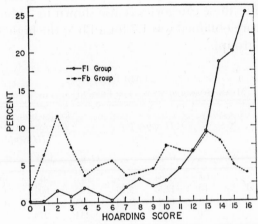

Fig. 1. Distribution of individual hoarding
scores (H scale) for the two groups of *Ss*. The area
under each curve is equal to 100.

each *S*, i.e., from 480 scores in the F1 and 612 scores in the Fb group.
The curve for the F1 group shows a concentration of high hoarding
scores. Its shape approximates a J curve and is similar to the distribution curve for the black-hooded parents, except that the latter's
mode was at 14 (25 per cent of the scores). These two curves have low
frequencies for H scores below 11. The shape of the distribution curve
for the Fb group is more complex; it may be considered either rectangular or bimodal, with maximum frequencies at scores of 2 and 13,
respectively. The distribution curve for the Irish parents is not of
the expected J curve shape with a maximum at the low end of the
scale, but it has a flat top between scores of 1 and 7, fluctuates between
8 and 12, and declines rapidly for higher hoarding scores. The modal
frequency for this distribution is at 2 (11 per cent of the scores). The
shape of this curve may be partially explained by the fact that some of
the Irish rats collected relatively large amounts of pellets for a few
days after their onset of hoarding and hoarded little during the subsequent trials. Figure 1 expresses clearly the difference in distribution
of scores between the F1 and Fb groups.

DISCUSSION

Hoarding behavior of rats is dependent on several known factors, such as age and the experimental arrangement, and on unknown variables which may be related to variations in the daily hoarding of individual rats under seemingly controlled experimental conditions. In the previous investigation (3) the effects of many of these factors were reduced by conducting simultaneous hoarding trials with rats from several strains. However, this was not possible in the present investigation in which Ss from different generations were compared. Moreover, in order to obtain reasonably large samples of Ss it was necessary, because of limited facilities, to conduct successive trials with groups of Ss in each of the generations.

In spite of the limitations imposed by the nature of the experiment, the hoarding behavior of the F1 and Fb groups could be compared. The F1 group exhibited a relatively uniform and high-level hoarding activity, whereas the distribution of mean scores of the Fb group showed greater variability, and the curve for individual scores (Fig. 1) suggests a bimodal distribution. Comparisons between these distributions, for relatively large groups of Ss, support the hypothesis of the genetic basis of hoarding.

The high-level hoarding of the F1 group suggests that genetic dominance is involved. A trait which is determined by a single dominant gene should appear in every member of the F1 generation. The Fb generation (backcross to recessive parent) should then segregate into two equal groups, one exhibiting the dominant, the other the recessive trait. This type of segregation may be readily observed for physical traits, which can be expressed by indices based on absolute scales of measurement. A behavioral trait, like hoarding, however, can only be measured on a relative scale, which permits comparisons among groups of Ss for this trait. When comparing the present groups of Ss with each other, the H score of 8.5, which is near the median of the scale, may be considered the point separating the high- from the low-hoarding Ss. According to this criterion, 90 per cent of both the black-hooded parents and the F1 group, but only 10 per cent of the Irish parents, were high hoarders. Among the Fb group 51 per cent of the Ss were high hoarders and 49 per cent low hoarders. These results are in general agreement with those expected if a single dominant gene were involved.

Distributions of measurements which are frequently obtained for inherited behavioral traits may be accounted for by Tryon's hypothesis of "independently assorting multiple Mendelian factors" (4, p.

349). An investigation of this hypothesis would require data about the hoarding behavior of additional hybrid strains, such as the F2 generation and its backcrosses to the original parental strains. Since these stains were not bred in the present experiment, the multiple gene hypothesis could not be examined.

The genetic character of hoarding may be a sex-linked factor. In this case *S*s with Irish mothers should segregate into high-hoarding females and low-hoarding males. This hypothesis could not be investigated, because there were only two *S*s in the F1 group with Irish mothers, and in the Fb group only six *S*s came from Irish females—three females that were high hoarders and three males, of which two were high hoarders. In order to test the sex-linked hypothesis, further investigations should be conducted which employ the appropriate breeding procedures.

When breeding the black-hooded with the Irish rats, the latter's fur color and agouti characteristics were dominant. Consequently, all *S*s in the F1 and Fb groups resembled the Irish rats in physical appearance. It was therefore not possible to relate hoarding to physical characteristics.

In the previous investigation (3) the two parent strains also differed significantly on measures of onset of hoarding. In the present study both of *S*s showed a wide range of onset of hoarding, and there were no differences between the groups on this measure. Onset of hoarding therefore does not appear to be influenced by the genetic factors which determine the amount of pellet collection.

The results of the present investigations support the hypothesis of the genetic basis for hoarding behavior in rats. The simplest interpretation, consistent with the present data, suggests that a single dominant factor is primarily responsible for the obtained differences in hoarding performance among the strains of rats investigated. However, the hypothesis of multiple genetic factors may not be excluded.

SUMMARY

In the previous investigation (3) two strains of rats were found that differed significantly in their hoarding behavior. Subjects from the high-hoarding strain were mated with *S*s from the low-hoarding strain. The offspring, the F1 group, were given hoarding tests when approximately six months old. The *S*s in the F1 group were then backcrossed to the low-hoarding parent strain, producing the Fb group, which had hoarding tests when about five months old.

The distribution of hoarding scores from *S*s in the F1 group was similar to that for their high-hoarding parents. The hoarding scores for the Ss in the Fb group, however, were widely distributed, and the group's mean score fell between the means for the two parent strains. The distribution of scores for the Fb group showed a bimodal tendency, with maxima for low- and high-hoarding scores, respectively.

The results of this investigation support the hypothesis that hoarding behavior is influenced by heredity.

REFERENCES

1. MORGAN, C. T. The statistical treatment of hoarding data. *J. comp. Psychol.*, 1945, **38**, 247–56.
2. SRB, A. M., AND OWEN, R. D. *General genetics.* San Francisco: W. H. Freeman, 1952.
3. STAMM, J. S. Genetics of hoarding: I. Hoarding differences between homozygous strains of rats. *J. comp. physiol. Psychol.*, 1954, **47**, 157–61.
4. TRYON, R. C. Individual differences. In F. A. Moss (ed.), *Comparative psychology.* New York: Prentice-Hall, 1942.

STUDIES IN EXPERIMENTAL BEHAVIOR GENETICS:

I. THE HERITABILITY OF PHOTOTAXIS IN A POPULATION

OF DROSOPHILA MELANOGASTER

JERRY HIRSCH
Columbia University

and JAMES C. BOUDREAU
University of California, Berkeley

It has frequently been observed that individual differences (IDs) in behavior can be inherited; e.g., Tryon (11) has reported on the inheritance of maze-learning ability, and Kallmann and Baroff (5) on the inheritance of behavior pathologies. The present paper extends the study of the inheritance of IDs in behavior to a part of the phylogenetic series at which experimental behavior genetic (BG) analysis is feasible, viz., the genus *Drosophila*. The behavior chosen for BG analysis is the reaction to light, phototaxis—an apparently innate or unconditioned response. Taxes have the advantage of representing relatively constant S–R relationships: the repeated presentation of a single stimulus value appears to elicit, depending on the method of measurement, either a characteristic response or a characteristic probability of response. Both the characteristics of the response and the probability of the response have been shown to vary as a function of two parameters, the value of the stimulus presented and the strain of organisms stimulated (1, 8).

Brown and Hall have measured strain differences in phototaxis. The immediate purpose of the present study is to measure IDs in, and to estimate the heritability of, phototaxis within a single strain. (Roughly, "heritability," h^2, refers to that portion of the total variance due to additive genetic causes [6, p. 111].) This is one of several studies of *Drosophila* behavior in which an experimental attack is being made on the long unresolved question of whether abilities are under the control of one general factor (9) or many specific factors (10).

At present three *Drosophila* behaviors are under study: phototaxis, geotaxis (3), and eating rate (2).

METHOD

Experimental Design

Individual differences in phototaxis were measured in a **Y** maze by the method of mass screening (4). The measurements consisted of ten mass-screening trials, which in the foundation population had the reliability, $r_{tt} = 0.673$ (4. Formula 6).

Selection pressure was applied, and a system of assortative mating was used, i.e., the highest-scoring animals within the high strain and the lowest-scoring animals within the low strain were bred together, respectively.

Behavioral Analysis

Apparatus. Individual differences in the approach to light were studied in the **Y** maze shown in Figure 1. The maze consisted of three 5-in. lengths of acrylic

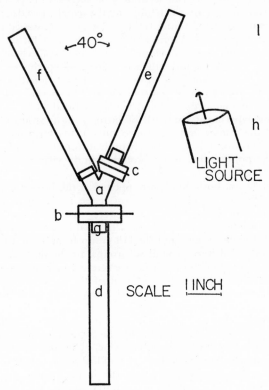

Fig. 1. Apparatus for measuring the reaction of *Drosophila* to light.

tubing, *f, e, d,* having ½-in. inside diameter. These tubes were attached to a **Y** joint, *a,* having ½-in. outside diameter and ⅜-in. inside diameter. Tubes *d* and *e,* which served as the starting path and the lighted arm of the **Y** respectively, were attached to the center unit, *a,* by plastic sleeves, *b* and *c.* Both sleeves were fitted with sliding plastic "doors" 0.02-in. thick to prevent premature approach to the choice point and retracing after a choice.

All parts of the maze were painted black on the outside with the exception of the starting tube, *d,* and the lighted tube, *e.* To eliminate reflections, the

cotton plunger in the starting tube was dyed black. The attrahent was light reflected from cotton at the end of Arm *e*. Although the same tube (Arm *e*) was
always illuminated, the illuminated side was varied after each block of two trials
(tests have shown that the tubes themselves do not act as stimuli). This was accomplished by rotating the entire front section of the maze 180° on the **Y** joint and
shifting the light to the other side. A microscope light was placed at *h* and focused
on the cotton at the end of *e*. The distance from the light source to the cotton
was 6 in. The illumination at this distance is 100 ft-c., as measured by a Weston
illumination meter, Model 756. Thus, the stimulating source of light was indirect.
This was neccessary because in preliminary studies using a direct suorce, i.e., a
light shining through *e* to *d*, it was evident that secondary reflections were being
set up in the starting arm, *d*, and that these constituted competing attrahents
with the result that many flies never left the starting tube.

   Procedure. The sexes were run separately on successive days. Each generation
the males were run one day after hatching and the females two days after hatching.
The role of heredity in determining IDs in behavior was assessed by the response
of the population to selection. Virgin females are necessary for selective breeding.
Since *melanogaster* females remain virgin for only the first 7 to 8 hr. after hatching,
the cultures were cleared of all flies the day before an experiment, and only those
flies that hatched in the following 7 hr. were tested. Occasionally, to obtain larger
samples, flies were collected over two consecutive 7-hr. periods. Hence, the maximum age difference among the animals never exceeded 14 hr.

   The behavior experiment consisted of introducing a group of flies into the
starting tube of the **Y** maze and inserting a plug of black cotton behind them to
seal the tube. The cotton was immediately pushed forward to within 0.5 in. of the
door to the choice point so that all flies would be in the vicinity of the choice point
at the start of a trial.

   A trial lasted 30 sec. Both doors were opened at the beginning of a trial, and
30 sec. later the door to the illuminated arm of the **Y** was closed. In this way, on
each trial the flies that approached the light were separated from the others. That
is, on Trial 1 the initial group of flies was separated into two pass-fail subgroups.
On Trial 2 both the pass group and the fail group from Trial 1 were tested and
were in turn subdivided into pass-fail subgroups. In the method of mass screening, the subgroups obtained on one trial are retested separately on the next trial
and further subdivided. A complete account of the method is given elsewhere
(4). In this experiment ten mass-screening trials were used; therefore, the distribution of final scores ranges from 0 through 10.

   Dyes were added to the medium on which the flies were raised. Bismark brown
was used for the low strain and Nile blue for the high strain (tests have shown that
reversing the colors does not affect the behavior). The colors were ingested along
with the food. Since the females of the high and low strains could be distinguished
by the colors they had absorbed, they were run in the apparatus together. It was
necessary, however, to run the males in separate groups, since they did not show
the colors clearly.

Genetic Analysis

   Subjects. The Ss were 3,424 fruit flies, *Drosophila melanogaster*, Formosa wild
type. The initial sample of animals was obtained from regular stocks in the genetics laboratory of the zoology department of the University of California,
Berkeley. The flies were raised on standard *Drosophila* medium (to which color
had been added) in ½-pt. culture bottles at 25° C.

   Mating system. Selection pressure of variable intensity was applied under a
system of restricted assortative mating. Animals were mated on the basis of
phenotypic merit without regard to family relationship. In the foundation popu-

lation animals with similar extreme phototactic scores were mated. In all filial generations the same selection criteria were applied with the further restriction that matings were always within and never between the two strains established by selection from the foundation population. Thus, the high and low strains were reproductively isolated, and inbreeding undoubtedly increased down through the generations.

If a sufficient number of animals received extreme scores, i.e., 0 or 10, only members of these classes were chosen for breeding. If not, individuals in adjacent classes were also used for breeding. The intensity of selection pressure increased because the percentage of animals receiving extreme scores increased as selection progressed. Selection was carried on over 29 generations with the exception of Generations 10, 11, 12, and 13, when mass mating was permitted (within the separate strains) and no behavior tests were made.[1]

RESULTS

Male and female data have been combined except for Generations 7, 8, and 9, for which female data alone are presented. In these generations the males were given only enough test trials to identify the extreme scorers for breeding. Data are not available for Generations 10 through 13 or for Generation 16, when the apparatus broke.

Figure 2 presents the percentage of trials on which the light was approached by the high and low strains over 29 generations of selection. Clearly, there is an early response to selection, and despite fluctu-

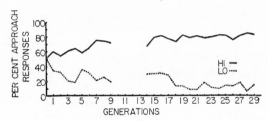

Fig. 2. Percentage of trials on which light was approached per generation.

ations the expected values of the selected strains show progressive divergence from the foundation population value of 51.6% to asymptotic values of approximately 80.0% for the high strain and 15.0% for the low strain.

Figure 3 presents the distribution of phototactic scores for the foundation population and for filial Generations 1, 2, 7, and 29. Inspection of the figure reveals that selection effects marked changes in dispersion as well as in central tendency. The changes in dispersion are

---

[1] As the medium on which to establish the basic principles of BG, *Drosophila* is thus an animal quite superior to the laboratory mammals such as mice, rats, or guinea pigs. Compare the present results, obtained in about a year, with the Tryon study (11), which required over 15 years.

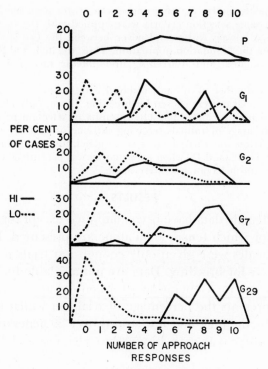

FIG. 3. Distribution of light-approach scores for
Generations 0, 1, 2, 7, and 29.

shown in Figure 4, where the ratio of the variance of each selected
generation to that of the foundation population is plotted.

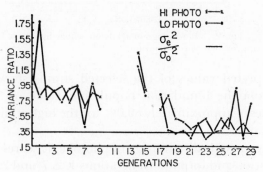

FIG. 4.   The ratio of the variance of each selected
generation to the variance of the foundation popu-
lation, σ_i^2/σ_o^2, for the "high" and "low" phototactic
strains, σ_e^2/σ_o^2 is the asymptote predicted from the
reliability of the foundation population scores (see
text).

It has been predicted that the limits of selective breeding would depend upon the reliability of the ID measurements in the foundation population (4, p. 410), i.e., when the variance in the selected lines decreases to the size of the variance error of measurement in the foundation population, further selection should be ineffective, since at that point the method of observation is no longer discriminating among individuals. In the present study the foundation population measurements have a reliability $r_{tt} = 0.673$, a variance $\sigma_0^2 = 6.38$, and a variance error of measurement $\sigma_e^2 = \sigma_0^2 (1 - r_{tt}) = 6.38 (1 - 0.673) = 2.09$ (4, Formula 8). Hence the ratio of the variance of the selected strains to that of the foundation population should approach the asymptote:

$$\frac{\sigma_e^2}{\sigma_0^2} = 2.09/6.38 = 0.327$$

In Figure 4 it can be seen that the variance ratio for the high photo strain appears to be settling down near the line 0.327. The variance ratio for the low strain, however, has not stabilized enough yet to determine whether it is approaching the predicted asymptote.

Next, let us examine the extent to which IDs in phototaxis are genetically determined. If it is assumed that the average of the variances of the two selected strains over Generations 28 and 29 represents an upper limit to the variability to be expected in an isogenic line, then we have available a conservative estimate of the heritability, h^2, of phototaxis in the foundation population under the present experimental conditions.

All methods of estimating heritability rest on measuring how much more closely animals with similar genotypes resemble each other than less closely related animals do. . . . Variation within isogenic lines is wholly environmental. Comparing this with the variation in an otherwise similar random breeding population may give an estimate of heritability (7, p. 92).

For the high strain $\sigma_{28}^2 = 2.88$ and $\sigma_{29}^2 = 2.08$; for the low strain $\sigma_{28}^2 = 1.63$ and $\sigma_{29}^2 = 4.51$. The average of these four variances is $\bar{\sigma^2} = 2.77$. Hence: $h^2 = (\sigma_0^2 - \bar{\sigma^2})/\sigma_0^2 = (6.38 - 2.77)/6.38 = 0.566$, i.e., at least 57% of the phenotypic variance is genetic variance. This is a conservative estimate because the value of the reliability coefficient sets an upper limit to the values an estimate may take (as calculated, h^2 is 84% of the reliable phenotypic variance). Furthermore, h^2 contains only the additive portions of the genetic variance; it does not include variance due to dominance or to epistasis (i.e., dominance of nonallelic genes).

No estimate can be made of the heredity-environment interaction because only a single stimulus condition has been employed.

DISCUSSION

The aim of the present experiment has been both exploratory and descriptive. Its purpose has been to examine the possibility of studying IDs in behavior and their genetic bases in a species on which detailed genetic analysis can be performed.

The results which have been reported indicate that the study of *Drosophila* behavior is quite feasible, that IDs in performance can be measured in groups both reliably and efficiently by the method of mass screening, and that the ID's variance contains a large genetic component to which the techniques of experimental genetics may now be applied.

Since the present data have been obtained with a laboratory stock considered to be rather inbred [2] and therefore not very heterogeneous genetically, it is to be expected that a larger genetic variance would be found in a less inbred natural population. These findings have implications for psychological theory.

Theory testing in psychology is usually done on human Ss or on laboratory strains of animals which, it is reasonable to assume, are genetically much less alike than our *Drosophila*. (The Formosa stock has been maintained in the laboratory in small cultures for more than 20 years. Inbreeding has, therefore, had over 700 generations in which to exercise its homogenizing influence. Within the same period of time laboratory strains of rats would have completed about 70 generations. Furthermore, *Drosophila melanogaster* have only 4 independently assorting pairs of chromosomes whereas rats have 21 and human beings at least 23.) If large genetic differences do exist in the populations now being studied by psychologists, it should be of interest to determine in what ways stimulus control of behavior depends upon the genotype under stimulation.

SUMMARY

Behavior genetic analysis of the unconditioned response, phototaxis, has been carried through several steps: Individual differences in phototaxis have been measured reliably and efficiently in a *Drosophila* population by the method of mass screening. The genetic determination of individual differences in behavior has been demon-

---

[2] Personal communication from Th. Dobzhansky.

strated by the response to selection, and the heritability has been estimated to be more than one-half the phenotypic variance.

REFERENCES

1. BROWN, F. A., AND HALL, V. A. The directive influence of light upon *Drosophila melanogaster* Meig and some of its eye mutants. *J. exp. Zool.*, 1936, 74, 205–20.
2. DURKIN, R. D. Eating behavior of *Drosophila melanogaster*. Unpublished honors study, Psychol. Dept., Columbia Univer., 1957.
3. HIRSCH, J. Behavior genetic studies of individual differences in *Drosophila melanogaster*. *Amer. Psychologist*, 1956, 11, 450–51. (Abstract)
4. HIRSCH, J. AND TRYON, R. C. Mass screening and reliable individual measurement in the experimental behavior genetics of lower organisms. *Psychol. Bull.*, 1956, 53, 402–10.
5. KALLMANN, F. J., AND BAROFF, G. S. Abnormal psychology. *Ann. Rev. Psychol.*, 1956, 6, 297–326.
6. LERNER, I. M. *Population genetics and animal improvement.* Cambridge: Cambridge Univer. Press, 1950.
7. LUSH, J. L. *Animal breeding plans.* Ames, Iowa: Collegiate Press, 1945.
8. SCOTT, J. P. Effects of single genes on the behavior of *Drosophila*. *Amer. Naturalist*, 1943, 77, 184–90.
9. SPEARMAN, C. *The abilities of man.* New York: Macmillan, 1927.
10. TRYON, R. C. A theory of psychological components—an alternative to "mathematical factors." *Psychol. Rev.*, 1935, 42, 425–54.
11. TRYON, R. C. Genetic differences in maze-learning ability in rats. In *Yearb. nat. Soc. Stud. Educ.*, 1940, 39(I), 111–19.

ON LOCOMOTORY MOVEMENTS IN BIRDS AND THE INTENTION MOVEMENTS DERIVED FROM THEM

by

A. DAANJE

(Eindhoven, Holland)

(adapted from the original Dutch manuscript by N. TINBERGEN)

I INTRODUCTORY

As all observers of animal behaviour know, many activities may occasionally be performed incompletely. This is especially true of locomotory movements. Walking, for instance, in a bird, may be seen in numerous degrees of intensity, arrangeable in a sliding scale from full intensity down to an almost imperceptible indication of it. Heinroth seems to have been the first to have called attention to these low intensity movements; he called them "intention movements" because the trained behaviour student can derive from their study a knowledge of what the animal is intending to do in the next few moments.

It has become clear to me that intention movements are, at least in birds, of much more common occurrence than is usually realised, and that a better knowledge of them could promote our insight into the factors underlying behaviour to a considerable degree. In order to recognise intention movements however it is imperative that the full intensity of the corresponding movements should be well known. A close study of locomotory movements, therefore, is the first step in a study of intention movements.

In this paper I want first to give a description of various types of locomotion in birds, especially of the start, as it is these first phases that are usually found in the intention movement. Most attention will be given to the movements of the legs, and less to those of the wings, because I am better acquainted with the phenomena of jumping and walking than with bird flight. When I have had to consider particulars of flight, I have mostly drawn from the extensive observations of Lorenz (1933) and Stolpe and Zimmer (1939).

Following upon the chapter on locomotion I will present a number of descriptions of more or less easily recognisable instances of intention movements. This will be followed by a chapter tending to show how such intention movements may have undergone certain changes or may have merged with other movements as a result of which it may be difficult to recognize them as derived from intention movements.

Although I have tried to study as great a variety of species as possible, I am quite aware of the limited scope of my study. Circumstances prevented me from studying birds more closely in Zoological gardens. Further, my observations are concerned with the mechanics of locomotory movements, and many anatomical and physiological aspects are ignored, being irrelevant to the present problem. Further, my use of the literature has been limited to papers in which full attention is given to this special aspect of locomotion. Lastly, I must stress the tentative nature of many of my interpretations. An intention movement can only be recognised as such with certainty after a thorough study of the behaviour pattern of the species concerned. I naturally desired to draw my examples from a great variety of species: therefore I was led to include observations, the interpretation of which still contains elements of uncertainty.

In spite of these limitations I think it justified to present this paper as a sketch of the probable origin of a number of hitherto little understood behaviour elements.

I am much indepted to Prof. Dr. E. J. Slijper and Dr. N. Tinbergen for their valuable criticism and advice, and to Mr. P. Sevenster for making most of the drawings.

II LOCOMOTORY MOVEMENTS OF THE HIND EXTREMITIES

A bird on the ground or in a tree may move in two ways: (1) hopping on both feet at the same time or (2) walking or striding with alternately moving feet. Many species only hop, others again hop or walk according to circumstances (see Stresemann 1927–1934). According to Stresemann the hop takes considerably more energy than walking or running. Many kinds of hopping birds get over this difficulty to a certain extent by avoiding using both feet at exactly the same time, instead placing them one after another. One and the same foot remains in advance of the other in a series of successive leaps. The hind foot gives the impetus and the jump is developed to its full extent by the foremost foot so that the movement becomes supple and less jerky, as can be seen, *e.g.,* in the Magpie. When going slowly a Magpie walks; at higher speeds it hops with the feet laterally behind each other; at still higher speed it proceeds with both feet side by side and pushing off simultaneously. This last method is never used for more than a short time.

The hopping type of locomotion, considered by Böker (1935) as the primitive type characteristic of the tree living ancestors of birds, will be treated first.

The Hop

A bird, for instance a Blackbird, about to take a hop to a higher branch, partially folds its legs (chiefly by bending the heeljoint), lowers its breast, so that the hipjoint is strongly bent, and draws in its head and neck, so that the backpart of the head is almost on and between the shoulders with the neck forming a more strongly curved S than in the attitude of rest. In taking the hop it begins with stretching the legs, raising the breast relative to the haunches (the hipjoint) and the neck rapidly changes from the S–form into an almost straight line. Shortly before and during alighting the opposite bending movement follows. Finally, after landing, it stretches itself from this "doubled up" position into the position of rest. Mechanically seen, this movement is best compared to the movement of a loosely coiled spring, that it pushed in and then relaxed, so that the spring jumps up. The maximum effect is reached when the stretching is performed by the whole spring. In much the same way, a leaping bird does not confine the stretching to the legs but uses the muscles of legs, body and neck.

When a bird makes a still larger leap, the wing is also moved. At first sight this may make the impression of incipient flight, but I believe that it is really something very different. When a man jumps with both legs at the same time, he not merely huddles up partly with his legs, bends his back and shortens his neck, but he also bends his elbows and even clenches his fists. When he jumps the arms go upwards and laterally forwards, the clenched fists are relaxed. Then the arms move backwards. This has nothing to do with flying, swimming or rowing in the air. I think the most important function is that of supporting the energy of the jump, the arms acting as additional springs, laterally fixed to the main spring. When the automatic movement of the arms is hindered, a much smaller leap will be the result, even in spite of a higher expenditure of energy.

The movement of the arms of a leaping bird is much the same. The relative lightness of the bird arm renders it of less importance in this respect than the arms of man. Moreover, the bird arm with its large carrying planes supports the bird during the leap. Although this latter function now probably overshadows the "spring" function, I nevertheless think the spring function is not to be neglected.

Finally in treating the jump we have to consider the movements of the tail. Many birds erect the tail just before jumping. During the start it is gradually lowered until it is almost in line with the body axis. At the same time it is spread to a certain extent. One function of the lowering of the tail might be the following. When the bird does not merely jump but actually flies up, the turning down and spreading of the tail may help in directing the flight. According to Lorenz (1933), a bird starts with fluttering wing movements (*"Rütteln"*). In this type of flight, the pressure centre of the wings usually lies a little in front of the centre of gravity of the bird, so that the back part of the body would be inclined to sink down if the tail were not spread out and pushed down a little.

It may be that the spreading of the tail in a jumping bird has something to do with flight. The initial erecting and the subsequent gradual lowering however has a function in the jumping. If the tail were kept in line with the body axis, the full weight of the tail would have to be carried right at the start. By first erecting and then gradually stretching the tail, its drag is coming into play gradually.

The parts of the body behind the hip joints carry out a similar movement, as they cannot help executing a downward movement as a result of the upward movement of the forepart of the body. The same line of argument could be applied here.

The tail movement just described is only found in few birds; the majority of them simply drag their tails along. This suggests that the movement of the tail is of little importance—which can easily be understood since the mass of the tail is, as a rule, very slight. But even in species that show no discernable tail movement in a normal hop, the movement of the tail does occur in a hop of high intensity.

The preparation for the jump may therefore be described as follows: the legs are bent, the breast is lowered, the neck is drawn in, the hind part of the body and the tail are pushed up and the wings are

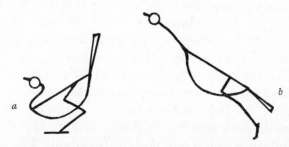

Fig. 1.   Scheme of a. the first and b. second phase of the jump by a bird.

slightly expanded (Fig. 1a). When the actual jump follows, legs and neck are stretched, the breast moves upward, the abdomen and tail are pushed down and the wings may make a single stroke (Fig. 1b).

All these movements can best be seen in larger, more slowly moving species, especially when executing large jumps. The smaller the bird and the smaller the jump, the smaller the amplitude of movements. In a hopping House Sparrow for instance, the legs seem to be the chief or may be the only parts of the body that make the bird move. Yet one should not conclude too hastily that the other movements are absent, for I know by experience that absence of movements may be only apparent, the movement being visible under exceptionally favourable conditions only. I once observed a House Sparrow which had some feathers stuck to its neck. These feathers, enlarging so to speak the neck's movements, clearly indicated that at each hop the neck was stretched and refolded. I also saw the movements in a hopping Chaffinch, a species in which the neck movements are very conspicuous during walking.

Fig. 2. The huddled and the stretched phase in under water swimming of *Podiceps nigricollis* Brehm. From a film by Frank and Neu in Stresemann, 1927–1934.

Figure 2 shows that there is a type of under water swimming that closely resembles hopping.

Walking

For a discussion of the movements during walking it will be necessary to select three types, *viz.*, (1) Domestic Hen, (2) Wagtail, (3) Duck.

Domestic Hen. Except for the movements of the legs the most distinct movement in a hen when walking is that of head and neck. With each step the head is brought forward and backward again. This head movement is linked up with the leg movement as follows. At the moment the leg which moves forward through the air (abbreviated: the air leg) almost reaches the ground and the most distal part of the leg on ground (ground leg) just passes backward under the body's gravity centre, the head reaches its most backward position. The stretching of the neck now begins, simultaneously with the stretching of the ground leg, which is now pushing backwards. The head reaches its most foreward position when the ground leg is stretched and is about to leave the ground. Now that this leg, which now has become air leg, moves forward, the head is withdrawn, to be pushed forward

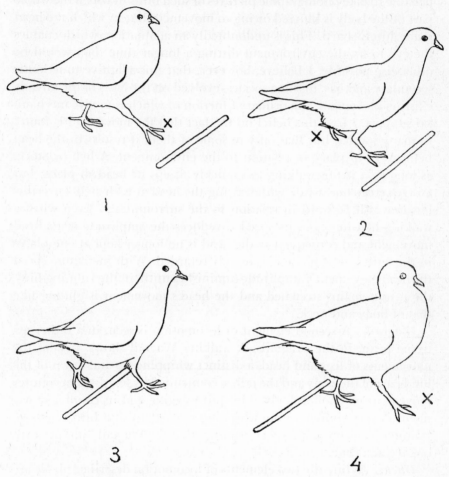

Fig. 3. Sagittal horizontal head movement of a walking Pigeon in connection with the movements of the legs. The feet in the figures, indicated with a cross, were not sharp in the original photographs, which proves that they were still moving as "air leg." For further explanation, see text. From a film by Thauer and Peters, 1938.

again when the other leg is stretched. Four phases of this movement are given in Figure 3.

It will be clear that the head is brought forward each time one of the legs is stretched. In other words, each step is a hop with one leg, and walking is alternate hopping. At each step the head gives mechanical assistance in exactly the same way as in each hop.

The movements of the head in walking have often been noticed and interpreted in another way. In some birds the head, when being drawn back, is kept at the same place in relation to the environment. It is possible to take photographic pictures of such birds in which the whole part of the body is blurred owing to movement but in which the head is absolutely sharp. This is undoubtedly an adaptation, which enables the eye to fix the environment during a longer time than would be otherwise possible. I believe, however, that this adaptive function is secondary and has, in some species, evolved on the basis of the already existing movement, the primary function of which is to give mechanical support. I base this belief on the fact that the movement is found in many species, but that only in some of them it results in the head being kept in place in relation to the environment. A hen or Stork, as long as it is not walking too quickly, keeps its head in place; but an Oystercatcher, while withdrawing the head at each step, nevertheless moves it forward in relation to the surroundings. Even when a walking hen increases its speed it reduces the amplitude of its head movement and consequently the head is no longer kept at one place; in the withdrawal phase it is merely retarded. With increasing speed the head movement's amplitude diminishes until, in the running bird, the neck remains stretched and the head's movement is gliding like that of body and neck.

Wagtail. A second element of locomotion is seen, in a rather extreme form, in the Wagtails. A walking Wagtail shows, besides the movements of legs and head, a distinct whipping up and down of the hind part of the body and the tail, accompanied by less distinct counter movements of the forebody. This tail wagging and its counter movements is very similar to the whipping movement of a bird's body in jumping. The only difference, again, is that the Wagtail "jumps" with one leg at a time.

Ducks. While the two elements of locomotion described above are taking place in a sagittal plane, the most striking movements of walking Ducks (waddling) do not. In Ducks, the pushing motion of the hind leg, pushes the body forward, and at the same time lifts the body at its side and turns it in a horizontal plane around the foremost leg. This lifting and turning element of walking is so conspicuous in Ducks because of (1) the relative shortness of their legs, (2) the wide distance between the legs and (3) the nearness of the center of gravity to the ground.

These three elements, *viz.*, the rhythmic withdrawal of head and neck, the tail wagging, and the waddling are by no means confined to these types because they are "specialists" which each show one of the elements in a very conspicuous form. Most, if not all, birds, show all these elements. Withdrawal of the head for instance is seen in slowly walking Pigeons, Rails, Cranes, *Tringa* species, Common Curlew, Ibis, Oystercatcher, Wagtails, Larks, Starling, Crows, Magpie, White Stork, Herons and foraging Black-headed Gull. It is even present in Ducks, although it is difficult to detect and shown only under favorable circumstances. It is difficult to see in the Lapwing because it runs too fast; but one can detect a slight forward movement of the head at the beginning of the run which is not withdrawn until the end.

Birds, such as the Lapwing, the Black-headed Gull and Terns, which take very short steps, *i.e.*, whose legs execute only a small angle displacement, show either very small head movements or none at all. A Heron, when striding almost erect and taking small steps, does not make the head movement; should however it take large steps with the body almost horizontal, as in foraging, then the head movements become very noticeable.

While in the Wagtail the tail moves even in relation to the abdomen, in Crows and other Song birds, in the Flamingo and possibly in many other birds one gets the impression that the tail moves merely as a consequence of the body movements.

Waddling, while most distinct in Ducks, Geese and Swans, is also seen in Pelicans, Cormorants, Parrots, and Crows. The Swallows and the Nightjar, though also short-legged, hardly show the waddling, because they always walk with such small steps. The Woodpeckers, also short-legged, always hop, even when on the ground and therefore do not waddle at all.

It will be clear therefore, that most birds show all the movements. Depending on the proportions of various parts of the body, on speed of motion, on the angular-displacement of the legs *etc.* now one of the elements, now another is more prominent. Absence of an element can only be established after very careful observation, because a movement may be hardly detectable, as is especially the case in species that have "specialised" into one of the types of locomotion. Other species, like, *e.g.*, the Crows, are non-specialists; showing all types of movement more or less equally developed.

III THE INTENTION MOVEMENT

As has been pointed out by Heinroth (1910) and by Lorenz (1935, 1941), an animal may under the influence of weak internal or external stimulation, perform incomplete movements. Because it is often possible to judge from these fragmentary or incipient movements what part of the behaviour pattern is activated at the moment, or in other words what the animal intends to do, Heinroth called such incipient movements intention movements *("Intentionshandlungen")*. Apart from the instances of intention movements in Ducks mentioned by Heinroth and Lorenz, relatively few intention movements have been described in literature. Yet my studies of locomotion have convinced me that intention movements are not at all rare in birds. For various reasons however they are not always readily recognisable. I will begin my description with the more obvious cases.

Intention Movements of Walking or Hopping

The most striking case is the initial phase, the bow. An alarmed Robin will perform one or more bows before it actually flies away. From the more or less erect resting posture, it rapidly lowers its breast, at the same time moving the hind part of the body and the tail upward. With a pronounced bow the wingtips are also moved upward and probably the legs are somewhat folded and the head drawn back. After this bow, the bird stretches itself again, raising the foremost part of the body and lowering the hind part. After what has been said about the jump it will be clear that the bow is nothing but the first phase of the jump, and that the subsequent stretching is the incipient form of the next phase of the jump, performed on the spot. The identity of these intention movements with the actual jump is obvious when, with growing alarm, the bird finally jumps or flies away.

Another example of this same type of bow is provided by the Magpie. When relatively strongly motivated, the Magpie also makes a very deep bow, raises the tail and the backpart of the body, and spreading the tail while doing so, but folding it again at the highest point. Also, it bends the heel joints and flaps the wing tips. From this highest intensity performance down to the merest indication there is a whole scale of increasingly incomplete movements. With decreasing intensity the wing movements are dropped first, then the actual bowing becomes less pronounced and finally only the tail flapping remains. This sequence of "fading" is clearly seen in the series of movements made after perching on a branch, when the locomotion impulses under the influence of an after-discharge, are gradually dying down. Besides this type of bow, which is very frequent, the Magpie, sometimes shows another type in which the bird bows slowly downward, putting up the tail and bending the legs, but remains in this position for rather a long time, sometimes fluttering its wings. The springing up follows after some time. This type of the bow is executed by one bird of a pair in front of the other. It is followed by flying away, the other bird following.

The Lapwing and many other waders when alarmed perform a movement which I believe to be derived from the bow, and which I propose calling the plovers' bow (following german usage, where it is called the *"Regenpfeiferknicks"*). An alarmed Lapwing raises the fore part of the body and stretches the neck a little, resuming the original posture immediately afterwards. This movement is very similar to the second phase of the robin's bow. The omission of the first phase of the bow may be connected with its omission in most cases of actual flying-away, when the Lapwing, having a rather horizontal normal position, does not bother to lower its forebody but jumps right up. Only when strongly alarmed does a Lapwing execute a deep bow. I observed this only once, in a bird with a broken wing which was being attacked by a Kestrel. This Lapwing bowed, and springing up made counter attacks.

This omission of the first phase can be observed in many birds that can fly up without jumping. I even saw it in a tame Duck that was reacting to food in my hand. Even when standing in a quite upright position it was able to jump up for more than 10 cm, using its toes only.

The intention movement of a Kingfisher, a bird that, when searching for fish, has a quite erect bearing, does not include the downward phase either but it raises the body some times before it flies off to the sighted prey to catch it.

The Little Owl may execute either one of the two phases. Upon the approach of a human it may duck, and remain ducked for some time (Fig. 4). When the enemy moves, it may keep up the erect posture for some time again and, upon the next movement of the enemy, duck down again.

In the case of the plovers' bow and of the Little Owl's movements one again meets with a different interpretation in literature in which quite another function is emphasized. It is generally supposed that these movements, by enlarging the parallax, help the bird in three dimensional analyses of the visual field. I believe, in both cases, but more especially in the owls, that this function certainly is not primary but that it may have evolved secondarily from the intention movement. My main argument is the fact that the intention movements are so widely distributed and occur in so many cases where nobody would attach any function in three dimensional vision to them. Also, I believe that the movements that help in three dimensional vision are, even in owls, different from the mere intention movements. Räber (1949) in his extremely thorough study of prey catching in owls, describes and figures in the Tawny Owl movements preceding the actual swooping down on the prey. The head is not only moved in vertical but also in a horizontal direction. According to Räber, these movements are, superficially, similar to intention movements, but fundamentally different (p. 16). I think it quite possible, however, that these fixation movements have evolved from the intention movement, in much the same way as the fixation of the head in some birds when walking may be a secondary development on top of the primary function of withdrawing the head at each step.

Such secondary developments may also be suspected in other, quite different cases. The crouching movement of an alarmed Lark, for instance, is quite obviously the first phase of the bow. It has evolved into an adaptation correlated with the cryptic colouration, and together they have the function of concealing the bird from visual feeders like predatory birds. This type of adaptive colouration and behaviour has evolved in many species.

In the Bittern, an inhabitant of reed beds, the second phase of the intention movement has evolved into a cryptic posture, the so called pole posture (Fig. 5). Both birds, Lark and Bittern (to chose only two examples) are forced, upon approaching danger, to do something in

Fig. 4a. and b. The ducked and the erected attitude of a frightened Little Owl.

the way of escape, but they freeze in one of the phases of the intention movement, *viz.* in the phase that has the greatest selective value in relation to the given environment and its own colouration. In the Bittern, adaptation has even gone so far as to make the bird take up its position very gradually.

The first phase of the bow is displayed by the Bittern under different conditions, *viz.* when the enemy approaches it very closely, which, from the viewpoint of selection, means that the chances of being noticed are greater than those of escaping unnoticed. This posture

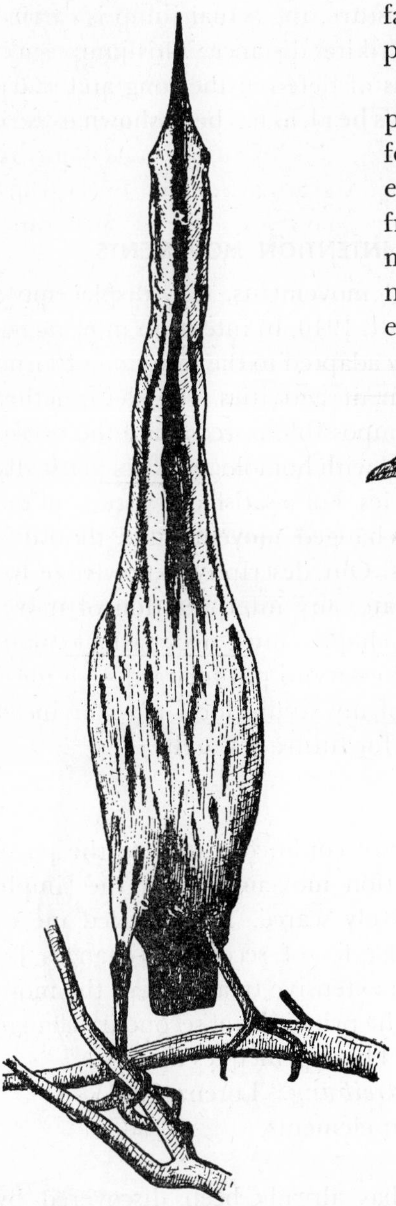

FIG. 5. The pole attitude of the Bittern. From a photograph by Schut in Portielje and Schut, 1938.

FIG. 6. Attitude of an alarmed Blond Ring Dove. From a photograph by Craig, 1909.

is adopted by a quick movement. The bird bends its legs, withdraws its head, and lifts its wings. On top of this, and certainly connected with its secondary value as a threat, the feathers are fluffed and the wings are spread, so as to make the bird appear as large as possible to the enemy. From this posture, the actual jump is carried out when the enemy comes within striking distance. This jump again has a secondary function as a means of defense: the long and sharp bill is thrusted towards the opponent's head, as has been shown experimentally by Portielje (1926).

. . . .

IV RITUALIZED FORMS OF INTENTION MOVEMENTS

Just as in other types of derived movements, *e.g.*, displacement activities (Tinbergen, 1940, Kortlandt, 1940, b) intention movements may be ritualized, that is, secondarily adapted to the function of social releaser. So in ritualized displacement activities, the deformation may be of such an extent that it is impossible to recognise the origin of the movement unless it is compared with homologous, less markedly ritualized movements in related species. For a satisfactory study of the origin of derived and secondarily changed movements a thorough comparative description is necessary. Our descriptive knowledge being still in a highly fragmentary state, any interpretation of movements as I am going to give in this chapter must necessarily remain highly speculative. Yet I think it necessary to put forward such ideas as I have developed in the course of my study; for I am convinced that some of them will prove fertile for future research.

Principles of Secondary Change

In the foregoing chapter I have not confined myself to the pure, unchanged, original types of intention movements, for the simple reason that these seem to be relatively scarce. This has led me to touch several times upon the principles of secondary changes involved. Before proceeding to a more extensive treatment of the more highly ritualized types I will discuss the principles of secondary change which I have encountered thus far. These principles are:

(1) Exaggeration. ("*Mimische Übertreibung*," Lorenz, 1941).
(2) Shifting thresholds of component elements.
(3) Loss of coordination.

Exaggeration. This principle has already been discovered by previous observers, and has been discussed by Lorenz, 1941. A good example is the tail whipping of the Magpie, and that of the Wagtails.

I am not quite certain whether exaggeration always springs from the same source. In the case of the Magpies' tail I believe it is connected with a function as a social releaser. I think however that exaggeration may in other cases be the result of the suppression of a movement by another drive. I have observed Willow Warblers continuously fluttering their wings while on the ground. One never sees this to such an intensity in Willow Warblers foraging in the tree. I am inclined to think that the inclination to flee to a safer tree was suppressed by the inclination to feed on some special food on the ground, and that this was the cause of the exaggerated wing fluttering.

Shifting Thresholds of Component Elements. Problems of threshold concern us here in two respects.

First, the intention movement as a whole is built up of various elements (movements of head, legs, wings, tail) that lead a more or less independent life within the whole. As I mentioned above, not all the elements have the same threshold for the general excitation evoking the movement as a whole. Thus in the Magpie the first sign of motivation is movement of the tail, while the other components, having a higher threshold, appear with increasing motivation.

As a general rule it seems that usually the most distal parts have the lowest threshold. This is the case in the tail wagging of dogs. I believe tail wagging in dogs to be the intention movement of walking. It is not, as is often supposed a sign of joy. Fierce dogs, growling or barking while on a chain or in the kennel wag their tails just as intensely as any dog let out by its master. The tail wagging is the lowest intensity of walking; with increasing motivation, as every dog owner knows the wagging movement will extend forwards, until at first the hind body is wagging, then the forelegs beat the ground alternately and finally the hind legs also "walk" on the spot.

Corresponding tail movements are shown by cats, when they prepare to jump, not only to catch prey, but also to reach a higher window. Often the whole tail moves, but sometimes only the extreme tip.

Now the relation between the thresholds of the components appears to vary considerably from species to species. As will be clear from many of the instances cited in the foregoing chapter, some species use mainly the tail in the intention movements, others the head, others the legs. This shift in the thresholds may even go so far that some of the elements are completely "lost." To complicate the matter still further, the thresholds may even change in one individual in the course of time—an instance of which is provided by the Teal, which as a rule bobs the head before flying up, but occasionally lifts

the wingtips. Even such an "element" as tail wagging is a system containing separate elements, and these elements, as we have seen, lead
their own life too. Thus in some species the downward movement,
in others the upward movement, in others again the lateral movement has become prominent.

   Loss of Coordination.   As was set forth in the first chapter, there is,
during locomotion as well as in the original intention movements, a
very rigid coordination in tempo between the separate elements; for
example—rhythm of the head, the legs, the tail and the wings. This
synchronisation may break down in some cases, and in order to understand this phenomenon fully it is necessary to study the mechanism
of coordination as far as it is known.

   Coordination between limbs has been studied by Von Holst, mainly
in fishes, but also in other animals, including man.

   Von Holst found that in many fishes the oscillations of the pectoral
fins, the dorsal fin and the caudal fin are synchronous. In the Labrus–
Sargus type for instance the pectorals alternate, and the dorsal, caudal
and anal fins are synchronised both with each other and with the
pectoral rhythm.

   Under certain circumstances, this coordination may break down,
that is to say, whereas each fin still oscillates regularly, their rhythms
are no longer synchronized but are entirely independent of each
other. Both complete (absolute) synchronisation and complete lack
of synchronisation are observable in fish after severance of the connections between spinal cord and the brain. Also, external stimuli,
while apparently necessary to initiate the movements, are not necessary for the synchronisation. The coordination between the various
fin rhythms, therefore, is entirely an intrinsic faculty of the spinal

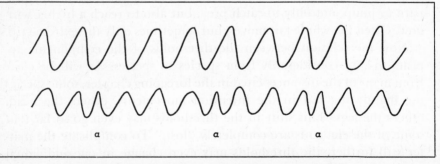

Fig. 10.   The magnet effect in *Labrus*. Above: rhythm of the pectorals (dominant).
Below: rhythm of the dorsal fin (dependent) influenced by the pectorals' rhythm. After
Von Holst, 1937.

cord. This faculty has been studied more closely by Von Holst, who showed that synchronisation was due to an influence exerted by the spinal mechanism responsible for the rhythm of another fin. This influence responsible for synchronisation, the exact nature of which is still unknown, was called by Von Holst the magnet effect. The magnet effect, exerted by one rhythm upon the other, tends to slow down or to speed up the frequency of the dependent rhythm until it coincides with that of the dominant rhythm.

Von Holst discovered further that the magnet effect did not always secure complete synchronisation but often influenced the dependent rhythm in a "half hearted" way, in that it succeeds in forcing its rhythm upon the dependent fin when the phase difference is not too great, but fails to do so in case of greater phase differences (Fig. 10). He called this relative coordination.

Von Holst also found a type of relative coordination which does not affect the tempo but the amplitude of the dependent rhythm. A dominant fin may increase the movements of a dependent fin when they are moving in a certain phase relationship (*e.g.*, synchronously) but suppress the dependent rhythm in the contrary phase relationship. This effect upon the amplitude was called the superposition effect (Fig. 11).

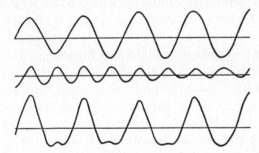

Fig. 11. Schematic representation of the superposition effect. Above: rhythm 1, of a sinusoid character, with increasing amplitude. Center: rhythm 2, of a sinusoid character but with smaller and decreasing amplitude. Below: result of superposition of the two rhythms. After Von Holst, 1937.

The phenomena of relative coordination seem to be much more frequent in fish than in land Vertebrates, although Von Holst found some instances in the latter, even in Man. Yet I think the phenomenon is more common in birds than Von Holst seems to think. The coordination between the two legs, it is true, is always absolute, but

the movements of head and (or) tail are often very loosely coordinated
with those of the legs.

Owing to the differences in thresholds of the elements involved in
locomotion one element (1) may, when locomotion begins very
gradually, come in action well before the element with the next
higher threshold (2) steps in. As long as (2) does not act, its possible
influence on (1) does not show itself. Now if (2) is dominant to (1),
the rhythm and amplitude of (1) suddenly change when (2) comes in
action. The following may serve as an example. In a walking domestic
hen the movements of the head are absolutely synchronised with those
of the legs. The head makes one oscillation at each oscillation of each
leg, so that each leg makes one oscillation in the time the head makes
two oscillations (phase relation 1:2). Now when a hen starts walking
slowly, the head movement is the first to set in, and follows its own
"local" rhythm. After some head oscillations the legs may begin to
step, but in a very low tempo, so that the phase relation may be 1:6.
After a while the leg movement may be speeded up and the head
movement slowed down, the relation will become 1:4 and finally 1:2.

When the movements during the 1:4 phase relationship are studied
more closely it will be seen that not all head movements are exactly
alike. Those which coincide with the leg movement as in normal
locomotion are reinforced, those in between are weakened. This is
relative coordination of quite the same type as described in fish by
Von Holst.

The influence of the magnet effect on the tempo of the oscillations
can be observed for instance in the Moorhen. When the bird is a little
alarmed it tips up its tail; then follows a rather slow movement with
the legs. The tempo of the leg movement gradually increases while
the rhythm of the tail becomes retarded until at a certain moment the
phase relation 1:2 of the oscillations of legs and tail is almost reached.
The rhythm of the tail however is still a little too fast; the magnet
effect is too feeble to achieve absolute coordination and the tail movement gets more and more ahead in relation to the leg movements
until at a certain moment the difference in time between the two
oscillations becomes so great and the influence of the magnet effect
so feeble that again the tail moves at its own higher frequency, inserting one quick oscillation; after which both movements of tail and
legs coincide again in about the relation 1:2. Such insertions of a
quick oscillation may be repeated more often till finally absolute
coordination is reached.

.   .   .   .

Display Flights. The intention movements treated thus far may be derived from walking or jumping or from flying up. Actually, there does not seem to be a sharp boundary between jumping away and flying away, and therefore there is no need to discuss separately the intention movements of flying away.

During actual flight however, and especially during the start, we may observe intention movements indicating a tendency to increase the speed and these intention movements may have developed into signals by exaggeration. This can be done in two different ways, *viz.*, (1) by speeding up the rhythm or (2) by increasing the amplitude. The two principles may be illustrated by a human example: when playing with a child and trying to make it believe that we want to overtake it we may either take very long but very slow strides, or we may make very frequent but exceedingly small steps. Both procedures carry the impression of rapid locomotion.

As a rule smaller birds seem to use increase of tempo rather than amplitude, while taller forms increase the amplitude at the expense of tempo. We saw the two methods applied in the exaggeration of walking. A disturbed Hen makes frequent but small head movements, whereas displaying Ducks may overdo the amplitude of the head movements. The Robin may meet an intruder now with frequent small bows now with large and slow bows (Lack, 1939).

House Pigeons taking to flight at the appearance of a Sparrow Hawk start with some extra-ordinarily large wing strokes in which the wings touch above the back. This has evolved into an auditory signal, and the movements and sounds of this wing clapping often cause all the inhabitants of the pigeon loft to fly up. It is difficult to state with certainty whether the increased amplitude is proportionate to an increase in speed of locomotion or whether there is an excess due to exaggeration. From the fact that the wings are actually clapped together with force one would conclude that there is much exaggeration that is mechanically worthless.

The male of the Black-tailed Godwit executes his display flight (ceremonial flight, Huxley and Montagne, 1926) with large slow strokes of the wings, turning its body from side to side and spreading the tail. No increase in speed is effected.

Increase in amplitude with resulting wing clapping is also practised by the male Nightjar (Stülcken and Brüll, 1938). Again the speed is not at all increased.

Increased frequency, resulting in what is commonly called wing trembling, is seen in a number of Passerine birds in the beginning of the reproductive period. In the House Sparrow the male does it during display, and the female when "saluting" her husband. While this is usually done while sitting on the substratum both male and female may fly around with trembling wings, when they are preparing for a second brood, a fact not mentioned in my paper on the House Sparrow (Daanje, 1941). During this trembling flight the actual speed of flight is less than during normal flight. The same type of trembling flight is seen at the mating time in both sexes of the Chiffchaff, in the male Great Spotted Woodpecker, and presumably in many other small birds. The Magpie which shows the trembling when sitting, does not do it in flight.

Swifts show the trembling flight just before copulation takes place in the air. As a rule the trembling is only shown by the female but occasionally the male also shows it. Sometimes a pursuit with both birds trembling their wings may be observed without a copulation following. While in normal flight the wings beat at a rate of about 280 a minute this is increased till about 360 a minute in the trembling flight. The speed of flight is notably less than normal (Daanje, 1944).

Among many Song birds the wing trembling is an invitation to mating.

Begging Movements. The young of many species of Passerine birds show the same movements when begging for food. As I pointed out in my paper on the House Sparrow (1941) this type of wing trembling has something to do with flight and, in young Swallows for instance, it may become true flight when begging increases in intensity, the birds really lifting themselves up into the air. It is remarkable however that the movement has no forward component. Failure of a forward component is fairly common in intention movements of locomotion, as for instance in the pole attitude of the Bittern (Fig. 5), the alarmed posture of the Blond Ring Dove (Fig. 6), the bow of the Little Owl (Fig. 4) the vertical head movement of the Kestrel, Lapwing, and presumably in the bow of Magpie and Robin, *etc.*

Young Wagtails do not only flutter their wings but also wag the tail, another indication of locomotory intention. Fledged Wrens show, in addition to the wing trembling, a very quick rhythmic moving up and down of the head and fore part of the body; doubtless a symbol of hopping. Quieter bows are performed by fledglings of the Song Sparrow (Nice, 1943) and by the begging young of the Little Owl (Haverschmidt, 1946).

A very remarkable begging movement is shown by young Moorhens. Very young chicks in particular may run around, flapping the "wing" alternately. Moreover the wings move in coordination with the running legs in the same way as the arm movements of Man are coordinated with his leg movements, which suggests that the wing movements support the leg movements. If its primary task were to help in maintaining equilibrium the wing movement would be irregular. This coordination of leg and wing movements of the Moorhen can best be studied in very young chicks when they swim away as fast as possible from an enemy, for instance the observer. This is very difficult to detect in running individuals, as their movements are usually too quick. Once I saw a halfgrown young one change over from the alternating wing movement into the synergistic movement. It was fleeing over a flat bank, waving its wings alternately. However, when it reached a slope, which had to be climbed, the alternating movement was (gradually?) replaced by the synergistic movement. In running, the alternating movement apparently gave the best support, in climbing a lift with the wings was of more help.

Very young Moorhens, waving the wings alternately, when running towards the parent to be fed, continue these wing movements till they are fed. This can be observed very well when the young are stopped by reaching the water, where the parent is approaching with food. The wing movements get visual support from the red color at the tips of the wings.

In the Moorhen and in many Song birds, begging is also accompanied by a stretching of body and neck towards the parent, and of the tail backward. This too might belong to the intention of rapid locomotion. With decreasing intensity the stretching of the body is first abandoned, then the head is withdrawn and finally the trembling of the wings is diminished. The forward stretching component is also found in the pre-mating posture of female Passerines, and in the pre-mating posture of a female Mallard. The mating posture of the Cormorant is also a clear instance of a locomotory intention movement, as I showed above. The invitatory movements of the female Robin are similar to those of the Cormorant. Apart from the normal Passerine invitation posture the female of the Robin will, if the male does not respond immediately, perform a lateral swaying movement of the neck or a head movement up and down (Lack, 1939).

Finally I want to mention the remarkable movements of some displaying Song birds, such as the Hedge Sparrow, in which only one wing is flapped. Now one wing flicks out, now another. These movements may be alternated with quite synchronised synergistic move-

ments of both wings or with movements of both wings, that are
approximately synchronised but shifted in time. Although these movements correspond in many respects with the fin movements of fish,
studied by Von Holst, it would be too speculative to make an attempt
at any interpretation until more comparative data are available.

SUMMARY

This paper is intended to show that a great number of movements in birds, the
origin of which has not hitherto been understood, are intention movements or
movements derived from them.

Pure intention movements (Heinroth, 1910) being low intensity forms of innate
behaviour patterns, are as a rule, the very first parts of an activity. Because many
instinctive acts begin with a locomotory movement towards something (food, or a
mate, or an enemy) most intention movements are low intensity forms of locomotion.

In order to recognise pure intention movements therefore it is necessary to
study the form of locomotory movements first. This is done in Chapter II, in which
special attention is given to hopping and walking. It is shown that hopping involves not only the feet, but also movements of the body, the neck, the wings and
the tail. Walking is "one-sided hopping," in which both feet are used alternately,
and in which each foot is supported by body, neck, tail and wing movements.

Chapter III discusses a number of intention movements.

Chapter IV shows that the majority of intention movements are difficult to
recognize because they have undergone a secondary evolutionary change (ritualisation) as an adaptation to a newly acquired function, that of acting as a social releaser.

Comparison enables us to trace a number of principles involved in this secondary change, *viz.:* (1) exaggeration, (2) a shifting of thresholds of the component
elements and (3) loss of coordination between the component rhythms.

Applying these principles, many so-called display, threat and begging movements can be understood as ritualised intention movements.

Owing to the extreme scarcity of accurate comparative studies it is, in most
cases, not possible to do more than make a guess as to the origin of a given movement. And although the available facts for the relatively better known groups such
as the pigeons, the ducks, and the Gallinaceous birds, support my relatively speculative conclusions, I should like to emphasize the need of accurate comparative
studies aimed at a tracing of the origin of derived movements.

LITERATURE

ALLEN, A. A. (1934). Sex rhythm in the Ruffed Grouse (*Bonasa umbellus* Linn.)
    and other Birds. — The Auk, Vol. LI.
BERG, B. (1929). Tookern. — Berlin.
BERNHARDT, P. (1940). Beitrag zur Biologie der Schellente (*Bucephala clangula*).
    — Journal f. Ornithologie, Vol. LXXXVIII.
BÖKER, H. (1935). Vergleichende biologische Anatomie der Wirbeltiere. Vol. I. —
    Jena.
CRAIG, W. (1909). The Expressions of Emotion in the Pigeon I. The Blond Ring
    Dove (*Turtur risorius*). — The Journal of Comparative Neurology and Psy-
    chology. Vol. XIX.
—— (1918). Appetites and Aversions as Constituents of Instincts. — Biol. Bull. Vol.
    XXXIV.

DAANJE, A. (1941). Über das Verhalten des Haussperlings (*Passer d. domesticus* (L.)). — Ardea, Vol. XXX.

—— (1944). De vliegende Gierzwaluw (*Apus a. apus* (L.)). — Ardea. Vol. XXXIII.

HAVERSCHMIDT, F. (1940). Observations on the breeding habits of the Little Owl. — Ardea, Vol. XXXIV.

HEINROTH, O. (1910). Beitrage zur Biologie, insbesondere Psychologie und Ethologie der Anatiden. — Verhand. d. V. intern. ornithol. Kongr., Berlin.

HOLST, E. VON (1937). Vom Wesen der Ordnung im Zentralnervensystem. — Die Naturwissenschaften, Vol. XXV.

—— (1938a). Neue Versuche zur Deutung der relativen Koordination bei Fischen. — Pflügers Archiv, Vol. CCXL.

—— (1938b). Über relative Koordination bei Säugern und beim Menschen. — Pflügers Archiv, Vol. CCXL.

—— (1939). Entwurf eines Systems der locomotorischen Perioden-bildungen bei Fischen. — Zeitschrift f. vergl. Physiologie, Vol. XXVI.

HUXLEY, J. S. AND F. A. MONTAGUE (1926). Studies on the Courtship and Sexual Life of Birds VI. The Black-tailed Godwit. (*Limosa limosa* (L.)). — The Ibis, Vol. II.

KLUYVER, H. N., J. LIGTVOET, C. V. P. OUWELANDT AND F. ZEGWAARD (1940). De Levenswijze van den Winterkoning, *Troglodytes tr. troglodytes* (L.). — Limosa, Vol. XIII.

KORTLANDT, A. (1940a). Eine Übersicht der angeborenen Verhaltensweisen des mitteleuropäischen Kormorans (*Phalacrocorax carbo sinensis* (Shaw and Nodder)), ihre Funktion, ontogenetische Entwicklung und phylogenetische Herkunft. — Archives néerl. Zool. Vol. IV.

—— (1940b). Wechselwirkung zwischen Instinkten. — Archives néerl. Zool. Vol. IV.

LACK, D. (1939). The Behaviour of the Robin, I and II. — Proceedings of the Zoological Soc. of London, Vol. CIX.

LORENZ, K. (1933). Beobachtetes über das Fliegen der Vögel und über die Beziehungen der Flügel- und Steuerform zur Art des Fluges. — Journal f. Ornithol., Vol. LXXXI.

—— (1935). Der Kumpan in der Umwelt des Vogels. — Journal f. Ornithol., Vol. LXXXIII.

—— (1941). Vergleichende Bewegungsstudien an Anatinen. — Journal f. Ornithol., Ergänzungsband III.

NICE, M. M. (1937). Studies in the life history of the Song Sparrow, I. — Transactions of the Linnaean Soc. of New York, Vol. IV.

—— (1943). Studies in the life history of the Song Sparrow, II. — Transactions of the Linnaean Soc. of New York. Vol. VI.

PORTIELJE, A. F. J. (1925). Zur Ethologie bezw. Psychologie der *Rhea americana* L. — Ardea. Vol. XIV.

—— (1926). Zur Ethologie bezw. Psychologie von *Botaurus stellaris* (L.). — Ardea, Vol. XV.

PORTIELJE, A. F. J. AND W. F. H. SCHUT (1938). Dieren zien en leeren kennen. — Amsterdam.

RÄBER, H. (1949). Das Verhalten gefangener Waldohreulen (*Asio o. otus*) und Waldkäuze (*Strix a. aluco*) zur Beute. — Behaviour, Vol. II.

SIEWERT, H. (1932). Störche. — Berlin.

STOLPE, M. UND K. ZIMMER (1939). Der Vogelflug. — Leipzig.

STRESEMANN, E. (1927-1934). Aves in Kükenthal-Krumbach, Handbuch der Zoologie. Vol. VII. — Berlin und Leipzig.

STÜLCKEN, K. UND H. BRÜLL (1938). Vom Nestleben der Nachtschwalbe (*Caprimulgus e. europaeus*). — Journal f. Ornithol. Vol. LXXXVI.

THAUER, R. UND G. PETERS (1938). Sensibilität und Motorik bei lange "überleben-den Zwischen-Mittelhirntauben." — Pflügers Archiv. Vol. CCXL.
TINBERGEN, N. (1937). Über das Verhalten kämpfender Kohlmeisen (*Parus m. major* L.). — Ardea. Vol. XXVI.
—— (1940). Die Übersprungbewegung. — Zeitschr. f. Tierpsychologie. Vol. IV.
—— (1942). An objectivistic study of the innate behaviour of animals. — Bibliotheca biotheoretica. Vol. I, pars 2. Leiden.
VERWEY, J. (1930). Die Paarungsbiologie des Fischreihers. — Zool. Jahrbücher, Abt. F. allg. Zool. u. Physiol., Vol. XLVIII.
WHITMAN, C. O. (1919). The Behavior of Pigeons. Vol. III. — Washington.
YEATES, G. K. (1936). On the fighting of the Blackcock. — Brit. Birds. Vol. XXX.

MORPHOLOGICAL AND ETHOLOGICAL NOTES

ON A HYBRID BETWEEN A DOMESTIC DUCK AND A

DOMESTIC GOOSE

by
HOLGER POULSEN
(Zoological Gardens, Copenhagen)

Although interspecific crosses, especially those between species of different genera, are rare in nature, interbreeding is much commoner in captivity. The Copenhagen Zoological Gardens possess two hybrids between *Branta canadensis* L. and *Anser albifrons gambelli* Hartl., which were captured 1944 in Sarquaq in West Greenland. These birds, incidentally, were the only existing proof of the breeding of the Canada Goose in Greenland (Verbal information from Dr. F. Salomonsen).

When species which are not known to interbred in nature do so in captivity, we are usually concerned with individuals which have been kept in isolation from their own species. Under these conditions the reproductive drive may become extremely strong, so that the threshold for stimuli releasing reproductive, especially sexual, behaviour is considerably lowered. In such cases individuals of other species may be accepted as partners although they offer stimuli which would normally be inadequate to release sexual reactions. The sexual drive may even become so strong that sexual behavior occurs *in vacuo*.

Until recently, interest in problems of interbreeding was focussed mainly upon the question of what species would hybridise, and upon the morphological features and fertility of the hybrids. During the last few years, however, hybrids have received attention from behaviour students. In comparative ethology it is important to know the behaviour of hybrids, and to compare it with that of the parent species. The behaviour of a hybrid is not always intermediate between that of its parents, but may show more primitive traits (Lorenz, 1941, p. 201): it may thus elucidate many interesting problems.

In July, 1947, the Zoological Gardens acquired a hybrid between a domestic duck and a domestic goose from a farmer. I was particulary interested in studying the behaviour of this hybrid because the behaviour of the ancestral forms (the Mallard, *Anas platyrhyncha* L., and the Grey Lag-Goose, *Anser anser* L.) is so well known from the studies of Heinroth (1911) and Lorenz (1941). So far as I know, there has been only one previous record of such a hybrid (Taibell, 1930). Hybrids between the corresponding wild forms are unknown.

At the farm where this hybrid was reared, the stock of breeding ducks and geese consisted of an old drake and two ducks, and a young gander and two geese. The drake was the dominant bird, and never allowed the gander into the pond, where it would normally have copulated. It was for this reason that the drake was able to copulate with the geese in spite of the presence of the gander.

The parents of the hybrid were a wild-coloured domestic duck (male) and a white parti-coloured domestic goose (female). The hybrid has the superficial appearance of a duck, but closer examination shows that it has points in common with both ducks and geese. Its colour is white with a few blackish-grey spots. The legs and bill are orange-yellow. It has a short curved neck, like that of a duck. The wings are rather long, and reach to the tip of the tail, as in geese, but they are not so broad as the wings of geese. The tail is rounded like that of geese, not pointed as in ducks. The plumage is completely straight, and not furrowed on the neck as in geese. Although it is a male, the upturned feathers on the tail normally characteristic of a drake are not present. The legs are short and rather slender, and the hind toe is compressed as in ducks: in geese the hind toe is round. The tarsus is reticulated, as in geese, but the scutes are arranged in a row along the front, as in ducks. At first the bill appears to be very much like that of a duck, being wide and with the upper-side concave in profile, but it is higher at the base than that of a duck. The upper-bill has a furrow along the edge, as in ducks, but the nail at the end is so large that it occupies the entire tip: this nail ends in a sharp edge projecting from the tip of the bill. On the tip of the under-bill there is also a wide goose-like nail. As in ducks, the edges of the upper-bill project over the under-bill and the cutting edge of the upper-bill is not concave. The transverse ridges are placed on the insides of the upper and lower jaws, and not on the edges as in geese, but the shape of these ridges is intermediate between the thin ridges of ducks and the tooth-like knots of geese. The nostrils are longitudinal, projecting, and placed in the middle of the bill as in geese: the nostrils of ducks are not projecting and are placed nearer to the base of the bill. The shape of the boundaries between the bill and the head-feathers is intermediate between ducks and geese. The edge of the eyelid is feathered as in ducks, but the edge itself is thicker and orange coloured, as in geese. The iris is bluish-grey, certainly inherited from the white goose.

The behaviour of the hybrid is intermediate between that of ducks and geese. It bites off the grass, just like geese, but uses only the tip of the bill and not the sides. The sides of the bill are shaped like those of ducks, who pull off the grass and quack in the grass, and are thus not suitable for biting grass. The walk is rather waddling, but this is not so marked as in ducks, and goose-like elements are also distinguishable. When swimming it quacks like a duck.

The hybrid dominates the other birds in the enclosure irrespective of their size. When it is chasing or threatening other birds it never stretches its neck forward as geese do, but keeps the body upright and the neck curved. When attacked it hisses and shows a threat display quite like a drake, with curved neck and extended tail feathers. Its voice is more like that of a duck than that of a goose; but although itself a male, it has the deep coarse note of the female instead of the more subdued note typical of males. Its voice also has some goose-like characters, but it never utters the loud cries typical of geese.

Although it is a male, it has never shown any tendency to mate, nor any courtship display. I therefore tried to produce this with hormone injections.

The hormones used were gonadotropic and male sex hormones. The gonadotropic hormone I obtained from Mr. H. Kjems (Løvens kemiske fabrik, Copenhagen) and the testosterone from Mr. E. Wilken (Ciba, Copenhagen), to whom I wish to express my thanks. I would also like to thank Dr. E. Møller–Christensen, who gave me advice as to the correct dosage.

At first I used Antex Leo (Løvens kemiske fabrik), a gonadotropic hormone in aqueous solution (8.5% NaCl) extracted from the urine of pregnant mares. 2,000 int. units were injected in the chest muscles between Sept. 24th and Oct. 11th, but gave no results. The bird was then given Physex Leo (Løvens kemiske fabrik), a gonadotropic hormone in aqueous solution (4.5% NaCl) obtained from the chorion of human females. 7,500 int. units were administered between Oct. 19th and 27th, and the same amount was given again between Nov. 6th and 14th. The behaviour of the bird still did not change, and it showed no sexual interest in other ducks or geese. Another attempt

with Antex was made between Feb. 19th and March 17th. Although
10,000 int. units were injected, the bird still showed no courtship
display. Finally 40 mgms of testosterone proprionate (Perandren,
Ciba) in oil were given in four injections between March 31st and
April 11th. This also failed to produce any result. The hybrid never
showed any sexual interest towards other birds, neither at this time,
nor later when the other ducks and geese were showing their courtship display. It did, however, show some social responses to other
birds; these were given only to geese (Bean Goose *Anser fabalis* L.,
and Snow Goose, *Chen caerulescens* L.), and never to Mallard (*Anas
platyrhyncha* L.) nor to domestic white ducks.

Although considerable research has been done on the effects of
hormones on the appearance of the treated animals, their effects on
the sexual behaviour of birds have been studied very little until recently. Nevertheless there is sufficient evidence to show that hormones
do normally influence sexual behaviour (See summary in Beach, 1948).
For instance, Emlen and Lorenz (1942) implanted testosterone pellets
in free living Valley Quail (*Lophorty californicus vallicola* Ridg.).
The treated birds showed pairing behaviour on the second day. Noble
and Wurm (1940) have demonstrated that injections of testosterone
radically alter the behaviour of Black-crowned Night herons (*Nycticorax n. hoactli* Gml.). The same is known for Anserine birds.
Beach (1942, cited in Beach, 1948, p. 33) states that a sexually inactive
Canada gander (*Branta canadensis* L.) exhibited intense courtship
and mating following injections of testosterone propionate.

The reason for the ineffectiveness of the hormone treatment on the
hybrid was not that the bird was too young. Domestic ducks and geese
become mature when they are one year old. Moreover, precocious sexual behaviour can be elicited in birds of wild as well as domesticated
species. Noble and Wurm (1940 b) injected immature Black-crowned
Night herons (*Nycticorax n. hoactli* Gml.) with testosterone propionate and observed that the treated individuals reacted like sexually active males. According to Hamilton (1938), and Noble and Zitrin
(1942), young male chicks injected with testosterone propionate show
adult courtship display. Further, it is known that treatment with male
sex hormones will induce normal mating behaviour in castrated male
birds, such as fowls (Davis and Domm, 1941; Domm, Davis and
Blivaiss, 1942; Davis and Domm, 1943; all cited in Beach, 1948, p.
33), the Laughing Gull, *Larus atricilla* L., (Noble and Wurm, 1940
a.) and Black-crowned Night heron, *Nycticorax n. hoactli* Gml.,
(Noble and Wurm, 1940 b.). The fact that these immature or castrated

birds showed the innate patterns of sexual behaviour after hormone treatment shows that the central nervous mechanisms necessary for those patterns are already fully developed. In the case of the hybrid we must conclude that the ineffectiveness of both gonadotropic and male sex hormone was due to the absence of a response from the nervous system. In fact it is clear, both from the hormonal experiments and from the behaviour of the hybrid in spring, that the bird did not possess the nervous mechanisms necessary for these patterns of sexual behaviour. This can not be due to domestication, for both the domestic duck and the domestic goose each have their own elaborate courtship display.

Other hybrids between different genera of Anserine birds also lack the courtship display. For instance, Lorenz (1942, p. 313) mentions that a hybrid between the Mallard, (*Anas platyrhyncha* L.) and the Muscovy Duck (*Cairina moschata* L.) did not show any courtship display, whereas Heinroth (1906, p. 4) states that male hybrids between domestic ducks and Muscovy Ducks copulate with other ducks and have an intermediate courtship display.

I have not yet been able to study the sexual organs of this hybrid. They can not be examined until its death. At present I only know that it is a male, because I have seen its copulatory-organ by squeezing the anus.

SUMMARY

A hybrid between a domestic duck (male) and a domestic goose (female) acquired by the Zoological Gardens, Copenhagen superficially resembled a duck, but by a closer examination it was shown that morphologically and ethologically it showed characters of both duck and goose. Although it is a male it has never shown any sexual activity. I therefore tried to activate it by hormone injections. Treatment with gonadotropic hormones and with sexual hormone were both ineffectual. Therefore I conclude that this bird does not have the nervous mechanisms underlying the sexual patterns, because it is known that castrated male birds and young male birds show sexual activity when treated with hormones.

LITERATURE

BEACH, F. A. (1942). Analysis of factors involved in the arousal maintenance and manifestation of sexual excitement in male animals. — Psychosom. Med. IV, pp. 173–98.
——, (1948). Hormones and Behavior. — N. York.
DAVIS, D. E. AND L. V. DOMM (1941). The sexual behavior of hormonally treated domestic fowl. — Proc. Soc. Exper. Biol. & Med. XLVIII, pp. 667–69.
—— AND L. V. DOMM (1943). The influence of hormones on the sexual behavior of the fowl. In Essays in Biology. — Univ. California Press, Berkeley, California.
DOMM, L. V., D. E. DAVIS AND B. B. BLIVAISS (1942). Observations on the sexual behavior of hormonally treated brown leghorn fowl. — Anat. Rec. LXXXIV, pp. 481–82.

EMLEN, J. T. AND F. W. LORENZ (1942). Pairing responses of freeliving valley quail to sex hormone pellets implants. — Auk. LIX, pp. 369–78.

HAMILTON, J. B. (1938). Precocious masculine behavior following administration of synthetic male hormone substance. — Endocrinology XXIII, pp. 53–57.

HEINROTH, O. (1906). Beobachtungen an Entenmischlingen. — Sitzungsber. Gesellsch. naturforsch. Freunde. Berlin. pp. 3–4.

—— (1911). Beiträge zur Biologie, namentlich Ethologie und Psychologie der Anatiden. — Verh. V. Int. Orn. Kongr. Berlin, 1910. pp. 589–702.

LORENZ, K. (1941). Vergleichende Bewegungsstudien an Anatinen. — Journ. Orn LXXXIX, pp. 194–294.

—— (1943). Die angeborenen Formen möglicher Erfahrung. — Zeitsch. f. Tier psychol. V, pp. 235–409.

NOBLE, G. K. AND M. WURM (1940a). The effect of hormones on the breeding of the laughing gull. — Anat. Rec. LXXVIII, Suppl. pp. 50–51.

—— AND M. WURM (1940b). The effect of testosterone propionate on the black-crowned night heron. — Endocrinology. XXVI, pp. 837–50.

—— AND A. ZITRIN (1942). Induction of mating behavior in male and female chicks following injections of sex hormones. — Endocrinology. XXX, pp. 327–34.

TAIBELL, A. (1930). Descrizione di un ibrido fra l'anatra e l'oca. — Bolettino de Zoologia. II, pp. 75–81.

THE EVOLUTION OF NEST-BUILDING BEHAVIOR

IN APICOTERMES (ISOPTERA)[1]

ROBERT S. SCHMIDT
University of Chicago

INTRODUCTION

The relative non-existence of ethological fossils (with such exceptions as fossil tracks and burrows) and the transitory nature of movements and behavior patterns makes the study of the evolution of behavior extremely difficult. It is not surprising that the number of papers dealing with this subject is so small compared to the vast literature of the evolution of morphological structure.

The nests of the African genus of termites, *Apicotermes,* present unique material for the study of the evolution of behavior. These species-specific structures are tangible products of the nest-building behavior of the entire colony, and permit an ethological study of a supraorganism in contrast to an organism. They are relatively permanent and may be studied in the laboratory at leisure. The known nests present an unusually complete phylogenetic series, and it can be expected that this series will be considerably improved as future collections fill in existing gaps. In this genus, the nests show phylogenetic relationships much more clearly than do the morphological characteristics of their builders. Emerson (1938) summarizes the attributes of termite nests as follows:

> Termite nests may be used as examples of behavior evolution because they are morphological indications of behavior patterns, they express the behavior of a population, the patterns are hereditary, there is a natural control over any Lamarckian influence, evolutionary sequences are available, adaptive modifications may be demonstrated, and coordination mechanisms may be partially analyzed.

Of the many types of structures (nests, webs, cases, etc.) produced by various organisms, the nests of termites present one of the best materials for the study of the evolution of behavior, and the nests of

---

[1] A dissertation submitted to the Department of Zoology, University of Chicago, in partial fulfillment of the degree of Doctor of Philosophy.

Apicotermes are far superior in certain respects to the nests of other termites. In *Apicotermes*, the nest of each species is unusually characteristic of that species in contrast to the nests of many of the other termites which often vary conspicuously only between genera. Such a complete phylogenetic series of so many species within a single genus is also rare among termites.

This type of study will probably be criticized by some, who will point out that a description of the nest does not describe the actions or processes performed in building the nest. This cannot be denied. However, it must be emphasized that this paper deals not with a *description* of the nest-building behavior but with the *evolution* of this behavior. There can be little doubt that the nests of *Apicotermes* are valid indicators of the phylogenetic relationships of the behavior producing them.

The known nests of *Apicotermes* have been described in detail by Desneux (1918, 1948, and 1953) and the termites themselves by Emerson (1953). Both of these workers have discussed the phylogeny

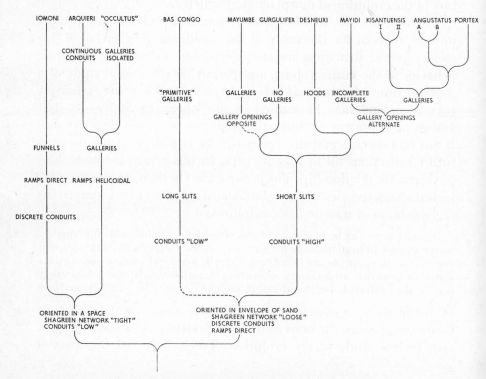

Fig. 1. A hypothetical phylogeny of *Apicotermes* based on nests.

KEY TO NESTS OF APICOTERMES

A. Oriented in a space. Discrete internal slits absent, or if present opening into funnels. Shagreen network adhering closely to surface. Ramps helicoidal except in *A. lamani.*
    B. Internal slits opening into funnels. Ramps direct. ......*A. lamani*
    BB. Circular galleries present. Ramps helicoidal.
        C. Conduits continuous. ....*A. arquieri*
        CC. Galleries with neither internal nor external openings. ......
                A. "occultus"
AA. Oriented in envelope of sand. With discrete internal openings. Shagreen network loosely applied and easily broken off. Ramps direct.
    B. Internal silts long (mean greater than 4.5 mm.) and less than half-way from floor to ceiling. Heavy shagreen network uniformly covering external surface. ....Bas Congo
    BB. Internal slits short (mean less than 4.5 mm.) and more than half-way from floor to ceiling. Light shagreen network scattered over external surface.
        C. Galleries absent. No overhanging of upper lips of external conduit openings. ....*A. gurgulifex*
        CC. Galleries complete, or partially enclosed by overhanging upper lips of external conduit openings.
            D. External and internal openings of galleries opposite. ....*Mayumbe*
            DD. External and internal openings of galleries, when complete, alternate.
                E. Galleries not in complete form.
                    F. Upper lip of external conduit opening projecting downward but not quite reaching wall at distal end. ....*A. desneuxi*
                    FF. Projecting upper lip of external conduit opening often fusing with wall at distal end. ...*Mayidi*
                EE. Gallery in complete form.
                    F. Opening of conduit into gallery forms a large tooth. Width of conduit at center about ½ or more of width of internal slit.
                        G. Tooth large. Sides of conduit more or less parallel. ....*A. kisantuensis* I
                        GG. Tooth smaller. Conduit narrowing at the center ....*A. kisantuensis* II
                    FF. Opening of conduit into gallery in form of small tube or very slight tooth, or not raised at all. Width of conduit at center about ¼ or less of width of internal conduit opening.
                        G. Internal opening a slit.
                          H. Opening of conduit into gallery forming a small tooth. ....
                              A. angustatus A
                          HH. Opening of conduit into gallery smooth or forming slight tube. .....
                              A. angustatus B
                      GG. Internal opening a pore. ......*A. porifex*

of the genus (Emerson, 1952a, 1953 and Desneux, 1948, 1953). This paper, leaning heavily upon the work of these two men, will attempt to deal with the phylogeny of the genus in greater detail, using additional data as well as occasional reinterpretation of some previous data. Certain aspects of the evolution of these nests will then be discussed.

METHODS

Sources and Types of Material

Measurements were taken from three sources. The only nests available for study were some fragments in the custody of Dr. A. E. Emerson at the University of Chicago. These nests were received from the Musée Royal du Congo Belge, T. E. Snyder, Professor P.-P. Grassé, and Dr. J. Desneux. This collection was especially useful in that it provided the most accurate set of measurements made. Extensive use was made of photographs in the 1948 and especially the 1953 papers of Dr. J. Desneux. Radiographs were made of the nest walls of the specimens in Emerson's collection.

Radiographs of Nest Walls

Radiographs were obtained by merely laying the nest fragment on a piece of film and irradiating from above. The film was kept small to reduce errors resulting from the curvature of the nest. The nest and film were exposed at about one meter from the target in order to reduce errors due to divergence of rays. Kodak Super Ortho-Press was wrapped in black paper and used as film. The results were reasonably satisfactory, although use of better materials and techniques might possibly have given somewhat better resolution of certain wall structures. The best resolution was obtained at about 30–50 kv., depending upon the nest fragment used. A few of the more interesting radiographs are shown in Figure 1.

Methods of Measuring

The size and accessibility of the structure determined the method by which it was measured. Nest structures smaller than 1 cm. were generally measured by an ocular micrometer in a dissecting microscope. Measurements of less than 1 cm. from photographs were usually made with fine-pointed calipers, the distance between the points of the calipers being determined by placing them against an ocular micrometer with a 1 cm. scale. Measurements greater than 1 cm. were made with calipers and a metal rule calibrated in millimeters. Areas were measured with a planimeter. In a few cases the area was too small to be measured directly by this method. The area was then enlarged with a microscope and camera lucida and the enlarged area determined with a planimeter.

Accuracy of Measurements

A number of sources of error are inherent to the methods used in this study. An extensively used character is the length of the internal slit. These are internal openings of conduits that pass through the nest wall. Errors in the measurement of these slits result from the difficulty in actually defining the structure. Slits are often closed to varying degress with sand or mortar, making it very difficult to determine the exact limits of the structures. Because of this, different observers might obtain slightly different measurements due to different concepts of slit limits. However, several checks used indicate that the measurements of these structures are somewhat more accurate than one would suspect from the difficulty just mentioned. Slits measured from radiographs gave results similar to those obtained directly from the nest. Measurements of a small number of slits, the conduits of which had been sectioned horizontally also provided a good check. Such horizontal sections through the conduits exposed the slit free from obstructing material, thus providing the most accurate measurement of this structure. Although this is the obvious solution to the difficulty of slit measurement, it is not practicable at present. This method would require the almost complete destruction of the portion of nest being used, which would, of course, be inadvisable with such rare material.

The use of photographs of curved structures also introduces errors that are difficult to avoid. So far as possible, only those portions of a photograph were used in which the object photographed was in focus and in a plane parallel to the plane of the film. Even so, much of the variability of data from photographs is undoubtedly due to such factors as curvature.

It would be expected that the distance between centers of external parietal openings would be slightly greater than the distance between the centers of the corresponding internal parietal openings of the same nest because of the radial arrangement of these structures. . . .

Some of the larger samples of measurements of the length of the internal slit, interval between slits, and distance between centers of external pores were checked to see if they fitted the normal curve. It was found that they fitted reasonably well.

Choice and Arrangement of Data

Both the vertical and horizontal curvature of the nest vary along its vertical axis. This usually results in the wall structures of the two poles being somewhat different from the rest of the nest. Since the poles were generally not available for study, measurements have been restricted to the equatorial, central portions of the nest wall. It also seemed advisable to exclude portions obviously modified by such factors as the presence of an adjacent ramp or a root passing through the wall. Only the most accurate data obtained have been presented. Data have been excluded for which the accuracy was for some reason questionable (e.g., due to excessive curvature or unknown magnification in the case of a published photograph). When sufficient data have been available directly from a nest fragment, these have been given preference over data obtained from photographs. . . .

Highly accurate nests measurements and large samples will not be possible until nests may be spared for dissection and more extensive collections are available.

.   .   .   .

DISCUSSION

There is no evidence to contradict the assumption that nest-building behavior in termites is innate and instinctive. Certainly, colony founding by a single pair of reproductives would eliminate the possibility of workers (which appear only after these reproductives have left the parent colony) learning these behavior patterns from earlier generations of workers. Innate or instinctive behavior is considered here to be those movements or acts, occurring in response to a specific set of stimuli, for which previous performance as a result of these stimuli is not necessary for the functional completeness of the neural pathways controlling that behavior. The repetition of the behavior pattern, in such instances, is initiated by genetic factors passing from one generation to another through the germ plasm. Lehrman (1953) seems to consider most behavior learned. However, his reasoning is rather difficult to follow and his arguments seem to be largely semantic. Although criticizing the use of "instinct," he offers no adequate substitute.

Teleology and anthropomorphism have no place (when used literally) in the study of innate behavior. An extreme example of such use is seen in a paper by Bugnion (1927). For instance, in discussing the evolution of defense behavior in termite soldiers, he says that "the origin of most of these instincts is a reasoned and conscious action."

Emerson (in Allee *et al.*, 1949) states that "the evolution of behavior results from similar forces and follows patterns similar to those characteristic of morphological evolution, and . . . both depend upon physiological development and genetic interactions." As early as 1898, Whitman (1899) remarked that "instinct and structure are to be studied from the common standpoint of phyletic descent."

To a certain extent behavior is determined and modified by the physiological (e.g., hormonal) processes and the morphological equipment of the organism. Behavioral changes would therefore be expected to parallel evolutionary, genetic changes in morphology and physiology. Evidence also indicates direct genetic changes of the nervous system itself. Further discussion of this subject is beyond the scope of this paper. An excellent general review of ethological evolution is given by Tinbergen (1951, chaps. 7 and 8).

A remarkable difference is seen between the degree of radiation of behavior and structure in the two neuter castes of termites. The morphological features of the workers show minimum radiation. Such conservative characters are of great value in determining the relations between genera and higher categories, but are relatively useless in species identification. On the other hand this caste shows considerable variation of behavior, as illustrated by the many nests types already known for *Apicotermes*. In contrast, the soldiers show considerable morphological adaptation, hence proving the most useful specimens for species determination but often being of less value than the morphologically conservative workers for relating higher categories. The known behavior differences of soldiers within a genus are relatively small.

Nest-building behavior in *Apicotermes* illustrates particularly well several principles analogous to structural evolution. These will be discussed in greater detail.

Adaptation

The nests of termites have obviously evolved toward a high degree of social homeostasis, providing considerable regulation of the environment (e.g., temperature and humidity) and protection from enemies (e.g., predators and fungi).

A high selective advantage of the various systems of wall perforation is indicated by their occurrence in all known nests of *Apicotermes*, with the exception of *A.* "*occultus.*" It is generally assumed that the function of such structures is to permit the exchange of gases between the interior and exterior of the nest (Desneux, 1953; Emerson, 1953). Although there is no supporting experimental evidence, this seems to be a safe assumption, for the carbon dioxide tension in such underground nests must become very high, and the oxygen tension rather low.

However, the assignment of a particular function to a structure without experimental verification sometimes involves a certain degree of hazard. This is suggested here by the fact that although the function of the perforation systems as a whole seems to be for gas exchange, the evidence concerning the specific function of the circular galleries within this system is rather contradictory. The importance of the galleries cannot be denied, for they appear to have originated independently four times.

Certain factors suggest that the function of the circular gallery may be something other than gas exchange *per se*. A preliminary experiment has been made comparing the rate of diffusion across models of the walls of various species of *Apicotermes* nests. The meager data thus far obtained suggests that the galleries may have little or nothing to do with the rate of diffusion, this apparently being determined (as might be expected) by the size of the smallest parietal opening (in most cases the external opening). If this is at all indicative of the actual situation, it is interesting to note the possible significance of the decrease in conduit width in the *A. kisantuensis-A. porifex* series. If diffusion is proportional to the perimeter of the smallest (external) opening of the gallery, the larger size of the internal slit would be of no advantage to the species from the standpoint of gas exchange. Therefore a narrowing of the conduit could take place without adverse effects upon the "ventilating system" but possibly with some advantage such a increased protection from water, predators, or fungi. Such a possibility is also consistent with the presence of wide conduits in *A. gurgulifex* and *A. desneuxi*—both without galleries (and without the small external openings of galleries) and therefore able to take full advantage of the greater rate of diffusion offered by wide slits. In the case of nests with galleries, the lower rate of diffusion would presumably be compensated for by added protection. It cannot be overemphasized, however, that the experiment mentioned here was preliminary and the result can be considered no more than suggestive. Additional work with this method is in progress and it is hoped that it may give some instructive results.

The somewhat similar nests of the South American termite

Procornitermes lespesii also have circular galleries and are subterranean in hollow cavities (Emerson, 1952b). However, the galleries of these nests have neither internal nor external openings (apparently never had them) and therefore could not function directly for gas exchange (except possibly to produce thinning of the wall). It is, of course, possible that the function of the galleries in *Procornitermes* may be entirely different from that in *Apicotermes*.

The regulation of internal nest temperatures against external fluctuations has been suggested as a possible function of the galleries (Desneux, 1953; Emerson, 1952b). It is questionable, however, whether the relatively slight temperature changes to which these termites are subjected, being subterranean and tropical, would provide the selective pressure for the evolution of such apparently important structures. It is difficult to see how the primitive stages of gallery evolution could provide increased temperature control. Maintenance of high temperatures within the nest could also be a function, although this would meet with some of the same objections just noted concerning possible protection from external temperature changes.

Desneux (1953) suggests that the nests of the *A. kisantuensis-A. porifex* series, once completed, may be enlarged according to the spatial needs of the inhabitants. He shows several photographs suggesting that secondary galleries may be built on the outside of a completed nest and that the inner, original galleries may then be removed. The evidence for this is still not conclusive, however. It has been found that at least some species of *Apicotermes* have colonies composed of a number of nests of various sizes (Desneux, 1953; Grassé and Noirot, 1948b). Grassé (1952) considers colony enlargement to take place by addition of another nest. Perhaps colony growth takes place by both of these methods.

Thus it appears that the direct participation of circular galleries in the regulation of gas exchange across the nest wall is open to serious question. The most likely function seems to be protection of the conduits from soil water, predators, fungi, parasites, or some other factor. Such a function would not be inconsistent with the apparent method of origin. The overlapping upper lip (possibly lower lip in *A. arquieri*) could quite conceivably provide protection for the conduits even though a function of temperature or diffusion regulation is more difficult to imagine. Protection, especially from water, is also suggested by the downward slanting funnels of *A. lamani*. The conduits of most species also slant downward and outward. An exception to this is the inward slanting continuous conduits of *A. arquieri*. It should be noted, however, that none of the present evidence on the function of the galleries is adequate, and a final answer to this problem must await further data. These structures may even function in several ways or have changed their function during the course of their evolution.

The partial closure of internal parietal slits by sand and mortar has already been noted as interfering with slit measurement. Because of the variation in the degree of closure within a nest and between nests from different localities, Desneux (1953) has suggested that the degree of closure may be determined by local gas exchange needs. If such a regulation exists, it would be impossible at present to know whether the degree of slit closure is irreversibly determined by the conditions present when the slits were originally built, or whether they may be later modified as environmental conditions change.

As the field of ethology advances, it might be expected that behavioral homeostatic mechanisms will be found to be more common. A few such mechanisms known for other groups of animals will be mentioned here. Richter (1942–1943) has shown that certain surgically produced hormone deficiencies in rats would modify the animal's dietary preferences in such a way as to largely compensate for the physiological disturbances caused by the operation. For instance, if a parathyroidectomized rat was provided with both ordinary water and water with calcium added, it would drink sufficient amounts of the calcium water to prevent excessive symptoms due to the removal of the parathyroid. He also found that hypophysectomized rats, now incapable of adequate heat production, built much larger nests than normal animals.

Some of the well known homeostatic mechanisms of bees have been reviewed by Chauvin (1954). For instance, periods of increased activity during the winter prevent the temperature of the cluster from dropping to a fatal low, and by fanning, bees are able to increase air circulation within the hive.

Convergence

If the phylogeny presented here is approximately correct, the circular galleries probably have evolved independently four times. The two main branches, the *"occultus"* and the *porifex* groups, are quite different and the lowest member of each branch is without these structures. The galleries of the Mayumbe nest have been shown to be formed in a manner peculiar to that nest and therefore have probably evolved independently. The Bas Congo nest, although uncertain as to position, seems to have arisen from stock without galleries and is not very closely related to other groups with galleries.

Although examples of convergent evolution are numerous, few show such repeated convergence within a single genus. For instance, the presence of striking display behavior by the males of certain species of crabs, squid, fish, lizards, and birds is noted by Tinbergen (1953). Social parasitism is found among the cowbirds, cuckoos, weavers, honey-guides, and ducks (Friedmann, 1929). Mimetic resemblances are also known (Cott, 1940). Mosauer (1930, 1935) has discussed the similarity in locomotion on loose sand of the sidewinder of the Southwest United States and the African sand viper of the Sahara Desert. Friedman (1946) notes that the African pipit (*Macronyx*) and the American meadow-lark (*Sturnella*) show a number of ethological (e.g., song, nests, turning away from an approaching observer) as well as morphological similarities. Rain-shedding structures have evolved independently in nests of the Amitermitinae, Termitinae, and Nasutitermitinae (Emerson, 1938). The similarity of the nests of *Procornitermes* and *Apicotermes* has already been noted (Desneux, 1953; Emerson, 1952b). Cases of convergence within a single genus are more easily found for morphological than for ethological characteristics; for instance, the independent origin of terminal tail rackets in two birds, *Dicrurus remifer* and *D. paradiseus* (Mayr and Vaurie, 1948).

Regression

The modern theory of regressive evolution is based largely on the following factors (Emerson, in Allee *et al.*, 1949):

1. Most genes (pleiotropic) affect more than one character.
2. Most characters (polygenic) are affected by more than one gene.
3. Each gene mutates at a specific statistical rate.
4. Most mutations are deleterious.
5. Entire organisms or populations are selected, as well as the parts of each.

A structure, physiological process, or innate behavior pattern would be expected to remain functional as long as it is maintained by a positive selection pressure. Loss or reduction of this positive pressure may lead to regression. Such loss or reduction might result from an environmental change, bringing about conditions to which the character is not as well adapted, or under which it is detrimental. In the latter case there would be a negative selection pressure against the character. However, regression may also occur in the absence of negative pressure (Wright, 1929). Wright (in Emerson, 1938) states that "the type allele in each series is that which has the most favorable net effect on all characters. If one character loses in importance relative to others, there will be a shift in the alleles in many series with degeneration of the character losing importance as a consequence of the increased development of the others." Therefore a neutral character will eventually regress because of the lack of positive selection pressure maintaining it and because of the shift of alleles in favor of other characters. Regressive evolution is thus seen to bring about increased total adaption rather than decreased adaption as the term "degeneration" so often seems to imply. This theory explains not only the loss of characters, but also the temporary retention of neutral or slightly detrimental characters. Because of the large number of genes involved in any one character, the generally slow rate of mutation, and the fact that most mutations are deleterious, the regression of a character (through the shift of alleles mentioned above) would be expected to take considerable time.

. . . .

The Use of Behavior in Building Phylogenies

In any study of phylogeny it is of the utmost importance to use and correlate all available data from all available sources. A failure in this respect is seen in Kemner's (1927) classification of Javanese termite nests and the classification of caddis flies (based upon feeding behavior and case) by Milne and Milne (1939). Although these workers present valuable information concerning the constructions of these insects, Emerson (1938 and personal communication) notes that their phylogenies based upon behavior are not verified by the morphological data. Since both behavior and structure have evolved by similar methods, one is not *a priori* more important than another in determining phylogenetic relationships. A truly accurate phylogeny must be able to accommodate data on all organismic characteristics. Obviously the structural properties of an organism have not evolved completely apart from its behavior. Selection, of course, is applied to each whole integrated organism or organismic unit such as the supraorganism.

The importance of behavior as an indicator of phylogenetic relationships is finally being recognized. The use of behavior in this manner emphasizes the similarities between the evolution of ethological and morphological characters. So far, relatively few studies of comparative behavior relate more than a small number of species. More investigations comparing large numbers of closely related species are to be desired. A few interesting studies will be briefly noted here.

Emerson (1938) has made a comparative study of termite nests largely at the family and generic level. He also deals with the nest-building behavior of the termites themselves and discusses the evolutionary implications of termite nests. Many of the papers of Grassé and of Grassé and Noirot deal with termite nests and nest-building behavior [e.g., the construction of the royal cell in *Cephalotermes rectangularis* (Grassé, 1939)]. Grassé's 1944 paper on the nests of the Macrotermitinae shows that behavior may also characterize higher taxonomic categories.

An outstanding study of the evolution of behavior is the work of Lorenz (1941) on the calls and mating behavior of some of the Anatinae. His diagram of the phylogenetic relationships between the species studied correlates a number of morphological as well as behavioral characteristics. In some cases he has been able to arrange series, showing the evolution of a highly modified behavior pattern from a more primitive pattern. Delacour and Mayr (1945) state that such ethological characters as pair formation, displays, nesting and feeding habits, are of more value than certain previously emphasized morphological characters. For instance, bill shape is so adaptive that it can be used for little more than species identification.

Petrunkevitch (1926) notes the value of such characteristics as type of web and manner of caring for the egg cocoon for spider classification. Early workers in the field were often over-enthusiastic in their use of behavior, occasionally making errors resulting from the confusion of analogous with homologous behavior. This again emphasizes the importance of using all available evidence in building a phylogeny.

Friedmann (1929) finds that the phylogenic series, *Agelaioides badius—Molothrus rufo-axillaris—M. bonariensis—M. aster,* is indicated by nesting behavior and song as well as by zoogeography and structure. The first bird in this series has no courtship display, incubates its own eggs which are laid in the nests of other birds, and has a "primitive, formless type of song." The next two species show a simple courtship display, are parasitic, and have a more or less typical cowbird song. The last in the series has a more elaborate display, is parasitic, and has a clearer song. The behavior of two captive young males of *M. aster* is of interest. The development of mating behavior during their first spring showed a recapitulation of the behavior of their more primitive relatives until the adult behavior typical of the species was finally exhibited. These birds had been raised in the absence of others of this species. Friedmann (1948) makes a similar report on the parasitic breeding habits of African cuckoos. However, the data are not as complete as in the case of cowbirds. . . .

The phylogeny of *Drosophila* has probably been studied by more methods than has that of any other group. To these methods may be added the studies of Spieth (1952) on the mating behavior of this group. He found that the ethological data for the species of *Drosophila* that he studied closely paralleled the data from other methods. He also has suggested a hypothetical ancestral mating pattern.

The identification of caddis fly larvae is greatly faciliated by the cases built by so many of them. Identification is often made on the basis of case alone, little attention being paid to its inhabitant. For instance, Needham and Needham (1941) give a key to Trichoptera larvae, based mostly on case characteristics.

Crane (1941) has made extensive studies of the crab *Uca*. She makes the following statement concerning their courtship display:

"Each species proved to have a definite, individual display, differing so markedly from that of every other species observed, that closely related species could be recognized at a distance merely by the form of the display. Furthermore, related species had fundamental similarities of display in common, and series of species, showing progressive specialization of structure, in general showed similar progression in display."

Chapin (1917) found that the generally accepted classification of the Ploceidae, based mostly on the length of the tenth primary, was largely artificial. In both subfamilies (as regrouped by Chapin) there appeared to be a convergent shortening of this feather. In regrouping the members of this family, Chapin made considerable use of nesting behavior. In one of his subfamilies pensile, intricately woven nests are found, while in the other subfamily nests are neither pensile nor woven.

SUMMARY

Termite nests are species-specific products of the nest-building behavior of the colony. The subterranean nests of *Apicotermes* provide unique material for the study of the evolution of behavior. Each species builds a very specific type of nest which shows distinct similarities to and differences from nests of other species of the genus. Nest characters show phylogenetic relationships more clearly than do the morphological characteristics of the termites. Nest-building behavior in termites is probably entirely innate or instinctive, at least according to the definition of "instinct" given here. Ethological evolution seems to be directed by the same forces as is morphological evolution. The nests of *Apicotermes* show particularly well several phenomena found also in the evolution of structural characteristics. Termite nests have evolved toward a high degree of social homeostasis, providing considerable regulation of the environment and protection from enemies. Wall perforations, apparently functioning to permit gas exchange between the interior and exterior of the nest, must be of considerable adaptive advantage, since they occur in the nests of all but one species of *Apicotermes*. Circular galleries possibly function by protecting these perforations from ground water and enemies that might otherwise enter the nest. Galleries may have evolved convergently as many as four times within the genus. Vestigial, partially regressed galleries are seen in one nest that has completely lost the openings of the galleries. Another nest seems to be in an earlier stage of this regression. The apparent method of gallery construction within a single nest seems to recapitulate stages in the evolution of these structures. These nests show radial symmetry and replication of structures. *Apicotermes* provides an excellent illustration of the supraorganism concept.

LITERATURE CITED

AHMAD, M. 1950. The phylogeny of termite genera based on imagoworker mandibles. Bull. Am. Mus. Nat. Hist., 95: 37–86.

ALLEE, W. C., A. E. EMERSON, O. PARK, T. PARK, AND K. P. SCHMIDT. 1949. Principles of Animal Ecology. W. B. Saunders Co., Phila.

BOYDEN, A. 1947. Homology and analogy, a critical review of the meanings and implications of these concepts in biology. Am. Midl. Nat., 37: 648–69.

BUGNION, E. 1927. The origin of instinct, a study of the war between the ants and the termites. Trans. C. K. Ogden. Psyche Monographs No. 1.

CHAPIN, J. P. 1917. The classification of the weaver-birds. Bull. Am. Mus. Nat. Hist. 37: 243–80.

CHAUVIN, R. 1954. Aspects sociaux des grandes fonctions chez l'abeille la théorie du superorganisme. Insects Sociaux, 1: 123–29.

COTT, H. B. 1940. Adaptive Coloration in Animals. Oxford Univ. Press, N.Y.

CRANE, J. 1941. Crabs of the genus *Uca* from the west coast of Central America. Zoologica, 26: 145–208.

DARWIN, C. 1877. The Origin of Species. New edition from the 6th British edition. D. Appleton and Co., N.Y.

DAVIS, D. E. 1940. Social nesting habits of the smooth-billed Ani. Auk, 57: 179–218.

——. 1942. The phylogeny of social nesting habits in the Crotophaginae. Quart. Rev. Biol., 17: 115–34.

DELACOUR, J., AND E. MAYR. 1945. The family Anatidae. Wilson Bull., 57: 1–55.

DESNEUX, J. 1918. Un nouveau type du nids de termites. Rev. Zool. Afric., 5: 298–312.

——. 1948. Les nidifications souterraines des *Apicotermes*, termites de l'Afrique tropicale. Rev. Zool. Bot. Afric., 41: 1–54.

——. 1953. Les constructions hypogés des *Apicotermes*, termites de l'Afrique tropicale. Ann. Mus. Roy. Congo Belge, Série in 8°, Sciences Zoologiques, 17: 1–98.

EMERSON, A. E. 1938. Termite nests—a study of the phylogeny of behavior. Ecol. Monogr., **8**: 247–84.

——. 1947. Why termites? Sci. Monthly, **64**: 337–45.

——. 1951. Termite studies in the Belgian Congo. Deuxième Rapport Annuel, 1949, Inst. Rech. Sci. Afr. Centr., pp. 149–59.

——. 1952a. The supraorganismic aspects of the society. Coll. intern. C.N.R.S., **34**: 333–54.

——. 1952b. The neotropical genera *Procornitermes* and *Cornitermes* (Isoptera, Termitidae). Bull. Am. Mus. Nat. Hist., **99**: 475–540.

——. 1953. The African genus *Apicotermes* (Isoptera: Termitidae). Ann. Mus. Roy. Congo Belge, Série in 8°, Sciences Zoologiques, **17**: 99–121.

——. 1954. Dynamic homeostasis: a unifying principle in organic, social, and ethical evolution. Sci. Monthly, **78**: 67–85.

FRIEDMANN, H. 1929. The Cowbirds. Charles C. Thomas, Springfield, Ill.

——. 1946. Ecological counterparts in birds. Sci. Monthly, **63**: 395–98.

——. 1948. The parasitic cuckoos of Africa. Wash. Acad., Sci., Monograph No. 1.

GRASSÉ, P.-P. 1937. Recherches sur la systématique et la biologie des termites de l'Afrique Occidentale Française. Ann. Soc. Ent. France, **106**: 1–100.

——. 1939. La reconstruction du nid et le travail collectif chez les termites supérieurs. Jour. Psychol. norm. et path., 1939, pp. 370–96.

——. 1944. Recherches sur la biologie des termites champignonnistes (Macrotermitinae). Ann. des Sc. Nat., Zool., 11ᵉ série, **6**: 97–172.

——. 1952. La régulation sociale chez les Isoptères et les Hyménoptères. Coll. intern. C.N.R.S., **34**: 323–31.

GRASSÉ, P.-P., AND C. NOIROT. 1948a. Sur le nid et la biologie du *Sphaerotermes sphaerothorax* (Sjöstedt). Ann. des Sc. Nat., Zool., 11ᵉ série, **10**: 149–66.

——. 1948b. La biologie et les constructions du termite *Apicotermes arquieri* n. sp. Comptes rendus Acad. Sci., **227**: 735–36.

HINGSTON, R. W. G. 1932. A Naturalist in the Guiana Forest. Edward Arnold and Co., London.

KEMNER, N. A. 1927. Aus der Biologie der Termiten Javas. Xᵉ Congrés Internat. de Zool., Budapest. Deuxième partie, pp. 1097–117.

LEHRMAN, D. S. 1953. A critique of Konrad Lorenz's theory of instinctive behavior. Quart. Rev. Biol., **28**: 337–63.

LORENZ, K. 1941. Vergleichende Bewegungsstudien an Anatinen. Jour. f. Ornithol., **89**: 194–294.

MAYR, E., AND C. VAURIE. 1948. Evolution in the family Dicruridae (birds). Evol., **2**: 238–65.

MILNE, J. M., AND L. J. MILNE. 1939. Evolutionary trends in caddis worm case construction. Ann. Ent. Soc. Am., **32**: 533–42.

MOSAUER, W. 1930. A note on the sidewinding locomotion of snakes. Am. Nat., **64**: 179–83.

——. 1935. The reptiles of a sand dune area and its surroundings in the Colorado desert, California. Ecol., **16**: 13–27.

NEEDHAM, J. G., AND P. R. NEEDHAM. 1941. Guide to the Study of Fresh-Water Biology. Comstock Pub. Co., Ithaca, N.Y.

PETRUNKEVITCH, A. 1926. The value of instinct as a taxonomic character in spiders. Biol. Bull., **50**: 427–32.

RICHTER, C. P. 1942–1943. Total self-regulatory functions in animals and human beings. The Harvey Lectures, **38**: 63–103.

SCHNEIRLA, T. C. 1946. Problems in the biopsychology of social organization. Jour. Abnormal and Soc. Psychol., **41**: 385–402.

SPIETH, H. T. 1952. Mating behavior within the genus *Drosophila* (Diptera). Bull. Am. Mus. Nat. Hist., 99: 385–474.

TINBERGEN, N. 1951. The study of Instinct. Oxford Univ. Press, Lond.

——. 1953. Social Behavior in Animals. Methuen and Co., Lond.

VAN DER KLOOT, W. G., AND C. M. WILLIAMS. 1953. Cocoon construction by the Cecropia silkworm. Behaviour, 5: 142–74.

WEISMANN, A. 1893. The all-sufficiency of natural selection. Contemporary Rev., 64: 309–38.

WHITMAN, C. O. 1899. Animal behavior. Biol. Lect. delivered at Woods Hole, summer of 1897 and 1898.

WRIGHT, SEWALL. 1929. Fisher's theory of dominance. Am. Nat., 63: 274–79.

CHAPTER 3

THE BEHAVIORAL CONSEQUENCES
OF INHERITING SPECIAL SENSORY STRUCTURES

The present treatment of sensory effects upon behavior must necessarily be limited to highlighting a representative few. First we will make some comments about basic concepts and methods of investigation. Then we will present a number of phylogenetic comparisons for several sense modalities, focusing on the behavioral consequences of inheriting special sensory structures.

The distinguished biologist, Jakob von Uexküll, has probably stressed more than anyone else the behavioral implications of an animal's perceptual tools. This he did in a candidly mentalistic, organismic, and vitalistic frame of reference. We will attempt to achieve the same point in a mechanistic framework.

The Stimulus. The concept of stimulus was defined in Chapter 1 but will be reviewed here. A stimulus is always relative to a particular class of organisms. By class is meant species, age grouping, and designation of intactness or normality (representative or nonrepresentative members of a species). Given this qualification, a stimulus can be defined as a specifiable object or event which is potentially capable of eliciting a response. This means that the object or event has been observed reliably to elicit a response in representative members of a particular class of organisms at some time or another. The emphasis here on structural intactness and species affiliation is one way of pointing out that what can be a stimulus depends on the receptor systems of the animal. Since stimuli alone elicit responses, all behavior is in some way dependent upon an animal's sensory structures.

In turn, many instances of stimulus reception depend upon the kind of responses an organism can make: an animal receives a particular pattern of kinesthetic stimulation when it moves a particular way, a human being hears himself talk only when he speaks, and so on. The response-produced kinesthetic or auditory stimulus then determines, at least in part, the subsequent behavior (a feedback system). Some of the highly specialized instances of sensory feedback, as seen in the sonar systems of bats and porpoises, will be considered in detail later.

Methods for the Identification of Stimuli. Whether an object or event can be called a stimulus, or a change therein can be called a stimulus difference, is basically a problem in psychophysics. But with lower animals the direct, language-oriented methods of psychophysics are not possible. Instead the determination of a stimulus or stimulus difference usually depends upon one of the following testing techniques.

1) *Detection.* The animal reliably makes an innate or unconditioned response which indicates that the stimulus is detected. Examples are as follows: the startle or other overt responses to sound; the optokinetic or optomotor responses (nystagmus) which are elicited by a moving *articulated* field, as by a series of moving stripes which differ in brightness or hue; an initial preference for a particular foodstuff; failure of fowl to peck grain under low levels of illumination; an invertebrate's reliable positioning of itself at a certain point in a *gradient* of stimulation, as when the cockroach approaches and stays in a region of 80 percent humidity; a naïve rat's accurate judgment of distance when jumping; and the *change* in behavior which occurs whenever the opportunity is available to investigate a *change* in the stimulus situation (see Chance and Mead, 1955 **, Chapter 9).

2) *Conditioning.* The question to be answered by this method is: Can the object or event serve as a conditioned stimulus in a conditioning experiment, when the circumstances for conditioning are optimal (see Chapter 10)? With this method positive results can be interpreted more clearly than negative results. If conditioning occurs, then the environmental manipulation which was used as the conditioned stimulus *is* a stimulus for the animals tested.

3) *Discrimination learning.* The popular trend in discrimination learning is to use operant techniques, where rate of responding (lever-pressing, key-pecking, etc.) in the presence of one "stimulus" as opposed to the rate of responding in the presence of another is the measure of learning. Essentially, in discrimination learning, the animal must learn to respond to one aspect of the environment in a way that is different from the way it responds to other aspects of the environment. Typically, the occurrence of a response to one stimulus aspect is followed by reward, while the same response to other aspects is nonrewarded. If the organism can learn the discrimination, then the environmental manipulation constitutes a true stimulus difference. For a definitive identification of the stimulus, however, one must be cer-

tain that only one type of receptor input is being manipulated at any one time. This last point becomes especially critical in the study of color vision. This is true because variations in wave length result in brightness changes as well as hue changes (chromatic changes). A similar problem can arise when an animal is learning a size discrimination. It is often difficult to differentiate between a size and brightness dimension or between a size and position dimension (a large white circle is brighter or reflects more light than a small one and extends either closer to the floor or closer to the ceiling than a small circle). So far we have been discussing difficulties involved in interpreting positive results. Negative results also can be ticklish to interpret. Failure to learn a discrimination, instead of being due to sensory incapacity, may be due to the fact that the conditions for learning are unduly complicated. In an experiment on color vision, for example, the exercise of precise experimental controls could produce an apparent failure of discrimination.

Phylogenetic Comparisons

Audition. When the analysis of the sense of hearing is broadened to include more than the sensing of vibrations by means of a cochlea, then many phyla are capable of hearing. Although evidence below the arthropods is scanty, insects are quite sensitive to sound. Sensitivity even to ultrasonic frequencies has been observed in species of grasshoppers, and auditory communication among several species of insects during sexual behavior has been quite well established.

> ROTH, L. M. An experimental laboratory study of the sexual behavior of *Aedes aegypti. Amer. Midl. Nat.,* 1948, **40**, 265–352.
>
> The antennae of male mosquitoes are hearing organs attuned to receive the sounds made by the female mosquito. The male flies toward the source of sound, seizes the female and copulates. All of these responses can be elicited by a tuning fork vibrating at 275–700 cycles per second. Very young males are often molested because their frequencies are in the same range as mature females. The very young females emit frequencies which are outside of this range and are therefore ignored. The males' response is abolished if the antennae are waxed and is restored when the wax is removed.

Fish hear by means of the lateral line system which developed from tactile organs, and as such this system is a precursor of the mammalian auditory organ. Lower frequencies seem to be perceived by fish most adequately (300 cycles and below), with little or no pitch discrimination. For fish, which cannot see much beyond 20 or 30 feet nor receive odors very rapidly, the lateral line system is its best distance receptor.

The frog, according to the early work of Yerkes, can hear from 50 to 10,000 cycles, but additional study of hearing in the amphibia is badly needed. Snakes presumably do not hear airborne sounds, but groundborne vibrations are undoubtedly heard. Such a receptor system is of course adaptive for an animal which glides along the ground most of the time. Although the experimental evidence is meager, there is evidence that other reptiles such as crocodiles, alligators, turtles, and lizards are also able to hear.

In birds the ear is developed to the point where it can be said to have an uncoiled cochlea. Accordingly, hearing is well developed though perhaps somewhat more restricted in range than for man. Pitch discrimination is good as witnessed by birds' ability to mimic and to distinguish a species' call.

Hearing is excellent in all mammals, and many mammals hear in an upper range that is inaudible to man. The rodent, the dog, the cat, even the chimpanzee have much higher upper limits than man's 20,-000 cycles. But the bat takes the prize, for its upper range ends at about 98,000 cycles. The excellent hearing in mammals brings up a point that needs to be made when man's hearing is being compared with the hearing of other mammals. The dog, for example, has keen hearing over a wide range but it is very unlikely that it has keener hearing than man within the range to which humans are maximally sensitive. At the point of maximum sensitivity in man (around 2,000 cps) his hearing is so acute that any increase in sensitivity would let him hear the molecular action of the air. The behavioral implications of the dog's wide, sensitive range of hearing is that the dog excels in tasks requiring auditory vigilance (the watchdog, the sheep dog, etc.). In the same vein, many rodents are nocturnal and depend on a wide, sensitive range of hearing to detect predators.

The most dramatic behavioral consequence of special auditory structures is the phenomenon of echolocation as exemplified by the bat and dolphin (porpoise) and as described in the selected studies. Rats appear to possess a similar ability even when they do not produce the sound which is reflected (Riley and Rosenzweig, 1957 *); and at least one species of bird, the oilbird of Venezuela, navigates in complete darkness in an underground cavern. This bird emits short clicks of about 7,000 cycles per second and uses these low frequency reflected sounds to discriminate and localize objects, though somewhat ineffectually (Griffin, 1954). One interesting feature of echolocation is the fact that it involves sound production as well as sound reception. Yet, in this regard, sonar is not unlike other sensory feedback systems as used by all animals. The blind man walking with a cane is a good example of feedback mechanisms.

ANDERSON, J. W.   The production of ultrasonic sounds by laboratory rats and other animals. *Science,* 1954, **119,** 808–9.

High frequency sounds are produced by the laboratory rat and various other mammals (flying phalanger, squirrel monkey, guinea pig, and marmoset). The laboratory rat is able to emit pure tones between 20 and 30 kilocycles per second, tones which have no audible component for man. The ability to hear above 20 kilocycles has also been established for the laboratory rat.

GRIFFIN, D. R.   More about bat "Radar." *Scien. Amer,* 1958, **199,** 40–44.

Ounce for ounce and watt for watt the bat is one billion times better at echolocation than the radar and sonar systems developed by man.

KELLOGG, W. N.   Echo ranging in the porpoise. *Science,* 1958, **128,** 982–88.

Several experiments were run to determine the echo-ranging abilities of the bottlenose dolphin when experimentally blindfolded. These studies dealt with the subject's reaction to submerged targets and its ability to avoid obstacles and discriminate between objects in the water. It was definitely concluded that the porpoise uses echo ranging to locate and avoid objects.

RILEY, D. A. AND ROSENZWEIG, M. R.   Echolocation in rats. *J. comp. physiol. Psychol.,* 1957, **50,** 323–28.

Rats were blinded and required to run toward the unblocked alley of a T–maze to a food goal. A small speaker and microphone were placed at the choice point and directed alternately at the open and closed alleys. It was found that discrimination was better when the microphone and speaker were directed at the blocked alley, and when hearing was impaired there was a sharp decrement in performance. Microphones were placed near the rats during the trials and it was found that their own cries did not correlate with avoiding the barriers.

The range of auditory frequencies around 50,000 cycles yields sharp reflections. Thus when an animal like the bat is capable of hearing in this range, the detection of reflected sound is greatly facilitated. Other special structures such as the shape and size of the pinna of the bat's ear are also involved in perfecting the bat's sonic discriminations.

The main behaviors affected by echolocation are navigation and food-seeking. The porpoise, because of echolocation, can feed and navigate at night as well as in deep, turbid waters. And bats catch insects to eat by means of echolocation (Griffin, *et al.,* 1960 **). In turn certain species of moth appear to hear optimally in the range of frequencies of the cries emitted by bats while in flight (30,000 to 70,000 cycles). Thus the moth is adapted for defense by means of its sensory apparatus.

Vision. A comparison of visual functions among animals shows them to differ in a variety of ways. While birds appear to have better visual acuity than man, this is not necessarily because birds can see detail better (though hawks, eagles, and vultures may exceed man in optical acuity to some extent). Rather, the rate of integration of detail is much faster. That is, the bird, with densely packed cones throughout a wide area of the retina together with one or more fovea, is capable of high resolution over a visual angle of 70 to 80 degrees. Man on the other hand would have to scan laboriously this wide area piece by piece with repeated foveal fixation. Because of its rapid rate of visual integration the bird can find its food from the air quickly and accurately.

> DONNER, K. O. Visual acuity of some passerine birds. *Acta Zoological Fennica*, 1951, 66, 1–40.
>
> Birds were required to learn a discrimination problem and then were tested for visual acuity at six different intensities of illumination. Morphological acuity (resolving power) of the eye was also determined and was shown to correlate fairly closely with behavioral results. The birds were superior in visual acuity to all other vertebrates with the exception of some primates and showed a significant decrement in visual acuity with a decrease in illumination.

Honey bees and ants can apparently perceive the plane of polarized light from the sky. This permits the bee, for example, to orient with respect to the sun when only a patch of blue sky is visible. The successful foraging bee can then communicate to the other bees in the hive the direction of the food source by means of a properly oriented dance (Von Frisch, 1956 **). The bee, as well as other insects with compound eyes, can also distinguish ultraviolet light which presumably aids in the identification of certain flowers. On the other hand, the compound eye, made up of many units or ommatidia, seriously limits form discrimination. This is because each rod-like ommatidium is oriented at a different angle and thus is stimulated only when the light enters at the angle of orientation.

> SMITH, F. E. AND BAYLOR, E. R. Bees, Daphnia and polarized light. *Ecology,* 1960, 41, 360–63; AND JANDER, R. AND WATERMAN, T. H. Sensory discrimination between polarized light and light intensity patterns by arthropods. *J. Cellular & Comp. Physiol.,* 1960, 56, 137–60.
>
> These two studies represent a controversy over whether or not insects can perceive the plane of polarized light. The first study argues this interpretation and offers evidence to the effect that polarized light supplies special brightness patterns—different patterns of reflection and scatter depending upon the plane of orientation. In other words, the explanation is extraocular. The second study takes the affirmative view and concludes that the mechanism for such perception is in the retinular cells of the ommatidium.

Annelids or segmented worms are light sensitive throughout the body surface; thus each half of an earthworm, when cut in two, can respond to light. Owls can see almost as well in the dark as diurnal birds can see in the daylight. Beyond the fact that the rods of the owl's eye are structured like cones in that they possess one-to-one connections with ganglion cells, there is no known explanation of the owl's excellent visual acuity in darkness.

HESS, W. N.   Reactions to light in the earthworm, *Lumbricus Terrestris.*
J. Morphol. & Physiol., 1924, **39**, 515–42.

This experiment was a composite of several subexperiments to test the
worm's overall reaction and sensitivity to light and its behavior in the
presence of light following removal of various anatomical structures. It was
found that light-adapted worms responded more positively to stronger light
than dark-adapted worms, that excessively stimulated worms were more
positive to stronger light than unstimulated ones, and that sexually mature
worms were more positive to stronger light than the sexually immature. A
slight decrease in the number of negative reactions occurred up through
the removal of the third segment, but when the cerebral ganglia were removed, the ratio of positive-negative reactions was reversed (i.e., more
positive than negative reactions). When the ventral nerve chord was severed
(between 5th and 6th segments), the front portion of the worm had the
usual negative reaction to light, but the posterior portion reacted positively.
From this it was concluded that the cerebral ganglia seemed to be the controlling factor in negative reactions to light. All segments were found to be
somewhat sensitive to light, at least on some part. The anterior and posterior
segments were more light sensitive than the middle segments, and the middle
portion of each segment was the most sensitive part.

One of the most interesting optical adaptations is found in the eye
of the horse. The eyeball of the horse, instead of being roughly spher-
ical, is oval shaped and oriented slantwise in the head, with the pupil
and nonelastic lens situated near one end. Such a shape and orientation
make possible the simultaneous accommodation (focusing) for near
objects and distant objects. Thus, while a horse is grazing, distant objects, including potential predators on the horizon, are also in focus.
When rays from the near object fall on the more distant section of the
retina, the rays from a distant object can still be in focus because they
fall on the close section of the retina. In addition, both the location
of the eyes on the side of the head and the shape of the head adaptively
provide the horse with wide, flat panorama (Williams and Wierzbowski, 1962).

As one proceeds up the phyletic scale from the higher invertebrates
there seems to be no marked improvement in brightness discrimination. However, when it comes to visual acuity primates generally have
better acuity than the lower mammals. This is especially true when
primates are compared with nocturnal mammals such as the opos-
sum and rat. A visual angle of one minute of arc (at the retina) can be
detected by most primates, including man, while for the pigmented
rat, the acuity threshold is in the region of 26 minutes of arc.

BRIDGMAN, C. S. AND SMITH, K. U.   The absolute threshold of vision in cat
and man with observations on its relation to the optic cortex. *Amer. J.
Physiol.*, 1942, **136**, 463–66.

The absolute brightness threshold for man, completely dark adapted,
varies between 10^{-7} and 10^{-8} millilamberts (ml). In this experiment the

average brightness threshold determined for six cats was 8.2 × 10⁻⁸ ml. The average determined for the human subjects was 5.8 × 10⁻⁷ ml. In other words, the cat's threshold is approximately one seventh that of man's. This value is lower than any value ever reported for any human or for any other infrahuman animal. The great sensitivity of the cat's eye is presumably based on a superior lens system and the wide pupils opening—not on any feature of the retina.

In the vertebrates, form vision is present from the fish to the primates. In the lower forms of invertebrates, except the octopus, form vision is absent or minimally present. Higher forms of invertebrates, such as the ant, are capable of discriminating complex patterns.

Color Vision. Of all the visual phenomena studied, color vision has probably been the most widely investigated; and the rat has probably been the most frequent object of study. Yet we are still not certain whether the rat sees color or not. If it does, the ability is primitive and seems to be limited to distinguishing red from achromatic colors and from the remainder of the spectrum. The point we are making is that the determination of color vision in animals is extremely difficult. The chief complication, as mentioned earlier, is that brightness as well as hue varies with wave length (for the rat, blue is the brightest region and red the darkest). When a discrimination is established between two wave lengths, it may well occur in terms of brightness. Since perceived brightness is in part an organismic variable, one cannot use physical measures, or one's own eye, or even the average eye of the animals being tested in order to control the brightness variable.

Nevertheless, the research on color vision seems to indicate that color vision is distributed here and there through the phylogenetic scale, though it is mainly limited to vertebrates and to the insects and cephalopods (squid and octopus) among the invertebrates. When innate or unconditioned reactions are elicited by color, as when fish change color to adapt to the background or when chicks show a natural preference for pecking at colored objects, then the presence of color vision is more easily determined for the species. It is now quite well established that most species of fish see color, especially teleost fish. Color differentiation has been determined in amphibia by the optokinetic method. And reptiles, such as the turtle, appear to have rudimentary color vision.

All diurnal birds appear to have excellent color vision. The range of discrimination is similar to that of man but with fewer discriminable hues, as illustrated in the study by Hamilton and Coleman (1933 *). The adaptive value of good color vision for the bird is quite apparent. Food objects and the sex and species of other birds are frequently differentiated by color. Color vision in most mammals, however, is poorly developed, having questionable status in dogs, cats, rodents, and many other mammals. Color vision appears full blown only among the primates, where it is comparable to that of man (see Miles, 1956 **).

HAMILTON, W. F. AND COLEMAN, T. B. Trichromatic vision in the pigeon as illustrated by the spectral hue discrimination curve. *J. Comp. Psychol.*, 1933, 15, 183–91.

Pigeons were used to determine the degree of wave length discrimination in diurnal birds. Pigment stimuli were used to establish the hues to which the pigeon would respond, and spectral stimuli were used for more specific determinations. The results indicate that the pigeon's eye is only slightly less sensitive to differences in wave length than the eye of a normal man over a comparable spectral range (700 mμ — 460 mμ) and support the conclusion that the pigeon has a tri-receptor visual apparatus.

In species where both olfaction and audition are well developed, color vision is less important and often not present. The dog, with its keen hearing and with its well-developed sense of smell, as described in the study by Kalmus (1955 **), is a case in point. On the other hand, birds which have poor olfactory sensitivity as well as rudimentary taste perception have well-developed color vision. In other words, when behavior depends heavily upon vision, color vision has increased importance. A rule of thumb to assess the presence of color vision in a species is to see if the males and females of the species are differentially colored as, for example, in birds and fish. The number of possible stimulus differentiations is substantially increased by the existence of a color dimension (hue plus saturation differences). Thus specific adaptations and greater complexity of behavior are possible.

The Chemical Senses. Reactions to chemical stimuli are primitive and pervasive, representing a fundamental property of all animal life. Chemoreception includes the traditional senses of smell and taste, but these are mainly mammalian modalities. Undifferentiated chemical sensitivity is present in lower animal forms, as illustrated in protozoa and planaria where no specific receptors can be identified. The sensitivity to chemical stimuli is high in almost all lower forms of animal life, which is quite adaptive because most of them live in water.

A variety of higher forms of *invertebrates* also exhibit high chemical sensitivity. In insects, with differentiated receptors, there is marked sensitivity to sugars, as contrasted with the sugar sensitivities found in man and other mammals. Fish are presumably capable of distinguishing individuals of their own species solely on the basis of olfaction, and the homing ability of salmon is presumably based on olfactory stimuli

(Hasler and Larsen, 1955). Among the mammals, swine as well as the dog have a highly developed sense of smell. Olfaction seems to be the pig's major sense modality and is closely tied in with its rooting behavior. In France, for example, pigs are used to search for truffles, a delicacy which grows well beneath the earth's surface.

ANDERSON, A. L.   The sensitivity of the legs of common butterflies to sugars. *J. Exp Zool.,* 19, 63, 235–59.

A number of common butterflies possess legs which are more or less sensitive to contact with chemical substances (species-specific sensitivities are present). This particular sense may be regarded as the sense of taste since it assists in the detection of food.

CRAGG, J. B. AND COLE, P.   Laboratory studies on the chemosensory reactions of blowflies. *Ann. Appl. Biol.,* 1956, 44, 478–91.

Various species of blowflies were tested by use of a choice-chamber technique to determine their reactions to sheep wool and other materials. Only female flies were attracted to the wool and those showing the greatest attraction were fertilized females having daily access to meat. Even without all of the olfactory organs intact, two of the species tested showed some response to wool when tested on a damp floor.

HODGSON, E. S.   Electrophysiological studies of arthropod chemoreception, II. Responses of labellar chemoreceptors of the blowfly to stimulation by carbohydrates. *J. Insect Physiol.,* 1957, 1, 240–47.

Only those sugars which stimulate a "sugar" receptor in the labellar hairs, as detected electrophysiologically (spike potentials), evoke a feeding response. This was true for 23 sugars tested. There was also a fairly good quantitative relationship between these two events—a clear correlation between receptor activity and behavior.

Undetermined Sensory Effects.   The question is still open as to what is the sensory basis of certain behaviors. What determines, for example, the cyclical behaviors of many organisms with respect to time of day, season of year, phase of the tide, etc.?

BROWN, F. A.   Living clocks. *Science,* 1959, 130, 1533–44.

Various experiments and hypotheses were referred to in drawing conclusions about the rhythmic cycles of organisms. It was suggested that there are two rhythm processes, one of which is referred to as a basic stable rhythm and the other as a more labile (unstable) rhythm. Both of these processes operate within an open system in accordance with the organism's inherent periods of oscillation and its rhythmic geophysical environment. All other periods are described chiefly as functions of light and temperature.

AUDITORY SCANNING IN THE DOLPHIN[1]

W. N. KELLOGG
Florida State University

The purpose of this report is to present an analysis of a unique behavior pattern of the bottle-nose dolphin or porpoise, *Tursiops truncatus* (Montagu), as it locates objects by echo ranging in water. This marine mammal—which is actually one of the smaller of the toothed whales—is known to avoid obstacles in its pathway while swimming and to locate fishes for food by sound reflection or by echolocation (Kellogg, 1958; 1959a). To accomplish such a result, it sends out trains or series of short staccato sound pulses, the echoes from which are reflected back to the animal's ears (Kellogg, Kohler, and Morris, 1953). Porpoises have been shown experimentally to be able to discriminate between food-fishes of different size and to select one fish from another by this method after visual cues have been effectively eliminated (Kellogg, 1959b). The man-made or mechanical analogue of porpoise echo ranging in water is represented by Navy sonar or by the marine fathometer.

Locating a Small Target

In swimming toward a small target such as food-fish held beneath the water, a dolphin can often be seen to move its head and trunk alternately to the right and left. Movements of this nature have been reported in a single captive specimen by Schevill and Lawrence (1956) and have been described in two additional animals by Kellogg (1958, 1959a).

Oscillating head movements occur only (1) while the animal is emitting trains of sound pulses and (2) when the target toward which it is swimming cannot be visually identified because of the turbidity

[1] Contribution No. 110 from the Oceanographic Institute of Florida State University. The observations reported in this paper constitute a part of a longer program of research supported by the National Science Foundation (grants No. G920 and G1730). Some of the underwater acoustical equipment used to listen to and record porpoise sonar signals was loaned by the Office of Naval Research (contract Nos. Nonr 531 and Nonr 1502). The porpoises were donated by the Marine Studios of Marineland, Florida.

of the water. Observations of the phenomenon indicate that a complete cycle takes place in from 2 to 3 sec. This activity has been noted at distances up to 10 ft. from the target and it continues until the dolphin gets close enough to seize or take the bait.

Moving the target slowly in a direction perpendicular to the animal's line of approach causes him to turn continuously so as to keep the target in the median plane. There is no interruption in the angular oscillations under such conditions. If the target is moved rapidly, there is an appreciable and clearly observable latency in the orienting behavior which results. The aim of the porpoise lags behind the actual position of the target at any instant. If the direction of movement of the target is abruptly reversed, the animal will overshoot the turning point (Kellogg, 1959b).

The speed of forward motion in such cases has been calculated for one animal and has been found to be quite slow. In 172 measurements made over a period of 4 weeks it averaged .34 ft./sec. with a standard deviation of .06 ft./sec. and a range of .44 ft./sec. (The average of .34 ft./sec. is roughly equivalent to .2 miles per hr.) The magnitude of the arc of oscillation of the head and body is estimated at approximately 10 degrees, or 5 degrees on either side of the median plane. What takes place is diagrammed schematically in Figure 1.

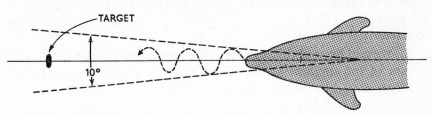

Fɪɢ. 1. Auditory scanning in the bottlenose dolphin. When echolocating a small target, such as fish, the porpoise approaches by oscillating its head to the right and left through an arc of about 10 degrees. This behavior undoubtedly involves binaural localization as well as echolocation.

Significance of the Behavior

The only adequate interpretation of this activity appears to be that the animal is orienting to the echoes of its own sound signals which are reflected back from the target it is approaching. The original sound-pulses broadcast by the dolphin are not highly directional—probably no more so than the human voice. But the echoes returning from an object at a fixed point in space would vary continuously as the locus of the animal's ears changed with reference to the source of the echoes.

The oscillation of the head is exactly what one would expect in the pin-pointing of an object by means of reflected sound. It is the same sort of activity in which a human being would engage if he were employing binaural localization. The head movements of the dolphin would constantly modulate the phase and intensity differences of the echoing sound waves reaching each of the ears. They would also alter the time interval between the emission of a pulse-signal and the return of its echo to each ear. The continuation of the process as the animal swam forward would enable him to determine with great precision the direction from which the echoes came.

Auditory Scanning

Since the noises which make up the echoes are emitted by the dolphin itself, the activity as a whole amounts to a kind of scanning by sound. We suggest the term *auditory scanning,* therefore, as a good name for both the acoustic and the general behavior comprising this elaborate pattern of activity. The parallel with optics is enhanced if auditory scanning is compared to visual scanning which is conducted at night with the aid of a searchlight.

From the standpoint of the organism, auditory scanning may be thought of as more complex than visual scanning, for it represents a combination of two already complex processes. Auditory scanning consists of (1) the emission of a continuous series of sound-signals for the purpose of echolocation and (2) binaural localization. It might be characterized as "binaural-echo-localization."

Above and beyond this activity is the perceptual process itself. The stream of information produced by auditory scanning must be instantly analyzed by the amazing brain of the animal. Greatly enlarged cerebral hemispheres, particularly in the temporal region, give an anatomical clue to the remarkable acoustical ability which the dolphin possesses. The mechanical counterpart of such a receptor system would be a sonar apparatus with one transmitter and two independent receivers, plus an electronic computer capable of decoding and processing the data—all within a single compact unit.

SUMMARY

As the bottle-nose porpoise swims toward an underwater target it frequently oscillates its head from side to side through an arc of about 10 degrees, at the same time emitting trains of sound signals. The phenomenon is accounted for as a combination of echolocation and binaural localization. It is given the name of auditory scanning.

REFERENCES

KELLOGG, W. N.   Echo ranging in the porpoise. *Science,* 1958, **128**, 982–88.

KELLOGG, W. N.   Auditory perception of submerged objects by porpoises. *J. Acoust. Soc. Amer.,* 1959, **31**, 1–6. (a)

KELLOGG, W. N.   Size-discrimination by reflected sound in a bottlenose dolphin. *J. comp. physiol. Psychol.,* 1959, **52**, 509–14. (b)

KELLOGG, W. N., KOHLER, ROBERT, AND MORRIS, H. N.   Porpoise sounds as sonar signals. *Science,* 1953, **117**, 239–43.

SCHEVILL, W. E., AND LAWRENCE, B.   Food-finding by a captive porpoise (*Tusiops truncatus*). *Breviora (Mus. Comp. Zool., Harvard),* 1956, **53**, 1–15.

COLOR VISION IN THE MARMOSET[1]

RAYMOND C. MILES
Montana State College

Research concerned with the topic of animal color vision indicates that the primates, in contrast with most other mammals, possess some degree of color vision (2, 3, 4, 7, 12). Since no investigation has failed to find this ability in primates, it appears that color discrimination may be a universal characteristic of this order (3, 6, 8). The object of the present experiment is to extend the above comparative research by investigating color vision in a more primitive primate, the marmoset (11).

The standard learning-set procedure has been used by Miles and Meyer (11) to compare the marmoset's intellectual capacity with that of the macaque. After extensive testing, the marmoset revealed a respectable primate-like learning curve; the macaque, however, achieved the same status after one-tenth as many problems. These two species were again compared by an identical delayed-response procedure, and the marmoset fared much better than it had on learning sets, but was still far inferior to the macaque (9).

Thus, the marmoset is clearly inferior to the macaque in learning ability; it would be of interest to determine whether or not the marmoset shows other deficiencies, such as color blindness. If this rather lowly primate species does possess color vision, the generalization that all primates have this feature in common will receive further support.

METHOD

Subjects

The Ss were two experimentally naive adult common marmosets, genus *Callithrix*, one female and one male. During the experiment the Ss were allowed to eat for 30 min. immediately after each test session; their diet consisted of apples, oranges, bananas, bread, eggs, and a vitamin mixture.

Apparatus

The marmosets were tested in a rectangular plywood box which was very similar to a conventional Wisconsin General Test Apparatus (5). In order to

[1] This research was carried out at The Ohio State University and was supported by funds allocated by the University Advisory Committee on Research Grants.

accommodate the marmosets' small size, the proportions of the apparatus were reduced by approximately two-thirds. The equipment consisted essentially of a restraining cage which was separated from a test compartment by evenly spaced vertical bars. An opaque screen, which could be raised or lowered by *E,* was located directly in front of the restraining bars (11).

The test compartment was equipped with a movable tray which could be advanced toward, or withdrawn from, the restraining cage. Located near the front edge of the test tray and spaced 8 in. apart were two circular foodwells, 1 in. in diameter. The tray was painted flat black, with the exception of a small 2-in.-square white patch around each foodwell; the rest of the apparatus was painted dove gray. A circular diffusing surface of white cardboard, which was replaced when soiled, was glued to the top of each test object.

Above each foodwell was a lamp component which projected a circular patch of light upon the test object or, when an object was displaced, upon the white area around the foodwell. Luminance was randomly varied by the insertion of Wratten neutral filters of densities 0.05, 0.50, 1.00, 1.50, and 2.00. Corning color filters were utilized to vary spectral composition. The color filters selected were those that yielded to the human observer the sensations of blue, green, and red; color specification numbers for the filters were 5-58 (blue), 4-64 (green), and 2-61 (red). The filters were sufficiently separated so that there was virtually no overlap (less than 1 per cent) in their spectral transmissions.

Procedure

The marmosets were first trained to enter transport cages and were then adapted to the test situation. Both *S*s were given 50 trials in which it was necessary to displace one stimulus block in order to receive the test reward, a small square of cooked white-of-egg or apple.

The testing routine consisted of the following sequence: Each test trial began with the opaque screen closed. Food was placed in the appropriate foodwell and the filters were inserted. The tray was advanced so that the diffusing surfaces of the test objects were illuminated. The opaque screen was then raised and the *S* permitted to make one choice. A daily test session consisted of 50 trials.

The first problem was blue-positive and red-negative; the second, blue-positive and green-negative; and the third, green-positive and red-negative. For any given problem, the food was always in the foodwell under the test object illuminated by the positive stimulus. Position of the correct stimulus varied from trial to trial according to a Gellermann (1) series. The brightness relation of the two stimuli was altered at random every five trials by the insertion of neutral filters of different densities. Other controls were: observing the *S*s through one-way glass, smearing both foodwells with the food to eliminate odor cues, and reinserting the filters every trial to counteract differential noise cues.

Both *S*s were tested on a given problem until the slower learner attained the criterion of 19 correct responses in 20 trials. As a final control, before any problem was considered learned, the positive stimulus was paired with a stimulus having a density of 0.05 for 10 trials and then with one of 1.50 for 10 more trials to ascertain whether or not there had developed a tendency to respond on the basis of brightness differences. Each *S* was tested for a total of 330 trials.

RESULTS

Figure 1 illustrates the results in terms of percentage of correct responses as a function of number of trials. The learning curve represents the averaged performances of both *S*s. Both animals learned each of the three discriminations to the criterion of 19 correct responses in 20 trials.

Neither S experienced great difficulty in learning the first (blue-positive, red-negative) discrimination. The next problem (blue-positive, green-negative) was learned very rapidly because of positive transfer effects. The final problem (green-positive, red-negative) proved to be more difficult. This was to be expected, since the previously negative stimulus (green) was now positive, and it therefore cannot be inferred that any particular hue was less readily discriminated than any other. When the positive stimulus was paired with stimuli of radically different-brightnesses, no interference with the discrimination was found.

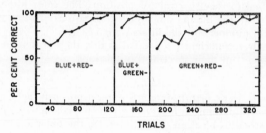

F~IG~. 1. This graph summarizes percentage of correct choices as a function of trials. Each point is a mean score for both animals and for a block of 20 trials.

DISCUSSION

The animals readily learned a discrimination based upon color differences. Although brightness was varied over a considerable range, and the positive color was paired with very light and very dark negative stimuli, the differences in brightness failed to confuse the Ss. It can therefore be concluded that the marmoset has some form of color vision.

Although this animal is intellectually retarded in comparison with most other primates, it apparently possesses the primate characteristic of advanced development in the visual modality (10, 11). The experimental value of the marmoset is enhanced by the fact that it perceives color, since its rather smooth cortex will make possible some excellent and basic psychosurgical research on vision.

This experiment should be regarded as only preliminary. The next step should be an extensive investigation to determine whether or not this primitive primate will show the expected marked deficiency in the long-wave-length end of the spectrum (3, 6, 8).

SUMMARY

This experiment was designed to determine if the marmoset, genus *Callithrix,* can discriminate color. The Ss were presented with two circular test objects, each of which had a circle of light projected onto its surface. Hue and luminance of the circle of light were varied with filters. The fact that the Ss readily learned discriminations based upon blue, green, and red color combinations indicates that the marmoset, like other primates, does possess some form of color vision.

REFERENCES

1. GELLERMANN, L. W.   Chance orders and alternating stimuli in visual discrimination experiments. *J. genet. Psychol.,* 1933, **42**, 206–7.
2. GREGG, R. M., JAMISON, E., WILKIE, R., AND RADINSKY, T.   Are dogs, cats, and racoons color blind? *J. comp. Psychol.,* 1929, **9**, 379–95.
3. GRETHER, W. F.   Color vision and color blindness in monkeys. *Comp. psychol. Monogr.,* 1939, **15**, No. 38.
4. GUNTER, R.   The discrimination between lights of different wave lengths in the cat. *J. comp. physiol. Psychol.,* 1954, **47**, 169–72.
5. HARLOW, H. F.   The formation of learning sets. *Psychol. Rev.,* 1949, **56**, 51–65.
6. MALMO, R. B., AND GRETHER, W. F.   Further evidence of red blindness (protanopia) in cebus monkeys. *J. comp. physiol. Psychol.,* 1947, **40**, 143–47.
7. MEYER, D. R., MILES, R. C., AND RATOOSH, P.   Absence of color vision in cat. *J. Neurophysiol.,* 1954, **17**, 289–94.
8. MILES, R. C.   Color vision in the squirrel monkey. *Amer. J. Physiol.,* 1955, **183**, 645.
9. MILES, R. C.   Delayed-response learning in the marmoset and the macaque. *J. comp. physiol. Psychol.,* 1957, **50**, 352–55.
10. MILES, R. C.   Learning set formation in the squirrel monkey. *J. comp. physiol. Psychol.,* 1957, **50**, 356–57.
11. MILES, R. C., AND MEYER, D. R.   Learning sets in marmosets. *J. comp. physiol. Psychol.,* 1956, **49**, 219–22.
12. MILES, R. C., RATOOSH, P., AND MEYER, D. R.   Absence of color vision in guinea pig. *J. Neurophysiol.,* 1956, **19**, 254–58.

THE DISCRIMINATION BY THE NOSE OF THE DOG OF INDIVIDUAL HUMAN ODOURS AND IN PARTICULAR OF THE ODOURS OF TWINS

By H. KALMUS

Galton Laboratory, University College; London

Francis Galton's suggestion (1875) that "it would be an interesting experiment for twins who were closely alike to try how far dogs can distinguish between them by scent," has to the author's knowledge never been put to any deliberate experimental test. What evidence exists on this point, has arisen from chance observation and points to the conclusion that dogs may not be able to distinguish between the body odours of identical twins. For instance, in a letter dated 15th October, 1952, from Mrs. John W. MacArthur to Professor Penrose, the following experience which was brought to the knowledge of the late John W. MacArthur, Professor of Genetics of Toronto University, is recorded:

"In a prospector's camp in Northern Ontario was a nearly blind great dane, Silva. She was not a friendly dog, but she had a passion for one prospector and fawned on him delightedly whenever he came to camp.
"One day a stranger appeared for the first time and to the surprise of those present, Silva greeted him with great affection. Upon enquiry by the camp crew it was found that the stranger was the identical twin of the particular prospector, whom Silva had such a passion for, and that he had never been there before nor seen the dog before."

The fact that a dog can pick out an individual from others may appear commonplace but for the fact that recently there are indications that sweats may be as different and as characteristic genetically as bloods and salivas (Penrose, 1953). In phenylketonuria, for instance, abnormal substances are found in the sweat (Jervis, 1950) which are believed to give it a characteristic smell.

In the present paper controlled experiments are described, concerning the discriminatory powers of dogs' noses and, in particular, their limited ability to distinguish between the body odours of twins.

Discrimination of People Other than Identical Twins

If confusion by a dog of the odours of identical twins is to be taken as proof of the exceptionally high chemical similarity between the twin partners, it must first be established that the same dog can discriminate with ease and reliability between the body odours of people who are not identical twins, i.e., between unrelated people, and members of one family. The first task was thus to select good dogs and to explore the conditions under which they can work successfully. According to their training two types of dogs were found and two different types of experiments were gradually developed, namely retrieving, which was performed either indoors or in the open, and outdoor tracking, of which there were two schemes; this will be described later.

The nine dogs used in these experiments varied greatly in intelligence, perseverance and the degree to which they had been trained. Four were young male Alsatians trained for police duty by individual police officers; one male Doberman Pincher and an old male Labrador were also police dogs, and there was one bitch, a German Pointer (Jagdhund), who however, was "multihandled," i.e., she could be made to work by several people. The two other bitches used, both Alsatian and several years old, were show dogs and particularly good at retrieving.

Seventeen men, nine women and five children were used in these experiments, all of whom were Europeans with the exception of one male African. The task was either to single out a handkerchief scented by a particular person or to find a track laid by a particular person among tracks laid by four to ten others.

The task of finding a particular human individual, or a track, or a scented object, is given to the dog by its human handler and the problem is solved by the co-operation of the two. The first precaution in experiments concerning discrimination by a dog's nose must thus be that the person who handles the dog should not know the answer to the problem and should have no preference for any particular solution; in this respect animal psychologists and police have to be particularly careful. Löhner (1924) describes how a trained goat seemed to learn individual human scents with great ease, but failed completely as soon as its owner did not know the correct answer. In the present experiments dog and man were never at the site while scented objects were laid out or tracks were being laid.

The limitations of a dog's understanding, although varying a great deal, nevertheless imposed a severe restraint on experimentation. Thus, on most occasions the dog had to be gradually and repeatedly taught its task, proceeding from the simpler to the more difficult (see experiment on p. 121), and it was also patted or rewarded when successful and discouraged after failures.

Only an exceptional dog can, during any one experimental session, change from searching for one person's odour to searching for another's odour. Thus experiments were as a rule so arranged that only one odour was tried on any half day on one dog. There was little sign of "nose fatigue" in the experiments, but after one hour or so most dogs lost interest and their performance became erratic. It was then little use to persevere with the experiment.

Retrieving Experiments

These were a version of the retrieving tests usual at dog shows. The procedure was as follows: first, a number of marked handkerchiefs,* one of which was scented for a few minutes in a person's armpit, were laid out in a straight line in the absence of dog and handler. These were then called in and the dog made to sit down; it's muzzle was then clasped for about half a minute by the hands of the person who had scented the handkerchief. Indoors (Fig. 1), the dog was commanded

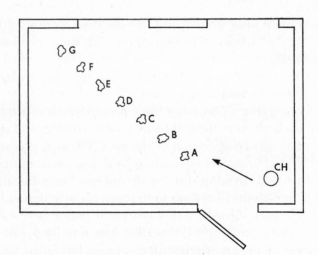

Fig. 1. A row of handkerchiefs (A–G) laid out in a room for retrieving. The person whose body odour is sought for sits in the chair, Ch.; the dog is led in by the door, made to sniff the person's hands and sent off in the direction of the arrow.

---

* Three dozen handkerchiefs were washed, ironed and stored for a few days before every experiment by a person not taking part in the experiments. They were then handled by means of plastic forceps.

to walk over the handkerchiefs and to seek and bring back the scented one. Outdoors (Fig. 2), the dog was sent obliquely against the wind

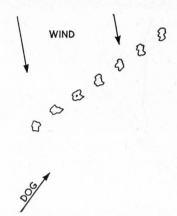

Fig. 2. A row of handkerchiefs laid out in the open.

and at a slight angle to the row of handkerchiefs. Usually the dog brought back the scented handkerchief the the first attempt but sometimes it overshot and only brought it back when returning or at a second attempt. In any case, the next step in the experiment was only taken after success in this task. This second step considered of asking the dog to pick out the "right" handkerchief not among a row of unscented ones (blanks) but among handkerchiefs scented in the armpits of other people.

The results of several such experiments indicated that although there was some variation in the day-to-day performances of some individual dogs, nevertheless a few dogs were very sure in retrieving. These were subsequently used in the twin experiments.

Tracking Experiments

These were performed in two different ways. The first type (Fig. 3) of tracking consisted of a number of people walking into a field side by side for about 100 yards, where one of them dropped a handkerchief, glove, cap or similar object. After a further 25 yards or so the people fanned out and when they reached a distant hedge or a row of trees, either hid behind the hedge or climbed the trees so that they were not visible from the field. The dog was then led from the car C to the point where the men had entered the field, and put on the scent on a tracking line. He picked up the dropped object and followed one track, and it was then ascertained whether he had followed the right one. A new field had to be used for each such experiment and the di-

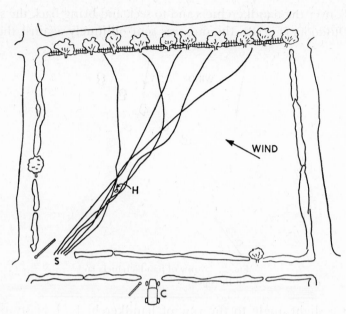

FIG. 3.   Fanning   out   tracks.

rection of the wind had to be taken into account as direct air scent
interferes with the tracking. The outcome of these experiments was
that those police dogs, which were advanced in their training, were
quite reliable in picking out the correct track among a number of
incorrect ones.

The second type of tracking experiments followed the design given
by Budgett (Fig. 4). A person walked from the lee side (1) into a field
until he reached a point P where he stuck a pole or branch into the
ground and also dropped an object at 2. He then walked on at an angle
until he reached the hedge at 3 and continued behind it to 4, where
he hid. Another person starting from the same point 1 passed the pole
and the dropped object and continued towards 5 and 6; after returning to P he walked towards 7 and 8, returning to P for a second time,
then proceeded to the hedge at point 9, i.e., opposite the first person,
and finally hid at 10. The handler and a dog on a tracking line were
then summoned from the car C to position 1 and the dog put on the
track. The dog picked up the dropped object, which the handler took
from him and later gave it back to him to sniff. In the neighbourhood
of P the dog had a choice of 5 tracks by the second person and one
track of the first (to whom the object belonged), and it was then seen
whether he followed the correct track or one of the five wrong ones.
Table I shows that Kim, a well trained Police dog, made very few mis-
takes when the two people laying the tracks were not identical twins.

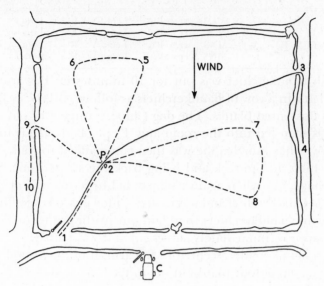

Fɪɢ 4. Budgett's layout.

TABLE I.
Bᴜᴅɢᴇᴛᴛ's Lᴀʏᴏᴜᴛ

Name of Dog	Sex	Age	Breed	Follows Correct Track from	Follows One Wrong Track from	Remarks
Kim	M	18 mos.	Alsatian	6		Follows wrong track
				6		for about 50 yds. then casts back and finds correct person.
Kim	M	18 mos.	Alsatian	6		
				6		
Kim	M	18 mos.	Alsatian	6		

TWIN EXPERIMENTS

Retrieving and tracking were used in the experiments with different results. Four pairs of apparently identical twins were tested, three female and one male. Previous experience makes it very improbable that the body odours of fraternal twins would be more similar than the body odours of sibs of different age; none were so far tested.

One retrieving experiment is described in some detail: Two identical twin sisters, (T_1 and T_2), aged 14, their sister (S) aged 12, their father (F) all living in one household, as well as four non-related people (P, K, L, R,) were tested in a room in the fashion illustrated in Figure 1. The twin sisters were extremely similar in every respect. The blood antigens of the family were:

Father (F)	O	MsMs	rr	P+	Le(a+)	K—	Lu(a—)	Fy(a+)
Mother	A₂B	N S	rr	P+	Le(a—)	K—	Lu(a—)	Fy(a—)
Twin sisters (T₁ & T₂)	A₂	MNS	rr	P—	Le(a—)	K—	Lu(a—)	Fy(a+)
Sister (S)	B	MNS	rr	P+	Le(a+)	K—	Lu(a—)	Fy(a+)

A fresh handkerchief was put for 10 minutes in T_1's armpit and then laid 4th in a row of handkerchiefs as follows, B B B T_1 B, where B means unscented blanks. The dog Chloë, a three year old Alsatian bitch, was then led into the room and T_1 put both hands for half a minute over her muzzle. She was then commanded to walk over the handkerchiefs and to seek and bring back the scented one. She first played about, but when again commanded to retrieve, brought back the correct handkerchief and was patted. Chloë was led out of the room and the same handkerchiefs were laid out in the sequence B B T_1 B B.[1] She was now immediately successful and was patted.

Next, a handkerchief, scented in the armpit of the second twin T_2 was placed among four blanks in the order B T_2 B B B. Chloë, when led in, sniffed the hands of T_1; sent out, she brought back T_2 without hesitation. She was not patted on this occasion. It was now considered that Chloë understood the situation. She was clearly able to pick out a handkerchief scented by T_1 from among blanks and she also retrieved T_2 instead. The significance of the acceptance of T_2 for T_1 was then assessed by offering T_1 and T_2, or both, among a number of handkerchiefs scented by other people. Using the same procedure as before, Chloë, after sniffing T_1's hand was confronted with the sequence S L K T_1 P R F. She playfully picked up S, the first one belonging to T_1's younger sister, then dropped it and retrieved T_1. She was patted and given a biscuit. The experiment was repeated with the sequence F S P T_1 L R and was immediately successful.

Now T_2's handkerchief was put into the sequence F S P L T_2 R, from which T_1 was missing. T_1's hand was sniffed, but T_2's handkerchief was retrieved without hesitation. This time Chloë was patted and rewarded. The experiment was then repeated with the sequence P S T_2 L R F and Chloë again retrieved T_2. In a second repetition Chloë overshot T_2 in the sequence S R F T_2 P L, but when she turned back and worked the handkerchiefs from the far end, she picked up T_2 and brought it back. She was patted and rewarded. At this stage it was concluded that Chloë accepted, in the absence of the "correct" scent and from a sample of body odours containing those of a younger sister and her father, as well as non-related people, only the body odour of her monozygotic twin sister.

The next experiments were designed to show whether, when the

---

[1] Persons and handkerchiefs scented by them are denoted by the same letter.

body odours of both twin sisters were in the series, a preference for the correct one could be detected. First, T_1 and T_2 were offered among unscented handkerchiefs (blanks). Working the series B B T_2 T_1 B B Chloë retrieved T_2, which was the first she came across, and after this was removed, and the row rearranged closing the gap, she retrieved T_1 when led in again. No difference in the certainty of reaction or in any other way was observed.

For the next experiments the handkerchiefs, scented by the twins were laid out among six handkerchiefs, scented by their father, sister and four non-related people, in the following sequence: R K S T_2 F T_1 P L. Chloë, after sniffing T_1's hands, retrieved T_2 which was first on her way without hesitation, and after its removal and the arrangement of the rest she retrieved T_1, again without any observable difference in behaviour. An interval of 10 minutes ensued, during which Chloë was fed and given water. A training run was put in, in which Chloë successfully picked out T_1's handkerchief among seven handkerchiefs, none of which were scented by T_2. Finally, the sequence P T_1 S K T_2 L F R was offered Chloë; she overran T_1 and retrieved T_2, and when the gap was closed and she was sent out again she retrieved T_1.

The conclusion from this series of experiments is that in the circumstances stated Chloë accepted the identical twin sister's body odour for the original one and, when offered handkerchiefs from both among several scented with other people's body odours, indiscriminately retrieved that which she first came across. The dog did not seem to prefer the scent of either a younger sister or the father of the twin, to the odour to which she had been trained.

A similar set of experiments was performed with two identical twin sisters, aged 23, both post-graduate students living together. Their blood antigens were as follows:

O MsNs R_1R_1 P+ Le (a−b+) K−Lu (a+) Fy(a+)

The same dog was used. The results are summarised on page 124.

The results of tracking experiments, while also indicative of a great similarity between the odours of identical twins, nevertheless suggested, that in this situation good dogs might be able to distinguish by smell between identical twin partners. Budgett's layout (Fig. 4) was used for each experiment, and a new field for every set of tracks. The results of two such experiments were as follows:

26th December, a cold day with wind and drizzle. The two identical twins, married men aged 33 who had lived in different places for several years, had the following blood antigens in common:

A_1 NsNs Ror P+ Le (a−) K− Lu (a−) Fy (a−).

Sequence						Chloë, after sniffing T_1's hand, retrieved
B	B	T_1	B	B		T_1 Patted
B	T_1	B	B	B		T_1 Fed on biscuit
B	B	B	T_2	B		T_2
R	P	T_1	O	H		T_1 patted
K	O	R	P	T_1	H	T_1 patted, fed on biscuit
H	P	R	O	T_2	K	T_2 after overrunning and working back
O	J	T_2	K	R	T_1 P H	T_2 which is first in the way
O	J	K	R	T_1	P H	T_1
H	T_2	J	B	K R T_1 P O		T_2
H	J	B	K	R T_1 P O		Refusal to bring any handkerchief back. Second try
H	J	B	K	R T_1 P O		T_1

10 minutes pause, while fresh handkerchiefs were scented in all armpits for 5 minutes.

Sequence						Chloë, after sniffing T_1's hand, retrieved
W	T_2	R	P	T_1	L M	M The last one brought back. Failure! Chloë scolded.
W	T_2	R	P	T_1	L	T_2
W	R	P	T_1	K L		T_1 Chloë patted
P	L	T_2	N	T_1	R W	T_2
P	L	N	T_1	R W		T_1

A Police dog Kim, an Alsatian male aged 18 months, was used. In two preliminary tests, Kim twice picked out the track of one of the twins from five tracks of an unrelated person. He was next set on the double tracks made by the twin brothers. After picking up a glove of the twin brother, used in the preliminary experiment, he unhesitatingly followed his track, although it bent on the crossing point and there were five tracks laid by the other twin brother. When the experiment was repeated in a new field, Kim followed the right track for about 50 yards but then lost it, presumably owing to the strong wind. Casting about he found it again and followed it to where it left the field through the hedge (point 3). Here, however, Kim lost the track again, and when led back to the starting point, he got confused and followed several of the false tracks. The experiment was then repeated on new tracks laid in a fresh field. The force of the wind had by then increased to such an extent that Kim tracked about two yards to the lee side of the tracks, and in this way after some time on the right track he got onto one of the false ones. Finally, the air scent of the "correct" twin was picked up and Kim ran to him directly, i.e., not following any track, and barked at him. Bad weather made continuation of the experiment impossible.

31st January, a frosty, but sunny, day. Two identical twin sisters aged 32, unmarried and living in one household, having the following blood antigens in common:

O MsMs R_1r P+ Le (a−) K− Lu (a−) Fy (a+)

A male Alsatian Kim, 19 months old was used.

In a preliminary experiment, Kim picked up the handkerchief of one twin and followed her track among five other tracks of an unrelated person. In the next experiment, the handkerchief scented by the first twin sister was deposited at P by the unrelated person, who also laid the five tracks, and the single track was laid by the second twin sister. Kim picked up the handkerchief of the first twin and followed the track of the second twin for most of the way, in preference to the five tracks of the unrelated person. At the very end, Kim picked up the air scent from the first twin and running to her barked. In a new field the first twin sister dropped her handkerchief and laid the single track, while the second laid the five fold track. Kim picked up the handkerchief and followed the track of the first (=correct) sister. He did so again, when the experiment was repeated in a new field.

After this experiment the dog, walking between the two sisters got somewhat excited and presumably confused. When given the handkerchief of the first twin to smell at and asked to "speak," he sniffed at both girls several times and finally barked at the first (=the right) one.

From these experiments one might conclude that Kim accepts in the conditions stated, i.e. mainly in the absence of the correct odour, the odour of an identical twin sister, but that when both odours are available he is able to discriminate between them.

DISCUSSION

The above statement may also explain why some tracking experiments revealed the power of the highly trained canine nose for discriminating between the body odours of identical twin partners, whereas the retrieving experiments did not reveal any sign of this. The difference is very likely to be found in the variation between the situations in the two types of experiments. A tracking dog, casting about is more or less simultaneously confronted with a mixture of the odours of the two twin partners and can pick out the right one, but a retrieving dog sniffing at each handkerchief in turn, is at any particular moment confronted with one odour only. If this is sufficiently similar to the one remembered, the dog retrieves. The situation may be likened to visual recognition if one considers that one might easily pick out one identical twin from among a group of people, when shown the photograph of the other, but that when both partners are simultaneously available, their distinction becomes quite feasible.

It would be tempting to suppose that scent discrimination between different people must be based on differences between complex mixtures of a number of chemical substances, and that it would be more of a quantitative than of a qualitative nature. Differences in the odour of bees from various colonies have been recently shown (Ribbands and Kalmus, 1952) to be dependent on diet and thus are presumably of this nature. However, several observations exist which are difficult to reconcile with the assumption that the scent discrimination by dogs depend solely on quantitative differences. (1) As shown previously (Löhner) as well as in the above experiments, regional differences in body odours of one person, e.g., those between the arm pits, the palms and the soles, though markedly different for the human nose, do not prevent the dog from recognising that they all belong to the same individual and from distinguishing them from the body odours of others. (2) Evidence for this point of view also comes from an old observation by Romanes (1885), and an experiment described below.

Romanes describes how he took his terrier to Regent's Park on a Bank holiday, when the Broad Walk was swarming with people. When the terrier's attention was diverted by a strange dog, Romanes suddenly made a number of zig-zags across the Walk, then stood on a seat and watched the terrier picking up his scent and tracking his footsteps over all the zig-zags he had made until it found him. In order to do this it had to distinguish its master's trail from at least a hundred others quite as fresh, and many thousands of others not so fresh, crossing it at all angles.

This observation is paralleled by the following experiment. Gretchen, an 8-year-old Alsatian bitch, had learned to pick out one person's handkerchief in the manner illustrated in Figure. She was then offered a handkerchief among others scented in the armpit of this particular person as well as in the armpit of another person, also represented by herself among the other handkerchiefs. In two experiments the bitch nevertheless twice picked out the doubly-scented handkerchief. She also picked out the correct handkerchief when the armpit smell was overlaid (for the human nose at least) with the smell of Collidine, or pentadecanoline.

The role of environmental factors in the origin of individual odour differences, e.g., of diet, clothing, or personal hygiene, is difficult to assess, and, apparently, as long as one deals with healthy people it is not very great, but it seems sufficient to enable a well trained dog under optimal experimental conditions to distinguish between some twin partners, who were to all appearances identical.

On the other hand twin partners were the only people observed, whose scents in different circumstances could consistently be substituted for each other without the dogs' noticing it.

From all this one might tentatively conclude that the volatile substances responsible for the discrimination by dogs of individual odour differences are the result of numerous innate metabolic differences, and that this chemical aspect of human individuality is possibly based on polyallelic differences in several chromosome loci.

SUMMARY

Controlled experiments are described showing that Police dogs trained to follow human tracks, and show dogs trained to retrieve objects scented by people, can distinguish fairly reliably between the body odours of different individuals, including the members of a family. The individuality of a person's body odour as perceived by the dog's nose is not greatly dependent on the region (e.g. palm, armpit, sole) from which it emanates, although these regional odours appear quite different to the human nose. The individual odour of a person is perceived by the dog even when mixed with another person's body odour, or with some strongly smelling substances.

In retrieving experiments the body odours of identical twin partners offered in succession are accepted for each other and there is no indication that the dogs perceive any difference.

In tracking experiments in which two body odours are offered simultaneously and mixed up, those of identical twin partners are distinguished by the dogs. However, when the odour of one twin is offered in place of the odour of the partner, and in the latter's absence, it is picked out from the odours of other people. Thus, the odours of identical twin partners, although more similar than those of any other people tested, can nevertheless be distinguished by well trained dogs.

ACKNOWLEDGMENTS

Thanks are due to Captain John Rymer-Jones, Assistant Commissioner, and Superintendent S. E. Peck, of the Metropolitan Police, and Lieut. Col. A. F. Wilcox, Chief Constable of Hertfordshire, for permission to work with personnel and dogs under their command, to Sgt. Boath, Inspector P. J. Matthews and Inspector J. Hickman, and others, for assisting me with their police dogs, and to Miss B. V. Pindar for work with her two show dogs.

I am also grateful to my colleague Dr. Sylvia D. Lawler for the blood grouping.

Last, but not least, I must thank the numerous participants in the experiments.

REFERENCES

BUDGETT, H. M. (1933). *Hunt by scent.* London: Eyre & Spottiswoode.
FR. GALTON (1875). *Anthropological Miscellany: the history of twins and the criterion of their relevant powers of nature and nurture.*

JERVIS, G. A. (1950). Excretion of phenylalanine and derivations in phenylpyruvic oligophrenia. *Proc. Soc. exp. Biol. N.Y.,* **75,** 83.

KALMUS, H., AND RIBBANDS, C. R. (1952). The origin of the odours by which honeybees distinguish from their companions. *Proc. roy. Soc. B.,* **140,** 50.

LOHNER, L. (1942). Uber menschliche Individual—und Regionalgerüche. *Arch. Ges Physiol.,* **202,** 25–45.

PENROSE, L. S. (1953). Human biochemical genetics. *Advanc. Sci.,* *10,* 56–64.

ROMANES, G. J. (1885). *Mental evolution in animals.* London: Kegan Paul.

THE "LANGUAGE" AND ORIENTATION OF THE BEES

KARL VON FRISCH *

University of Munich
(*Read by Donald R. Griffin, Harvard University, April 20, 1956*)

IN A bee hive (Bienenstaat) there is in force a well-organized division of labor. While the young worker bees care for the domestic affairs, the care of the brood and comb construction, the older bees fly out to collect nectar and pollen to feed the colony. There is a further division of labor among the collecting bees. In the first place, only a very few bees, the scouts, fly out independently to discover new sources of food. Most of the bees wait in the hive until they receive directions to make their way to a particular goal. Secondly, the assemblage of collecting bees is divided into working groups each of which seeks out one particular kind of flower. The size of the working groups is proportional to the productivity of the available flowers. At any given time the largest group of bees will be at the flowers where the best crop is available. This is all very sensible; but how is it possible?

A scout bee may find a good source of food near the home hive—it can be a flower with pollen or nectar or, in an experiment, a glass dish with sugar water. When the scout returns to the hive, she performs a round dance on the comb (Fig. 1). This dance indicates symbolically to her hivemates that they should fly out and search around the hive. Inactive bees sitting near the dancer are thus aroused and stimulated to fly out. While they are still trooping after the dancer on the honeycomb, touching her with their antennae which bear the olfactory organs, they learn the kind of flowers for which they must search. Every species of flower has a specific odor. It clings to the scout bee which has collected from the flower, and it clings also to the nectar which she feeds the bees surrounding her during slight hesitations in her dance. The new collectors search for this odor and thus succeed in

---

* On November 11, 1955, the Society in Executive Session voted to award the Magellanic Premium to Dr. von Frisch in recognition of his studies of animal sense organs and his analysis of the dances of bees. The Magellanic Medal was presented to Mr. Horst Pelckmann, First Secretary to the German Embassy, on behalf of Dr. von Frisch on April 20, 1956.

finding the correct goal. They too dance upon returning to the hive and after all subsequent collecting flights for as long as they find an abundant food supply. In this way the worker group becomes larger and larger as long as it is successful.

The liveliness and duration of any one of these dances depend on the sweetness and quantity of the nectar which the bee has found during the preceding collecting flight. The larger the helpings at the restaurant thus patronized, so to speak, the livelier the dance; the livelier the dance, the more new bees are attracted. And so the size of the worker group for each of the plants blooming at one time is regulated relative to the yield of the flowers.

If the species of flower discovered in this way is more than 50 or

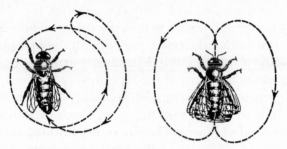

Fig. 1. Round dance (left) and wagging dance (right) of the bee. From K. v. Frisch, Sprechende Tänze im Bienenvolk, München, 1955.

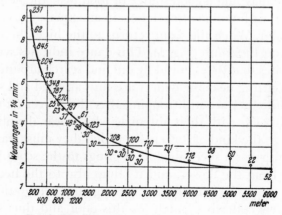

Fig. 2. The expression of distance by bees. Abscissa: distance of the feeding place from bee hive in meters, ordinate: number of wagging runs per quarter minute. The points on the curve are average values: the accompanying figures give the number of single observations. From K. v. Frisch, Sprechende Tänze im Bienenvolk, München, 1955.

100 meters from the hive, then the round dance is supplanted by the "wagging" dance (Schwänzeltanz) (Fig. 1). The bee now moves in a straight line while wagging her abdomen vigorously; then she runs in a half-circle back to the starting point, and again the wagging course (Schwänzellauf), then a half-circle to the other side, and so forth. The wagging dance means, like the round dance, that there is something to fetch outside. The flower species is identified by its odor, and the available yield through the spirit and duration of the dance. But in addition, this dance form conveys information about the distance to the goal and about the direction in which it lies.

The distance of the feeding area is shown by the rhythm of the dance. The more distant the food, the more slowly the turns of the dance follow one another, the fewer wagging courses occur therefore in a given time (Fig. 2).

The direction of the Schwänzellauf conveys the direction of the goal, with reference to the position of the sun. This point is most clearly seen when the dance takes place on a horizontal surface and under a clear sky. One can observe it under these conditions if in warm weather part of the bee population loiters on the landing board just outside the hive entrance and some of the homecoming bees stop here to give up their load and to dance. They orient themselves in such a way that during the wagging course the sun is seen on the same side and at the same angle to their path as was the case on their flight to the feeding place. They thus point directly to the goal (Fig. 3). The bees which troop after the dancing scout bees perceive this relationship relative to the sun, and since they assume this same position on flying out, they fly in the direction of the goal.

Most of the time, however, the returning bees dance inside the pitch-dark hive—on the vertical honeycomb. Then the angle to the sun's position is translated into an angle relative to the force of gravity according to the following rule: The direction toward the sun is indicated by a wagging course straight up. A direction 60° left of the sun is rendered by a wagging course 60° to the left of the upward direction, and so forth (Fig. 4). It has been possible to show experimentally that bees which are aroused by the dances on the honeycombs and fly out to the food hold very exactly to the distance- and direction-data imparted to them.

To indicate direction in this way it is necessary to know the sun's position. What do the bees do when the sky is cloudy? The answer is as simple as it is surprising: they see the sun through a complete cloud cover. This can be demonstrated when one lays the observation hive on its side. On the horizontal surface the dancers orient their wagging course directly toward the goal. Under a cloudy sky they show the correct direction if they have a free view of that portion of the sky where, invisible to us, the sun stands behind the clouds, but their dances are completely disoriented if a board is interposed in the sun's direction and only cloudy sky is visible in other directions.

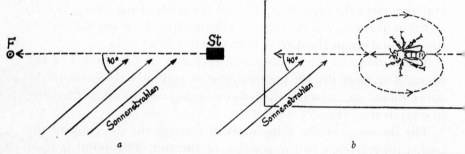

FIG. 3. The expression of direction by bees on a horizontal surface. (*a*) When flying from hive (St) to feeding place (F) the bee pays attention to the angle between the sun and its goal. (*b*) After returning to the hive the bee maintains the same angle to the sun in its wagging run on the horizontal surface and thus points the way to the goal.

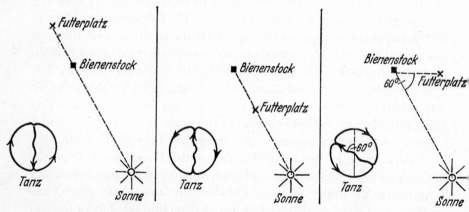

FIG. 4. The expression of direction in the dance on vertical surfaces in the bee hive. Middle: the feeding place lies in the direction of the sun, the bee moves upward in its wagging run. Right: the feeding place 60° left from the position of the sun, wagging run 60° to the left of straight upward. Left: feeding place opposite the direction of the sun, wagging run straight downward.

This perception of the sun through the clouds does not depend, as one might think, upon perception if infrared light, but rather on the sensitivity of the bees to ultraviolet light. Ultraviolet between 4,000 and 3,000 Å represents a distinct color for the bee's eye, and quantitatively their greatest visual sensitivity lies in this region. If under cloudy conditions, and with the hive horizontal, one places glass filters of selective spectral transmission above the dancers, one sees oriented dances only under those filters which transmit ultraviolet light in a particular range, and disoriented dances under filters which strongly filter out the ultraviolet. Whether, and to what degree, the visible and infrared light is transmitted has no bearing on the degree of orientation of the dances (Fig. 5a and b).

Should the sun stand behind a hill or be already set, the information system of the bees is undisturbed. But this is only the case if the sky is clear or at least a patch of blue sky is visible, for the blue light of the sky is to a large extent polarized, and its plane of polarization has a regular relationship to the position of the sun. Thus the bees have one more advantage over us in that they perceive the plane of polarization extremely well and can put it to use for their orientation. If the horizontal hive is shaded with a piece of fiberboard so that the bees cannot see any sky, their dances are disoriented and cannot indicate the direction of the feeding place. But if one makes a hole in the shade so that a tiny piece of blue sky is visible, for example to the north, remote from the sun, immediately their dances are precisely oriented and point to the goal. If a polaroid film is held over the dancers, one can change the direction of the dances at will by turning the polaroid. The details of these experiments prove unequivocally that it is indeed by means of the plane of polarization of the polarized sky light that the bees orient themselves. The analyser for polarized light, to which they owe this ability, is located in the sensory cells of the compound eyes.

A problem seems to arise if the bees use the sun and the related polarized light pattern of the sky as a compass to inform their comrades of the direction of a goal. The magnetic compass always points to the north, but the sun is constantly changing its position. At first I thought that it would be useful only within short intervals of time, during which the sun's position would not shift significantly. An experiment has convinced me that I was wrong. Bees can also use the sky compass over long periods; they are capable of this because they possess a remarkable sense of time and because they are familiar with the daily path of the sun. One might say that they know just where it belongs at every hour of the day.

The experiment which led to this conclusion was the following: we transported a hive of bees to an unfamiliar region, opened the flight-hole in the afternoon and induced a group of marked bees to feed at a point 180 meters northwest of the hive during the afternoon

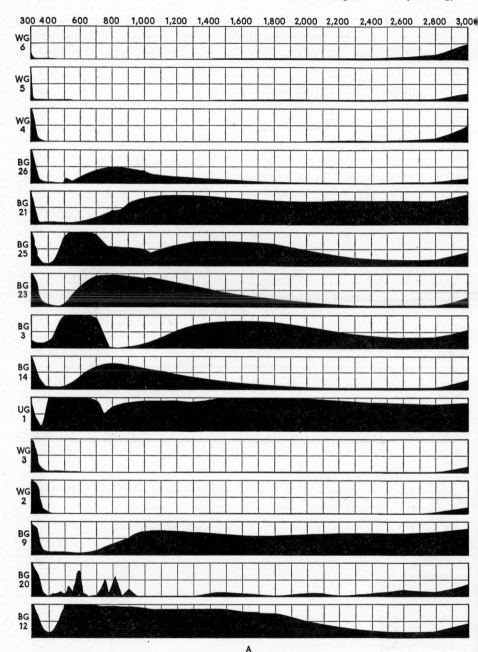

A

FIG. 5. Transmission of various glass filters (manufactured by Schott) in the spectral region from 300–3000 millimicrons. Under the filters of the left hand column (*a*) the bees could orient themselves by the sun even under overcast skies (though they did so only uncertainly

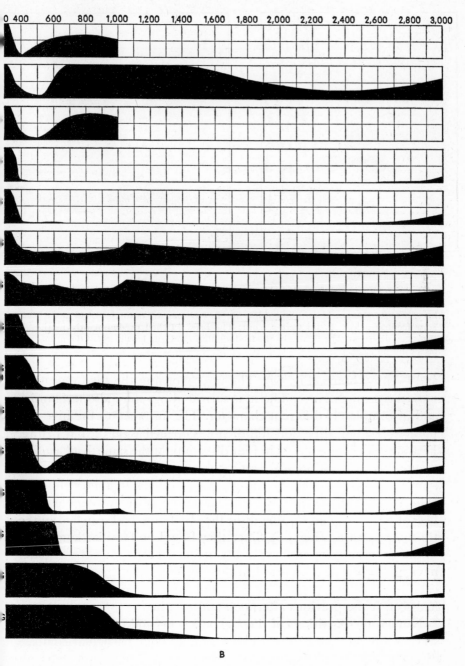

0 400 600 800 1,000 1,200 1,400 1,600 1,800 2,000 2,200 2,400 2,600 2,800 3,000

B

ith the five lower filters); with the filters in the right hand column (*b*) they were wholly
isoriented.

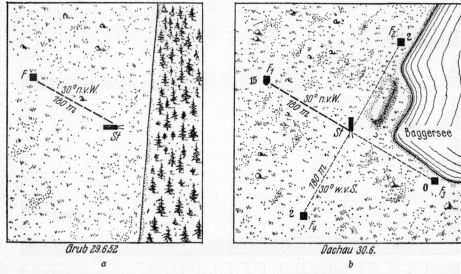

FIG. 6. (*a*) Training of numbered bees during the afternoon to fly from the bee hive (St) to a feeding place (F) 180 meters to the northwest. (*b*) The following morning the bee hive was moved to a wholly different location in territory where the bees had never been. Four feeding places (F_1–F_4) were set out. The bees searched predominantly in the accustomed direction. The figures by the feeding places indicate how many of the numbered bees came to each.

and evening hours (Fig. 6*a*). The next morning the hive was again moved a great distance. The new surroundings were also unfamiliar and of completely different character. The entrance to the hive was pointed in a new direction and then was opened as on the day before. Feeding tables were placed in four directions at the same distance, 180 meters. At each feeding place sat an observer who caught every bee as soon as it arrived so that she could not send others. In a short time the collecting bees from the day before appeared in overwhelming numbers at the northwest feeding dish; they therefore had searched in the training direction (Fig. 6*b*). Since they found no familiar landmarks in the unknown region, they could only have been guided by celestial navigation. And this occurred in the morning when the sun was in a completely different position from the direction in which the bees had seen it the previous afternoon and evening.

Numerous repetitions of these experiments and other types of observation besides prove that the bees can find one particular compass direction repeatedly whatever the time of day. Hence, the sun and the related polarized light pattern of the sky play an indispensable role for the bees, not only in the communication of direction, but in their general orientation as well.

A compass based on the sun's position and the polarized light pattern of the sky coupled with a reckoning of the time of day has been found in other Arthropods. The phenomenon is probably of even more general occurrence than we yet realize. But the bees remain unique in the use of the sun-compass not only for individual orientation, but also for the communication of exact information, thus placing it in the service of the community.

I certainly did not expect that the bees would help me to the great pleasure and honor which come to me today with the conferring of the Magellanic Premium by the American Philosophical Society. After all, it is these wonderful creatures who should have earned the prize rather than I, who have only described what they do.

THE ECHOLOCATION OF FLYING INSECTS BY BATS

DONALD R. GRIFFIN, FREDERIC A. WEBSTER
AND CHARLES R. MICHAEL
Biological Laboratories, Harvard University

When bats are hunting insects they adjust the pattern and tempo of their high frequency orientation sounds in a way that seems quite appropriate for active echolocation of small moving targets but distinctly unsuited for the passive detection of insects by listening for their flight sounds. (Griffin, 1953; 1958). The most obvious change is a marked rise in the pulse repetition rate just as the bat closes in on its prey. For example, *Eptesicus fuscus* often emits only four or five pulses per second in straight cruising flight, with silent intervals of 200 milliseconds between them; but during insect pursuit the same bat may shift to a "buzz" in which the pulses are separated by only five milliseconds. Similar flight patterns and vocal responses can be elicited by tossing into the vicinity of a hunting bat imitation insects such as pebbles or plagets of wet absorbent cotton. What little sound these make can scarcely resemble that of a real insect.

Yet this type of evidence is indirect and not wholly satisfactory, since some bats certainly do respond to the sounds made by buzzing insects (Moehres, 1950; Kolb, 1959). Studies of insect pursuit behaviour in the laboratory have recently enabled us to make four significant extensions of earlier studies under natural conditions: (1) a more detailed description of the bats' hunting tactics, (2) measurements of the high rates at which small insects are captured, (3) estimates of the minimum distances at which they are detected, and (4) selective masking experiments with low and high frequency noise which demonstrate conclusively that at least under some circumstances insects such as *Drosophila* are intercepted by echolocation.

It is convenient to distinguish three phases of insect hunting behaviour which appear always to be present with varying degrees of distinctness in bats of the family Vespertilionidae. The first or *search phase* is fairly straight flight in which the pulse repetition rate is relatively low, although the bat is evidently ready to attack flying insects.

138

The second or *approach phase* begins when the bat first reacts to an insect, either by turning towards it, by increasing the pulse repetition rate, or both. Here the interval between pulses shortens progressively though often irregularly, as the bat apparently locates its prey more accurately and flies toward it. A *terminal phase* ensues when the bat is fairly close to the insect and emits a burst of pulses at a very high rate, the buzz. A similar buzz is emitted on dodging small wires or just before landing, but the buzz of an insect catch seems typically to last longer and to include more closely spaced pulses. In *Myotis lucifugus,* the species we have studied most thoroughly, the search phase involves pulse-to-pulse intervals varying from about 50 to 100 milliseconds or more; in general the larger the room the longer the intervals in this phase. The approach phase has intervals between about 50 and 10 milliseconds, and in the buzz the pulses are separated by only 4 to 7 milliseconds. Intervals of more than 50 milliseconds are thus characteristic of cruising or search, 50 to 10 milliseconds approach, and less than 10 milliseconds the terminal phase of very close pursuit or actual capture of the insect.

METHODS

Although small insects are apparently detected and pursued one at a time, the bats we have studied were much more likely to begin active hunting when large numbers of insects were on the wing. Even at best we have found that only a small fraction of the *Myotis lucifugus* released in rooms filled with flying insects undertake serious hunting; many will slowly starve and would doubtless die eventually in a room where other individual bats catch hundreds of insects every day. Two or three sessions of a half-hour or less on different days are usually sufficient to find the good catchers, provided that the bats are wide awake, warm, and active when tested. The 90 per cent or more that did not show signs of hunting after several such sessions were released.

A good catcher identifies itself by making obvious interception manoeuvres, turning sharply, suddenly climbing or diving for a few inches, or merely by pulling up abruptly in the midst of fairly straight flight. Often the interfemoral membrane can be seen to turn upwards and forward, and the head may be thrust down into it very rapidly and out again. If the room is quiet, one can hear with the unaided ear the faint audible clicks which accompany each pulse of high frequency sound during the search or approach phases. The buzz accompanying the actual catching manoeuvre is usually more clearly audible. With adequate lighting the actual capture of insects may be seen, but this has been much less obvious than the flight manoeuvres or the faint audible buzzes.

We have studied insect hunting in three different rooms, all about 8 feet high. The first, at the Vero Beach Laboratory of the Florida State Board of Health, was 8 ft. $\times$ 16 ft., the two used later in Cambridge, Massachusetts, were 12 ft. $\times$ 32 ft. and 11 ft. $\times$ 16 ft. All of these rooms had walls which reflected high frequency sound quite well, and in all cases the bats must have received strong echoes from walls, ceiling, and floor along with the much fainter echoes from their insect prey. This "clutter" may well have been what discouraged most bats from hunting indoors.

Sufficient numbers of insects might be obtained by light traps or other means of attracting wild insects, but we have reared mosquitoes and fruit flies by standard methods (Galtsoff, *et al.*, 1959). It was necessary to stir the insects into flight every few minutes in order to elicit continuous hunting. The actual densities of flying insects varied widely, both in space and time; but the great majority of catches were probably made at densities of no more than three or four insects per cubic foot.

Since insect capture by bats is a rapid process, and since the small insect is often very difficult to see at all, we were anxious to record the hunting behaviour by single photographs and motion pictures. With single photographs, even when the insect as well as the bat is shown, it is difficult to be certain what part of a complex sequence of events is recorded. Multiple flash stroboscopic photographs have been very useful, and at a flashing rate of five to ten per second the successive images of a flying bat are sufficiently separated, except in turns or hovering manoeuvres. Insects can be photographed better with multiple than with single flashes, because a row of specks equal in number to the flashes is less likely to be confused with dust on the film. We have used both still and motion picture cameras in pairs, spaced 0·5 or 1 metre apart, in order to obtain more accurate information about the positions of bat and insect, by simultaneous cross bearings.

In many experiments a tape recording was made of the bat's orientation sounds with a plastic dielectric condenser microphone (Kuhl *et al.*, 1954), a suitable amplifier, band pass filter, and an Ampex tape recorder. Each flash of a strobe light can easily produce a recognizable electrical signal on the tape, so that when oscillograph pictures of the bat's sounds were later prepared from the tape recordings it was quite feasible to identify each flash and determine its time of occurrence relative to the recorded sounds from the bat.

Illumination and background surface are of great importance because bats are very dark and tend to blend into most backgrounds if photographed by reflected light. It is relatively easy to obtain silhouettes of flying bats against a white background, and if the background is marked off with a grid of contrasting lines, the bat's position can be determined with one camera by making parallax corrections (Grinnell and Griffin, 1958). If two lights are employed, the separation between the two shadows of a bat can be used to determine its distance from the wall. We were not able to use this method to photograph mosquitoes or *Drosophila,* however, and turned instead to a very dark background of black velvet with lateral illumination either by flood lamps or an electronic flash. By careful arrangement of the lamp or lamps it was possible to photograph both bats and individual fruit flies on 16 mm. film. The flies appeared only as specks, but in many cases a careful study of the film with a time motion study projector permitted unequivocal identification of the flies by their characteristic movement. Catches were recognized by the approach of a bat to a particular fly followed by the disappearance of the latter as the bat flew on. A dust speck could easily be mistaken for a single image of a fly, but dust varied randomly from frame to frame while flies remained in approximately the same place or moved progressively. Furthermore dust specks were not intercepted by the bats.

1. Hunting Tactics

Most of the pursuit and interception manoeuvres requires less than one second and are extremely difficult to observe directly. We therefore photographed the bats and insects and recorded simultaneously the pattern of the orientation sounds. Each of the catches for which full or fragmentary sound and position records were obtained was preceded by the customary search and approach phases defined above, although there were some catches or apparent catches of mosquitos without a full-fledged buzz. In such cases the pulse-to-pulse interval dropped from about 90 milliseconds in the search phase only to about 40 or 50 milliseconds. This shift from search to approach phases provides the best indication yet available of the distance by which a bat has already detected some small object, such as a wire or an insect. In two mosquito catches for which excellent records were obtained there was a clear drop in this interval at about 100 centimetres and at about 30 centimetres respectively from the probable position of the mosquito. That is, the interval showed a marked drop at these distances from the spot where, a fraction of a second later, the bat was to emit its sharp buzz. Mosquitos can therefore be detected at appreciable distances, but further discussion of this topic is best deferred to Section 3.

The manner in which the frequencies within each pulse varied during these catching manoeuvres is also of interest. In the search phase, before any apparent reaction to the insects, the pulses were about two milliseconds in duration, the intervals between pulses were roughly 80–100 milliseconds, and the frequency dropped in each pulse from about 75–85 kilocycles at the start to 37–45 kilocycles at the end. This is the typical octave of frequency sweep in a *Myotis* pulse, although the actual frequencies were slightly lower than on some other occasions. During the two pronounced buzzes mentioned above the pulse durations fell to 0.5 milliseconds, or sometimes a little less. The estimated frequencies within these and other very short pulses ranged from about 25 to 30 kilocycles. Our recent and technically much improved records thus require an important modification of the first description of frequency patterns during insect catching (Griffin, 1953). It is now clear both for *Myotis* and *Eptesicus* during the pursuit of real and imitation insects that in the terminal buzz the frequencies are distinctly *lower* than in the search phase (previously referred to as "crusing," an appropriate term for *Eptesicus* under natural conditions but much less apt for *Myotis* catching insects at high rates in a small space).

During the pursuit of an insect the actual lengths of the pulses of sound in air drop, in proportion to the pulse duration, from about 70 cm. to 15 cm. The distance travelled by the bat between pulses varies with its flying speed, but before and just after detection (indicated by the drop in pulse-to-pulse interval) the bats were flying at 2 to 3 metres per second, or 2 to 3 millimetres per millisecond. One of the longer intervals thus represents 200–300 mm. of travel, while during the two clearest buzzes the bat's speed was about 70 cm./second or 0.7 mm./millisecond. Since one pulse was emitted every 5 to 7 milliseconds, the bat was now travelling only about 3.5 to 5 mm. between pulses. The velocity of sound in air is about 340 mm./millisecond, so that the wave lengths of the orientation sounds were about 4 to 8 mm. in the search phase, but increased during the buzz. The catching manoeuvres and their relationship to the pattern of the buzz will be described in more detail in a later paper.

2. Rates of Insect Capture

a. Mosquitos. In April, 1958, at the invitation of E. T. Nielsen several bats were brought to his 8 ft. × 16 ft. flight chamber at Vero

Beach, Florida, which contained initially about 2,000 mosquitos (*Culex quinquefaciatus*). Several *Myotis lucifugus*, one *M. subulatus*, one *M. subulatus leibii*, two *Pipistrellus subflavus*, and two *Plecotus rafinesquii* were set free in this room for 10–15 minutes at a time, and certain of the *Myotis* hunted actively. These were left in the chamber overnight, and in the morning the mosquito population had fallen to roughly 200–300. Although none of the *Pipistrellus* or *Plecotus* was ever observed to hunt actively, a few of the *Myotis* were so successful that we could estimate the rate of insect capture not only by counting audible buzzes, but also by measuring the rate at which the bats gained weight (See Table I). Many factors might reduce the weight gain—evaporation of water from skin or lungs, urination or defaeca-tion—but since the bats were closely watched we could be sure that they did not eat or drink anything but insects caught on the wing. Their gain in weight thus represents a conservative minimum esti-mate of the weight of insects captured.

It was not practicable to restore the population of mosquitos to its original level during these experiments, and on some of the subse-quent days only a few hundred were present in the flight chamber. Yet in eight cases listed in Table I accurate weighing demonstrated high rates of mosquito catching. On other occasions the same bats gained very little, or even lost weight while flying in the same cham-ber. In these cases observation and listening for the faint audible com-ponents of the buzzes confirmed that they were hunting much less actively. The mosquito population was so low on 5th April that it was supplemented by releasing in the same room several dozen large crane

TABLE I.

RATES OF MOSQUITO CATCHING BY BATS AT THE VERO BEACH LABORATORY, APRIL 1958. The average weight of six of the mosquitos used (*Culex quinquefaciatus*) was 2.2 milli-grams.

Bat	Date	Duration of Flight (Minutes)	Weight Gain (mg.)	Mosquitos Caught per Minute
M. lucifugus	April 1	30	350	5.3
Number 5	April 4	31	100	1.5
(Wt. 5.7 gr.)	April 4	9.5	73	3.5
	April 5	15	55	1.7
M. lucifugus	April 2	10	125	5.7
Number 7				
(Wt. 5.7 gr.)				
M. subulatus leibii	April 2	21	77	1.7
(Wt. 3.7 gr.)	April 4	24	264	5
	April 5	15	312	9.5

flies (*Brachryprenna*). These weighed about 19 mg., but the bats usually dropped the legs and wings, uneaten, and the bodies weighed only about 12 mg. During the 15 minutes when the *M. subulatus leibii* was observed to gain 372 mg. it was clearly observed to catch no more than 4 or 5 crane flies along with many mosquitos. It seems most likely that less than 60 mg. of its 372 mg. weight gain consisted of the crane flies, so that its rate of mosquito catching is listed in Table I as 312/15 or 21 mg. per minute. This bat was thus catching about ten mosquitos per minute or one every six seconds.

b. Drosophila. During the spring and summer of 1959 large numbers of *Drosophila* were reared in an 11 ft. $\times$ 16 ft. flight chamber and out of many *Myotis lucifugus* which were allowed to fly in this chamber, four, designated below as TR, S, B and TL, began active catching immediately when first allowed to fly in this room. The fruit flies were unfortunately not maintained in pure culture, but only two species were present. *Drosophila robusta* weighing 3 mg. on the average, and *D. melanogaster* with an average weight of 0.6 mg. On several occasions certain of these bats gained as much as 29 mg./minute while catching only fruit flies in this room. Sustained catching rates of 20 fruit flies per minute were observed, and two flies were often taken within one second (For details see below, especially Table III). These rates of weight gain were in satisfactory agreement with the number of visible pursuit manoeuvres and audible buzzes which were often noticeable every few seconds, and are also quite similar to the estimates reported by Gould (1955; 1959) for the same species hunting under natural conditions.

3. Distances at Which Insects Are Detected

a. Procedures. This subject was studied by a minor modification of the photographic method used to measure the distance at which small wires are detected (Grinnell and Griffin, 1958). Bats and fruit flies were photographed in an 11 ft. $\times$ 16 ft. flight room with bright lateral illumination against a dark velvet background with a 16 mm. Auricon sound-on-film camera. The bat's orientation sounds picked up by the microphone were rectified into low frequency clicks by a detector circuit, and supplied to the input of the sound camera. Each bat pulse was registered, on the same piece of film as the pictures, as a click which contained no information about the original frequency, only rough information about pulse duration and intensity, but accurate information about pulse repetition rate or interval between pulses. This camera operates at 24 frames per second, with its shutter open about 1/50th second. While the images were small and slightly blurred by the bat's motion, they sufficed to show its position within one or two inches every 24th of a second. Actually the position shown was the projection of the bat or fly against the opposite wall, and estimates of the distance between the two are subject to parallax errors in either direction. The apparent distance was greater than the actual distance when bat and fly were equally far from the camera, but less when one was behind the other. We could make only rough estimates of the bat's distance from the camera or the opposite wall, and hence we did not attempt to apply parallax corrections. But a long series of such single camera pictures allowed approximate estimates of the distance of detection and provided a most helpful background for more accurate determinations of bat and insect positions with paired cameras.

Detailed analyses were made of 34 catches or attempted catches by one *M. lucifugus*, S, 26 by another of the same species, B, and six by a *M. keenii septentrionalis*. In each of these 66 cases graphs were prepared showing, on a common time base, the pulse-to-pulse intervals, the vertical and horizontal positions of the bat and fly, and the apparent distance between them, that is, the distance between their images on the wall opposite the camera.

b. Special Aspects of Insect Pursuit Behaviour Relevant to Measurements of the Distance of Detection. Before proceeding to analyse these data on distance of insect detection it is important to review certain aspects of the bat's behaviour during these insect catching manoeuvres. In several cases the bat began its pursuit by taking off from the wall where it had previously been resting, and flew out to catch a fly which may well have been detected before take-off. In many other instances, however, the detection clearly occurred while the bat was flying; often many flies were caught during a continuous flight; and sometimes the bat did not land until hundreds of catches had been made. When starts from the wall were eliminated along with cases where the bat was turning away from the wall, catching another insect, or executing some other special manoeuvre at the start of the search phase, the pulse-to-pulse interval during search varied from 48 to 85 milliseconds, with the range from 50 to 60 milliseconds predominating. On the average the clear drop below 50 milliseconds occurred about 0.5 second before the catch; and after that time almost every approach phase included a steady drop in interval. In all cases the actual detection must have taken place somewhat earlier than the vocal reaction of shortening the pulse-to-pulse interval. But since we have no way of estimating the bat's reaction time we will conservatively consider that detection occurred at the moment when the first pulse was emitted after an interval significantly shorter than that characteristic of the search phase.

The actual number of pulses emitted during the approach phase varied between 4 and 22; the average for the two *M. lucifugus* was 8.1 and for the *M. keenii* 10.6. These pulses are presumably used to track the moving insect. The terminal buzz contained anywhere from 3 or 4 to 15 or 20 pulses separated by 5 to 10 milliseconds. We have no way of determining whether the last pulse of the search phase served for detection, or whether several searching pulses at roughly 50-millisecond intervals were required. The number cannot be very large, however, because of the numerous cases described in the next section in which one catch was completed and a second detection and interception begun within a remarkably short period of time.

c. Double Catches. In six of the 66 cases selected for careful study there were two catches or attempted catches within less than one second. The actual period between catches was ¾ second for the *M. keenii*, ½ second for *M. lucifugus*, and three cases of about ½ second plus one of ¾ second for *M. lucifugus* B. In all cases the two flies were intercepted by distinct manoeuvres, and it seems probable that the second insect was located only after the first had been seized. (In one of these six cases the first fly was attacked but missed). Hence only a short interval of time and a few pulses are necessary for a successful search phase and detection. One of the clearest examples of double catches within one second is illustrated in Figure 1. The positions of bat and fly were not clear until after the moment when the sound track first became adequate to show the tempo of the orientation sounds, but the latter part of the first approach phase was clearly photographed. The most significant aspect of this sequence is the time between the two catches. The next pulse to follow the first buzz came at a long interval (118 milliseconds) after the last pulse in the buzz. This is a common feature of these records, and it may well represent the time needed to remove the insect from interfemoral membrane where it is often "pouched" immediately upon capture or which it may strike before being seized in the teeth. Then three pulses were emitted at intervals of about 62 milliseconds, a value quite similar to the search phases just before and after the two catches. The next pulse came at an interval of only 17 milliseconds and clearly represented the beginning of the second approach phase. Only four pulses were emitted during the search phase between the two catches,

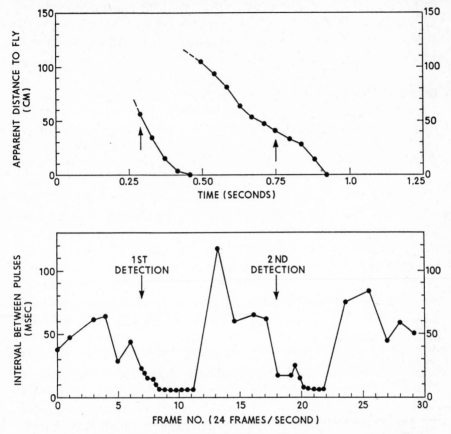

Fɪɢ. 1. A typical double catch within half a second. The upper graph shows as a function of time the apparent distance between the bat and the two *Drosophila*, that is, the separation between their images against the wall opposite the camera. Parallax errors may render these distances too high by 25 per cent. Each point on the lower graph shows on the same time base the interval separating one pulse of sound emitted by the bat from the previous pulse. Arrows mark the first vocal reaction to each fly, conservatively designed as the point of detection. During the two buzzes there were more pulses than could be plotted as separate points. Note that only four pulses were emitted in the search phase for the second catch (between 0.6 and 0.7 second).

hence the second fruit fly must have been detected by means of no more than four echoes. The reactions of these bats must thus be very rapid, and the information extracted from a very few pulses must suffice to locate the small target presented by a *Drosophila*.

   d. Results Obtained with One Camera. Almost every one of the 66 cases of fruit fly catches analysed graphically provided a clear indication of the point at which the search phase gave way to the approach phase, thus demonstrating that the fly had already been detected. When the apparent distances of detection were averaged without parallax correction, the values were 73 cm. for the *Myotis keenii*, 55 cm. for *M. lucifugus* S, and 73 cm. for *M. lucifugus* B. The extreme values of these estimated distances of detection were 21 and 135 cm. Our next step was to average the individual values of pulse-to-pulse interval as a function of apparent distance from the fly. The mean value of the interval thus obtained showed an increase out to a distance of about one metre. This might be interpreted as evidence that detection occurs at this distance, but the flight patterns and other circumstances such as proximity to the walls differed so much in these several cases that average curves are of somewhat doubtful significance. We therefore selected 16 cases where parallax errors seemed minimal, when the bat did not start from the wall, and when the search phase was relatively uncomplicated by immediately previous manoeuvres. On averaging these for each bat, the mean pulse-to-pulse interval was found to increase rather smoothly to reach a plateau value at 70 cm. for *M. lucifugus* S, 55 cm. for B, and 90 cm. for the *M. keenii*. Parallax errors render these values too high by perhaps 20 or 25 per cent, but detection at half a metre would appear to have been common, and an occasional detection may well have occurred at one metre.

e. Measurements with Two Cameras.   After these records had been analysed we made a further effort to determine the distance of detection more accurately by using two 16 mm. motion picture cameras to photograph many *Drosophila* catches by two *M. lucifugus*, TL and TR, which were two of the better catchers under our experimental conditions. Both were Auricon sound-on-film cameras operated by synchronous motors at 24 frames per second. Each received the same input of rectified pulses from the microphone, and each photographed a clock with minute and second hands. To aid in correlating the two films, the field of each camera also included a clock hand that revolved once per second and an oscilloscope with the horizontal sweep set at 20 per second. Careful study of several hundred feet of paired films permitted the selection of 11 clear cases in which a *Drosophila* catch could be unequivocally located on both films, i.e. both bat and fly were depicted throughout search, approach, and terminal phases, and there was no doubt concerning the matching of individual frames of the two films. In each pair of pictures the bat or fly appeared against the different spots on the grid on the opposite wall, and lines could be drawn on a floor plan of the room from the positions of the camera to these projections on the wall. The intersections of these lines located bat or fly within one to two inches. The same accuracy could equally well have been achieved in the vertical

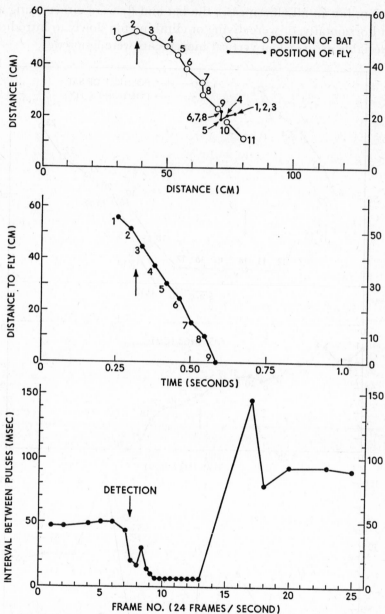

FIG. 2. Positions of bat and fruit fly and the pattern of orientation sounds during the catch. The upper graph shows a floor plan of part of the flight room some distance from the walls in which the zero point is arbitrarily selected to show the bat's position, and that of the fly, as determined by cross bearings from two motion picture cameras. The middle graph shows the distance separating bat and fly, and the numbers on the upper graph and middle graphs refer to frames of the film. The lower graph shows, on the same time base as the middle graph, the intervals between pulses. The arrow indicates the assumed point of detection. As in Figure 1 the buzz contained more pulses than can be depicted individually.

position, but in all eleven cases the bat and fly were either flying almost horizontally, or were diving or climbing too slowly to introduce appreciable errors when vertical movements were ignored.

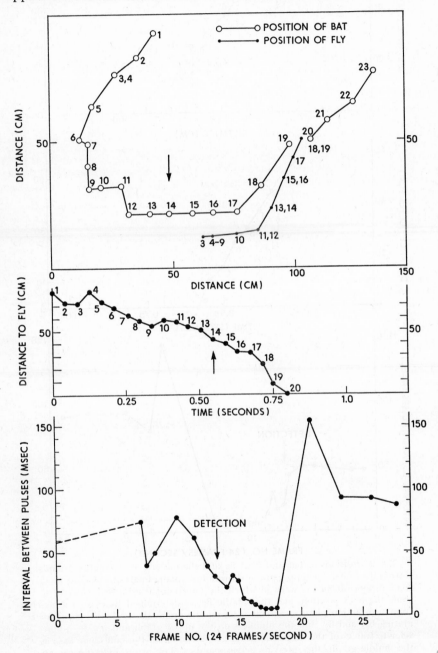

FIG. 3. Positions of bat and fly, together with the pattern of sound emission in another catch manoeuvre. For details see legend for Figure 2.

For these eleven cases we thus obtained fairly precise plots of the positions of bat and fly every 24th of a second, and from these we could measure the distance from bat to fly. We could then plot the pulse-to-pulse interval on the same time base as the distance separating the bat from its target. Three samples of the resulting combined graphs are shown in Figures 2, 3, and 4; these are representative, although they include more clear-cut shifts from search to approach phase than some of the other cases. All eleven cases permit fairly accurate estimates of the distance of detection, however, and these distances are listed in Table II, along with the angular position of the fly relative to the bat's flight path at the time when the search phase ended and the approach phase began. It is quite evident that these more accurate measurements confirm the tentative conclusion reached above that detection commonly occurred at about half a metre. The shortest measured distance of detection was 23 and the longest 83 cm.

The motion pictures suggest that the bat turns towards its prey within a small fraction of a second after detection. It is also of con-

TABLE II.

DISTANCES AND DIRECTIONS AT WHICH *Drosophila* WERE DETECTED BY TWO *Myotis lucifugus*. Detection is assumed to occur when the pulse-to-pulse interval first drops below the level characteristic of the search phase. Direction is given relative to the bat's flight direction at the time of detection.

Catch No.	Bat	Dist. of Detection (cm.)	Direction of Fly at Time of Detection (Degrees)	Remarks
1	TR	62	15°L.	Bat had just turned away from wall, fly moving toward bat, detection may have occurred earlier, perhaps at 80 cm.
2	TL	52	5°R.	Bat approaching at 90°
3	TL	68	60°R.	Approach from behind fly
4	TR	23	50°L.	Oblique approach from behind fly
5	TR	34	15°L.	Fly almost stationary, straight approach
6	TR	45	45°R.	Fly stationary, straight approach (Fig. 3-14)
7	TR	27	40°R.	Oblique approach from behind fly
8	TL	42	15°L.	Approach from behind fly (Fig. 3-15)
9	TL	83	35°R.	Fly approaching bat, detection may have been at almost 90 cm.
10	TL	56	35°R.	Approaching at about 90° (Fig. 3-16)
11	TR	40	70°R.	Bat out of field of one camera during part of approach phase
Average distance of detection		48		

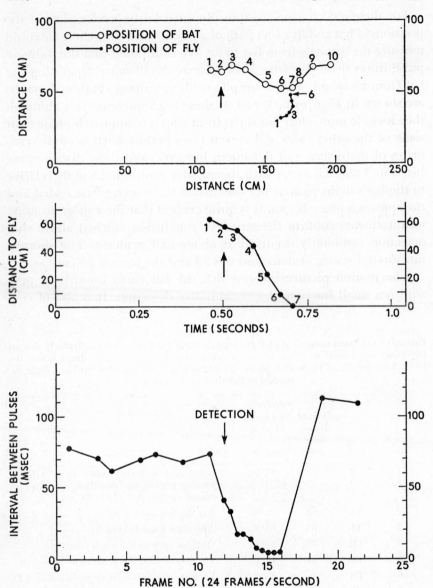

Fig. 4. Positions of bat and fly together with the pattern of sound emission in a third catch manoeuvre. For details see legend for Figure 2.

siderable interest to note that many detections seem to have occurred at considerable distances even though the fly was not directly in front of the bat. Indeed there is little if any correlation between the angular position of the fly at the time of detection and the distance at which detection occurred. Since these bats usually seem to face in approximately the direction they are flying, at least in the search phase, this indicates that *Drosophila* can be detected from anywhere within a cone of perhaps 120°.

4. Selective Jamming Experiments with Low and High Frequency Noise

The evidence presented above suffices to show that small insects such as mosquitos and fruit flies are detected rapidly and at distances of about 50 cm. But even when taken together with the marked adaption of the tempo of orientation sounds, this evidence does not prove conclusively that the insects are detected by means of echoes. It would still be logically possible to postulate that detection was achieved by hearing sounds of the insects' wingbeats. *Drosophila* were selected for the above experiments partly because their flight is very quiet, so that detection by passive listening would be more difficult than in the case of mosquitos or many of the larger flies and beetles. Furthermore, Williams and Galambos (1950) have measured the wave form of the flight sounds from a single *Drosophila funebris* beating its wings while attached to a small wire. The fundamental frequency under these conditions was about 180 cycles per second, and while the waves were complex enough to demonstrate the presence of strong harmonics, there do not appear to be any above the 10th at appreciable amplitude. The sound of a single *Drosophila* is very faint; Williams and Galambos used a 640AA condenser microphone at 1:5 cm. from the fly but did not estimate the absolute sound pressure level.

We have measured the sounds emitted by *Drosophila melanogaster* when 20–30 at a time were placed in a small glass bottle (about 50 millilitres) covered at the top by gauze. When the flies were strongly agitated and buzzing vigorously the r.m.s. sound pressure level was 25–30 decibels above 0.0002 dyne/cm.^{2} at 15 cm. from the gauze covered end of the bottle. This sound level, measured with a calibrated 640AA microphone, must have been considerably higher than that from a single fly in flight at 50 cm. from a hunting bat; probably the level reaching the bat's ears at this typical distance of detection would have been below 20 decibels. The observed frequency was between 500 and 800 cycles/second which is considerably higher than that measured by Williams and Galambos. It seems probable that resonance phenomena associated with the bottle may have accounted for this difference, but for present purposes the important point is that 20 or 30 flies, aided by the bottle's resonance, produced such a low sound pressure level.

If these bats detect fruit flies by hearing their flight sounds, it should be possible to mask these low frequency and low intensity sounds from the fly without employing a masking noise of high enough frequency to interfere with the bat's echolocation. Our best microphones when used together with an ultrasonic spectrum analyser could detect no ultrasonic components in the flight sounds of *Drosophila,* even though adequate to reveal sounds as faint as 25–30 decibels, above 0.0002 dyne/cm.^{2} We can thus exclude the possibility that *Drosophila* are detected by hearing ultrasonic components of their flight sounds, unless these components lie below this level of intensity. For selective masking experiments we therefore set up a simple apparatus to generate noise over the frequency band from about 50–15,000 cycles/ second. It consisted of a Grason–Stadler noise generator, a 20-watt high fidelity audio amplifier, and a combination of a standard 8-inch dynamic loudspeaker with an Electrovoice driver loudspeaker for the higher audible frequencies. This sytem filled the small flight room with a noise so loud that we had almost to shout when we wished to communicate. For comparison with this loud low frequency noise a rather weak thermal noise in the bat's frequency range was also used for certain experiments. It was generated by a General Radio type 1390A noise generator, a broad band amplifier which delivered into four Isophon electrostatic loudspeakers about 50 volts r.m.s. These loudspeakers gave a declining output above about 25 kilocycles/ second, but still emit an appreciable signal to 55 kilocycles, and a weaker signal at least over much of the range from 55 to 100 kilocycles. For some experiments electronic filters were used to restrict the frequency band of the low or high frequency noise. The low frequency noise sounded roughly equal in intensity throughout the small flight room used for observations of *Drosophila* catching, but the intensity of the high frequency noise undoubtedly varied widely from point to point, and it was not measured. Measurements with a calibrated 640AA microphone placed the overall sound pressure level of the 100–5,000 cycles/second band of the low frequency noise at +87 decibels re 0.0002 dyne/cm.^{2} Its spectrum level did not vary greatly from 100–8,000 cycles/second as judged by ear and by measuring the level passed by a narrow band filter moved gradually across the frequency range from 100–10,000 cycles/second. The noise level was thus approximately 50 decibels per cycle bandwidth or 20–30 decibels more than the *overall* sound level of several *Drosophila* flying inside a small bottle.

When *Myotis lucifugus* which had previously been good fruit fly catchers were exposed to these two noises the results were consistent and unequivocal. The low frequency noise had no noticeable effect; the bats continued to catch flies as rapidly in this noise as in the quiet.

The high frequency noise, however, produced a marked decrease in the number of pursuit manoeuvres, the number of buzzes, and in the rate at which the bats increased weight while hunting. They did not stop hunting altogether, but usually made many fewer attempts to catch fruit flies, and then landed. If the high frequency noise was switched off they would often resume hunting almost at once. Excluding measurements obtained when the bat appeared tired or when the flies were scarce, the average rate of *Drosophila* capture was 9.5 per minute in the quiet and 11 per minute in the low frequency noise. Nor was there any appreciable difference between experiments in the dark and in the light. The results of the several experiments summarized in Table III thus provide strong evidence against the possibility that under these conditions fruit flies were intercepted by passive listening to their flight sounds.

TABLE III.

RATES AT WHICH *Myotis lucifugus* CAPTURED *Drosophila* IN LOW AND HIGH FREQUENCY NOISE

Rates of capture are based on the measured rate of weight gain divided by an assumed average weight of 2 mg. for the fruit flies, and hence are minima. Bat TR was used July 2–27, 1959, and bat TL August 23–24.

Date and Time	Conditions of Noise and Light		Interval between Weighings (Min.)	Rate of Insect Capture (Flies per Min.)	Remarks
July 2	0.05–5 kc.	dark	10	7.5	
July 18	0.05–5 kc.	light	10.5	11	
July 19	0.05–5 kc.	light	15	14.8	
July 20	0.05–5 kc.	light	12.8	4.7	
July 22 2:06	Quiet	light	12	6	
July 22 2:22	0.05–15 kc.	light	6.7	14.2	
July 27 1:40	0.1–15 kc.	light	3	13.5	
July 27 1:51	20–100 kc.	dark	3	—	Lost 1.7 mg./min.
July 27 2:00	Quiet	dark	3	11.7	
July 27 2:12	40–100 kc.	dark	3	1	
July 27 2:19	0.1–15 kc.	dark	3	3.8	Flies scarce
July 27 2:27	Quiet	dark	3	3.4	Flies scarce
Aug. 23 2:32	0.1–15 kc.	light	6	13.7	
Aug. 23 2:44	20–100 kc.	light	6	—	Lost 11 mg./min.
Aug. 23 2:56	Quiet	light	6	9.3	
Aug. 23 3:07	40–100 kc.	light	6	—	Lost 10 mg./min.
Aug. 23 3:18	0.1–15 kc.	light	6	6.9	
Aug. 23 3:31	Quiet	light	6	3.2	Bat tired
Aug. 24 4:00	0.1–15 kc.	light	3	13.1	
Aug. 24 4:13	20–100 kc.	light	4	—	Lost 29 mg./min.
Aug. 24 4:24	Quiet	light	4	10.9	
Aug. 24 4:32	40–100 kc.	light	4	—	Lost 7.5 mg./min.
Aug. 24 4:41	0.1–15 kc.	light	4	10.1	
Aug. 24 4:47	Quiet	light	4	7.8	Bat tired, flies scarce

DISCUSSION

When one watches a six-gramme bat chasing two-milligram fruit flies with dextrous, agile, and split-second manoeuvres, it is natural to wonder whether it obtains enough food from such tiny insects to equal metabolic energy required to catch them. Even the best catchers in our experiments have required supplementary feeding of meal-worms, but this was primarily because we could not keep enough fruit flies on the wing to furnish a normal night's catch. The metabolic rate of a flying bat has been estimated as roughly 100 calories per gramme per hour or 600 calories per hour for a six-gramme bat (Griffin, 1958). The caloric value of a *Drosophila* does not seem to have been measured, but a reasonable approximation is probably the value of 2241 calories per gramme listed by Trager (1953) for newly emerged adults of the fly *Ophyra cadaverina*. When our bats were catching ten fruit flies per minute (conservatively assumed to average 2 milligrams in weight) they were taking in food at a rate of roughly 2,700 calories per hour, provided the above assumptions are correct. Even though the supreme exertion of insect interception may require somewhat more than 600 calories per hour, the game does seem to be worth the candle.

Since *Myotis lucifugus* can detect echoes from *Drosophila* at 50 centimetres or more, it is appropriate to inquire what the intensity of such echoes would be. This will depend upon the sound level emitted by the bat, the frequency chosen for consideration, and the effective size of the fruit fly; but an approximate formula for the necessary computation is available (Griffin, 1958, p. 349). In the search phase the r.m.s. intensity of the outgoing pulse at 100 millimetres from the mouth of a *Myotis lucifugus* is about 100 decibels above the standard reference level of 0.0002 dyne/cm.[2] This is the maximum value when the pulse is at its highest amplitude, and this peak amplitude occurs at roughly 60–70 kilocycles, so that the strongest component of the echo corresponds to a wave length of about 5 mm. For simplicity let us assume that the *Drosophila* returns an echo of 5 mm. sound waves equal to that from a rigid sphere of 2 mm. radius, a rough approximation but one that we cannot improve upon until actual target cross sections of insects for bat pulses are measured. Making the above assumptions one can compute that the echo from a *Drosophila* would have an r.m.s. value of about 30 decibels at a distance from bat to fly of 50 cm., approximately the distance by which our records show detection to have occurred. This calculation assumes that the inverse square law applies to both the emitted sound beyond 10 cm. from the bat's mouth, and to the echo from the fruit fly. It also takes into account the $2\frac{1}{2}$ decibels of atmospheric attenuation at 68 kilocycles over a round trip distance of 1 metre. If the fly were detected at one metre, rather than 50 cm. the echo would be reduced by sixteen fold, or by about 12 decibels. This, together with another $2\frac{1}{2}$ decibels of atmospheric attentuation, would reduce the echo to 15 decibels, only slightly above the human auditory threshold at those frequencies where it is lowest.

Detection by bats of an echo having an intensity between 15 and 20 decibels appears plausible, except that the human auditory threshold of sound intensity rises sharply as the duration of a tone is decreased below about 200 milliseconds (Steven, *et al.*, 1951, pp. 1,020-22). These data suggest that a 1–millisecond pulse might have a threshold 100 times, or about 20 decibels higher than one lasting 200 milliseconds. Since 0 decibels is approximately the human threshold under favourable conditions, it does not strain credulity to postulate that a bat could detect one-millisecond pulses at 15 decibels especially since there is good reason to believe that the auditory brains of bats are highly specialised for the detection of short pulses of high frequency sound (Grinnell and Griffin, 1959).

Another important question concerns the choice of 68 kilocycles, or a wavelength of 5 mm. as the most easily detectible portion of the echo. Other factors being equal, higher frequencies or shorter wavelengths would return somewhat stronger echoes, but higher frequencies are not present at as high intensities in the emitted pulse, they suffer more atmospheric attenuation, and furthermore in the case of spheres with a 2 mm. radius the increase in echo is not very rapid between 68 and 120 kilocycles, the highest observed frequency in *Myotis* pulses. Lower frequencies are actually used during the interception phase, down to about 25 kilocycles in some cases. But of course the distance is then much shorter, and to a first approximation the echo intensity varies inversely as the fourth power of the distance. While the echo of a 25 kilocycles component would be weaker than that of 68 kilocycles by a factor of about six, the shorter distance would more than offset this.

These echoes which the bat seems to detect at a level of about 30 decibels may come from any direction within a cone of roughly 120°. Nor is mere detection enough for the hungry bat; it must localise the direction from which the echo is coming and execute and appropriate turn within a fraction of a second. The probing pulse of sound emitted by a *Myotis* has a rather broad angular spread, although the higher frequencies at the start of the pulse are more sharply concentrated into the forward direction than the lower frequencies at the end. It is possible that in each of the cases shown in Table II where the angular position of the fruit fly was far removed from the flight path of the bat the animal hapepned to have its head turned in that particular direction at the moment of detection. But photographs of flying *Myotis* indicatee that during the search phase the head is ordinarily pointed in the direction of flight, so that it seems more likely that echoes can be detected from anywhere within a fairly wide zone in front of the animal. The initial localization may not be precise, and the need for more accurate bearings may well explain the shortening of pulse-to-pulse interval during the approach phase. But an eventual understanding of the physiological mechanisms of echolocation must include not only the detection of insect echoes at a level of roughly 30 decibels, but their almost instantaneous localizations as well.

Finally we should compare the difficulty of jamming the echolocation of small wires (Griffin and Grinnell, 1958) with the cessation of insect hunting in high frequency noise. It should be borne in mind that in the jamming experiments collisions with wires were presumably unpleasant enough to motivate their detection. But we have no way of ascertaining how strongly our bats were motivated to continue hunting when the noise was switched on. Insect hunting has been elicited only with difficulty, even in the quiet, and it is not surprising that high frequency noise would discourage it. In our jamming experiments with wires the bats preferred not to fly and they tried to avoid the difficult task of echolocating small wires in the noise. While we could make some of them do this by forcing them to fly in an array of wires, we have no comparable way of forcing bats to attempt insect catching in the noise. Furthermore, wires are larger in one dimension and are stationary, rather than moving targets, Bats often slow down on approaching wires, but insects are intercepted at flight speeds of at least one metre per second.

It is remarkable that our very loud low frequency noise did not reduce the rate of insect catching at all, and that the good catchers, TR and TL, caught approximately as many fruit flies in this noise as in the quiet. In human masking experiments low frequencies are found to mask higher tones more easily than the reverse, but the auditory system of a *Myotis* is clearly able to make sharp frequency discriminations (Grinnell and Griffin, 1959), and it must be able to distinguish

30 decibel echoes at 60 or 70 kilocycles from a noise covering the band from 0·1 to 10 or 15 kilocycles at a level of about 50 decibels per cycle bandwidth.

Another question might be phrased as follows: since bats can apparently hear echoes from wires at a signal-to-noise ratio of − 35 decibels (Griffin and Grinnell, 1958), why not assume that they can also hear *Drosophila* wings beat 30 decibels below a 50 decibel per cycle bandwidth noise at lower frequencies? This question leads directly into the problem of critical bands for the hearing of bats, a problem discussed elsewhere (Griffin, 1958, pp. 373-75). But regardless of the uncertainties surrounding this problem, it is difficult to believe that bat hearing or *Drosophila* flight sounds could have so narrow a bandwidth as one cycle per second. Hence the noise effectively competing with the flight sounds must be greater than 50 decibels. Even if we assume that the overall level of the *Drosophila* flight sounds (about 20 db. re 0.0002 dyne/cm.^{2}) is spread over as narrow a bandwidth as 10 cycles/second, the competing noise would have a level of 60 decibels or 40 decibels above the sound level from the fly.

It should be reiterated that we are not suggesting that all detection of insect prey by all bats under all conditions is based upon echolocation. The observations of Moehres (1950), Kolb (1959) and others are sufficient to demonstrate detection of relatively noisy insects, and we have also observed bats suddenly respond to a buzzing blow fly and turn towards it from a distance of several feet. Quite clearly both active echolocation and passive detection are important in the feeding behaviour of bats under natural conditions. We have considered only the former, because of its intrinsic interest, and because its importance had not been fully recognized heretofore.

Further experiments now in progress seem likely to throw additional light on the intricate and rapid flight manoeuvres executed during insect pursuit and interception, the ways in which the various membranes are employed, and the accuracy of localization of the insects. These studies will be reported elsewhere, together with a consideration of the information processing involved in the tracking of small moving targets.

SUMMARY

1. Bats of the genus *Myotis* (*M. lucifugus, M. subulatus leibii* and *M. keenii septentrionalis*) have been studied while pursuing and cap-

turing small insects under laboratory conditions. It is apparently important to provide fairly large numbers of such insects in order to elicit insect catching behaviour indoors.

2. Insect catches are individually directed pursuit manoeuvres; each insect is detected, located, and intercepted in flight within about half a second.

3. Certain individual bats caught mosquitos (*Culex quinquefaciatus*) and fruit flies (*Drosophila robusta* and *D. melanogaster*) at remarkably high rates which could be measured conservatively by the gain in weight of the bat. Sometimes a bat would average as many as 10 mosquitos or 14 fruit flies per minute during a period of several minutes. In four cases motion pictures showed two separate *Drosophila* catches within half a second.

4. The orientation sounds of the hunting bat are adjusted in a manner that seems appropriate for the echolocation of single insects one at a time. There is a *search phase* before the occurrence of any apparent reaction to the insect. In this phase the frequency drops from about 100 to 50 kilocycles during each pulse of sound, and the pulses are emitted by *M. lucifugus* at intervals of 50 to 100 milliseconds.

5. When an insect is detected the search phase gives way to an *approach phase* characterized by a progressive shortening of the pulse-to-pulse interval and, if necessary, a sharp turn towards the insect. In this phase the pulse duration may shorten somewhat, but the frequencies remain approximately the same as in the search phase or drop slightly.

6. When the bat is within a few centimetres of the insect there is a *terminal phase* in which the pulse duration and interval between pulses shorten to about 0.5 millisecond and 5 or 6 milliseconds respectively. Contrary to a conclusion reached earlier on the basis of much less adequate data (Griffin, 1953), the frequency *drops* in the terminal phase, sometimes to 25 or 30 kilocycles. This is the buzz, which also occurs in many cases when the bat is dodging wires or landing.

7. The distance from the insect at which detection occurs can be judged by the shift from search to approach patterns. This distance of detection is commonly about 50 cm. for *Drosophila,* and it occasionally may be as much as a metre with fruit flies or mosquitos.

8. Two *M. lucifugus* which had become adept at catching *Drosophila* in the laboratory were exposed to broad band thermal noise either at low frequencies (0.1-15 kilocycles) or high (20–100 kilocycles). The low frequency noise had an approximately uniform

spectrum level of about 50 decibels per cycle band width (re 0.0002 dyne/cm.^{2}) from 0.1 to 8 kilocycles. It was thus very loud compared to the flight sounds of *Drosophila* which have a fundamental frequency of a few hundred cycles/second and a maximum sound pressure level of 20–25 decibels at the distances of detection by these bats. The high frequency noise was of low and varying intensity, but it discouraged or prevents insect catching. The low frequency noise, on the other hand, had no effect on insect catching; the bats gained weight in this noise (and in the dark) just as rapidly as in the quiet. Although bats sometimes detect insect prey by passive listening to sounds emanating from the insects themselves, these experiments appear to us to establish conclusively that small and relatively silent insects are often detected by echolocation.

ACKNOWLEDGMENTS

We are happy to acknowledge much co-operation, assistance, and support without which these experiments would not have been possible. Financial support has been provided through a contract between the Office of Naval Research and Harvard University, and reproduction of this paper in whole or in part for the purposes of the United States government is authorized. Instrumentation and extremely helpful advice and suggestions have been contributed by the Lincoln Laboratory, Massachusetts Institute of Technology, especially by David A. Cahlender, J. J. G. McCue, and N. Durlach, and also by A. F. Lagon of the General Radio Company. The initial stimulus for these experiments came from Dr. E. T. Neilsen, and the first observations were made with his collaboration at the Vero Beach Laboratory, Florida State Board of Health. Mosquito eggs were supplied for subsequent experiments by Dr. Paul A. Wolk of the U.S. Public Health Service. In many experiments we were materially assisted by A. Boass, C. Gifford, and A. D. Grinnell. Our photographic recordings of bats and insects have depended to a large extent on stroboscopic lights developed by H. E. Edgerton, Massachusetts Institute of Technology.

REFERENCES

GALTSOFF, P. S., LUTZ, F. E., WELCH, P. S. AND NEEDHAM, J. G. (eds.) (1959). *Culture methods for invertebrate animals.* New York: Dover Publications.

GOULD, E. (1955). The feeding efficiency of insectivorous bats. *J. Mammal.,* 36, 399–407.

GOULD, E. (1959). Further studies on the feeding efficiency of bats. *J. Mammal.,* 40, 149–50.

GRIFFIN, D. R. (1953). Bat sounds under natural conditions with evidence for the echolocation of insect prey. *J. exp. Zool.,* 123, 435–66.

GRIFFIN, D. R. (1958). *Listening in the dark*. New Haven, Conn.: Yale University Press.

GRIFFIN, D. R. AND GRINNELL, A. D. (1958). Ability of bats to discriminate echoes from louder noise. *Science,* 128, 145–47.

GRINNELL, A. D. AND GRIFFIN, D. R. (1958). The sensitivity of echolocation in bats. *Biol. Bull.,* 114, 10–22.

GRINNELL, A. D. AND GRIFFIN, D. R. (1959). The neurophysiology of audition in bats. *Anat. Rec.,* 134, 574.

KOLB, A. (1958). Über die Nahrungsaufnahme einheimischer Fledermäuse vom Boden. *Verh. Deutsch. Zool. Gesellsch.* in Frankfurt a. M. 1958, pp. 162–68.

KUHL, W., SCHODDER, G. R. AND SCHRODER, F. K. (1954). Condenser transmitters and microphones with solid dielectric for airborne ultrasonics. *Acustica,* 4, 519–32.

MOEHRES, F. P. (1950). Aus dem Leben unserer Fledermäuse. *Kosmos,* 46 (7), 291–95.

STEVENS, S. S. (ed.) (1951). *Handbook of experimental psychology*. New York: Wiley.

TRAGER, W. (1953). Chapter 14 in *Insect physiology* (K. D. Roeder, ed.). New York: Wiley.

WILLIAMS, C. M. AND GALAMBOS, R. (1950). Oscillographic and stroboscopic analysis of the flight sounds of *Drosophila*. *Biol. Bull.,* 99, 300–307.

CHAPTER 4

THE INNATE BEHAVIOR OF INVERTEBRATES

The present chapter will deal with three classes of behavior that are characteristic of invertebrates and are considered to be innate. The behavior classes are: kineses, taxes, and instincts. We will consider the defining characteristics of each class, subdivisions within the classes, and examples of behaviors typical of the class. In addition, theories regarding these behaviors and the relationships among them will be briefly discussed.

The concepts of kineses and taxes, as described herein, are based on the work of Fraenkel and Gunn (1961). The behavior patterns involved in kineses and taxes are particularly characteristic of invertebrates and involve the *orientation* or movements of these animals in their environments.

The concept of instinct as used in the present chapter and in later chapters is based primarily on the work of Lorenz (1950) and Tinbergen (1951). The behaviors subsumed under the concept of instinct are characteristic of higher invertebrates, especially insects, and many vertebrate forms. Such behaviors are usually involved in reproduction, fighting, and cooperation.

Kineses, taxes, and instincts have been characterized as being innate responses. Although this characterization follows general usage, it does not mean that the responses occur without external stimulation. Rather, they require stimuli or elicitors and may require a particular set of antecedent conditions. However, they do *not* require specific prior training such as is true for learned responses. In addition, the characterization of innate, is descriptive of behaviors that depend heavily on the biological organization that is typical for the individuals within the species. Thus, it is assumed that if a behavior is innate, different individuals within the species will react to the same stimulus in very much the same way given similar antecedent and immediate conditions (species-specific behavior).

163

The Relationship between Innate and Learned Responses

The details of the relationship between innate and learned behaviors are incompletely investigated and incompletely understood especially with regard to invertebrates. However, the present writers suggest that these behaviors are neither opposite nor parallel behavior processes but interlocking behavior processes. That is, learning is considered to involve the modification of innate responses. The modification may involve changing the stimulus which elicits the response, selection of particular innate responses from a larger pattern, or chaining together of a number of previously unchained innate responses.

Modification of innate behavior in terms of changing the eliciting stimulus is illustrated by classical conditioning (see Chapter 10); modification by selection of a particular response from a larger pattern or repetoire of responses, response differentiation, is illustrated by many instrumental learning tasks such as bar-pressing; modification by the chaining together of a number of innate responses is also illustrated by the typical instrumental learning task of bar-pressing in which the animal presses a bar and then obtains food or water. These types of behavior modifications, called learning, are not mutually exclusive nor is the list exhaustive. Detailed descriptions and analyses of the many examples of behavior modification considered as learning are presented in Chapters 10, 11, and 12.

Kineses

This class of behavior is defined in general as "undirected locomotory reactions, in which the speed of movement or the frequency of turning depend on the intensity of stimulation" (Fraenkel and Gunn, p. 10, 1961). Since kinetic responses are typically found in the behavior patterns of lower invertebrates, psychologists and students in psychology are somewhat unfamiliar with them. However, recognition of their importance is increasing as principles of behavior, such as conditioning, are extended to these lower animal forms. For example, a systematic change in the speed of movement from one place to another is frequently considered to be an index of instrumental learning and a systematic change in frequency of occurrence of turning responses is considered to be an index of conditioning for the flatworm, planaria (see McConnell, Chapter 10). When research is conducted with invertebrates appropriate control procedures are necessary to determine if the observed changes in speed of locomotion or frequency of turning is an innate or learned behavior change (VanDeventer and

Ratner, 1964*). In addition, such forms of innate behavior may be of interest to the psychologist as an aspect of the general study of the behavior of organisms.

Since the receptor systems of humans and other vertebrates with which we are familiar represent such high points of evolution, it is difficult to conceive of an animal's orienting by *undirected movements* which are associated only with increases in stimulus intensity. However, many species of invertebrates or their larval forms have receptor systems that are responsive only to intensity of stimulation and not to direction, distance, or quality of stimulation. For such species kinetic responses serve to alter the orientation of the animal. For example, the wood louse shows a kinetic response to changes in humidity. As the humidity is decreased the animal moves with increasing rapidity, and conversely as the humidity is increased it moves more slowly until it is relatively motionless at higher humidities (Gunn, 1937 *).

> GUNN, D. L. The humidity reactions of the wood louse, *Porcellio scaber. J. exp. Biol.,* 1937, 14, 178–86.
> A series of experiments were conducted to investigate the animal's responses to humidity and it was found that they survive well and remain relatively inactive in high humidity (near 90%) while they have high mortality and move almost continuously in dry air (below 30% humidity). When wood lice were put into an environment with a gradient of humidity from low to high, most of the animals moved into the area of high humidity and then became relatively motionless. The combined results of the experiments indicated that the animals were making *ortho-kinetic* responses to the humidity and changes in humidity. That is, they change their average rate of linear velocity as a function of the humidity of their environment.

The stimulus of humidity illustrates one of the aspects of a stimulus that is a determinant of the occurrence of kinetic responses as opposed to other types of responses. That is, humidity does not have a detectable direction or disance but for the wood louse, for example, a high level of humidity is important for the survival of the animal. An unfavorable humidity leads to activity which increases the likelihood of reaching a favorable humidity. Temperature and illumination are also reacted to as undirectional stimuli by many species of invertebrates. The occurrence of kineses for these animals depends on the characteristics of the organisms' receptor systems.

Two forms of kineses have been noted. One involves a change in speed of movement, the other involves a change in frequency of turning. An undirected response involving a change in the speed of movement is called an *ortho-kinetic response;* and undirected response involving a change in frequency of turning is called a *klino-kinetic response* (Fraenkel and Gunn, 1961). As previously suggested, the movement patterns of some species are typically ortho-kinetic and the movement patterns of others, such as the swimming reaction of paramecia, are *klino-kinetic*. Both ortho-kinetic and klino-kinetic responses can lead to the congregation of a number of individual animals in the same area. That is, a particular intensity of stimulation is assumed to have the same ultimate effect on the behavior of all of the individuals in the species. Thus, a large number of wood lice might be found in a single place of high humidity, but the path that each followed to get to that place would be expected to differ, since the reaction of the animals to humidity is a kinetic one.

The study by Hardy and Bainbridge (1951 **) illustrates an investigation of a kinetic response of larval crustaceans and several of the summarized studies illustrate the range of stimuli and species for which kinetic responses appear (Gunn, 1937 *; Hollis, 1963 *; Koehler, 1932 *; Reigert, 1959 *; Ullyat, 1936 *). As noted in these studies, both the stimulus and the form of the kinetic response are sometimes indicated by the name of the response. For example, an ortho-kinetic response that occurs to a change in intensity of illumination is called a photo-ortho-kinesis; an ortho-kinetic response that occurs to a change in temperature is called a thermo-ortho-kinesis.

KOEHLER, O. Sinnephysiologie der Susswasserplanarien. *Z. vergl. Physiol.*, 1932, **16**, 606–756.

This study, summarized from a detailed report by Fraenkel and Gunn (1961, p. 254 ff), investigated the responses of planaria to mechanical stimulation from water pressure. *Planaria alpina* were tested with streams of water squirted at them from a pipette. Three types of responses to the stream of water were noted. If the animal were resting, the stream first leads to a brief period of undirected activity, *rheo-kinesis*. The animal then turns and orients into the stream of water and if two streams are flowing, one on either side, the animal orients between them. These are the responses characteristic of *rheo-tropo-taxis*. When the intensity of stimulation is suddenly reduced by stopping the water flow the animal waves its anterior end around which is characteristic of *klino-tactic* response.

RIEGERT, P. W. The humidity reactions of grasshoppers. Humidity reactions of *Melanoplus bivittatus* (SAY) and *Comnula pellucida* (SCUDD). *Canad. Entomologist*, 1959, **91**, 35–40.

Individuals of two species of grasshoppers were tested in a number of physiological states for their reactions to humidity. The animals showed *ortho-kinetic* and also *klino-kinetic* responses in a test apparatus consisting of a piece of moist filter paper placed in the center of a covered dish. Normal adult and larvae hoppers become active in the moist areas and quiet in the dry areas of the dish. The activity consisted of linear and direction changing movements. Starved and moulting hoppers became quiet in the moist area of the test dish. As was found in research with other species, the humidity (moisture) receptors for the grasshoppers are located within the first eight segments of their antennae and removal of these segments eliminated responses to humidity.

ULLYOT, P. The behavior of *Dendrocoelum lacteum. J. exp. Biol.,* 1936, 13, 253–64.

The *photo-klino-kinetic* response of planaria was demonstrated and investigated in this study. It was found that under uniform environmental conditions planaria frequently change the direction in which they move and the rate of this change in direction is relatively stable. If the intensity of light shining on the planaria suddenly increases, the rate of change in direction also increases. This is the klino-kinetic response. The planaria then adapt to the higher intensity of illumination and the rate of change in direction of movement returns to the original level, although the illumination level is not changed. If only one spot of bright light is presented, the klino-kinetic response results in the animal's moving to an area of lower intensity of illumination and then reducing its rate of change in direction. This response is the ortho-kinetic response as described in the study by Gunn (1937*).

Taxes

Taxes are defined as movements of the animal *directly* toward or away from a source of stimulation. Fraenkel and Gunn (1961, p. 134) identify three types of tactic reactions: *klino-taxis, tropo-taxis,* and *telo-taxis.* It is important to note that the simple observation of an animal orienting with regard to a stimulus is not sufficient to allow the observer to determine what type of response is occurring. The specific classification of a response into one of these classes is made in terms of details regarding the stimulus, the characteristics of the response, and the form of the animal's receptor system. Kinetic responses involve undirected changes in rate of movement and occur to gradients of stimulation for species with simple receptors for intensity. Tactic responses involve movements toward or away from a source of stimulation and occur to very steep gradients of stimulation for which the source is identifiable.

The *klino-taxes,* as suggested by the prefix *klino,* involve orientation by bending or twisting. However, for the animal showing klino-taxes, the head or the body bends or swings from side to side while the animal moves rather directly toward or away from a source of stimulation. The bending or swinging is associated with the presence of a single intensity receptor with which the animal successively compares the intensity of stimulation on each side. This movement pattern is similar to that of the arm of a blind person who is walking down a narrow path swinging his cane from side to side to remain on the path. The arm holding the cane is oriented along the path, but this orientation is achieved by repeated swinging of the arm and cane from side to side.

Klino-tactic responses have been observed and studied in detail for the maggot larva for a number of common flies including *Musca domestica*, the house fly, and *Calliphora erythrocephala*, the blowfly (Fraenkel and Gunn, 1961, p. 59). In addition, the orienting movements of *Euglena*, earthworms (Adams, 1903 *) and some blood suckers (Wigglesworth and Gillet, 1934 *) can be described as klino-taxes.

ADAMS, G.   On the negative and positive phototropism of the earthworm *Allolobaphora foetida* as determined by light of different intensities. *Amer. J. Physiol.*, 1903, 9, 26–34.

A total of 30 worms were tested for their responses to light stimulation. The light source was located on the side of the animal. Movements toward the source were considered to be positive responses; movements away from it were considered to be negative responses. A jar of water was placed between the animal and the light source to control heat from the light. Animals were tested with light intensities from 0.012 candle meters (cm.) to 192 cm. Light intensities from 192 cm. to 12 cm. elicited approximately the same high proportion of *negative photo-klino-tactic* responses. Below intensities of 12 cm. progressively fewer negative responses occurred and at very low intensities (around 0.012 cm.) positive responses occurred.

WIGGLESWORTH, V. S. AND GILLETT, J. D.   The function of the antennae of *Rhodnius prolixus* and the mechanism to orientation to the host. *J. exp. Biol.*, 1934, 11, 120–39.

The responses to temperature gradients of a South American bloodsucker were found to be *thermo-klino-tactic* types of orientations. It was known that these bloodsuckers moved toward warm-blooded animals and this study investigated the type of movement, the stimulus, and the receptor system for this orientation. Blinded bugs were tested by being placed near test tubes full of warm water. The animals went directly toward the test tube. During the orientation movement, the animals' antennae waved back and forth; removal of the two antennae eliminated the orientation to temperature. However, removal of only one antenna did not interfere with orientation. The fact that the bugs could orient with a single antenna, which makes simultaneous comparison of stimulus intensity impossible, is part of the evidence leading to the conclusion that the response was klino-tactic.

Tropo-taxes are characteristic of invertebrates that have pairs of receptors that are sensitive to intensity of stimulation. In the presence of a very steep gradient of stimulation, such as a beam of light from an appropriate source, the movement pattern in tropo-tactic responses consists of direct movement toward (positive responses) or away from (negative responses) the source of simulation with no alternate bending or deviations in the movements. The original orientation toward or away from the source is achieved by the turning of the animal toward the more or less strongly stimulated side. When this turning has been achieved, there is equal stimulation at the two receptors, and direct movement toward or away from the stimulus occurs.

Two tests can be performed to verify the classification of a response as a tropo-tactic response. One test involves the behavior of the animal when two similar stimulus gradients are simultaneously presented. In this case, the tropo-tactic response leads to orientation between the two gradients, which is a way to equalize stimulus intensities on the two sides of the animal. The second test involves the behavior of the animal when the receptor on one side of the animal is eliminated so that equal intensities of stimulation on the two sides cannot be achieved. In this case, the animal makes continuous turning movements, *circus movements,* that are associated with the inequality of stimulation on the two sides. If light were used with a photo-negative animal that is blinded in one eye, the animal would continuously turn toward the blinded side; if a photo-positive animal were used, it would continuously turn toward the seeing side. Circus movements are also observed in intact animals. These occur if the animal is exposed to a large uniform field of stimulation for which a steep intensity gradient does not occur.

Portions of the study by Davenport, *et al.* (1960 **) illustrate a *chemo-tropo-tactic* response in worms and a *klino-kinetic* response in the same animal. This study and the study by Grosch (1950 *) illustrate the functions of these behavior patterns and some of the methods used for their analysis. The study by Mast (1923 *) with flies further illustrates the form of tropo-tactic responses and the stimuli to which they occur.

GROSCH, D. S. Olfactometer experiments with male braconids. *Ann. Ent. Soc. Amer.,* 1950, 43, 334–42.

A method for investigating responses of the wasp, *Microbracon hebetor* (Say), to chemical stimuli was determined, then a number of stimuli were tested using the method. The negative geo-taxis of the male wasp was used to get it to enter the choice point in a T or Y tube after the arms of the tube had been baited. Differential approach to the arms was used to indicate *chemotaxes.* Sweet syrups such as honey, molasses, and syrupy fruits elicited approach; fresh syrups made from simple sugars did not, and acidic or sour fruits elicited *negative-chemo-taxes.* Food deprivation up to six days increased the vigor of approach to positive stimuli. It was also found that males oriented toward and approached females in a large enclosed area as a function of chemical stimulants on the female.

MAST, S. O. Photic orientation in insects with special reference to the drone fly, *Eristalis tenax* and the robber fly, *Erax ruflibaris. J. exp. Zool.,* 1923, 38, 109–205.

The orientation of these flies to light and the characteristics of the photoreceptor mechanisms were studied in a number of experiments. In general it was found that the adult flies orient to light by *tropo-tactic* responses. That is, both eyes are involved in simultaneous comparison of the stimulus gradient that leads the flies to make strong and direct responses toward a light source (positive photo-responses). The strong responses are shown after a period of dark adaptation and if the wings have been removed, the flies walk directly to the light source. Unlike the typical tropo-tactic response, they orient directly to two parallel beams, if the flies are blinded in one eye. Thus, it was concluded that their receptors are advanced enough to allow simultaneous comparison under special conditions with only one eye that can respond differentially (like the mammalian eye, for example). Such a response, if it occurs generally, is considered to be a teleo-tactic response.

Tropo-tactic responses are sometimes identified in terms of the stimuli to which they occur. For example, a tropo-tactic response to water pressure, such as a directed stream of water, is called *rheo-taxis* and is characteristic of marine species. A tropo-tactic response to the earth's gravitational field is called *geo-taxis*. A variety of stimuli and receptors are involved in the orienting responses of invertebrates and most are not intuitively obvious to the observer. The pull of the shell of snails that produces the cue for geo-taxis (Crozier and Navez, 1930 *) and the bending of hair tufts on the locust that produces the cue for orienting into the wind (Weiss-Fogh, 1949 *) are two examples. However, in some cases the stimulus for an orienting response cannot be specified. This is true of the response to darkness illustrated in the study by Rao (1947 *). In this case it is not possible to distinguish between a response associated with avoidance of light and a response associated with approach to darkness.

CROZIER, W. J. AND NAVEZ, A. E.   The geotropic orientation of gastropods. *J. gen. Physiol.,* 1930, 3, 3–37.

Orientation to the earth's gravitational field, called *geo-taxis,* was investigated in the tree snail (*Liguus* sp.). The animal is normally negatively geo-tåctic, that is, it creeps up a vertical or sloping surface, such as a tree. The specific problem under investigation was to determine what sources of stimulation elicit the response. In general, it was found that the pull of the snail's shell on its body muscles provided the stimulus for orientation. Normally, the snail creeps upward if its shell is hanging downward. When the shell was pulled horizontally sideways by means of thread attached to it, the animal changed its orientation and crawled across the slope; when the shell was pulled upward, the animal turned and crawled downward. These findings also illustrate a reaction to gravitational fields that does not depend on specialized receptors such as statocysts.

WEISS–FOGH, T.   An aerodynamic sense organ in locusts. *Nature,* 1949, 164, 873–74.

Previous experiments and observations had suggested that a number of insects fly into the wind and this orientation was called *ameno-tropotaxis.* However, the kind of receptors that mediated these responses could not be identified. The present experiment reported the discovery of the receptors for responses to wind stimulation for the locust, *Schistocerca gregaria,* and probably for other grasshoppers. Tufts of hair on the front of the head of the locust were found. These tufts are sensitive to bending by currents of air and bending of the tufts leads the animal to fly. If the direction of air current is changed to the side, it leads the animal to change its orientation and turn again into the wind. This is characteristic of a tropo-taxis. Covering the tufts of hair with paint eliminated all of these responses.

Rao, R. T. Visual responses of mosquitos artificially rendered flightless. *J. exp. Biol.*, 1947, **24**, 64–78.

This study conducted with two species of mosquito (*Culex molestus* and *Anopheles maculipennis atroparvis*) investigated the perplexing question of *negative-photo-taxis* versus *skoto-taxis* in animals' orientation to light. That is, it has been suggested that some responses considered to be avoidance of light (negative photo-taxis) may be responses of approach to darkness (skoto-taxis). Experimental conditions can be arranged to make a differential test of which of these responses is being made. First the mosquitos (with wings removed) were tested on a plane with illumination from below and a black band at the perimeter. The animals consistently approached the black bands if they were at least 0.5 cm. wide and no more than 45 degrees off to the side. This suggested skoto-taxis. However, tests on which two black bands were presented simultaneously led to inconclusive findings. If the animals were orienting to black, they should have gone between the two bands. Observations with animals blinded in one eye also yielded equivocal results—some tests suggesting negative photo-taxis and some skoto-taxis.

Some higher invertebrates, particularly those with compound eyes such as the bee, orient directly to a source or beam of light. This response is called *telo-taxis*. Telo-taxis does not involve swinging from side to side as in klino-taxis nor does it involve establishing equal stimulation in a pair of receptors, as is true in tropo-taxis. Rather, it is a response that requires a receptor system that adjusts both to intensity and direction of stimulation. This is possible for some insects with compound eyes. If a bee is tested with two beams of light, the bee orients toward one beam and then toward the other but does not orient between them to balance the stimulation from the two sources. To illustrate the function of telo-tactic responses Fraenkel and Gunn point out (1961) that a bee must orient toward a specific flower and not between two flowers (a flower is considered as a source of light). In other words, the animal's orientation toward a light source must be direct and not involve a balancing of sources of stimulation. Theoretically, telo-taxis requires inhibition of stimulation from some receptors while others are responding; tropo-taxis requires balancing of the impulses from the receptors when the animal moves between two sources of stimulation, such as beams of light, that are of equal intensity.

Modification of Kineses and Taxes

A number of conditions modify kinetic and tactic responses. The effects of modifying stimulus conditions will be described in this section and the effects of modifying physiological conditions will be described in Chapter 6. Modifications of kinetic and tactic responses are indicated by a change in the intensity or vigor of the response or by a change in the sign of the response as, for example, from a positive tactic response to a negative tactic response. The types of stimulus conditions associated with these response changes are: (*a*) repeated or continuous presentations of the same stimulus, (*b*) successive presentations of different intensities of the same stimulus, and (*c*) simultaneous presentation of different stimuli that elicit different responses.

Repeated or continual presentation of the same stimulus leads to habituation or adaptation of kinetic or tactic responses. In this case, the animals respond with reduced intensity to repeated presentations of the stimulus until the stimulus no longer elicits response (Hollis, 1963 *). The rate at which the response loses vigor is a complex function of the intensity of the stimulus, the number of presentations and their durations, and the rest period between presentations. Recent studies by Clark (1960) investigated the adaptation of negative tropotactic responses to mechanical and photic stimuli for a species of marine worm. In these studies Clark found that as few as 40 2-second presentations of a light (40 watt) led to complete habituation of the response and the habituation lasted at least five hours.

HOLLIS, J. H. Habituatory response decrement in pupae of *Tenebrio molitor. Anim. Behav.*, 1963, 11, 161–63.
This study demonstrated the modification of an innate response in the pupae of the meal worm. Although the pupae are generally inactive some classes of stimuli such as electric shock and tactile stimulation elicit waving of the anterior portions called by the author "abdominal reflex" with some of the characteristics of a *klino-kinesis*. The shock was presented with a 30-second intertrial interval until the animals did not respond for 10 consecutive trials. A median of 20 trials was required to habituate the response to shock. It was then found that tactile stimulation elicited the response, although repeated trials with shock did not. This suggested that such innate responses can be modified and that the modification is not a function of generalized fatigue.

The relationship between *stimulus intensity* and kinetic responses is inherent in the definition of kinesis. That is, an ortho-kinesis is defined as a change in speed of movement as a function of a change in intensity of the stimulus, and a klino-kineses is defined as a change in amount or frequency of turning as a function of a change in the intensity of the stimulus. Tactic responses are also affected by changes in stimulus intensity and the specific cases of concern here are those in which the sign of the tactic response changes. *Euglena* is positively photo-tactic in weak light and negatively photo-tactic in strong light, (Mast, 1938). Similarly, the earthworm, *Lumbricus terrestris,* is photo-positive in weak light and photo-negative in strong light. That is, it approaches weak light and withdraws from strong light (Adams 1903 *; Hess, 1924).

One of the common effects of *simultaneous presentation of different stimuli* that elicit different taxes is a change in the sign of one of the tactic responses. A classic example involves the marine snail, *Littorina neritoides,* that reacts photo-negatively when right side up in the water (geo-taxis), photo-positively when upside down in the water, but regardless of geo-tactic orientation it always reacts photo-negatively when it is not in water (Fraenkel and Gunn, 1961, p. 298). Other examples of the effects of the interaction between stimuli and changes in the sign of a tactic response have been found for the drone fly, *Eristalis tena,* and its reaction to light as a function of temperature (Dolley and Golden, 1947), and mosquito larvae and their reaction to light as a function of vibration on the water surface (Fraenkel and Gunn, 1961, p. 334). The drone fly reacts photo-positively within a moderate range of temperatures and photo-negatively when subjected to temperatures on either side of this range. Mosquito larvae generally react photo-positively, that is, they orient toward light at the surface of the water, but they react photo-negatively when the surface of the water is disturbed. Here the adaptive functions of the interplay between two or more different taxes is nicely illustrated. The mosquito larvae move away from the surface of the water and away from the light when the surface has been vibrated as, for example, from the presence of a predatory fish. Another effect of the simultaneous presentation of stimuli that elicit taxes is the facilitation of the response to one of the stimuli. This has been shown in the case of planaria and their response to light (Van Deventer and Ratner, 1964*).

VAN DEVENTER, J. M. AND RATNER, S. C.   Variables affecting the frequency of response of planaria to light. *J. comp. physiol. Psychol.*, 1964, **57**, 407–11.
    The response of planaria to light was used as a learned or conditioned response in some recent works (discussed in Chapter 10). The present study investigated a number of conditions other than learning that affects this response. Planaria of two species, *Dugesia tigrina* and *Curtesia foremani,* were used. It was found that the responses to light, negative *photo-klino-taxes* in form, were affected by the temperature of the water in which the animals were tested, the light conditions under which they were kept, the shape of the trough in which they were tested, and the size of the animal being tested. The effects of the shape of the trough and the size of the animal were explained in terms of an interaction between the response to light and the response of positive *thigmo-taxis.* That is, smaller animals and those on a flatter surface remained more in contact with the surface (thigmo-taxis). This increased the likelihood of their responding to light.

Instincts

As suggested in the beginning of this chapter the concept of instinct refers to complex and innate stimulus-response patterns associated with reproduction, fighting, and cooperation. The stimulus in instinctive behavior is assumed *to release the innate response* if internal conditions are appropriate. The stimulus in kinetic and tactic responses is assumed *to orient* the animal without specific restraints from internal conditions. Thus, among other differences, such as releasing as opposed to orienting, instincts differ from kineses and taxes in terms of the importance of internal conditions, such as hormonal factors. The concept of releasing is used in the present sense very much the same way as the concept of eliciting is used in discussions of learned behavior.

Relationship between Taxes and Instincts. A tactic and an instinctive response frequently follow each other in the behavior of an organism and may be incorporated into a single larger pattern of behavior. Haskell, (1958) found that the song of the male grasshopper leads the female to orient toward and approach the male, a tactic response, after which the male's proximity to the singing female releases the instinctive pattern of mating with the female. Similarly, the presence of scented material near a beehive orients or directs sentry bees toward this material, contact with this material, particularly if it has a foreign odor, releases the instinctive attacking response. The complexity of the relationship between the specific characteristics of the releasing stimulus, and the attacking response to this stimulus are described in the study by Free (1961 **). It will be noted that Free is only concerned with measurement of the instinctive response, so it is not clear from his study if the infrequent attacks to certain stimulus materials were due to failure of the materials to lead to orientation toward them or failure of the materials to release the attacking response.

Other Characteristics of Instincts. The fact that a stimulus releases a complex response is not sufficient to lead to the classification of this S–R sequence as an instinct. For present purposes instincts are characterized as follows: (*a*) they require a releasing stimulus, (*b*) thresholds for the response change as a function of internal conditions, (*c*) occurrence of an instinctive sequence leads to a refractory period for that sequence, (*d*) releaser-response patterns are relatively specific for a given species, (*e*) learning is not necessary even for the first occurrence of the instinctive response, and (*f*) instinctive responses are primarily involved in behaviors that have adaptive biological functions for the species, such as reproduction, including mating and care of the young; fighting, including inter- and intraspecies examples; and cooperation. Some theoretical analyses of instincts will be considered in Chapter 5 and the details of the relationship of instincts and internal conditions will be considered in Chapter 6.

Some Examples of Instinctive Behavior. The behavior of higher invertebrates, such as crustaceans and insects, clearly illustrates some of the characteristics of instinctive reactions. The study by Grosch (1948 **) was designed to determine the releasing functions of olfactory stimuli in the mating reactions of male wasps. This study and the studies by Free (1961 **) and Wilson (1962 *) illustrate the importance of chemical sensitivity in the behavior of infrahuman species. These studies also emphasize the unlearned or innate aspects of instinctive behavior as shown by the fact that the mating reactions of the wasps observed by Grosch (1948 **) occurred in 24-hour-old insects that had been hatched in a laboratory and maintained away from adult individuals. Other examples of releasing stimuli and instinctive behaviors are seen in the study by Crane (1949 *) that describes the releasing functions of visual stimuli in the defensive and mating behaviors of spiders and the study by Wilson (1962) that discusses the total complex of instinctive behaviors of the digger wasp.

CRANE, J. Comparative biology of salticid spiders at Rancho Grande, Venezuela IV. An analysis of display. *Zoologica,* 1949, 34, 159–214.

Salticid spiders are ones that catch their prey by springing on them rather than catching them in webs. The stimulus that elicits prey-catching is visual, as is the stimulus for mating. This study investigated some of the specific stimulus characteristics that release mating and threatening display reactions of male salticids, *Carythalia xanthopa.* Males were tested with live males, live females, dead females, and models. The critical cue that differentially released threat (the response to a male) or courtship was the presence of a yellow area at the head of the test stimulus. Normal males have yellow scales on their palps that are raised in front of the head in display reactions. Uncolored models from twice normal size to half normal size elicited courting—if the models were roughly rounded and had lateral extensions (like legs) on them. Such models only elicited the first stages of courtship. As soon as the male touched the model it stopped its advances. These data indicate the excellent visual acuity of the salticids and some of the characteristics of stimuli that elicit threat or courtship.

WILSON, E. O. Chemical communication among workers of the fire ant, *Solenopsis saevissima* (Fr. Smith). 3. The experimental induction of social responses. *Anim. Behav.,* 1962, 10, 159–64.

The innate releasing functions of three and possibly four chemical agents produced by fire ants were studied under laboratory conditions following intensive study of the animal under natural conditions. The secretion from Dufour's gland generally led ants to approach. Depending on the details of the particular situation, approach was associated with foraging by following the odor trail, mass emigration, alarm recruitment, or settling. Secretions from the cephalic region of the ant led others to frenzied alarm; the third secretion, probably from the antennae, led to grooming. A moderate increase in carbon dioxide content in the air around the ants was identified tentatively as a chemical stimulus associated with settling of the colony.

From the selected and summarized studies it can be seen that research on instinctive behavior may take the form of an inquiry about the functions of specific releasing stimuli (assuming the responses are already known) or it may take the form of an inquiry about the responses that are involved in a particular instinctive pattern. In either case the research requires a thorough knowledge of the general characteristics of the species being studied and relevant ecological facts about the species. Such background information is also required for study of kinetic and tactic responses.

EFFECT OF PRESSURE ON THE BEHAVIOUR OF

DECAPOD LARVAE (CRUSTACEA)

A. C. HARDY AND R. BAINBRIDGE

Department of Zoology and Comparative Anatomy,
University Museum, Oxford

In an account of experiments with the copepod *Calanus finmarchicus* (Gunn.), Hardy and Paton[1] suggested that the behaviour in vertical migration of this and perhaps other plankton animals might be influenced by the differences in pressure at various depths. The following experiments have been made to test this hypothesis. Two vertical 'Perspex' tubes, each 20 in. tall and having an internal rectangular cross-section of 2 in. $\times$ 1$\frac{1}{2}$ in., were placed side by side. After filling with sea water, experimental animals were introduced and each tube was closed by a flanged, water-tight, 'Perspex' lid (tightly screwed down), and the pressure in one, called the experimental tube, was varied while that in the other, the control tube, was kept at zero. The pressure in the former was changed by raising or lowering a column of mercury which communicated with the tube through a freshwater buffer and a rubber diaphragm, designed to prevent contamination of the sea water by poisons from the mercury. The pressure was measured either by the height of the mercury column or by the level of the meniscus in a manometer and was recorded in terms of 'metres depth of water' equivalent to the number of atmospheres of pressure found.

Freshly caught plankton animals having been put in equal numbers into both tubes, the number found swimming in the upper half of each was recorded at intervals of 15 or 30 minutes, while the pressure in the one tube was varied according to the nature of the experiment. In order to eliminate the effect of light, the experiments were made in a dark room and the animals counted by looking at their silhou-

---

[1] Hardy, A. C., and Paton, W. N., *J. Mar. Biol. Assoc.*, **26**, 467(1947).

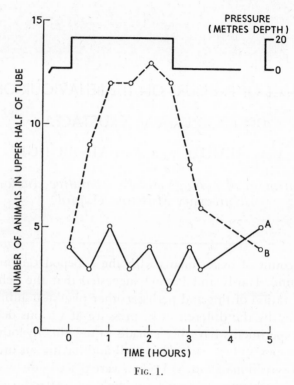

FIG. 1.

ettes against a screen illuminated by a red lamp which was switched on only for the short periods of counting.

While no effect of pressure on the behaviour of *Calanus* has been detected in any of many experiments so far performed, striking results have been obtained with mixed samples of Decapod larvæ which were almost entirely zœa and megalopa stages of *Portunus* and *Carcinus*. Figure 1 shows in a graph the results of an experiment in which 25 larvæ were placed in each tube and the pressure in the experimental one raised to the equivalent of 20 metres depth and, after 2½ hours, reduced to zero again (as shown in heavy line at top of figure); the points connected by the continuous line *A* show the number of larvæ in the upper half of the control tube at half-hour intervals, and those connected by the broken line *B* show the corresponding numbers in the experimental tube. Very similar responses were obtained to increases of pressure equivalent to depths of 5, 10, 15 and 20 metres; it was also shown that a gradually increasing proportion of the total animals in the tube was found in the upper half while the pressure was maintained at a constant value for two or three hours. These two findings are illustrated in the graph in Figure 2. Here the points connected by the thick continuous line *A* represent the average

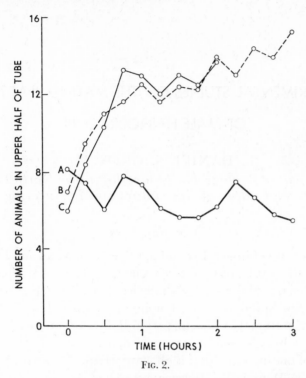

Fig. 2.

number of larvæ in the upper half of the control tube (pressure zero), at 15-minute intervals, in a large number of experiments in which 25 larvæ were placed in each tube. The points connected by the broken line *B* and by the thin continuous line *C* represent the average number of larvæ in the upper half of the experimental tube, in a similar number of such experiments, in which the pressure was raised just after the first observation was taken and maintained at the equivalent to 10 and 20 metres depth respectively. In other experiments very similar curves were obtained for larvæ under pressures equivalent to 5 and 15 metres depth; but these are omitted so as not to confuse the figure.

Experiments investigating the effects of pressure on these and other plankton animals will be continued, and attempts will be made to discover some pressure-sensitive organ in animals so affected. It seems likely that some such receptor may exist, since response to both increase and decrease in pressure is so rapid, but such an organ does not yet appear to have been demonstrated in any invertebrate animal. It is improbable that the slight changes in the rates of some chemical reactions due to changes in pressure could be the mechanism employed, because the rates of such reactions are affected so much more by quite small changes of temperature.

EXPERIMENTAL STUDIES ON THE MATING REACTION

OF MALE HABROBRACON

DANIEL S. GROSCH

*Department of Zoology and Entomology, The North Carolina
State College of Agriculture and Engineering*

INTRODUCTION

The majority of insects live solitary lives with males and females associating only just before and during mating. To ensure reproduction special attractive and recognition devices have developed which help insects to find suitable mates. For initial attraction of mates visual, auditory, vibrational or olfactory stimuli may be employed.

The view has often been expressed that in parasitic Hymenoptera the basis of mating attraction is olfactory [Fink (4), Murr (12), Parker (13), Cox (1), Daniel (2)]. However a search of the literature has failed to disclose reports dealing with controlled experiments on mating attraction. Therefore investigations were instituted using *Habrobracon juglandis* Ashmead, (*Microbracon hebetor* Say), an ectoparasite of Ephestia larvae bred extensively for about thirty years of genetic investigation by P. W. Whiting and students [see Martin (11)]. The present report is concerned chiefly with a type of behavior of the male termed the "mating reaction."

The mating reaction typically indicates male recognition of the presence of a female. It is an excited rapid flipping of wings just before the male dashes to the female and attempts to mount her. Grosch (7) found that antennae carry the important receptors of the stimulus (or stimuli) which evokes the mating reaction. As the inciting agency has been found singular in type or class, the singular form of the word stimulus is used throughout the paper. The present paper presents results of experiments designed to give information on (1) the nature of the stimulus; (2) the source; (3) the distance over which the stimulus is effective; and (4) the identification of the structural basis of the reaction. The discussion of male reproductive behavior includes consideration of what are termed nonspecific mating reactions.

MATERIALS AND GENERAL STATEMENT OF METHODS

Wasps were from eugenic wild type laboratory stocks. They were used twenty-four hours after emerging from the cocoons. This age seems best for mating reaction tests because males are old enough to be sensitive to mating stimuli but not so excitable that they lack discrimination.

The experiments were made in daylight (morning) at room temperature in the Marine Biological Laboratory, Woods Hole, Massachusetts. No tests were performed near bright artificial light or in direct sunlight.

Containers were shell vials (60 x 20 mm.). Before using, the vials were washed in water and dried overnight in a draft of air. Cheesecloth-covered cotton plugs were aired at least twenty-four hours before using.

After transfer to the test container males were allowed to quiet down before test materials or apparatus was introduced. In order to have a check on specificity of reaction, two males were used per test vial. A positive test was one in which both males responded with mating reaction during a given minute. Tests were called negative if no mating reaction occurred within ten minutes. Other than males of amputation experiments, no animals were etherized.

SPECIFIC METHODS AND RESULTS

Nature of stimulus: To investigate whether female products minus female structures could act as stimulus for the male mating reaction, two series of experiments were performed. In the first series, females were crushed on squares of absorbent paper and body fragments were removed. This preparation was placed immediately in a test vial of males. At the same time control vials were given clean paper squares. This series was followed by a second series of experiments which were similar except that controls were given paper on which males had been crushed.

All ten experiments of the first series showed positive mating reactions to the paper carrying female materials. Six of the reactions were immediate; all reactions took place before two minutes had elapsed. All controls to this series were negative.

In the second series, eight experiments were immediately positive; one was a delayed positive at five minutes and one was negative. All controls were negative.

These experiments indicate that female products can evoke mating reactions. However, papers from positive tests soon lost their effectiveness. This was demonstrated by removing papers from positive tests and placing them in new test vials of males. All attempts to obtain repeated positive tests failed if the preparation was older than five minutes. This is taken to be an indication that the responsible agent is volatile or diffusible.

Source of stimulus: In order to determine the bodily region with products capable of evoking mating reaction, different parts of females were placed in test vials containing males. In the first series of experiments females were transsected at the petiole. An abdomen was placed in one vial of males and the corresponding head and thorax in another vial of males.

In nine of ten experiments, males gave positive mating reactions to the female abdomen. These mating reactions were followed by attempts to copulate with the detached piece of the female. In two cases males succeeded in copulating with amputated abdomens. One of these copulations was so successful that the male walked around with the amputated female abdomen attached to his genitalia for at least ten seconds.

No mating reactions were obtained to female head and thorax. Often these parts were in motion and if there is a rhythm or vibration peculiar to the female presumably these parts were emitting it. In one test a head and thorax walked across the path of a male (about 2 mm. ahead of him). The male moved toward the object, investigated by tactile use of the antennae and then turned away without giving a mating reaction.

Because these results indicated the female abdomen as the source of the stimulus, a series of experiments was made in which the posterior half of a female abdomen was placed in one test vial and the anterior half in another vial of males. Fifty such experiments were made, with the following results:

Positive mating reaction to both parts .... 32 tests
Positive mating reaction to anterior only .... 14 tests
Positive mating reaction to posterior only .... 2 tests
Negative to both parts .... 2 tests

Of the 32 tests positive to both parts, 22 were immediate positives to both; 6 were immediate positives to the anterior and delayed positives to the posterior part (2 to 5 min.); and 4 were immediate positives to the posterior and delayed positives to the anterior part (2 to 5 min.).

These results indicate that scent glands of female *Habrobracon* although on the abdomen are not localized in the genital area. In this, the parasitic Hymenoptera, as represented by *Habrobracon,* differ from Lepidoptera [see Kellog (10) and Dickins (3)]. Indicated is a histological study to determine if unicellular scent glands such as are described for other Hymenoptera [Snodgrass (14)] are more numerous on the abdominal plates and the articular membranes in the anterior regions of the *Habrobracon* abdomen.

The distance over which the stimulus is effective: Vials containing males were connected to vials containing females by glass tubes of various lengths. Distance between vials could be increased by using a longer glass tube. The ends were inserted through corks which fitted the tops of test vials.

Positive mating reactions were obtained consistently with tubes 2 cm., 5 cm., 10 cm., and 15 cm. long (ten tests each). These positive tests were obtained at a distance in a system that precludes visual stimuli. When taken with results reported above, reception of a chemical stimulus is indicated. By definition this type of perception is olfactory.

Positive mating reactions were delayed three to five minutes after the system was closed in comparison with mating tests which are usually immediate when the male is in the same vial with a female or her products. Presumably this comparative lag in time is an indication of time needed for diffusion of the female scent. Mating reactions were especially frequent at or near the mouth of the tube connecting vials.

Typically, mating reactions were followed by excited ambulatorial movement of the males. However, these movements were not consistently directional. Males which gave a strong mating reaction at the mouth of the tube leading to the female would sometimes start off in the opposite direction. In some cases males started in the correct direction but apparently became confused for they turned around in the tube. It is possible that confusion of males is due to the closed system of relatively small volume in which graded intensity of stimulus cannot be long maintained. In systems of large or unlimited volume, gradations of diffused scent could be present which would direct males to a female. It seems possible that klino-taxis is the type of directive movement involved.

In reference to this criticism of methods on the basis of closed system is the suggestion that saturation of containers by odor of females is a hindrance even to normal laboratory mating of wasps. Parker (13) states that sexual activity of males is more pronounced and effective if parasitic Hymenoptera are not confined in a small space where the female odor may quickly saturate the air. He believes that males become satiated with the scent and are then not responsive to it.

Ten tests were run using a 20 cm. tube. However only eight were positive and the time between closing the system and observance of mating reactions was often as long as ten minutes. Experiments were not made with longer tubes because the time between closing the system and observing reaction was expected to be as long or longer than with the 20 cm. tube. Healthy males will not remain in the male vial longer than ten minutes for they tend to explore containers even though not excited by mating reaction.

Unexcited males were watched during their explorations. Mating reactions were seen to occur when males came within 5 to 10 cm. of the female vial. After mating reactions, the speed of males was visibly increased and movement was usually directed to females.

In one negative test (20 cm. tube) a male which had reached the female chiefly by undirected exploratory movements and had copulated, returned to the original vial. The male which had remained in the male vial then gave a mating reaction and attempted to mount the one which had just come from the female. This occurrence could be interpreted to mean that the successful male carried odor from the female which aroused the one that had remained in the male vial.

Identification of structural basis of reaction: Twenty-five males were etherized and their abdomens were amputated at the petiole. Two did not recover. The twenty-three which recovered were given females. Fourteen of these males responded with mating reactions and four of them persistently attempted to mount females.

Seven other males responded with atypical reactions when a female passed closely in front of them. This slight response consisted of tentative single movements of the wings with shifting of body position and waving of antennae. These seven with atypical reactions and two apathetic males which gave no reaction of any sort were probably not near the normal level of vitality as a result of the amputation. In three hours these nine were dead while the fourteen males of the positive tests lived about twelve hours. However, the males from the positive tests spent the last six hours of life motionless.

DISCUSSION

Specific mating reactions: Evidence from eyecoating experiments by Grosch (7) eliminates visual stimuli from those which might be responsible for evoking mating reactions specific for females. Present evidence eliminates other stimuli. Males showed no mating response to stationary or moving preparations of female head and thorax. Therefore presence or movement of a female perceived by vibrational or similar stimuli are not capable of summoning specific mating reactions. On the other hand males did respond to inanimate bits of paper which resembled females in no way except that female products were carried on the paper. The activity of excitement by chemical agents are indicated. Present evidence also indicates that reception can be effective at a distance. It appears that in a discriminating wasp the normally effective stimulus is female odor.

Antennae were shown to be the important receptors involved by Grosch (7). As distance chemoreceptors antennae thus function as olfactory organs. This identifies one function of the antennae but is not to be considered the only function.

These conclusions substantiate the general view that mating reaction in parasitic Hymenoptera has an olfactory basis (see Introduction). The suggestion by Genieys (6) that only tactile or other mechanical perception of female presence occurs is not supported.

Nonspecific mating reactions: All mating reactions which occurred during the present series of experiments were specific to the female or to female products. A total of 425 males was under observation. However no old, starved, or excited males were used.

Mating reactions are not always specific as in these controlled experiments. In the course of routine culture, wing flipping mating reactions are sometimes observed in vials containing only males. The behavior cannot be considered combative because typical mounting attempts may occur (although females have not been in the container for ten days). These reactions may be termed "nonspecific" to distinguish them from reactions evoked by female scent.

Two hypotheses may be postulated to account for observations made thus far on nonspecific mating reactions. Fraenkel and Gunn (5) stress the fact that when instinctive and reflex actions are involved, behavior of insects may not be purposive. On such a basis may be formulated the simplest hypothesis that nonspecific mating reactions are expressions of male excitability no more significant than the runing and flying activities of a generally agitated group of wasps. Any sudden change in environmental conditions might be responsible for sudden male excitement—changes in light when vials are removed from an incubator or protective container, changes in air current or pressure when a plug is removed or replaced, mechanical shock from handling or setting the vial down abruptly.

An alternate hypothesis is that stimuli to which there is ordinarily no response (male odor?) might evoke mating reaction if males lack discrimination because of a lowered threshold of sensitivity or an increased reflex excitability. Old or starved males have a lowered threshold of sensitivity. The majority of insect sense organs have the effect of increasing reflex excitability and most effective are the compound eyes according to Wigglesworth (17). Thus any of the environmental changes listed in the above paragraph may act to increase reflex excitability but probably most important is the strong stimulating action of direct light from the sun or from an electric bulb. It is known that Habrobracon are generally excitable by direct light and are positively phototropic at certain ages. However it should be kept in mind that Hase (8) found darkness no hindrance and Grosch (7) demonstrated that covered eyes were no obstruction to normal mating.

Male reproductive behavior as an interdependent series of reflexes: Fertilization of females is the chief purpose in male existence; therefore, the one basic activity or the main instinct of males is mating. This reproductive behavior consists of a series of actions which may form an interdependent sequence of reflexes. The links in the normal chain of events are (1) receive female scent. (2) give mating reaction, (3) go to female, (4) mount, (5) bend abdomen, (6) insert male parts, (7) perform rhythmic movements especially of the wings and abdomen. The activity termed the "copulation reflex" by Grosch (7) becomes a series of reflexes by splitting it into components.

If actions are interdependent each action is induced by the one which precedes it. Once started at any action of the chain, the performance tends to go to completion. Hingston (9) clearly showed that series even more complicated than this are typical of insects and that they often continue to completion even though there is no occasion for the actions. An interdependent series of mating reflexes would help explain why Habrobracon males mount and attempt copulation after a nonspecific mating reaction. It places importance on the reception and correct interpretation of stimuli and indicates the consequence of nonspecific mating reactions. The inference is that males have the choice to give or not to give a mating reaction (action 2) in response to a stimulus and probably have the choice of going or not going to a given wasp (action 3) but if once committed the male is swept along through the remainder of the chain of action. Thus he may attempt copulations with other males, completion of which is anatomically impossible.

Identification of structural basis of reactions: In general, anterior ganglionic masses exert a dominance over other arthropod nervous centers. This permits head sensitivity to play a controlling part in insect activities. Data reported for Habrobracon are consistent with this principle. Whiting's observations (16) on sex mosaics indicate that dominant reproductive behavior is determined chiefly by centers of the anterior nervous system, especially the brain. The present paper includes observations on non-mosaics which demonstrate that the abdomen is not needed for male reproductive behavior except to give the abdominal reflexes during actual copulation. Recognition of female presence, going to female, and mounting were all obtained with abdomenless males.

Local determination of reflexes: Locally determined activities of structural segments are characteristic of insect behavior. Evidence suggests that mounting in Habrobracon is chiefly determined by local thoracic ganglia. Being locally determined it may occur independently although it is normally one of a series of coordinated reflexes. Grosch (7) observed antennaeless males mounting females after chance close contact. These actions seemed to be in response to contact stimuli perceived by leg receptors and were immediately acted upon by the legs. There were no wing motions of the mating reactions. Interpretation that these mounting reflexes are locally determined is consistently with the principle that impulses excited by a stimulus are conducted to the nearest arthropod action parts which respond first and most strongly.

Parallel to this hymenopteran situation is Kellog's (10) historical discovery that male Lepidoptera which find females exclusively by odor, orient themselves for copulation by contact stimuli. It accounted for attempted mountings and copulations observed when two males accidentally came into contact. Probably some of the indiscriminate mounting of males in Habrobracon may be explained on this basis (however not those mountings which follow a nonspecific mating reaction).

SUMMARY

1. Specific mating reactions were evoked by paper on which females had been crushed and from which female fragments had been removed. No reactions were evoked by paper alone or by paper on which males had been crushed.

2. Female abdomens evoked specific mating reactions. Head and thorax preparations did not.

3. Although both anterior and posterior parts of the female abdomen evoked mating reactions the anterior fragment was more effective than the posterior. Suggested is a histological study of the distribution of unicellular scent glands.

4. The specific mating reaction stimulus is effective over a distance

of at least 20 cm. In a closed system of relatively small volume males may be confused on direction to females by lack of gradient of stimulus.

5. All evidence supports an olfactory basis for recognition of and attraction to the female. Odor perception is identified as one of the functions of the antennae.

6. Males deprived of abdomens give specific mating reactions and attempt to mount females. This is consistent with observations on sex mosaics that indicate dominant reproductive behavior to be determined by anterior nerve centers.

7. It is postulated that nonspecific mating reactions are either meaningless expressions of general excitability of males or that they are reactions by excited males to stimuli which are normally ineffective. Excitement may involve lowered threshold of sensitivity or increased reflex excitability.

8. The male reproductive performance is discussed on the basis of an interdependent series of reflex actions some of which are controlled by local ganglia.

REFERENCES

1. Cox, J. A. *Ascogaster carpocapsae* Viereck, an important larval parasit of the codling moth and the oriental fruit moth. *Tech. Bull. 188, N. Y. State Agr., Exp. Sta.,* 1932.
2. Daniel, D. M. *Macrocentrus ancylivorus* Rohwer, a polyembryonic parasite of the oriental fruit moth. *Tech. Bull. 187, N. Y. State Agr. Exp. Sta.,* 1932.
3. Dickins, G. R. The scent glands of certain *Phycidae* (Lepidoptera) *Trans. Roy. Ent. Soc.* London, 1936, 85, 331–62.
4. Fink, D. E. The biology of *Macrocentrus ancylivora* Rohwer an important parasite of the strawberry leaf roller (Ancylis complana Froehl.) *J. Agr. Res.,* 1926, 32, 1121–134.
5. Fraenkel, G. S. and Gunn, D. L. *The orientation of animals.* Oxford: The Clarendon Press, 1940.
6. Genieys, P. *Habrobracon brevicornis* Wesmael. *Annals Ent. Soc. America,* 1925, 18, 143–202.
7. Grosch, D. S. The importance of antennae in mating reaction of male *Habrobracon. J. comp. and phys. Psych.,* 1947, 40, 23–39.
8. Hase, A. Biologie der Schlupfwespe *Habrobracon brevicornis* (Wesmael). *Arbeit. a. d. Biol. Reichsanstalt f. Land u. Forstwirtschaft,* 1922, 11, 95–168.
9. Hingston, R. W. G. *Instinct and Intelligence.* New York: The Macmillan Company, 1929.
10. Kellog, V. L. Some silkworm moth reflexes. *Biol. Bull.,* 1907, 12, 152–54.
11. Martin, A. *An introduction to the genetics of Habrobracon Juglandis* Ashmead. New York: Hobson Book Press, 1947.
12. Murr, L. Über den Geruchsinn der Mehlmottenschlufwespe *Habrobracon juglandis* Ashmead. *Z. vergl. Physiol.,* 1930, 11, 210–70.
13. Parker, H. L. *Macrocentrus gifluensis* Ashmead, a polyembryonic braconid parasite in the European corn borer. *Tech. Bull. 230, U. S. Dept. Agr.,* 1931.

14. SNODGRASS, R. E. *Anatomy and physiology of the honey bee.* New York: McGraw-Hill, 1925.
15. ————: The mind of an insect. Ann. Rep. Smithsonian Inst. 1927, 387–416.
16. WHITING, P. W. Androgenesis in the parasitic wasp *Habrobracon. J. Hered.,* 1943, 34, 355–366.
17. WIGGLESWORTH, V. B. *The principles of insect physiology:* London: Methuen and Co., 1939.

THE STIMULI RELEASING THE STINGING RESPONSE

OF HONEYBEES

By J. B. FREE

Rothamsted Experimental Station, Harpenden, Herts

INTRODUCTION

Beekeepers believe that dark coloured clothes, strange scents, and jerky movements provoke honeybees to sting them (see Morse and Ghent, 1959). The present experiments investigate the effect of these and other factors on releasing stinging and ways to decrease it.

METHOD

Cotton wool was wrapped in muslin to make balls approximately an inch in diameter, which were suspended from thread and jerked in front of hive entrances or just above hives open at the top. Bees which stung left their stings, which have backward-sloping barbs, embedded in the balls.

No attempt was made to avoid handling the balls, except after odours had been deliberately added to them, so they all had some human odour.

RESULTS

Effect of Colour

The muslin coverings of the balls were white, black, blue or yellow. Two colours were compared at a time; 8 balls of each colour were arranged in a 4 × 4 latin square, and suspended by 2 inch threads from a 2 foot square hardboard background. The hardboard was covered with muslin dyed with one of the colours being tested. The balls were jerked over hives open at the top until they had been stung sufficiently for a comparison to be made. Five tests were made with each colour background (Table I).

In every test black balls were stung more than white, and blue more than yellow, particularly when the background contrasted with the black or blue balls. White balls were stung more than yellow in 4 of

190

the 5 tests with the yellow background, and yellow balls stung more than white in 4 out of 5 tests with the white background.

TABLE I.

EFFECT OF COLOUR IN CAUSING STINGING

Mean no. stings per test in balls of different colours			
White background		Black background	
White balls	Black balls	White balls	Black balls
6.8	36.6	24.8	38.0
Yellow background		Blue background	
Yellow balls	Blue balls	Yellow balls	Blue balls
16.2	44.6	15.0	26.4
Yellow background		White background	
Yellow balls	White balls	Yellow balls	White balls
22.8	33.8	40.2	22.2

TABLE II.

EFFECT OF PREVIOUS STINGS

	No. Times Stung	
	Balls with Stings Already Present	Fresh Balls
Trial 1	27	33
" 2	9	9
" 3	33	21
" 4	33	15
" 5	4	6
" 6	21	16
" 7	20	19
" 8	33	15
" 9	70	10
Mean	27.8	16.0

Effect of Previous Stings

Eight newly stung balls (mean of 4.6 stings per ball) were arranged in a 4 $\times$ 4 latin square with 8 fresh balls of the same colour. In 6 of 9 trials the balls with stings already embedded in them were stung more than the controls (Table II).

To overcome the possibility that nearness of the balls to each other influenced the result, further tests were made in which 2 balls were suspended 18 inches apart on the horizontal bar of a T-shaped wooden support and jerked in front of a hive entrance. One of the balls (experimental) had previously been stung (a mean of 5.6 times) and the other (control) had not; the positions of the 2 types were interchanged after each test. The results were as follows:

Balls containing stings stung more: 18 trials
Control balls stung more: 1 trial
Both balls stung equally: 4 trials
Mean no. additional stings in experimental balls: 2·3
Mean no. stings in control balls: 0·7

In all later tests only 2 balls were presented together and attempts were made to stop a test when only one of them had been stung.

The previously stung balls were probably stung more because of an odour associated with the stings, but they may also have acquainted the smell of some other substance the stinging bees perhaps secreted through their mouth-parts. To find whether the sting smell alone was sufficient, the abdomens of 2 recently decapitated bees were pushed against each experimental ball until they stung it, and these balls were then compared with unstung controls. The results were:

Balls containing stings stung more: 19 trials
Control balls stung more: 2 trials
Both balls stung equally: 4 trials
Mean no. additional stings in experimental balls: 4·0
Mean no. stings in control balls: 1·7

Effect of Smoke

The experimental balls had smoke from burning cardboard in a beekeeper's smoker blown over them for 30 seconds immediately before a trial. In 11 trials they were stung more than the controls, in 8 trials less, and in one trial as much (no significant difference). Similar trials were then made in which the experimental and control balls had recently received equal numbers of stings. The results were:

Experimental balls stung more: 5 trials
Control balls stung more: 15 trials
Both balls stung equally: 0 trials
Mean no. additional stings in {
    experimental balls: 0·90
    control balls: 1·65
}

Thus, although the smoke was not repellant, it decreased the stinging of previously stung balls ($P < 0.05$), presumably by masking the sting odour.

Effect of Colony Odour

Balls were kept in double-walled, wire-gauze cages between the combs of a colony for 24 hours in an attempt to impart the colony odour to them. They were then without further handling compared with clean balls. When presented to the colony in which they had been kept, the experimental balls were stung more times than the controls in 15 trials and fewer in 10 trials (no significant difference). When presented to another colony the experimental balls were stung more in 13 trials, the control balls more in 11 trials, and both were stung equally in one trial.

Balls were kept 24 hours in 2 colonies (A & B). One ball from each was presented to colony A and colony B on alternate trials. Bees of colony A stung balls kept in colony A more in 12 trials, balls kept in colony B more in 3 trials, and both balls equally in one trial. Bees from colony B stung balls kept in colony B more in 13 trials, and balls kept in colony A more in 2 trials. Therefore bees stung balls which had been in their own colony more than they stung balls from the other colony (P < 0.001).

Effect of Animal Scent

Balls were put in small glass dishes with voles or shrews for 1-3 hours before being presented to a colony, together with a clean control ball. The results were:

	Experimental balls kept with	
	Voles	Shrews
Experimental balls stung more:	19 trials	24 trials
Control balls stung more:	5 „	1 „
Both balls stung equally:	1 „	0 „
Mean no. stings in { experimental balls:	2·24	4·00
control balls:	1·00	0·40

When the experimental balls had human sweat (from the forehead) rubbed on them and control balls a few drops of distilled water the results were:

Experimental balls stung more:	21 trials
Control balls stung more:	2 „
Both balls stung equally:	2 „
Mean no. stings in { experimental balls 3·64	
control balls 0·64	

Effect of Repellents

Six drops of a possible repellent (i.e. dimethylphthalate, citronellol, methylsalicylate) were put on each experimental ball and 6 drops of distilled water on each control ball. Table III shows that the repellents decreased the frequency of stinging.

Both experimental and control balls were kept with voles for 3 hours before drops of dimethylphthalate were put on the experimental balls and distilled water on the control balls. The results were:

Experimental balls stung more: 0 trials
Control balls stung more: 24 trials
Both balls stung equally: 1 trial

Mean no. stings in $\begin{cases}\text{experimental balls: } 0\cdot24 \\ \\ \text{control balls:} \qquad 3\cdot28\end{cases}$

TABLE III.
EFFECT OF REPELLENTS ON STINGING

	No. Trials in Which:			Mean No. of Stings in:	
		Control			
	Balls with	Balls	Balls	Balls	
	Repellent	Stung	Stung	with	Control
Repellent	Stung More	More	Equally	Repellent	Balls
Dimethylphthalate	10	70	0	0.76	3.20
Citronellol	1	19	1	0.45	2.00
Methylsalicylate	1	19	0	0.10	2.74

Effect of Texture

It is often supposed that bees are more inclined to sting rough than smooth textured clothing (see Morse and Ghent, 1959). In the first experiment balls of muslin covered with wool were tested against balls of wool covered with muslin. All balls were dyed black. In 6 trials the muslin-covered balls, and in one trial the wool-covered balls, were stung more, and in 3 trials both were stung equally. However, during presentation the wool-covered balls had at least as many bees clinging to them as the muslin-covered balls and it seemed possible that the wool covered balls tended to have fewer stings because the bees could withdraw their stings more readily from them.

In the next experiment all balls had wool inside and muslin outside, but one ball in each trial had strands of wool wound round it to cover a total of about half its surface area, leaving ample space between the strands for the bees to sting the muslin. The results were:

Balls covered with wool and muslin stung more: 17 trials
Balls covered with wool only stung more: 2 trials
Both balls stung equally: 1 trial

Mean no. stings in balls covered with $\begin{cases}\text{wool and} \\ \quad \text{muslin:} \qquad 2\cdot30 \\ \text{wool only:} \qquad 0\cdot45\end{cases}$

Hence it seemed that the rougher texture of wool had more readily released stinging but possibly the odour of wool was also influential because although experimental and control balls contained wool, only the experimental balls had wool on the outside. However, when muslin-covered balls containing muslin and wool respectively were compared, the following results were obtained:

Balls containing muslin stung more: 17 trials
Balls containing wool stung more: 1 trial
Both balls stung equally: 2 trials

Mean no. stings in balls containing $\begin{cases} \text{muslin:} & 2 \cdot 4 \\ \text{wool:} & 0 \cdot 55 \end{cases}$

It is therefore unlikely that the smell of wool caused more stinging than that of muslin alone, although, because of the possibility that bee stings were more readily retained in balls made entirely with muslin, this has not been decisively shown.

Effect of Movement

One ball on a wire was held motionless 2 inches in front of a hive entrance. Another ball suspended from a cotton thread was jerked up and down about 6 inches further along the hive entrance. The results were:

Jerked balls stung more: 29 trials
Motionless balls stung more: 1 ,,
Both balls stung equally: 0 ,,

Mean no. stings in $\begin{cases} \text{jerked balls:} & 5 \cdot 0 \\ \text{motionless balls:} & 0 \cdot 3 \end{cases}$

Two balls were suspended by 3 inch threads from the ends of sticks and whirled in 6 inch circles at a hive entrance, one ball moving approximately twice as fast as the other. The results were:

Faster moving balls stung more: 29 trials
Slower moving balls stung more: 1 ,,
Both balls stung equally: 0 ,,

Mean no. stings in $\begin{cases} \text{faster moving balls:} & 2 \cdot 7 \\ \text{slower moving balls:} & 0 \cdot 2 \end{cases}$

DISCUSSION AND CONCLUSIONS

It is to be expected that the scent of mammals, many of which are natural enemies of honeybees, may encourage stinging and that once an object has been stung it is more likely to get further stings. Huber (1814) presented the stinger of a bee at a hive entrance and found that it was attacked.

Honeybees of the same colony have the same distinctive odour (v. Frisch and Rosch, 1926; Kaltofen, 1951; Kalmus and Ribbands, 1952) which is distributed over their bodies (Free, 1956; Renner, 1960) and results, at least in part, from absorption of scents inside their hives (Renner, 1960) in much the same way as with bumblebees (Free 1958a). Common intruders of a honeybee colony are honeybees from other colonies which have either arrived inadvertently (Free, 1958b) or with intent to rob (e.g., Cale, 1949). When recognized by their strange odour they are sometimes attacked (Butler and Free, 1952; Ribbands, 1954). Presumably balls which were kept inside a honeybee colony acquired something of its odour but it is difficult to understand why bees attacked balls kept in their own colony more than those kept in another.

Because the visual acuity of an insect eye is small, objects are more readily perceived when moving. Dead or 'model' bees are attacked when jerked among small numbers of bees in cages (Lecomte, 1951) or at the hive entrance (Butler and Free, 1952), and the jerky flight of robber bees induces guard bees to attack them (Free, 1954). Therefore it is not surprising that rapidly moving balls received more stings.

To reduce stinging, beekeepers should wear clean, light-coloured, clothing of smooth texture, and they should avoid rapid movement and sweating. Smoking the site of a sting will help to prevent further stings. Probably repellents can further decrease stinging.

SUMMARY

1. The factors inducing honeybees to sting were investigated by comparing the number of times cotton wool balls treated in different ways were stung.

2. Dark coloured balls were stung more than light coloured, particularly against dark backgrounds.

3. The odour of sting venom encouraged further stinging, but the effect was overcome by smoke. General bee odour did not encourage stinging and bees were more likely to sting balls with the odour of their own than of another colony.

4. Animal scent and the smell of human sweat encouraged stinging and various repellents discouraged it.

5. Bees probably sting materials of rough texture more readily than smooth.

6. Rapidly moving objects were stung more often than slowly moving ones.

REFERENCES

Butler, C. G. and Free, J. B. (1952). The behaviour of worker honeybees at the hive entrance. *Behaviour*, 4, 262–92.

Cale, G. H. (1949). Common practices in management. Ch. 9 of *The Hive and the Honeybee*. Ed. R. A. Grout. Hamilton, Ill.: Dadant.

Free, J. B. (1954). The behaviour of robber honeybees. *Behaviour*, 7, 233–40.

Free, J. B. (1956). A study of the stimuli which release the food begging and offering responses of worker honeybees. *Brit. J. anim. Behav.*, 4, 94–101.

Free, J. B. (1958a). The defence of bumblebee colonies. *Behaviour*, 12, 233–42.

FREE, J. B. (1958b). The drifting of honey-bees. *J. agric. Sci.,* 51, 294–306.

FRISCH, K. V. AND ROSCH, G. A. (1926). Neue Versuche uber die Bedeutung von Duftorgan und Pollenduft fur die Verstandigung im Bienenvolk. *Z vergl. Physiol.,* 4, 1–21.

HUBER, F. (1814). Nouvelles observations sur les abeilles H. Transl., 1926. Hamilton, Ill.: *American Bee Journal.*

KALMUS, H. AND RIBBANDS, C. R. (1952). The origin of the odours by which honeybees distinguish their companions. *Proc. roy. Soc. B.,* 140, 50–59.

KALTOFEN, R. S. (1951). Das Problem des Volksdufts bei der Honigbiene. *Z. vergl. Physiol.,* 33, 462–75.

LECOMTE, J. (1951). Récherches sur le compartement agressif des ouvrières *d'Apis Mellifica. Behaviour,* 4, 60–66.

MORSE, R. A. AND GHENT, R. L. (1959). Protective measures against stinging insects. *New York Sta. J. Med.,* 59, 1546–48.

RENNER, M. (1960). Das Duftorgan der Honigbiene und die Physiologische Bedeutung ihres Lockstoffes. *Z. vergl. Physiol.,* 43, 411–68.

RIBBANDS, C. R. (1954). The defence of the honeybee community. *Proc. roy. Soc. B.,* 142, 514–24.

ANALYSES OF THE BEHAVIOUR OF COMMENSALS

IN HOST-FACTOR.

1. A HESIONED POLYCHAETE AND A PINNOTHERID CRAB

By DEMOREST DAVENPORT, GEORGE CAMOUGIS
AND JOHN F. HICKOK
The University of California, Santa Barbara and Clark University

INTRODUCTION

On the whole, very little is known about the behavioural processes that enable animals which live in symbiosis with others to find their partners (Davenport, 1955, etc.). The responses of certain polychaete commensals to their hosts have been investigated and evidence presented that they are attracted to their hosts over considerable distances by chemical factors, which, though specific, are as yet unidentified. For such specifically acting agents we have used the generic term *host-factor*. Responses have been investigated with the use of a Y-tube olfactometer (Davenport, 1950) and a latex choice-apparatus (Bartel and Davenport, 1956). With such apparatus one may easily determine whether or not certain commensals find their host by chemical recognition, but one cannot readily identify any changes in behaviour brought about by the presence of host-factor. Some sort of apparatus was necessary which would enable us to identify and analyse in detail any such changes, particularly in those animals in which one subjectively can observe no clearcut, overt "searching activity." Many common species of this type (e.g. the facultotive commensal polychaete *Podarke pugettensis* Johnson) can be demonstrated, by statistical analysis of distribution data in the latex apparatus, to aggregate on the host, as a result of their response to a specifically-acting host-factor (Hickok and Davenport, 1957). But we needed to have at hand apparatus that would allow us to test critically the behaviour of certain species of which one could collect a few individuals and that at the same time would give us more precise answers to the questions: Just what does host-factor make the commensal do? Is the behaviour of the

198

commensal different in host-factor than out of it? Does its behaviour change as it moves across gradients? Can any such changes in behaviour be identified as taxes or kineses according to classical definitions (Fraenkel and Gunn, 1940; Kennedy, 1945)? Do any such changes have the effect of bringing the commensal closer to the source of host factor?

APPARATUS, METHODS AND MATERIAL

An olfactometer developed by Varley and Edwards (1953) for studying host-finding behaviour in parasitic insects was found to be adaptable to our needs. Our adaptation consists of an hexagonal trough (Fig. 1) 17 in. $\times$ 8¾ in. $\times$ ¼ in. in transparent plexiglass. This trough was made by cutting a hole of the above dimensions in a plexiglass sheet and cementing it to a whole sheet. Sea-water was introduced

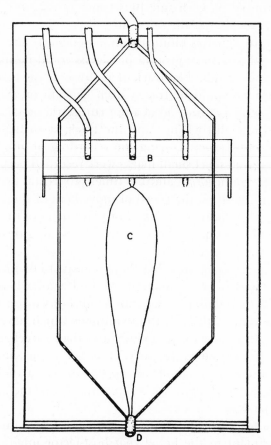

Fig. 1. Plexiglass test apparatus. A, inlet. B, plastic bridge with three pipettes. C, critical area. D, outlet.

through a tube (A) at one end of the trough. At (B) three streams of sea-water were introduced from drip-tubes set in a plastic bridge across the width of the trough. Non-circulating aerated sea-water was siphoned to the three tubes from three 3000-ml. beakers, which were maintained in a large aquarium water-bath at the temperature of the laboratory system (16.5°-18.0° at Santa Barbara; 19.0°-20.5° at Woods Hole). The flow from the drip-tubes was regulated by screw clamps. The middle beaker was used as a test chamber into which hosts and fluorescein (10^{-5} by weight) were placed. The inert dye has no effect on the behaviour of experimental animals, and it made the central stream carrying effective agents clearly discernible to the observer. In the very slow current flowing from one end of the trough to the other, this labelled experimental or central stream formed a spindle-shaped area (the critical area—C) from the central drip-tube to the outlet (D), limited on each side by streams of smoothly flowing un-labelled water moving at the same rate.

The entire trough was mounted on a wooden frame which had a slot in it so that a sheet of ground plexiglass could be introduced directly below the trough. The track or pathway being made by an experimental animal could be traced from beneath on this removable ground sheet, which at the end of a test run could be taken out of the apparatus without disturbance and the track permanently recorded from it on tracing paper. During the recording of an experimental track on the ground sheet small marks were recorded perpendicular to the track at the sound of an audible timer (10-second or 1-minute intervals, depending upon the speed of movement of the animal being tested). A wheeled distance-indicator or planimeter of the type used to measure distances on maps was used in determining distances travelled from the permanent records.

Past experience has shown that there appears to be little difference in the responsiveness of commensals to host-factor whether they are maintained in the laboratory separate from hosts or on them. It has been our general practice not to use animals which have been maintained in the laboratory for periods greater than a week, for after that commensals often become refractory. However, some commensal poly-chaete species(e.g., *P. pugettensis*) appear to retain their sensitivity to host-factor for long periods when maintained in the laboratory on their echinoderm hosts.

Hosts were placed in the central beaker not less than 12 hours before an experiment in the belief that host-factor might accumulate. Fluorescein was added just prior to the first test. In a standard test, the drip tubes would then be turned on, the clearly delimited central labelled stream allowed to become stable and an experimental animal introduced at a randomly selected spot near the bottom of the trough. Commensals were always handled with the greatest care using a camel-hair brush.

At the Marine Station of the University of California, Santa Barbara, a brief exploratory series of tests were conducted to determine the practicality of the apparatus as a tool with which to discern the presence of constant and identifiable responses to chemical agents. For this series the facultative commensal polychaete *Podarke pugettensis* Johnson was used, since it had already been demonstrated to respond specifically to an attractant released by the host. The results of this exploratory series led us to carry out extensive and more detailed experiments at the Marine Biological Laboratory, Woods Hole, where we used the obligate commensal crab, *Pinnixa chaetopterana* Stimpson.

In what follows it will be seen that, partly by necessity and partly as a result of experimentation, our methods of statistically analysing the pathways described by the two species differed; their method of movement and their behaviour in host-factor differed. The nature of the movement of an experimental animal in the apparatus will always in part determine the method of analysing pathways, e.g. pathways made by lengthened animals (polychaetes) which generally progress in the direction of the head will be quite different from pathways described by foreshortened animals (crabs), which frequently move sideways. Likewise, for example, pathways of animals which show little change in the rate of random turning (klinokinesis) when immersed in an agent, but marked tactic responses when crossing interfaces or moving through steep gradients will differ markedly from those animals which show a marked change in rate of turning but little evidence of directed responses (taxes). One must fit his method of analysis as best he can to the nature of the pathways of the animal concerned.

The statistical methods mentioned in the analyses which follow are described in detail in Siegel (1956). We have not accepted as significant probabilities of >0.01.

EXPERIMENTS

THE HESIONID POLYCHAETE *PODARKE PUGETTENSIS* JOHNSON

This worm is a facultative commensal which, on the Pacific Coast, inhabits mud-flats and wharf pilings and is commensal with two star-

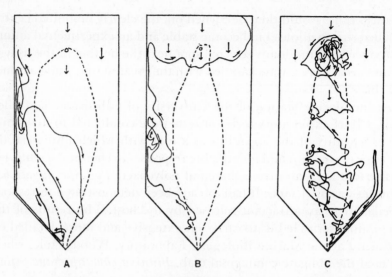

FIG. 2. Tracings of the tracks of *Podarke pugettensis.* A, free-living worm, central area containing fluorescein-labelled host-factor. B, commensal worm, fluorescein only. C, commensal worm, fluorescein-labelled host-factor.

fish, *Patiria miniata* and *Luidia foliolata.* Freeliving and commensal worms behave quite differently toward host starfish. With the aid of the latex choice-apparatus (Bartel and Davenport, 1956; Hickok and Davenport, 1957) it was shown that commensals are attracted strongly to hosts while free-living worms are not. Specificity studies were also made with the latex apparatus.

Tests with the plastic trough confirmed our earlier observations. Figure 2 shows the tracks of free-living and commensal worms under different conditions. In A it can be seen that the random wanderings of a free-living worm appear to be unaffected by the presence of host-factor, as was also shown in the latex apparatus. In tests in which commensals encountered a central stream containing fluorescein alone (Fig. 2B) was no indication of any response to the fluorescein. In Figure 2C, however, it can be seen that commensals are "behaviourally trapped" in a central fluorescein-labelled stream carying water from an aquarium containing the host. Results of this sort are hereafter spoken of as positives.

Analysis of pathways for data with which to discern the presence of kineses or taxes was conducted on a series of 12 such positives in the exploratory tests. What do these data show?

Chemokinesis

We wished to know whether with this apparatus it is possible to demonstrate that when a commensal enters host-factor there is a change in linear velocity (orthokinetic response). Subjectively, one sometimes observes an increase in speed immediately after a *Podarke* encounters host-factor. However, it soon became clear that the apparatus is not too wellsuited to give data which enables one to discern by statistical means the presence of changes in rate of linear movement under the different conditions within it, for frequently a randomly introduced animal encounters the critical area so soon after introduction that one is not given enough data on its behaviour prior to entrance to the critical area to be able to make comparisons between this and its behaviour after entrance. Wishing to compare rate of linear movement for a similar number of intervals both prior to and immediately after entrance to host-factor, we selected eight positives from the series in which each worm had spent the first five one-minute intervals after entrance *entirely immersed* in host-factor (40 worm-intervals in host-factor) and in which each had also tarried five minutes before entrance (40 worm-intervals in sea-water). The distances per interval (speed) in the two media were compared using the Mann–Whitney U–test (Siegel, 1956). The results of this treatment indicate that the difference in speeds in the two media may occur by chance with a $P < 0.50$. The order of magnitude of the speeds in the two media did not appear to differ significantly. However, that the occasional subjective observation of an apparent increase in linear velocity after entrance to host-factor is valid can be seen in the plot of distance vs. time (Fig. 3) for the track of one of the eight positives chosen for the statistical analysis above. At interval 11 the commensal was briefly exposed to host-factor at the constricted outlet of the trough and did not respond. But the velocity increased dramatically at intervals 14 and 15 after complete immersion in host-factor and then at 16, 17 and 18 dropped off towards the base rate. At interval 21 after a two-minute departure from host-factor the worm again speeded up after re-entrance.

One would wish to know whether upon a worm's entering host-factor a change in frequency of random turning (a klinokinetic response) can be discerned. An analysis was made of the frequency of change of direction for sections of the tracks inside and outside the host-factor stream. The number of changes in direction per cm. of track or per unit of time may be determined by the somewhat subjective method of Ullyott (1936) discussed in detail by Fraenkel and Gunn (1940). Figure 4 indicates the method of making these determinations; each numbered angle indicates a change in direction of not less than 5°, which angle was selected as the approximate minimum which could be so measured in the pathway of an animal which

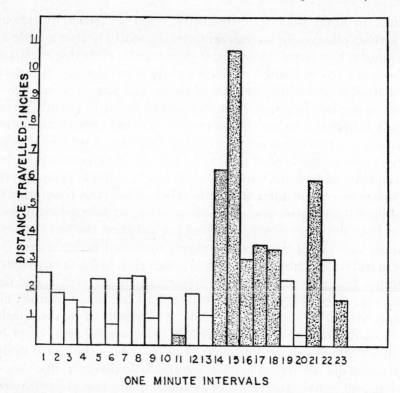

ONE MINUTE INTERVALS

FIG. 3. Orthokinetic response of a single *P. pugettensis* in fluorescein-labelled host-factor. Unshaded bars indicate distance travelled per interval when outside host-factor, shaded when in host-factor.

moves as does *P. pugettensis*. This method of determination is admittedly subjective because one is measuring movements which have been hand-recorded and hence subject to human error, and also because it obliges the experimentor to decide arbitrarily just what a change in direction is. The decision determines which turns are fractionated and which are not; arbitrarily in these studies a broad, sweeping curve was classified as a single change-of-direction. However, *P. pugettensis* rarely moves in this manner, changes in direction being generally followed by straight progressions of varying length. In our determinations, any turns occurring exactly at the interface of the host-factor stream were arbitrarily classified as having occurred outside the stream.

Twenty-five randomly selected one-minute intervals in host-factor showed a total of 198 turns as against a total of 113 turns for twenty-five randomly-selected intervals chosen from the tracks in sea-water prior to entrance. The frequencies of turning were computed from these data and compared using the Wilcoxen Matched-Pairs Signed-

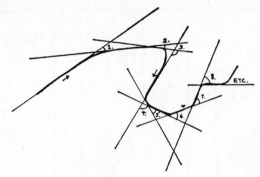

FIG. 4. Method of determining number of turns/cm. of track in *Podarke pugettensis*.

Ranks Test (Siegel, 1956). Such treatment indicates that the two frequencies differ with a $P < 0.1$ but $> .05$. Although our method of analysis is not well suited to discern minor differences which may be significant, these statistics support the conclusion drawn by the observer when he visually compares tracks made under the two conditions. There is certainly no dramatic change in the frequency of random turns such as we shall see occurring when *Pinnixa chaetopterana* enters host-factor.

Chemotaxis

One would wish to know whether with this apparatus it can be shown that contact with host-factor may result in directed responses (taxes). Data from twelve positives were analysed to determine whether on entrance to host-factor commensals turn towards the source more frequently than away from it. Turns toward the source are defined as turns with the sector enclosed by the 90° angle to right and left of the source. Turns away from the source are defined as those outside these sectors. The total number of turns towards the source from these tests was 83, while those away from the source totalled 26. The results were compared statistically using the Wilcoxen Test. The data differ significantly, the P being > 0.005.

The same tests were analysed for data on departures from the critical area. The total of turns toward the source on departure was 80, while the total away from the source was 30. This difference also appears to be significant ($P < 0.005$).

Rheotaxis

One would wish to know the extent to which rheotaxis is important in determining the pathway in a positive such as Figure 2C. Subjective observation indicated that worms seem to have a tendency to head into

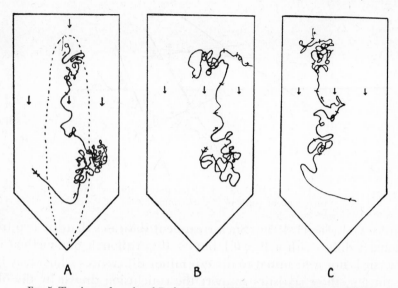

FIG. 5. Tracings of tracks of *Podarke pugettensis*. A, control positive. B, same worm, trough entirely filled with fluorescein-labelled host-factor. C, same worm, trough filled with fluorescein-labelled sea-water.

the slow currents of the trough. In six tests in which no host-factor was present (as in Figs. 2B, 5C) net displacement was upstream in all. The worms appear to show a weak positive rheotaxis. Is this positive response to current strengthened by the presence of host-factor?

To answer this a series of 12 runs were made in which four positives of not less than 30-minutes duration (Fig. 5A) were each immediately followed by a run of similar length in which the entire trough was filled with host-factor entering at the inlet (Fig. 1A) and at all three of the pipettes in the bridge (Fig. 1B). We assumed that under these conditions no concentration gradient of host-factor exists in the trough. Each worm was then immediately given a third run of equal duration in the trough filled with labelled sea-water alone. Examination of Figure 5 will show that under all three conditions there was no apparent difference in behaviour beyond the fact that in the positives (Fig. 5A) the pathways of the animals became restricted to the critical area as they approached the source of host-factor, while in the two controls (Fig. 5B, 5C) there was no such "behavioural trapping." In none of the runs of this series did the pathways of the worms appear any less devious when the animals were in a trough filled with host-factor (Fig. 5B) than when they were in a trough filled with labelled sea-water alone (Fig. 5C); there certainly appeared to be no greater tendency to orientate the body parallel with the current.

DISCUSSION

This exploratory series of tests with *Podarke* gave us clear indication that the plastic trough is a valuable tool with which to investigate the behaviour of aquatic animals in chemical gradients. The series was too brief to establish definitely the role of kineses and taxes in the responses to host-factor of *Podarke pugettensis,* but we nevertheless accrued data from which some preliminary generalities may be made.

Subjectively, one observes that the animals appear to be "physiologically trapped" in the host-factor stream and that they "climb up" it until they arrive in the vicinity of the source. The pathway described in Figure 2C as the commensal approaches the source is characteristic of positives, the worm moving in a more and more limited field as the critical area becomes limited, passing out of the area and in again. Analysis of our data from positives for evidence of directed response indicates that the existence of such responses can be demonstrated with a very limited number of tests. It was shown that as the animals "climb up" the critical area they turn *toward the source* in the great majority of passages in and out through the interface between the central and side streams. The central stream carrying host-factor is without doubt diluted, particularly at its margins, as it passes down the trough. A turn toward the source is therefore a turn toward the side of higher concentration. The consistent tendency of the worms to turn in the direction of higher concentration can be defined as a positive chemotropotaxis.

The implication of this response is that this polychaete exhibits remarkable sensory discrimination in its discernment of small differences in the concentration of host-factor on two sides of its head. It must frequently sense asymmetry when it crosses the steep gradient at the interface; it turns more frequently toward the source whether the gradient is rising (as it enters) or falling (as it leaves). This behaviour cannot be in response to changes in current rate. With careful adjustment of flow-rates no difference on the two sides of the interface occurs. Furthermore, we have evidence that host-factor does not strengthen the worm's weak positive response to current, and therefore this behaviour does not appear to constitute a change in the response to current (rheotaxis) as the animal crosses the interface. If host-factor strengthened a positive response to current, one would expect that absence of it on departure would in turn dampen this response. But the proportion of turns toward the source to those away from the source (83/26 vs. 80/30) is approximately the same whether the commensal is entering or leaving the host-factor stream, i.e. whether the animal is passing through a rising or a falling gradient. Although longer series of tests will be necessary to establish their importance in the behaviour of this worm, orthokinetic responses (changes in linear velocity) and klino-kinetic responses (changes in rate of random turning) may be of some significance in the behaviour of this animal elicited by host-factor. One cannot discount the possibility that in nature, particularly in rapidly rising gradients close to the host, they may, along with the strong tropo-taxis, effect "homing" on the host. Finally, the possibility that a klino-tactic response (successive testing of concentration in time) may be of importance also cannot be discounted, but this phenomenon cannot be demonstrated under the conditions of our experiments.

THE PINNOTHERID CRAB *PINNIXA CHAETOPTERANA* STIMPSON

During the summer of 1958 at Woods Hole it became possible to conduct extensive experiments with an obligate commensal, the crab *Pinnixa chaetopterana*, obtained from the tubes of the parchment worm, *Chaetopterus pergamentaceus* Cuvier. In the Woods Hole region the crab also inhabits the tubes of the terebellid *Amphitrite ornata* Verrill. On obtaining the material from the Supply Depart-ment, the tubes of the Chaetopterus were opened and discarded. Hosts and crabs were maintained separately in finger bowls and fresh mate-rial was obtained every few days.

Chemokinesis

Figure 6A shows four pathways made by a single crab in labelled sea-water (control) and may be compared with one of over 150 posi-tives made during the summer (Fig. 6B), the run in host-factor in this case having been made by the same crab immediately after the 4th con-trol.

Subjectively one may observe that when crabs first encounter host-factor, they very frequently stop at the interface for a variable period of time. Our records do not record the length of time of this stopping; they only show ten-second intervals on the track from which linear velocity can be computed. For this reason analysis to compare rate of linear motion before and after entering host-factor would not give valid results. There is, however, quite obviously no increase in linear velocity; indeed the cessation of linear movement on encountering host-factor may be defined as an akinesis.

When crabs move into host-factor there is a marked increase in the rate of random turning ("direct" klinokinesis—Kennedy, 1945). Often

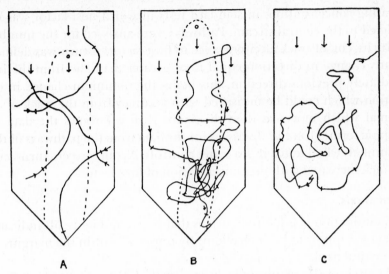

FIG. 6. Tracings of tracks of *Pinnixa chaetopterana*. A four tracks made by
a single crab, central stream carrying fluorescein labelled only. B, same crab
run immediately against fluorescein-labelled host-factor. C, track of a crab in
trough filled with fluorescein-labelled host-factor.

turning movements are so fine and rapid that it is difficult to make
accurate trackings of them. This is because animals very frequently
make very little net body displacement but simply pivot repeatedly
around their dorsiventral axis. For this reason our tracings show a reduction of the actual number of turns made. But the general devious-
ness of the pathway in host-factor can be seen in Figure 6B, in great
contrast to pathways when no host-factor is present (Fig. 6A). To demonstrate that this turning behaviour was not directed movement (a
taxis) we tested crabs in a trough entirely filled with labelled host-
factor, again by introducing host-factor at the same rate from all four
drip-tubes and assuming that under these conditions no concentration gradient or interface exists in the trough. As Figure 6C shows,
these pathways show repeated turning in contrast with controls (Fig.
6A) in which no host-factor was in the system.

Several workers have shown that in klinokinetic responses frequency of turns may be directly proportional to intensity of stimulation (Dethier, 1957). This is true of the responses of *P. chaetopterana*
to host-factor * "Full-strength" host-factor (4 hosts in 3000 c.c. of labelled sea-water overnight) was diluted with fresh sea-water to make 10
per cent and 1 per cent solutions. Twelve crabs were tested with in-

* Recently, similar behaviour has been observed in *Pinnixa tubicola* Holmes, a commensal of the terebellid *Eupolymnia crescentis* Johnson in Puget Sound.

creasing concentration, in standard tests in which host-factor was restricted to the central stream. Pathways were analysed for the number of turns/cm. of track after entrance to host-factor. A turn was defined as any change in direction equal to or greater than 30° from the immediately previous direction, this being the minimum change in direction which could be measured with accuracy from the track of an animal which moves as does this crab. Figure 7 shows the data in graphic form: C on the abscissa is for the data from the pathways of the 12 animals when tested in sea-water controls. As can be seen, turns/cm. of track increased with the concentration of host-factor.

Chemotaxis

Examination of a positive such as that shown in Figure 6B indicates that crabs appear to be "behaviourally trapped" within the margins of the critical area.

Analysis of the pathways from our total of 219 tests in which host-factor was restricted to the critical area shows a total of 375 crab-departures from the area, after the crabs had once entered it (Table I). The crabs returned in 215 cases and failed to return in 160. Assuming that crabs after any one departure have an equal chance of moving away from or re-entering the critical area, we may conclude that they re-enter more frequently than they depart, such numbers occurring by chance with a P of < 0.01 (as determined by a standard chi-square test).

One would wish to know whether once crabs have entered host-

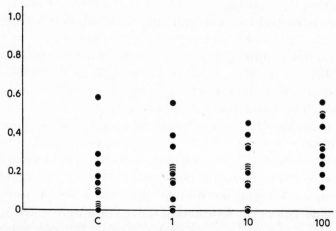

Fig. 7. Turns/cm. of track in pathways of 12 *P. chaetopterana* vs. per cent concentration of host-factor. C indicates sea-water controls.

factor there is a tendency for them to move toward the source. From the above sample of 219 runs in which host-factor was restricted to the central area we eliminated all runs in which crabs (perhaps because of high threshold, refractoriness after several runs or sensory adaptation) showed little response or tendency to be "physiologically trapped." This gave us 179 strong positives which we analysed for net displacement. Of these there was net displacement toward the source in 95, away from the source in 73, neither away from nor toward in 11. There is apparently no significant difference between the number displaced toward the source (95) and the number not so displaced (84). $P = 0.50$.

Rheotaxis

Controls in which no host-factor is present give no evidence that a positive rheotaxis is a factor in governing behaviour of these animals in the slow currents of the trough (Fig. 6A).

In order to be certain that the tendency of animals to remain in the critical area did not in part depend upon a response to current induced by the presence of host-factor, we analysed the net displacement of animals from 18 pathways described in the trough full of labelled host-factor which is without gradient. In each test a straight line was drawn from the point where the animal was introduced to the point where it first encountered the edge of the trough, at which contact responses affected behaviour. This line represents the sum vector of all the displacements carried out by the animal in reaching the edge. Figure 8 shows the angles of these vectors from the 18 tracks. There were 9 vectors within 45° of the X-axis and 9 within 45° of the Y-axis. There are 11 vectors pointing in the upstream direction and 7 in the downstream direction.

Specificity of Responses

In Table I we can compare the relative effectiveness of sea-water containing different polychaetes to affect the behaviour of the crabs, by observing the relative tendencies of crabs to be "behaviourally trapped."

It will be seen that crabs collected from *Chaetopterus* are as effectively trapped by the alternate host *Amphitrite* as by *Chaetopterus* (29 returns vs. 9 failures to return—P by standard chi-square test < 0.01). Pathways made against *Nereis* and *Arenicola* show no significant response to these worms. In all tests approximately the same total weight of polychaete was used.

TABLE I

Labelled Sea-water from	Total Tracks	Crab Departures	Returning	Failing to Return	P
Chaetopterus	219	375	215	160	<0.01
Amphitrite	19	38	29	9	<0.01
Nereis	28	33	9	24	not sig.
Arenicola	44	46	4	42	not sig.
Sea-water	35	37	3	34	not sig.

Nature of Host-Factor

A number of preliminary tests were conducted to give some infor-mation concerning the nature of host-factor:

(a) After hosts had been maintained in non-circulating, cooled and aerated sea-water overnight, they were removed. This sea-water was then tested for effect on behaviour. The water was found to elicit typi-cal responses 24 hours after removal of the worms, indicating relative stability of the host-factor at 20°C.

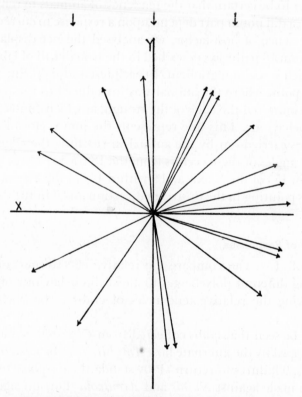

Fig. 8. Angles of vectors of net displacement from tracks of 18 crabs in trough filled with fluorescein-labelled host-factor.

(*b*) Host-factor-accumulate (4 worms in 3000 c.c. overnight) was heated to 90°-95° for 20 minutes, cooled and tested. All traces of activity had disappeared. Crabs used in these tests gave standard responses in non-heat-treated controls immediately after each test.

(*c*) Four hosts were placed in a large dialyzing bag and the bag suspended overnight in the test beaker. In the morning water from the beaker (the dialyzate outside the bag) had no effect on crab behaviour. When the bag was opened and the contents entered the system, the crabs showed standard responses.

(*d*) Approximately 3000 c.c. of "host-factor-accumulate," from which hosts had been removed in the morning, was divided into two equal parts. One part was treated with trypsin (final solution 0.1 per cent.) for 100 minutes prior to testing. A 0.1 per cent. control solution of trypsin in sea-water was also made up. Four crabs were each tested in four runs (for a total of 16) as follows: (1) in host-factor; (2) in sea-water plus trypsin; (3) in host-factor plus trypsin; (4) in host-factor a second time. In the 16 runs, 1 and 4 were always positive, while 2 and 3 were always negative. Finally, the pH of a 200 c.c. portion of host-factor, previously tested to insure activity, was adjusted to about 7.0. Then $(NH_4)_2SI_4$ was added to make an 80 per cent saturated solution. The solution was then placed for about 20 hours in a 5°C. cold room. When subsequently examined, only a trace of material, if any, was salted out.

All these tests would indicate that "Chaetopterus-factor" is a relatively time-stable protein.

DISCUSSION

P. chaetopterana shows a marked akinesis when it first encounters host-factor, after which (perhaps with brief sensory adaptation) a "direct" klinokinetic response appears. The intensity of the latter has been shown to be proportional to the concentration of host-factor; with a rise in concentration there is an increase in the rate of random turning.

Analysis of the data of passages through the interface by crabs indicates that at this point of steep gradient they are effectively trapped and return more frequently than they depart. But there does not appear to be a significant tendency for the animals to be displaced toward the source in any of our experiments. We must conclude that if chemotactic responses are of importance in the orientation of the commensals toward their host in shallow gradients, we have been unable to demonstrate the fact. It is entirely possible that such responses occur at high concentrations or in steep gradients, as is indicated by the behaviour of the crabs at the interface of the central stream.

One might suspect that a rheotactic response would be of some importance in an animal which lives commensally with a tubicolous current-producing host, but such a response does not appear to exist in this crab.

It is reasonable to propose, however, that an effective aggregating mechanism exists in *P. chaetopterana* as a result of its specific "direct" klinokinesis in host-factor. Personal communication with a number of workers who have been interested in such responses (Fraenkel, Wigglesworth, Dethier, etc.) indicates that there has been no experimental demonstration of the efficacy of a "direct" klinokinesis (rate of turning proportional to intensity of stimulation) in bringing about aggregation *at* or *near* the point of highest concentration or intensity of stimulus. In effect, any mechanism which reduces the length of straight runs (the net displacement) in a randomly turning organism moving at constant linear velocity will be as effective a "delaying" mechanism as an "inverse" orthokinesis in which linear velocity decreases with a rise in intensity of stimulation. There is some agreement that aggregation of "directly" klinokinetic animals will occur near the point of highest intensity only if they are slow adapting and that rapidly adapting animals would under such conditions tend to aggregate away from the highest intensity. Clearly, further experimental investigation of these phenomena is in order.

One may, nevertheless, assume that if such an aggregating mechanism existed in a symbiotic animal and if this was reinforced by strong directed responses at steep gradients, the animals would possess a most effective "host-finding" mechanism.

Finally, our experiments have indicated that the specificity of response is probably limited to the hosts of the species concerned, but it is of interest to note for a second time (Davenport, 1953) that a commensal collected from one host species responds strongly to an alternate host not closely related to its own. Preliminary investigations of the nature of the chemical agent concerned in recognition indicates that for the first time we have found an agent which is stable enough for further and more detailed investigations of its nature to be feasible. The evidence is that it is proteinaceous.

SUMMARY

1. A new apparatus is described for the investigation of the responses of aquatic animals to chemical agents.

2. With the apparatus it has been demonstrated in exploratory tests that in the facultative commensal polychaete *Podarke pugettensis* a positive chemotropotaxis is probably the most important behavioural mechanism involved in "host-finding." "Direct" orthokinetic and klinokinetic responses may aid the animal.

3. Detailed experiments with the obligate commensal pinnotherid crab *Pinnixa chaetopterana* indicate that this crab shows a strong "direct" kinokinesis in host-factor. Under the conditions of our experiments, chemotropotactic responses can be discerned in steep gradients. Rheotactic responses are not present.

4. The response specificity of this crab has been investigated. Evidence is presented that the host-factor concerned is a protein.

ACKNOWLEDGMENTS

This study was conducted under the contract of the senior author with the Office of Naval Research. The authors wish to express their appreciation to the staffs of the Marine Biological Laboratory, Woods Hole, and the Woods Hole Oceanographic Institution for their hospitality and co-operation. The technical assistance of Mrs. Diane Flynn is also gratefully acknowledged.

REFERENCES

BARTEL, A. H. AND DAVENPORT, D. (1956). A technique for the investigation of chemical responses in aquatic animals. *Brit. J. anim. Behav.*, 4, 117–19.

DAVENPORT, D. (1950). Studies in the physiology of commensalism. 1. The polynoid genus Arctonoë. *Biol. Bull.*, 98, 81–93.

DAVENPORT, D. (1953). Studies in the physiology of commensalism. IV. The polynoid genera Polynoë, Lepidasthenia and Harmothoë. *J. mar. biol. Ass. U.K.*, 32, 273–88.

DAVENPORT, D. (1955). Specificity and behavior in symbioses. *Quart. Rev. Biol.*, 30, 29–46.

DETHIER, V. G. (1957). Communication by insects: physiology of dancing. *Science*, 125, 331–36.

FRAENKEL, G. AND GUNN, D. L. (1940). *The orientation of animals, kineses, taxes and compass reactions.* Oxford: Clarendon Press.

HICKOK, J. F. AND DAVENPORT, D. (1957). Further studies in the behavior of commensal polychaetes. *Biol. Bull.*, 113, 397–406.

KENNEDY, J. S. (1945). Classification and nomenclature of animal behaviour. *Nature, Lond.*, 156, 754.

SIEGEL, S. (1956). *Nonparametric statistics for the behavioral sciences.* New York: McGraw-Hill.

ULLYOTT, P. (1936). The behaviour of Dendrocoelum lacteum. I. Responses at light-and-dark boundaries. II. Responses in non-directional gradients. *J. exp. Biol.*, 13, 253–78.

VARLEY, G. C. AND EDWARDS, R. L. (1953). An olfactometer for observing the behaviour of small animals. *Nature, Lond.*, 171, 789–90.

CHAPTER 5

THE INNATE BEHAVIOR OF VERTEBRATES

The previous chapter dealing with innate behavior of invertebrates emphasized three classes of innate behavior: kineses, taxes, and instincts. The present chapter on innate behavior of vertebrates deals primarily with instincts rather than kineses or taxes. This is due to the prominence of instinctive patterns in the behavior of vertebrates and to the paucity of research with vertebrates that deals with the other classes of innate behavior. The theory and data regarding instincts are extensive and in some respects controversial. In the present survey it is possible to present only the highlights of the theory and the data surrounding it. The next chapter, Chapter 6, presents the physiological model and physiological variables associated with instinctive and other innate reactions.

The Ethological Approach

The work of ethologists was introduced in Chapter 1 and referred to in subsequent chapters. Their contributions have been primarily in the analysis of instinctive behavior of both vertebrates and invertebrates. Since the majority of the ethologists are zoologists, they have certain orienting attitudes and hold certain assumptions that make their methods and theories somewhat alien to the mainstream of psychology. These attitudes are discussed by Tinbergen (1951) and Hinde (1959) and their effects may be noticed in the studies by Weikema (1961 **) and Bolwig (1959 **). Among these orienting attitudes are the following: (a) classification is a necessary preliminary for scientific analysis; (b) behavior occurring in a natural or seminatural setting is most appropriate for preliminary analyses; (c) the primary question about behavior is the question of why it occurs; (d) the answer to this question involves such considerations as evolutionary significance of behavior, adaptive function, and effects of specific stimulus factors. These considerations are called the "causes of behavior" by ethologists such as Tinbergen (1951).

The theory of instinct as elaborated by the ethologists Tinbergen (1951), incorporates the orienting assumptions that are stated above. However, none of the ethologists has yet made a complete classification and analysis of behavior. Tinbergen, focusing on instinctive behavior, has emphasized one question about this class of behaviors, namely, what is the relationship between specific stimulus factors and instinctive responses. Although Tinbergen (1951) and other ethologists, such as Lorenz (1950) and Baerends (1950), have investigated variables other than the stimulus that affect instinctive behaviors, their investigations have not yet yielded the body of data that the investigation of stimulus factors has.

Methods for Investigating Instinctive Behavior

Few topics in psychology have profited from the intimate interplay between field and laboratory research as has comparative animal behavior. The relationship is characterized informally but clearly by Tinbergen in his book *The Curious Naturalist* (1958) and by Lorenz in his book *King Solomon's Ring* (1952). The relationship is characterized formally by the same writers in other publications (Tinbergen, 1951; Lorenz and Tinbergen, 1957). Observations and reports of the behaviors of the animal in its natural surround, the field, are used to make general descriptions of classes or forms of behaviors characteristic of the species. These preliminary analyses then lead to more intensive study either in the field or in the laboratory. The field can be used for experimental study by arranging conditions in the field as, for example, by substituting eggs in nests or presenting restrained predators to animals in their natural surroundings. For those species and those behaviors that are not inhibited by laboratory conditions, formal laboratory investigation of instinctive behavior can also be undertaken. Laboratory conditions have been used extensively for the study of behavior of fish, young animals, and many species of birds.

After the behaviors of a species have been described through field or laboratory study, the investigator frequently attempts to determine the specific sign stimuli that are associated with the appetitive and consummatory response components for those acts that seem to be instinctive. This is done by systematic *reduction in the natural stimulus* until the specific characteristics in the natural stimulus that elicit the components of the instinctive acts are isolated. Hailman's study (1962 **) on the pecking of gull chicks is an illustration of this method.

Theory of Instincts

A number of the characteristics of instincts were listed and discussed in Chapter 4 in connection with the identification of instincts of invertebrates. There it was mentioned that (*a*) instinctive responses were often preceded by orienting, tactic responses, (*b*) the instinctive responses were released by specific stimulus configurations, and (*c*) these stimulus configurations were typically specific for a given species. These characteristics will be discussed in detail in terms of their relevance to instinctive behavior of vertebrates.

Appetitive and Consummatory Acts. The occurrence of orienting responses prior to the occurrence of the instinctive response, as frequently seen in invertebrates, is also seen in vertebrates. The generality of these observations has led Tinbergen, for example, to distinguish between two types of actions in the total instinctive pattern. The two components are called *appetitive acts* and *consummatory acts.* The appetitive component consists of the movements of the animal associated with orientation to and selection of particular stimuli. The appetitive components are neither stereotyped in form for the individual nor for different individuals of the same species. That is, unlike the innate consummatory acts, the form and sequence of appetitive responses vary from time to time and from individual to individual. Portions of the study by Weikema (1961 **) dealing with the mating of the bitterling fish illustrate the characteristic variability of the appetitive act. Both male and female fish show a variety of movements in their orientation toward the object, the mussel, into which the eggs will be placed and then fertilized. The orienting movements toward the mussel together with orienting movements toward the individual of the opposite sex can be considered the appetitive acts.

The consummatory acts for the bitterling are complex and involve a number of specific and closely articulated releaser-response sequences. However, the consummatory acts, unlike the appetitive acts, are relatively stereotyped or ritualized and cannot be repeatedly elicited at full strength even with repeated presentation of the appropriate stimulus. Lorenz, (1950) has called the consummatory acts *fixed action patterns* (FAPs) and has suggested that the inflexibility and species-specific characteristic of these responses make them useful tools for taxonomic classification of species.

The identification of appetitive and consummatory acts and the distinctions between them are not always apparent. Among the problems are: determination of the beginning of appetitive activity as, for example, the initial reactions of the male bitterling to the mussel or the female; and specifying the point between the termination of the appetitive action and the beginning of the consummatory action. In spite of these ambiguities, the distinction between appetitive and consummatory components of instincts is useful for description of innate behavior (Hinde, 1959, p. 572) and is similar to the distinction made in the analysis of general consummatory behavior that is presented in Chapter 9. In the context of a broad consideration of consummatory behavior, as in Chapter 9, the initial movements and orienting components are called *instrumental acts* and the final, more stereotyped components are called *consummatory acts*.

The Sign Stimulus in Instinctive Behavior. Ethologists have made intensive study of the stimuli that are associated with both appetitive and consummatory responses. Such stimuli are called *sign stimuli* by Tinbergen (1951) and *releasers* by Thorpe (1956). In typical instinctive acts such stimuli are assumed to represent only a small portion of the stimulus configuration. For example, in the now classic study of the behavior of male stickleback fish, Tinbergen (1951) reports that the "red belly" of the fish was the sign stimulus that elicited attacks even if this red belly were painted on a very crude model of a fish. Similarly Lack (1943) found that the "red breast" of the male robin was the sign stimulus for attack by other male robins. If a ball of cotton were daubed with red paint, this crude model elicited more attack responses than a robin that did not have a red breast.

The study by Hailman (1962 **) is a detailed investigation of the stimulus characteristics of the parent gull that elicit pecking (food-taking) in gull chicks. Hailman found that objects with the shape of the head and bill of the parent species were sign stimuli for this innate response. That is, the entire body was not necessary, nor was food in the bill necessary to direct pecking. The shape that conformed most closely with the shape of the head and bill of the parent species elicited the most pecking responses. For these animals it can then be said that the shape of the head and bill were sign stimuli for both the appetitive, orienting, component of the instinctive pattern and for the consummatory, pecking, component of the pattern. The study by Collias and Collias (1957 *) illustrates another investigation of food-taking responses of gull chicks for a species of gull for which color of the parent's bill was found to be the sign stimulus for orientation and food-taking.

A number of general ideas regarding sign stimuli (releasers) are useful in order to appreciate the application of the concept in the

analysis of instinctive behavior. It is assumed that the sign stimulus
for a particular response is readily detectable to the species in question and is present in the natural environment of the species. It is assumed that the sign stimulus appropriate for one individual of the
species is appropriate for others of the same species. That is, the sign
stimuli are species-specific. It is further assumed that the actual sign
stimulus for a particular appetitive reaction or consummatory reaction may involve only one stimulus characteristic or sensory modality,
though the stimulus as viewed by the experimenter may have a number of characteristics and involve a number of sensory modalities. For
example, Tinbergen (1951, p. 27) reports that the sign stimulus for
orientation toward a food object for the carnivorous water beetle,
which possesses a highly evolved visual system, is actually a chemical
stimulus and not a visual stimulus. Thus, the identification of the sign
stimulus involves extensive study of the animal in its natural setting
and careful control of the test stimuli. Some of the methods for such
investigations will be discussed in a later section. The study by Crow-
craft (1955 *) illustrates the first steps in an analyses of instinctive behavior, the study by Marler (1957 *) illustrates a later step. In both of
these the emphases of ethologists on identification of species—specific
responses and the eliciting stimuli can be seen.

CROWCROFT, P.   Notes on the behavior of shrews. *Behav.*, 1955, **8**, 63–80.
    Observations were made of the responses and eliciting stimuli for two
species of shrews that had been trapped and maintained in captivity. The
species were *Sorex araneus* and *Heomys fodiens.* Contrary to expectation, the
shrews did not canabalize each other and quickly habituated to the laboratory
cage. They selected dry grass or hay to construct a loose sphere of this material
that was the nest. The nest was constructed using simple and stereotyped responses. The fighting of the shrews involved posturing, screaming, and squeal-
ing. Only rarely did it involve biting. The responses in fighting were stereotyped and the response of one animal was a releaser for the response of the
other. Two types of digging responses were identified: one associated with
food-getting; the other associated with tunnel construction in which the animal drove his muzzle into the soil while the forefeet scratched the loosened
soil backward. The animals were observed to use the mouth to carry obstacles
such as stones out of the tunnel. Mating with the female was found to occur
during a post-partum period; otherwise the female viciously attacked the
male.

MARLER, P.   Studies of fighting in chaffinches (4) Appetitive and consummatory behaviour. *Brit. J. anim. Behav.*, 1957, **5**, 29–37.
    Several studies were undertaken to determine some of the stimulus fac-
tors associated with fighting among birds of a wild species, the chaffinch
(*Fringilla coelebs*). In one study each of a total of nine chaffinches was raised
in visual isolation from other birds from eight days after hatching until 100
days of age. The birds, including males and females, were then put in pairs
in cages. Fighting or other aggressive responses was observed in all of the pairs

and appeared to be precipitated by one bird getting too close to another. Similar results were found for captive chaffinches that were raised in groups. The enforced proximity between birds was associated with fighting. Observation of wild chaffinches during the winter indicated that they do not ordinarily fight unless special stimulus conditions occur. For example, one bird standing in an aggressive posture may be attacked by another or accidental nearness may elicit an attack. These results suggest that fighting is not a consummatory activity for the chaffinch during winter conditions and occurs primarily as a by-product of other stimulus conditions for this species.

Several apparent paradoxes regarding sign stimuli and instinctive reactions have been noted. One of these involves the finding that some stimuli that are created in the laboratory are more effective than natural sign stimuli in eliciting instinctive responses. Such stimuli, called *supernormal sign stimuli,* have been found to be effective with birds and grayling moths. The oyster catcher, a ground-nesting bird, selects the nest for brooding with the largest number of eggs in it; it also selects eggs for brooding that are double the size of normal oyster catchers' eggs. The generality of the principle of supernormal sign stimuli has not been established or have ethologists interpreted these findings. The view of the present writers is that the supernormal sign stimulus affects the orienting or appetitive component of the instinctive act insofar as it involves an increase in the sign stimulus aspect of the total stimulus complex or insofar as it involves an increase in contrast between the total stimulus complex and the sign stimulus itself. It is also hypothesized that increases in intensity or increases in degree of contrast beyond a certain amount leads to a reduction in the orienting functions of the stimulus in the same way that increases in intensity of stimulation beyond certain amounts lead invertebrates to change the sign (direction) of their orienting responses.

In contrast to the effects of supernormal sign stimuli is the observation that instinctive responses sometimes occur in the absence of a sign stimulus or in the absence of an appropriate sign stimulus. Such events have been called *vacuum responses* when instinctive responses occur in the absence of the sign stimulus and *displacement responses or activities* when the instinctive acts occur to inappropriate sign stimuli. These two sets of events are not considered to be related to each other at a theoretical level, although both are considered to be consistent with the concept of instinct as developed by Tinbergen (1951) and Lorenz (1950). According to Tinbergen (1951, p. 61) vacuum activities occur when the drive level (motivation) becomes so strong that the instinctive acts break through and occur in the absence of the sign stimulus. Critics of this interpretation, such as Armstrong (1950, p. 365), point out that minimal sign stimuli may be operating in cases in which vacuum activities have been reported. For example, the entire behavior pattern of insect hunting, killing, and swallowing has been reported for captive starlings in the absence of an insect, the usual sign stimulus associated with these responses. It has been suggested that the instinctive responses may have been elicited by a small object not noticed by the experimenter. In fact, there is general agreement that minimal stimuli may elicit components or complete patterns of instinctive activity, such as the hunting pattern observed in young kittens. The idea that minimal stimuli, such as a bit of dust, can elicit instinctive responses does not invalidate the principle of vacuum activity. Rather it can be considered to make a more objective principle of it. Thus, the principle of vacuum activity can be restated as follows: When drive level becomes very strong, instinctive acts break through and occur in the presence of minimal or inappropriate stimuli.

Displacement activities as discussed by Tinbergen (1951, p. 113) and Armstrong (1950, p. 361) are considered to occur when an animal is in a situation in which two antagonistic drives are operating. In this case the animal performs an incomplete instinctive act in the stimulus situation in which a different act is typical. Specifically, displacement actions are found under two conditions: (*a*) They occur when an animal is confronted by stimuli that are primarily relevant for approach and secondarily relevant for other responses. So the herring gull during a fight may stop fighting momentarily and pull a tuft of grass, a component of the nesting action. (*b*) They occur when the chain of sign stimuli and instinctive responses is broken by the absence of an appropriate sign stimulus. For example, after the initial components of the mating reactions of bitterling fish have occurred, the failure of the female to follow a male to the nest may lead the male to make inappropriate movements over the nest as if eggs were there. These movements, called fanning, are ordinarily associated with caring for the eggs and are considered a displacement act if the eggs are not yet in the nest. The analysis of displacement activities is similar to the psychological analysis of conflict in which it is observed that irrelevant responses, such as "nervous activity or aggressive acts," occur when an organism is responding to two antagonistic motives.

Tinbergen's and Lorenz's theory of drive is based on a model that drive or energy accumulates within the organism and inhibition of the energy is removed by a sign stimulus. The sign stimulus allows the energy to flow into pathways that activate the instinctive acts. The explanation of vacuum activity is based on this model. Both the general model and the explanation of vacuum activity have been criticized. Armstrong (1950, p. 364) describes examples of vacuum activity in which mimimal stimuli may be operating and the present writers believe that internal stimuli associated with deprivation and proprioception are classes of stimuli that can function as sign stimuli. Thus, minimal and internal stimuli may elicit responses that are described as vacuum activities. A more general criticism of Tinbergen and Lorenz's theory of drive has been made by Hinde (1959) who concludes that their theory is an oversimplification. The data regarding drive and consummatory behavior show these to be very complex processes. The relationships between eating, sham feeding, and stomach loading are a case in point. The relationships between copulation and intromission with and without ejaculation are another case in point (see Chapter 10 for details). While the portion of the theory of instinctive behavior that includes the energy model of drive can be criticized and modified, the other portions of the theory regarding releasing stimuli and species-specific responses, and the style of investigation of instinctive behavior certainly stand.

Analyses of Some Instinctive Behaviors

The ethologists have focused on behaviors that are relevant to the animal's natural environment and to the survival of the species. Thus, much of the research has concentrated on a limited number of classes of behavior. In the following sections three general classes will be considered in terms of patterns of instinctive acts. These are: reproduction, care of the young, and reactions to predators. Some of these behavior classes are also discussed in the chapter on social behavior, Chapter 8, which focuses primarily on the effects of the group on the behavior of the individual. The present chapter analyzes specific appetitive and consummatory responses and the sign stimuli relevant for these responses.

Reproduction. Because of the importance of reproduction for the survival of the species and the known complexities of behavior associated with it, students of animal behavior have undertaken detailed analyses of reproductive behaviors. Comprehensive studies of reproduction have been conducted with species of ducks, other birds and some common laboratory animals. A number of these studies are noted (Fisher and Hale, 1957 *; Baerends, *et al.*, 1955 *; Wood-Gush, 1954 *). In addition, portions of the studies of Weikima (1961 **) with fish and Bolwig (1959 **) with baboons deal with reproductive behavior.

BAERENDS, G. P., BROVWER, R. AND WATERBOLK, H. T.   On the ethology of *Lebistes reticulatus* Peters 1. Analysis of the male courtship pattern. *Behav.*, 1955, 8, 249–335.

This study presents a detailed description of the courtship of male fish of the species *Lebistes r.*, commonly called the guppy. A reliable sequence of courting responses by the male was identified. The sequence involves activities called: searching, approaching the female, following, posturing, luring, sigmoid response (arching the body), and a display jump or copulation. The sequence provided releasing stimuli for responses of the female that then elicited the next response of the male. It was also found that the males show a progressively changing pattern of black marks on their bodies. The specific pattern of marks, secondary sex characteristics, were associated with specific internal changes and behavior patterns. The marks and the degree to which they covered the body were associated quantitatively with the frequency or intensity of the responses associated with them. The activities shown by the male in courting were considered to be components of sexual, fighting, and escaping patterns.

FISHER, A. E. AND HALE, E. B.   Stimulus determinants of sexual and aggressive behaviour in male domestic fowl. *Behav.*, 1957, 10, 309–23.

The stimulus characteristics of the animal that release sexual and aggressive responses were investigated with male domestic fowl (chickens). Models and live birds were used as the stimulus animals. The posture of the model or live bird was found to be one of the most important aspects of the stimulus configuration. Specifically, a crouching bird reliably elicited sexual responses, namely waltzing, which is part of the courtship pattern, and copulation. A crouching bird did not elicit aggressive responses. An upright posture with raised hackle feathers inhibited aggressive responses among most of the males. Some males could be characterized as general reactors and others as specific reactors. That is, for some males sexual and aggressive responses were elicited by any of a broad range of stimulus configurations such as models, live birds, or standing birds; for others their responses were elicited only by very specific stimulus configurations. These differences may be related to differences in the early experiences of the birds such as imprinting.

WOOD–GUSH, D. G. M.   The courtship of the Brown Leghorn cock. *Brit. J. anim. Behav.*, 1954, 2, 95–102.

The display reactions involved in courting by male domestic fowl (Brown Leghorn cocks) were studied intensively with five mature and sexually experienced birds. Ten definite actions were performed by the males prior to attempts to mount the hen. The actions are called: *waltzing* in which one wing drops as the male approaches the female with short shuffling steps; *tidbitting* in which the male pecks and scratches at the ground and gives food calls near the hen; *wing-flapping* associated with raising the body to full height; *feather-ruffling* in which the neck is stretched with all of the feathers ruffed and shaken; *tail-wagging; head-shaking; preening; strutting* in which the male runs with legs slightly bent and both wings dropped; *sex calling*, a prolonged whine-like call; and *circling* in which the male walks around the hen with exaggerated high steps. These actions were not all performed in sequence or were they all shown on all occasions by the males. Each male emphasized some of the courting actions and not others. Actions such as tidbitting, head-shaking, and preening seemed to be displacement responses that occurred when the female was not responsive to the courtship.

The appetitive component of reproduction is typically called "courtship" and involves different responses and sign stimuli for males than for females of the same species. For example, the rounded belly of the female stickleback is one of the sign stimuli for the approach of the male, and the zigzag swimming pattern of the male is one of the sign stimuli for approach by the female. But among the sign stimuli for reproduction are incompatible ones which introduce fighting and withdrawal into the courtship pattern. These responses alternate in occurrence depending on the specific sign stimulus that is momentarily present and the relative strengths of the responses. For example, a female bird, fish, or mammal appears in many ways to look like a male. Thus, the male makes some responses toward the female as if it were a male and this leads the female to make abortive fighting and escape responses. When the female displays a characteristic female sign stimulus, such as the crouching of hens (Fisher and Hale, 1957 *), then the reproductive courtship component in the male predominates.

Visual stimuli, including display of colors, postures, and sequences of movements, are the typical sign stimuli associated with the appetitive or orienting component of reproduction for birds and fish. Tactile and proprioceptive stimuli are the typical sign stimuli associated with the consummatory component of reproduction. Some examples of sign stimuli are presented by Beach (1942 *) and Tinbergen (1959 *).

BEACH, F. A.   Analysis of the stimuli adequate to elicit mating behavior in sexually inexperienced rats. *J. comp. Psychol.*, 1942, 33, 163–207.

Normal male rats without prior sexual experience were tested with incentive stimulus animals including receptive females, unreceptive females, male rats, young female rabbits, and guinea pigs. The majority of male rats attempted to copulate only with the receptive female rats but some males, prior to sexual experience with receptive rats, attempted to copulate with other incentive animals. Other groups of male rats without prior sexual experience were treated surgically to eliminate one or more of the following sensory systems: olfaction, vision, cutaneous sensitivity of the snout and lips. No single modality was essential for copulation but animals deprived of one modality copulated less than the normal control males. Inexperienced males deprived of more than one modality did not attempt to copulate with the receptive female rat or any other incentive animal. Experienced males deprived of two modalities did continue to copulate with receptive female rats but elimination of three modalities abolished mating. It is concluded that visual, olfactory, and cutaneous stimuli from the receptive female are all relevant but not all necessary stimuli for mating of both inexperienced and experienced male rats.

TINBERGEN, N.   Comparative studies of the behaviours of gulls (Laridae): A progress report. *Behav.*, 1959, 15, 1–70.

The display (stereotyped postural responses) of various gulls (*Laridae*) are discussed and illustrated in this paper. Observations of the gulls indicated that the displays functioned as releasing stimuli for subsequent responses of other members of the species. Some of the displays that are identified are called: *upright posture,* associated with attack; *oblique posture,* associated with attack and escape; *choking,* involving repeated bending of the head downward and associated with threat near the nest; and *head-tossing* associated with soliciting food. These and other displays are analyzed into the categories of releasing stimuli that function to *increase distance* from another bird and those that function to *decrease distance* from another bird. The distance increasing displays are associated with territoriality and fighting, while the distance decreasing displays are associated with reproduction and relations between the parent and the young.

Nesting and Care of the Young. As is true for the study of reproductive behavior, the study of nesting and care of the young has been pursued most systematically with species of birds and fish. Some of the results of studies of nesting and care of the young are discussed by Tinbergen (1953), Hinde (1961), and Heinroth and Heinroth (1958). The location of the nest is usually determined by the territory that has been established by the male, but nest building among fish and birds may be performed by both males and females or by either one of the mates. The complex relationships between the sign stimuli and the actions involved in selecting a specific nesting location and constructing a nest have been analyzed in detail only for several species of birds, (Thorpe, 1956). These behaviors seem to depend on innate patterns, the effects of early experiences with nesting materials, and complex physiological timing mechanisms.

The behaviors involved in incubating eggs and caring for the young have the intricacy of the behaviors involved in nest building. As is true for building the nest, one mate cares for the eggs and the young for some species of birds and fish, for other species both parents do this. Hinde (1961, p. 406) suggests that in general the more highly evolved the species the greater the division of labor, with the female attending to the nest and the young. However, several reversals in this trend are known. Some species such as the cuckoo (*Cuculus canorus*) lay their eggs in the nests of other birds after which the young cuckoos throw out the young and the eggs of the host birds. This parasitic adaptation is possible since the young of the cuckoo usually hatch several days before the young of the host (Heinroth and Heinroth, 1958). The young cuckoos, being larger and more vigorous than the young of the host, are more salient sign stimuli to the host than its young and are stronger than any of the host's young which remain in the nest. Thus the cuckoos are better fed and otherwise cared for by the host.

Care of the young after hatching or birth involves some or all of the following behaviors: removing of the fetal material (placenta or eggshells), removal of feces, feeding, protection from predators and adverse environmental factors, and weaning from the parents. This classification is appropriate for most higher vertebrates and a number of species of fish. As was described in the analysis of reproductive behavior, the occurrence of these behaviors depends on sequential presentation of sign stimuli as the young and the parent innately respond to each other in a mutually dependent fashion. The analysis of sign stimuli for food-taking, described in the study by Hailman (1962 **) and in the study by Collias and Collias (1957 *), illustrates one aspect of these mutual and sequential actions with birds.

COLLIAS, E. C. AND COLLIAS, N. E. The response of chicks of the Franklin's gull to parental bill color. *Auk,* 1957, **74,** 371–75.

During breeding season the adult Franklin's gull (*Larus pipixcon*) has a red bill at which the chicks peck when the adult returns to the nest. This study was designed to investigate under laboratory conditions the function or effectiveness of the *red color* of the bill in eliciting pecking at it. A total of 35 Franklin's gull chicks were incubated in the laboratory and kept from seeing adult gulls until after they were tested. Each chick was tested individually when it was between 4 hours and 4½ days of age. During the test the chick saw two paper models of a gull head, one had a red bill, the other a green bill or white bill. The number of times each chick pecked each bill was recorded. The red bill (the parental color) was pecked seven times more often than the white bill and five times more often than the green bill. This indicates that the chicks could discriminate between the bills and that the red color is a more effective elicitor than either the green or white, although the chicks had no prior experience with such stimuli.

Weaning of the young from the parent involves physiological changes associated with the reproductive cycle of the parent plus the changing appearance of the developing young. Some of these changes are noted by Sanderson (1949 *) for weasels. When the movements and appearance of the young resemble those of mature members of the species, this elicits fighting with the parents which in turn elicits escape from the parent. Care of the young is also described in Chapter 8 in relation to the behavior of animals in groups. The behavior patterns involved in the removal of fetal material, removal of feces, and protection from predators are discussed by Scott (1958), Tinbergen (1953) and Heinroth and Heinroth (1958).

SANDERSON, G. C. Growth and behavior of a litter of captive long-tailed weasels. *J. mammol.,* 1949, **30,** 412–15.

A litter of eight weasels (*Mustela frenata longicauta*) were taken from a nest when about four weeks of age. Their eyes were open at this time and they did not avoid the observer's hand. The young ate many types of food including live and dead small animals. They appeared to have innate responses to small animals that permitted successful catching and killing of them. Specifically, they attacked them at the base of the skull. By about nine weeks of age the animals developed the characteristic weasel odor and a female became sexually receptive. The odor is undoubtedly a necessary stimulus to elicit approach by a male. The males were not sexually mature at the age at which the females were. This may be considered an adaptive device to preclude interbreeding within a single litter.

Reactions to Predators.   Nearly all species have other species that seek them as objects to be eaten. Thus it is not surprising that the prey species have evolved innate responses to their predators. In addition, morphological characteristics have evolved that are associated with eluding predators. Cott's (1940) review of the literature regarding protective coloration in animals indicates that such coloration reduces the chance that the animal is captured by a predator. But appropriate responses must occur for coloration to be effective, and for those species that do not have protective coloration the responses alone must be effective.

A number of different types of protective responses can be identified that occur in the presence of a predator or otherwise threatening stimuli. Among these are: (*a*) specific postures that enhance the protective coloration through camouflage or through warning; (*b*) escape; (*c*) attack, especially mobbing; (*d*) vocalization; and (*e*) distraction display. A number of these responses are commonly known and recognized but several require additional description.

The response of assuming a posture to enhance protective coloration "through warning" is especially well known in insects (Cott, 1940) and some species of fish. In coloration through warning the animal quickly exposes a part of his body that is marked or colored in a special way, typically like a large eye. This response momentarily startles the predator and allows the animal to escape. The response of some species of birds of raising their neck feathers and increasing their apparent size can be considered another example of using a warning posture. The response to a predator of *attack by mobbing,* is particularly common for smaller birds and involves repeated short dashes toward the predator by a number of animals at one time. Hinde (1954 *) reports an investigation of mobbing of owls by chaffinches. *Warning calls* associated with the presence of a predator are found for a number of species of birds and mammals especially during the time when the young are with the parents (Collias, 1960). The response identified as *distraction display,* also called injury feigning (Armstrong, 1954 *), is particularly common among ground-nesting birds, and involves movements in which the birds appear injured. The response is well documented for a variety of species, and an example is the following observation of a hawk's attack on a duck family: "The ducklings scattered and the mother immediately stretched out her head and neck, turned on one side, flapped a wing in the air and paddled in circles as though she were crippled" (Armstrong, 1942, p. 7). *Immobility reactions,* also called animal hypnosis, appear to be an extreme form of distraction display. In this case the animal, bird, amphibian, or mammal, becomes immobile and unresponsive, even to prodding or further attack by the predator (Ratner and Thompson, 1960).

ARMSTRONG, E. A.   The ecology of distraction display. *Brit. J. anim. Behav.,* 1954, 2, 121–35.

Display reactions to predators (innate postures and movements elicited by species-specific stimuli) of a number of species of birds are reviewed to discover the characteristics of the releasing stimuli (the predator stimulus), the forms of the display reaction and the relationship between the reaction and the natural habitat of the birds. It was found that a wide range of stimulus objects that move toward the bird's nest can elicit a display reaction for ground-nesting species. Among these are natural predators such as cats and dogs and humans or a camera pushed through the grass. The most typical display reaction of the adult bird is a *distraction display* in which the bird leaves the nest in a very conspicuous manner. The most common distraction display is *injury feigning* in which the bird flies or runs in an erratic pattern with a wing or leg held in an unusual posture. It is concluded that these displays are useful in distracting the predator from a nest on the ground and occur when the bird is tending both to defend the nest and to escape.

HINDE, R. A.   Factors governing the changes in strength of a partially inborn response as shown by the mobbing behaviours of the chaffinch (*Fringilla coelebs*). *Proc. roy. Soc. B.,* 1954, 142, 306–58.

The characteristics of the predator that are necessary to elicit the mobbing response by chaffinch were studied. The mobbing response is one in which a number of the birds fly around the predator, such as an owl, and make distinctive calls. It was found that counting the frequency of occurrences of the calls provided a quantitative index of the strength of the mobbing response. Using this measure, a number of stimulus objects were tested to determine what characteristics of an object elicited mobbing. Models of owls that were only roughly owl shaped elicited mobbing, as did stuffed owls of a variety of species. Repeated presentation of any of these stimulus objects led to a rapid reduction in the strength of the mobbing response with regard to all of the things that could elicit the response. In addition, the response never recovered to the level of the first presentation of the predator stimulus. This illustrates one of the fundamental types of modification of an innate response—habituation.

Analysis of these responses to predators indicates that they are elicited by specific sign stimuli, such as an object with the movements or shape of an owl (Hartly, 1951; McNiven, 1960 *). The specific response that occurs is a function of the distance between the predator and the prey. This is called the *defensive distance* by Ratner (in press) and its metric value is a complex function of where the animal ordinarily lives and hides and how fast it moves in relation to its predators.

McNIVEN, M. A.   Social releaser mechanisms in birds. *Psychol. Rec.*, 1960, 10, 259–65.

This study attempted to replicate findings reported by Tinbergen that the silhouette of a hawk swooping over birds, such as ducks, is an innate releasing stimulus for crouching or escape. Specifically, Tinbergen reported that the releasing configuration involved the approach of a "short-necked" winged object. In the present study domestic chickens, wild ducks, and wild pheasant were tested a number of times with the silhouette that was to elicit escape or crouching (short neck) and with the silhouette that was assumed to be neutral (long neck). It was found that the two silhouettes elicited the same number of escaping and crouching responses. However, the ways that the silhouettes were presented made a difference. On trials when the silhouettes swooped over the birds they made significantly more escaping and crouching responses than when the silhouettes sailed over them. This finding suggests that the form of the movement of an overhead object may be a more important aspect of the releasing stimulus than the direction of the movement.

Modification of Innate Behavior of Vertebrates

Two processes can be identified that are associated with modification of innate behavior. One is evolutionary adaptation that occurs over long periods of time and is associated with innate behaviors of the species. Such changes, associated with evolutionary adaptation, are of particular concern to the zoologist (Tinbergen, 1951, chs. 7 and 8; Hinde and Tinbergen, 1958). The other process associated with modification of innate behavior involves learning. In this case the change occurs during the life of the individual and is of particular concern to the psychologist. It has been previously stated that learning involves modification of innate responses, especially *reflexes and appetitive responses*. The specific types of modifications are discussed in Chapter 4 and abundantly illustrated in Chapters 10, 11, and 12. In other words, we are stating, as others have (Schiller, 1959), that innate responses are the raw material from which learned responses are shaped.

Students of learning do not ordinarily make detailed analyses of innate responses that are being modified. Rather, they label them with generic terms such as operant level, unlearned response hierarchy, or unconditioned responses and then proceed to investigate the modification of such responses. In addition, students of learning do not ordinarily work with the modification of the consummatory component of instinctive actions. Ethologists have made a number of attempts to modify such innate behaviors and have met with variable success. The variability of success seems to be a function of the fact that different aspects of innate patterns are differentially modifiable. By modifying species-specific behavior is meant eliciting responses with new sign stimuli, eliciting them with specific sign stimuli but not with similar ones, changing the usual sequence of innate responses, or inhibiting innate responses in the presence of usually effective sign stimuli. For example, Tinbergen (1951) reports that gulls will respond as foster parents to any gull chick until the chick is five days of age, after that age the chick will no longer be accepted (an example of limited modifiability). Conversely, gulls will sit on any eggs that are in their nests. That is, experience with one set of eggs does not modify the response to other eggs, although these other eggs are markedly different in appearance. Mating responses for monogomous species, such as gulls, terns, and geese are directed only toward the previously selected mate, although many receptive animals may be in the area.

Elimination or reduction of instinctive responses depends on giving the animals prior experiences with the releasing stimuli. This brings about *habituation* of the response. Thorpe (1956) considers habituation to be the most elementary form of learning or behavior modification and discusses examples of it for species in each phylum of the animal world. Hinde (1954 *) reports habituation of the mobbing response of chaffinch to a predator after only one presentation of the predator. Other experiments suggest that novel stimuli act as sign stimuli for approach and manipulation of the novel stimuli. The eliciting value of these stimuli also is rapidly reduced or eliminated by responses to them. The studies by Menzel *et al.* (1961 *) and Woods (1962 *) illustrate other features of prior experience that affect the eliciting value of novel stimuli. Menzel raised his chimps in restricted environments in order to test novel stimuli as sign stimuli. It is a good guess that if this had not been done, then the eliciting value of the stimuli would have habituated prior to the experiment. Woods showed that the eliciting value of a new environment is a function of the richness of the animal's environment shortly before the test.

MENZEL, E. W. JR., DAVENPORT, R. K. JR., AND ROGERS, C. M. Some aspects of behavior toward novelty in young chimpanzees. *J. comp. physiol. Psychol.,* 1961, 54, 16–20.

The effectiveness of novel stimuli as elicitors of approach and contact for higher vertebrates was studied with two young chimpanzees. Two males that had been raised in a restricted environment from birth until 21 months of age were tested at 25 and 27 months of age. Each animal had been given some experience with a small white cube and was then tested with a number of stimulus objects that were more or less different from the original cube. The more different the stimulus object the longer the chimps remained in contact with it. Tests with a number of completely different objects suggested that the first response to a novel stimulus is avoidance but habituation of this response leads the animal to approach similar objects.

Woods, P. J.   Behavior in a novel situation as influenced by the immediate preceding environment. *J. exp. anal. Behav.*, 1962, 5, 185–90.

Groups of laboratory rats were maintained for a 24-hour period in different environments ranging from restricted to enriched. The animals were then tested in an open field to determine what responses were elicited by this novel environment. The responses of each rat were noted in categories such as sniffing, locomotion, freezing, grooming, and lying down. By the end of the 24-minute test period, the rats previously kept in the restricted environment were making more exploratory responses than either of the other groups that had been living in more stimulating environments. While the investigatory responses, such as sniffing, showed high levels of occurrence for all animals when they entered the novel situation they then decreased in frequency for all of them.

Another striking instance of modification of innate behavior is seen in imprinting. In this case an object that the animal sees early in life becomes the focus for instinctive behaviors later in life. Imprinting is discussed in detail in Chapter 7 but for present purposes the point is that instinctive behaviors including following, courting, and copulating are controlled by the early experience of the animal. As seen in the natural situation, the object on which imprinting occurs is the parent; but as seen in laboratory and field experiments the object can be a person or a block of wood.

PECKING OF LAUGHING GULL CHICKS AT MODELS

OF THE PARENTAL HEAD

JACK P. HAILMAN

Downy chicks of the Laughing Gull (*Larus atricilla*) peck at a parent's bill and receive semidigested food held therein (Bent, 1921: 158), but they rarely peck when a parent is not present. This paper reports some field experiments that evaluate the importance of the shape and some other visual characteristics of the parental head as stimuli eliciting and directing the chick's pecking. The method utilized, that of counting chicks' pecks to colored, cardboard models, was patterned after that used by Tinbergen and Perdeck (1950) in their experiments on the Herring Gull (*L. argentatus*), and the results are compared with their findings and those of Weidmann (1959) on the European Black-headed Gull (*L. ridibundus*).

METHOD

During June 1959 my wife and I presented three series of five models each to chicks taken from their nests in the Laughing Gull colony on Green Island, located on the south side of Oregon Inlet, Dare County, North Carolina. Models were made of flat cardboard, colored with watercolor paints. (Figs. 1–3). Each chick was presented with one series of models only, and then returned to its nest. Ages of chicks varied from newly hatched (down wet with egg tooth present) to prefledged (flight feathers beginning to grow). The order of presentation of models was randomized (with a table of randomly selected digits) to compensate for habituation, or waning of responsiveness, with successive models (see Tinbergen and Perdeck, 1950). Each model was held and moved slightly in front of the chick for one minute, during which time the number of pecks at the model was recorded. It became apparent after running 10 presentations of models that some chicks were "unresponsive," that is, seemed to show no pecking at or even interest in the models. This unresponsiveness may be due to at least two causes: (1) recent feeding by parents in the wild, which reduces pecking, as demonstrated by Weidmann (1959) in the

233

Black-headed Gull; and (2) sleeping. After discovering this unresponsiveness of some chicks, I did not complete experiments on seven subsequent chicks that failed completely to respond to any of the first three models presented, and I discarded data of two chicks that had previously been recorded (neither of which had pecked at the first three models presented and had pecked less than four times at the remaining two models combined).

Results are arranged in Tables 1–3 with the mean number of pecks

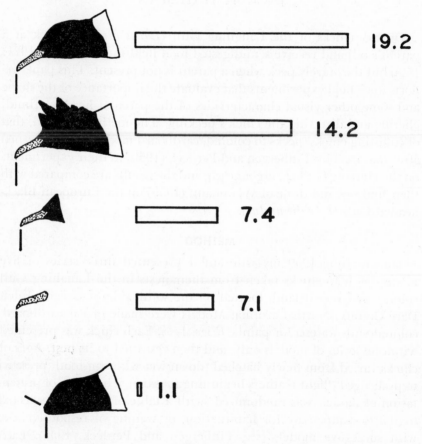

FIG. 1. Sketches of models used in the first series (from the top): standard, cock's head, bill and part head, bill only, head only. Horizontal bars show the mean number of pecks per minute received by each model (for transformed means and complete data see Table 1). Arrows indicate the parts of the models at which chicks most often pecked. Sketches in this and following figures were drawn from photographs of actual models used.

per minute indicated for each model in each series. Because of the heterogeneous variances, a square root (actually $\sqrt{n+1}$) transformation (Snedecor, 1956, 315–16) on the entire data was made prior to statistical analysis. Standard two-way analysis of variance calculation was carried out, and the transformed means of each column were calculated and compared by the method of smallest significant difference (*ibid.*, 294–95). The smallest difference that is significant at the 5 per cent level is included along with the transformed means at the bottom of each table so that significance of the difference between any two

TABLE 1

RESPONSIVENESS TO HEAD SHAPES

(See Figure 1)

Chick	Model:	Standard	Cock's Head	Bill and Part Head	Bill Only	Head Only
1		14	17	0	0	0
2		16	26	2	17	0
3		18	0	3	2	3
4		45	39	35	15	6
5		28	29	6	14	0
6		7	0	5	3	0
7		15	8	1	1	1
8		14	16	9	11	0
9		30	6	6	8	1
10		5	1	7	0	0
Mean pecks/minute		19.2	14.2	7.4*	7.1*	1.1*
Transformed mean		4.32	3.44	2.59	2.57	1.35

* Significantly less than standard model.
5% difference between transformed means: 1.26.

models may be judged. Columns in the tables are arranged in descending order of means from left to right, and asterisks indicate means that differ significantly from the most effective model of the series.

Each series of models contained a diagrammatic model of the Laughing Gull head in profile, hereafter referred to as the "standard" model (Figs. 1–3). Each other model in the series was like the standard except for a single characteristic. By comparing responses to the standard and to the other model, the relative importance of the altered characteristic is suggested.

RESPONSIVENESS TO MODELS

Presence and shape of the head. The first series of models tested the importance of the presence and shape of the head (Fig. 1). The standard model, a bill without a head, a bill with part of the head present, and a head without the bill were used. In addition, a "cock's head," patterned after the model of Tinbergen and Perdeck (1950), was included to test the effectiveness of a complete, but irregularly shaped, head.

Table 1 shows that the standard model was the most effective in the series (significantly better than all but the cock's head). The normal head without a bill was nearly ineffective as an eliciting stimulus, and just misses being significantly different from the bills with no head and just a portion of head. The cock's head is neither significantly below the standard nor above the bill with a portion of head.

Shape of the bill and bill tip. Since the bill appeared to be the pri-

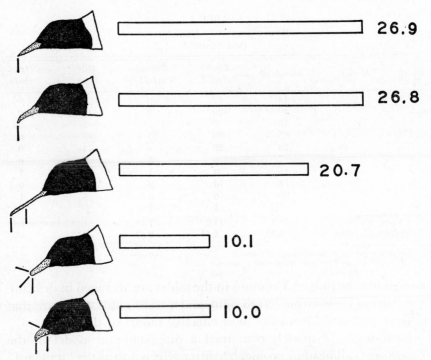

FIG. 2. Models used in the second series (from the top): pointed, standard, long-and-thin, rounded, short. Legend as in Figure 1.

mary component of the eliciting stimulus, a second series of models tested the importance of the shape of the bill (Fig. 2). In addition to the standard model, this series included a model with a more pointed bill tip, one with a more rounded bill tip, one with a very short bill, and one with an extremely long-and-thin bill, the last because Tinbergen and Perdeck (1950) showed that such a model of the Herring Gull evoked more responses than the normal model.

The standard and the pointed bill-tip models received significantly higher frequencies of response than did the other models, except for the long-and-thin bill model, which was neither significantly below the first two nor significantly above the last two.

TABLE 2

RESPONSIVENESS TO BILL SHAPES

(See Figure 2)

Chick	Model:	Pointed	Standard	Long-and-Thin	Rounded	Short
1		20	42	8	0	1
2		32	19	20	9	13
3		20	5	23	12	0
4		39	24	22	20	6
5		26	35	8	9	14
6		25	22	16	7	6
7		29	22	20	9	26
8		40	35	23	0	8
9		11	37	46	25	16
Mean pecks/minute		26.9	26.8	20.7	10.1*	10.0*
Transformed mean		5.20	5.14	4.42	3.07	2.95

* Significantly less than pointed and standard models.
  5% difference between transformed means: 1.42.

Other visual characteristics. The final series (Fig. 3) was designed to suggest other visual characteristics that might be important in eliciting the chicks' pecking. Responses to the standard model were compared with those to a more realistic representation of the Laughing Gull head, which contained an eye and details of the bill. A similar detailed head with simulated food in the bill was included in the series to test the hypothesis that the sight of food increased the chicks' pecking. The series was completed with detailed models of the head of two other species, the Herring Gull and the Ring-billed Gull (*L. delawarensis*), to test the importance of species—specific characteristics.

Table 3 reveals that the detailed and standard models were both significantly better than models of the other two species and surpris-

TABLE 3

RESPONSIVENESS TO OTHER VISUAL CHARACTERISTICS

(See Figure 3)

Chick	Model:	Laughing Gull	Standard	Herring Gull	Ring-Billed Gull	With Food
1		16	11	4	2	5
2		48	19	1	0	1
3		17	6	8	2	3
4		42	18	29	7	2
5		15	12	2	19	3
6		15	9	6	2	0
7		1	18	0	0	0
8		25	17	3	0	1
9		31	27	0	7	2
Mean pecks/minute		23.3	15.2	5.9*	4.3*	1.9*
Transformed mean		4.67	3.93	2.29	2.04	1.67

* Significantly less than Laughing Gull and standard models.
  5% difference between transformed means: 1.47.

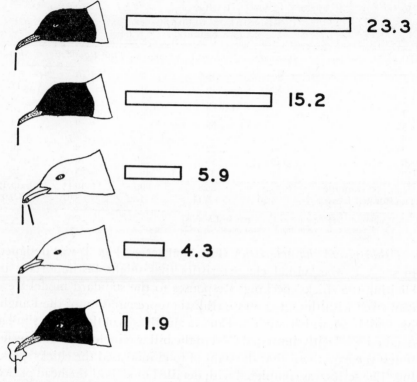

FIG. 3. Models used in the third series (from the top): Laughing Gull, standard, Herring Gull, Ring-billed Gull, Laughing Gull with food. Legend as in Figure 1.

ingly better than the model with "food." The last, which received very few responses, appeared to frighten the chicks, and they often turned from the model and attempted to hide in a near corner of the containing box.

PARTS OF MODELS PECKED

The particular place(s) on the models at which the chicks pecked were observed during the experiments. In models with normally shaped bills, pecking was usually directed at the tip of the bill. Thus only when the bill shape varied (Fig. 2) were other regions pecked. An exception to this rule was the Herring Gull model (Fig. 3); here pecking was directed to both the bill tip and the red spot on the lower mandible.

The second series (Fig. 2) showed some interesting variations in the direction of pecking. In both the standard and pointed-bill models, pecking was at the point of the bill, but in the rounded-bill model, pecking was indiscriminately aimed in the area of the end of the bill.

The short bill evidently caused confusion: pecks were delivered at the tip, at the edges of the bill where it meets the head, and even occasionally at the "corner" of red in the most proximal end of the bill. Finally, two areas of the long-and-thin bill were repeatedly pecked: (1) the tip of the bill itself, and (2) about halfway between the bill tip and the head.

DISCUSSION

From these preliminary experiments, it appears that the parental bill, and not the food itself, is the most important visual stimulus eliciting the chick's pecking. The long, narrow proportions and the pointed tip of the bill enhance its value as a stimulus, and the presence of the head improves the stimulus value of the bill.

The importance of some other characteristics remains tenuous. Because sample sizes were relatively small, the random presentations probably did not completely "smooth out" effects due to habituation. Therefore a few differences between models that are close to but not quite significant at the 5 per cent level may be considered briefly. For instance, in Table 1 the head lacking a bill received so few responses that it is probably less effective than the bill lacking a head (difference between transformed means: 1.22; 5 per cent significant difference: 1.26), demonstrating the relatively greater importance of the bill. However, the importance of the whole of the stimulus is suggested by the fact that the sum of responses to the head and bill separately is less than the total response to the two components together (standard model). Another characteristic from Table 1 of unproved importance is the normal shape of the head, since the cock's head is neither significantly below the standard nor above the bill with some head portion; it is possible, then, that the shape of the head does have some effect upon the frequency of response.

In a similar manner, Table 2 shows that the long-and-thin bill is not significantly different from either the standard or the round-bill models. The surprising effectiveness of the long-and-thin bill may be due, as suggested by Tinbergen and Perdeck (1950), to its resemblance to the frontal aspect of the parental bill. Since the adult gull's bill is compressed laterally, a chick viewing the parent's bill while standing under the parent between the latter's legs would see a long and thin aspect, in contrast to the thicker profile. Such a suggestion is particularly interesting because it may account for the effectiveness of the pointed bill-tip model in the second series. Perhaps chicks respond to a slightly hooked bill (standard model) as they would to the parental bill seen in profile, and respond equally as often to the thin, tapering point (pointed-bill model) as they would to the frontal aspect of the parental bill.

The species—specific differences found in the last experiment may depend on the color and pattern of the bill (and perhaps of the head), since the shapes of the Herring and Ring-billed gull models were identical with the Laughing Gull model. Actually, another series of models with varying colors of head and bill was presented to seven chicks, but no significant differences between models were uncovered, presumably due at least partly to the small sample size. Since bill color is an important component of the eliciting stimulus in other gull species (Tinbergen and Perdeck, 1950; Collias and Collias, 1957; Weidmann and Weidmann, 1958; Weidmann, 1959), further work on the influence of this component is being planned for evaluation under more controlled conditions.

Characteristics of the parental head that direct the response seem to be similar to those that elicit it. Pecks delivered to all three "corners" of the short-bill model suggest that chicks peck normally at the bill point itself. Pecks delivered to the long-and-thin bill halfway down its length suggest that chicks tend to peck a certain distance from the head along the bill. This assumption is further substantiated by pecks at the end of the rounded bill, which was normal in length but had no pointed tip.

COMPARISONS WITH OTHER SPECIES

At least two other species have been investigated with regard to stimuli that elicit pecking: the Herring Gull was studied by Tinbergen and Perdeck (1950), whose investigations are also related in detail in Tinbergen (1953, Chapter 22); and the Black-headed Gull was recently studied by U. and R. Weidmann (Weidmann and Weidmann, 1958; Tinbergen, 1958, Chapter 13; Weidmann, 1959). Neither the shape nor presence of the head has any effect upon pecking in the chicks of these two species. This is in contrast to the Laughing Gull, in which the presence (and possibly the normal shape) of the head increases the effectiveness of a normally shaped bill. In general, a long-and-thin bill is more effective than a bill of other abnormal proportions in both Herring and Black-headed gulls. Such a bill receives more responses than normal bills by Herring Gull chicks, but the same or fewer responses from chicks of the Laughing and Black-headed gulls. The shape of the bill tip is not important in the Herring Gull, but may be in the Black-headed Gull where a pointed tip received more responses than a rounded tip (U. Weidmann, pers. comm.).

The presence of simulated food on the bill increased the number of pecks from Black-headed Gull chicks, but not from Laughing Gull chicks. Weidmann (pers. comm.) used "food" that was the same color (red) as the bill, whereas the Laughing Gull "food" was white (Fig. 3). Tinbergen and Perdeck (*op. cit.*) presented a model with a small bump on the mandible, which was chosen over the plain bill by Herring Gull chicks. Perhaps the size and color of the projecting "food" are important.

In addition to stimuli that elicit the response, Tinbergen and Perdeck (*op. cit.*) found that the red spot on the bill and the actual bill tip direct the pecking of the Herring Gull chick. Interestingly, Herring Gull chicks also peck at the corner of the bill where it meets the head, emphasizing the importance of a point in directing the response.

The specific differences suggested above are tentative because different techniques and subjects of different ages were used in studying the three species. Increasingly objective techniques, like that of Collias and Collias (1957), will facilitate better comparisons. Weidmann 1959) suggests comparing newly hatched chicks before the first feeding, in order to equate experiences of the individuals. It is my feeling that a truly comparative study should include the full ontogenetic developmental sequences in each species.

ACKNOWLEDGMENTS

Mr. Verd Watson, Park Naturalist of the Hatteras National Seashore Recreation Area, and Mrs. Floy Burford were helpful in locating the Green Island colony. Mr. Charles Noble, Manager of Pea Island National Wildlife Refuge, helpfully allowed us to carry out the study at the colony. The manuscript benefited greatly from critical readings of an early draft by Dr. Peter H. Klopfer and Dr. Uli Weidmann, to whom I am much indebted. Advice on statistical methods was kindly offered by Dr. David L. Wallace.

SUMMARY

Chicks of the Laughing Gull (*Larus atricilla*) peck at the bill of the parent and thereby find regurgitated food held between the mandibles. Certain visual characteristics of the parental head were tested to determine their value as stimuli eliciting pecking by comparing the frequencies of pecking by chicks to various models (Figs. 1–3). Table 1 shows that a head with no bill is the poorest stimulus, that a bill with no head and a bill with some head evoke a modicum of pecking, and that a normal but diagrammatic Laughing Gull head is the best stimulus; a bill with an irregularly shaped head is possibly less effective than the standard diagrammatic model. Table 2 shows that a rounded bill tip and a short bill are less effective than the standard model and one with a pointed bill tip, and a model with a very long-and-thin bill is intermediate. Table 3 indicates that detailed models of two other gull species are significantly poorer stimuli than the diagrammatic model, as was a detailed Laughing Gull head with simulated food in the bill. However, a detailed head without food was as effective, perhaps more so, than the diagrammatic model.

Chicks pecked at the bill tips in all normally shaped models, but pecked indiscriminately around the end of the rounded bill-tip model. Pecks to the short bill were delivered to the tip, but also to the "corners" of red where the bill meets the head (Fig. 3). Pecks to the long-and-thin bill were directed to its tip and to a region about halfway down its length.

The stimuli that elicit and direct the pecking of the chicks of Laughing Gulls appear to differ somewhat from those to which chicks of other species of gulls react; however, the differences are not necessarily due to specific differences in the morphology of the adult heads. It is suggested that the best comparative study would involve comparisons of the ontogenetic development of pecking behavior.

LITERATURE CITED

BENT, A. C. 1921. Life histories of North American gulls and terns. U.S. Nat. Mus. Bull., No. 113. 345 pp.

COLLIAS, E. C., AND N. E. COLLIAS. 1957. The response of chicks of the Franklin Gull to parental bill color. Auk, 74: 371–75.

SNEDECOR, G. W. 1956. Statistical methods. Iowa State College Press, Ames, Iowa. 534 pp.

TINBERGEN, N. 1953. The Herring Gull's world. Collins, London. xvi + 255 pp.

TINBERGEN, N. 1958. Curious naturalist. New York. 280 pp.

TINBERGEN, N., AND A. C. PERDECK. 1950. On the stimulus situation releasing the begging response in the newly hatched Herring Gull chick (*Larus argentatus argentatus* Pont.). Behav., 3: 1–39.

WEIDMANN, R., AND U. WEIDMANN. 1958. An analysis of the stimulus situation releasing food-begging in the Black-headed Gull. Anim. Behav., 6: 114.

WEIDMANN, U. 1959. The begging response of the Black-headed Gull chick. Paper read before the 6th Inter. Ethol. Conf., Cambridge. 6 pp., mimeo.

AN ETHOLOGICAL ANALYSIS

OF THE REPRODUCTIVE BEHAVIOUR

OF THE BITTERLING (RHODEUS AMARUS BLOCH)

by

P. R. WIEPKEMA

(*Zoological Laboratory, University of Groningen,
Haren (Gr.), Netherlands*)

I. INTRODUCTION

1. Summary of the Earlier Literature and Scope of the Present Study

A long time elapsed from the first descriptions of the species *Rhodeus amarus* Bloch[1] (1782) to the discovery of its unusual biology.

First Döllinger (1818) and then Küster (1843), Vogt (1849), and Aubert (1856) found fish eggs in fresh-water mussels at different places in Germany, while Maslowski (1863) discovered them in Russia. The origin of these eggs remained unknown for some time. While Krauss (1858) described the urogenital papilla of the female bitterling and v. Siebold (1863), finding this papilla filled with eggs, called it an ovipositor, not until 1877 did Noll demonstrate the function of this ovipositor in the laying of eggs in the gill cavity of the fresh-water mussel. Olt (1893) examined the remarkable development of the embryos of the bitterling within the gills of the mussel. Sorge (1932) gave a valuable description of the anatomy and the histology of the female genital structure and elucidated much of the egg laying apparatus.

Although bitterlings possess this very peculiar mode of reproduction, it is not this characteristic of their biology that has received most attention. Wunder's study (1931) on the effect of injections of hormones on the nuptial colours of the male bitterling was the first of a long series of papers appearing on the endocrinology and histology

---

[1] *Rhodeus amarus* Bloch = *Rhodeus sericeus amarus* Bloch according to Berg (1948–49), cited by Pickford and Atz (1957).

of the bitterling. Pickford and Atz (1957) have given a valuable review and discussion of this subject.

The progress of the endocrinological and histological knowledge of the bitterling increased the need for an exact description and analysis of its behaviour, since previous descriptions. (Noll, 1877; Boeseman *et al.*, 1938; Duyvené de Wit, 1939; Bresse, 1946; Verster, 1955; Wiepkema, 1957) are of a qualitative nature rather than of a quantitative one. So the main reason to start the present study was to investigate quantitatively the causation of the behaviour of a species, of which many endocrinological and histological data are available.

Apart from this I have tried to find a reliable method to examine one of the central problems in this type of analytical behaviour studies, *viz.* the problem how to analyse the entire behaviour pattern of a species in such a way that the variables observed can be ordered according to sets of common causal factors, a problem originally raised by Tinbergen (1942) and Baerends (1941), when they postulated the concept of the hierarchical organization of behaviour.

There is much need for quantitative methods that use clearcut criteria and have a wide range of applicability for ordering behaviour patterns in accordance with common factors. In many instances the analyses have been made with the aid of concepts that are not clear, since it is often unknown by what parameters they have been measured.

A typical example of such a loose concept is the term tendency as defined and used by Marler (1956) in his analysis of the courtship behaviour of the chaffinch. According to Marler tendency is "the readiness to show a particular type of behaviour, as observed under natural conditions." Since in this way the term tendency does not refer to a definite set of operations by which it has been measured, little can be said on the nature of the mechanisms underlying these tendencies.

In addition this study may serve as a beginning for comparative ethological research on the different species and genera of the bitterling to clarify their evolution. Duyvené de Wit (1955) has already previously drawn attention to the possibility of such a comparative research on bitterlings.

2. Methods and Terminology

The present study was started with a qualitative description of the complete behaviour pattern of the species as advocated by Tinbergen (1951). To obtain quantitative data that could be expected to represent the complete behaviour pattern of the species satisfactorily, a limited number of behaviour elements or variables were selected. To increase the reliability of this selection a thorough knowledge of the complete behaviour pattern of the bitterling was needed. The variables were selected in such a way that they were (1) easily measurable, (2) not too rare in its occurrence, (3) biologically meaningful and (4) not entirely correlated with any other chosen variable. Of course this last criterium is a difficult one since as a rule one does not know anything of the correlations among the possible variables; decisions depend on qualitative impressions in this stage.

By recording the behaviour elements selected in different situations, information has been collected on their frequencies, their temporal association and the specific conditions in which their frequencies show a maximum or minimum (*cf.* chapters II and IV).

Since the frequency distributions of the variables fluctuate in space and time, the probability of their occurrence seems not to be constant. This probability I have called the tendency of the variable involved. Thus in this paper the tendency of a definite variable is measured by its frequency. The use of the term tendency in this paper is somewhat similar to the way Hinde (1955) uses and defines it.

To investigate the possible existence of causal factors controlling the occurrence of a number of variables in common, the correlations among these variables have been calculated on account of their temporal association. These correlations are subjected to factor analysis, by which is examined whether or not the occurrence of the variables observed can be described in terms of a smaller number of variables (Henrysson, 1957). These latter variables are called common factors and are considered to be of a more fundamental nature than the original ones. On account of this analysis groups of movements are distinguished which probably are characterized by common causal factors (chapter IV).

The positive correlations among the tendencies of a set of variables point to the existence of a common tendency typical of this set of variables. These common tendencies refer to the probability of the occurrence of a particular set of variables and are determined by the frequency observed of a definite variable and its correlation with the other variables.

The entire complex of external and internal factors, which correspond with the common factors obtained by factor analysis and which control the occurrence of the variables observed or of a group of variables, I have called a system. According to this definition the term system is very similar to the term drive as defined by Thorpe (1951), but the term system is preferred since "drive" has also other meanings (Hinde, 1956; 1959). I do not intend to propose a new and general meaning for the term system in ethology, but it was defined this way primarily to serve as a useful concept in examining the problems described in the present study. The term motivation which has been used sometimes in this paper refers to the same factors as the term system.

To indicate the internal factors corresponding with each tendency the term mechanism has been chosen. This term was needed when discussing the interaction of the causal factors underlying the different tendencies (chapter V).

Because the aggressive tendency of the male shows an increase after periods of strong fighting behaviour (*cf.* Tavolga, 1956 a; 1956 b), it was possible to examine the relationship between different levels of the aggressive tendency and of the tendencies to perform each of the sexual movements. In this way interaction problems between the aggressive and sexual mechanisms have been studied. The results of these experiments are compared with the results obtained from situations in which the levels of these tendencies varied under the influence of natural causes (chapter V).

3. Materials and Technique

The fish were obtained from fish-ponds of the "Nederlandse Heide Mij," from fish dealers, and from cultures in our laboratory; in all cases the fish were of Dutch origin.

During the non-reproductive period when no systematic observations were made males and females were stored together in large tanks of different size. Observations and experiments were made in smaller tanks (60 × 35 × 35 cm) containing one or more fresh-water mussels. The temperature of the water in the smaller tanks during the observations and experiments varied from 20–24° C. There was some vegetation of *Vallisneria*, *Elodea* and *Saggitaria* along the back and side walls of these tanks. The fish were fed with rolled oats, Tubifex, Daphnia, etc. In total about 500 fish have been observed.

. . . .

III. THE REPRODUCTIVE BEHAVIOUR

1. General Description

In early spring bitterlings, males as well as females, begin to show interest in the fresh-water mussels of the genera *Unio* and *Anodonta*.

Although I observed no preference of the bitterlings for either of the genera, I used only mussels of the genus *Unio* in the experiments reported.

The bitterlings swim around these mussels and perform reactions to them which are typical of the reproductive period. After some time the males start defending an area around a mussel. Other males or females are chased away, but ripe females are permitted to enter this area. These females are led by the males towards the mussel. During leading the male swims in front of the female and quivers with its entire body. The female deposits its eggs within the gills of the mussel by means of the long ovipositor. There usually are a number of spawning acts a day. Both before and after egg laying the male makes skimming movements over the siphons of the mussel. Simultaneously with skimming the male may eject sperm, which may be drawn into the inhalent siphon of the mussel and thereby reach any eggs lying within the gills. After a development of about 4 weeks the young fish leave the mussel through the exhalent siphon. There is no parental behaviour in the bitterling (Noll, 1877; Olt, 1893; Boeseman *et al.*, 1938; Bresse, 1946, 1950; Kristensen, 1952; Wiepkema, 1957).

According to Verhoeven and v. Oordt (1955) oestrus is preceded by a proöestrus during which high temperatures (18° C.) impair the development of the eggs, whereas such a temperature during dioestrus stimulates this development. In proöestrus, usually in February and March, no spawning takes place. After this, oestrus follows and lasts into June. Under laboratory conditions these phases can be shifted; *e.g.* by taking away the mussels the onset of oestrus can be postponed until May or June.

Each female may spawn during 1–3 months. Once every 6–12 days the ovipositor of the female becomes very long and during such a day eggs can be laid. There are 10–15 spawning acts a day and within oestrus each female may have 5–11 spawning days (Meltzer, 1947; Verster, 1955). The female deposits 1–4 eggs per spawning act, so I estimate the total number of eggs deposited by one female during the reproductive period to be 100–500. This low number and the large size of the eggs (diameter of 2–3 mm) correspond with a suggestion of Fabricius (1959) that territorial species generally have less numerous and larger eggs than non-territorial species.

2. Detailed Description of the Reproductive Behaviour Elements

Bitterlings have a number of movements typical of the reproductive

period. In this description these behaviour elements are classified in
the following way:

a. The behaviour of males and females towards the mussel.
b. The behaviour of a male towards another male.
c. The behaviour of a male towards a female.
d. The behaviour of a female towards males and females.

a. The Behaviour of Males and Females towards the Mussel. In
autumn and winter before the reproductive period bitterlings take
little or no notice of fresh-water mussels. When swimming they may
pass the mussels again and again without performing any reactions
to them.

In early spring, when the bitterlings begin to react to the mussels,
I observed the behaviour of 26 animals about 6 months old, which
had been isolated from mussels as soon as possible after hatching.
These animals were placed in heterosexual pairs in a tank with a mussel for 30 minutes. The observations gave the following results.

For some males and females there was no apparent difference in
their behaviour with and without a mussel. Other fish stopped swimming for a moment and looked at the mussel. After stopping four fish
made circling movements around the mussel. While fixating or circling around the mussel the fish approach it to about 3 cm, but did not
draw nearer. The mussel seemed to have both an attracting and a
repelling effect on them. The remaining nine fish arrived at the mussel after some fixating or circling. The first approaches to the mussel
appeared to be much slower than later ones. After approaching the
mussel the fish investigated the entire visible part of the mussel and
came to show a definite preference for the edge of the mussel with the
siphons. In most cases the mussel had not burrowed deeply into the
sand on the bottom, so a large part of the shell surface was exposed.

When investigating the siphons with its snout the fish may approach
the mussel from a number of angles. However after some time the
animal comes in the median plane of the mussel and performs the
head-down posture (Fig 5). In the head-down posture, which is performed both by the males and the females, the snout is usually just
above the exhalent siphon. The longitudinal axis of the fish forms an
acute angle with the bottom. Usually the fish performs the head-down
posture as sketched in Figure 5a, but sometimes the acute angle is
turned away from the mussel. The animal maintains its position
above the mussel by appropriate fin movements. In this paper head-
down postures refer to postures above the mussel, unless stated otherwise.

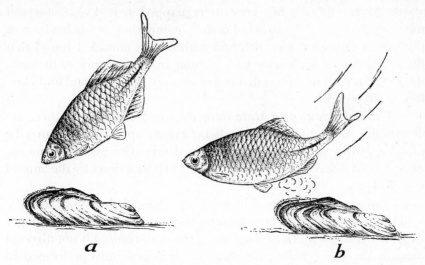

FIG. 5. (*a*) Head-down posture of the male above a mussel and (*b*) skimming of the male with sperm ejection.

The head-down posture is the starting point for the next typical movements, *skimming* of the male and *touching* of the female. These movements are both very rapid swimming movements in the median plane of the mussel over its siphons (see Fig. 5*b*), sometimes however, no more than a short almost horizontal movement over the siphons. Skimming of the male and touching of the female differ in that in skimming the males usually do not touch the mussel, while in touching the females do touch the mussel with their anal region. Touching of the female appears to be an attempt to place the anal region on the exhalent siphon of the mussel. Skimming and touching are identical in form with the fertilization and egg-laying movements respectively.

Comparing the reactions of these 26 animals one gets the impression that the behavioural differences observed have been caused by a differently advanced development of each animal. Some of them did not perform any reaction to the mussel, others did perform all the possible reactions to the mussel. If this is true the differences give us information about the normal development of the reactions of the bitterling to the mussel with increasing tendency for reproductive behaviour. The developmental sequence of these reactions would then be: swimming around in the tank without reactions to the mussel, fixating the mussel, circling around the mussel, approaching the mussel, investigating the mussel, head-down posture, skimming or touching.

The movements mentioned were not the only reactions shown to the mussel. While investigating or performing a head-down posture above the mussel, the fish very often snapped at it. I also observed much chafing on the mussel. Further, comparing the behaviour of the fish in the situations with and without the mussel, I found that the frequency of finflickering was greater in the presence of the mussel. I shall return to this occurrence of snapping, chafing and finflickering in chapter VI.

b. The Behaviour of a Male towards Another Male.   If there are only males in a tank with mussels behaviour appears which may be called agonistic (Scott and Fredericson, 1951). The normal sequence of agonistic behaviour shown after the first reactions to the mussel is as follows.

One of the males, after skimming, may spread the dorsal and the anal fin for a moment. Somewhat later these fins are spread for a longer time (3 to 6 seconds). In the beginning this *finspreading* is not directed towards the other males, but later on it is generally performed in front of or beside an opponent. Usually during the first days in early spring nothing more than finspreading will occur. Later on finspreading can be combined with swimming rapidly towards another male, usually directed to the head or the anal fin of the other male.

When two males are finspreading beside each other, one or both may perform jerking movements. *Jerking* is a lateral undulating movement of the entire body by which the opponent is pushed away (Fig. 6). The rate of jerking varies, but is never very rapid. Jerking is

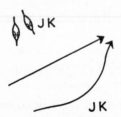

FIG.   6. Jerking. The arrows represent two fishes; the lowest arrow symbolizes jerking. Upper left, a frontal view of two fish, the right one jerking.

practically always attended with finspreading. In many instances following finspreading and jerking two males oriented in the same direction may swim along a straight or slightly curved line parallel to each other (Fig. 7). In this *parallel swimming* the fins are expanded and the distance between the two fish varies from 1 to 5 cm. If the fish have a head-tail orientation, they circle around each other. During parallel swimming there is a strong increase in the colouration of the males, especially of their heads and fins. Parallel swimming may or may not be followed by other agonistic movements.

FIG. 7. Parallel swimming.

In parallel swimming, one of the males may perform a *turning beat* which is a rapid turn of about 180° towards the opponent (Fig. 8).

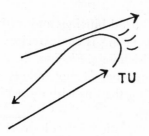

FIG. 8. Turning beat. The arrows represent two fishes; the lowest arrow symbolizes a turning beat.

The rapidity of the movement prevents observation of details in most cases, but sometimes it seems that the male performing a turning beat touches the opponent. The main effect of a turning beat appears to be the production of a strong water current brought about by the rapid turning. In most cases the fins are spread immediately before and after a turning beat.

Another very common agonistic movement is *head butting* which is strongly associated in time with chasing, the agonistic movement next to be discussed. In head butting, a male rushes at another male and pushes it with the anterior side of the snout or, if alongside the opponent, with the side of the snout (Fig. 9). In the latter case head butting resembles intensive jerking. Two males which are both per-

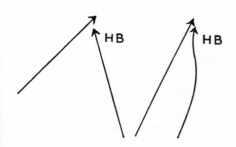

FIG. 9. Head butting. The arrows represent two pairs of fishes; to the left head butting with the anterior side of the snout, to the right head butting with the lateral side of the snout.

forming head butting push at each other's heads, but never show any sign of mouth fighting (Fig. 10).

FIG. 10. Head butting.

Chasing follows turning beats and head buttings and terminates an agonistic encounter of two males. Chasing is characterized by rapid swimming towards the other male which flees. *Fleeing*, the opposite of chasing, is a collective noun for a number of movements which are strongly associated in time, *viz.* folding the fins with crouching, *yielding* or slow fleeing and rapid fleeing.

Reproductive behaviour is accompanied by colour changes. As previously mentioned the bitterlings have a silvery tint during dioestrus. The upper part of the eyes is red or yellow and there is a bluish tail line. The females maintain this appearance throughout the whole reproductive period, but the colours of the males change. In early spring the first signs in the male of the coming reproductive period are a brightening of the red eyepatch and the blue tail line and a reddening of the anal fin. During agonistic behaviour the colouring of the male reaches a maximum. The entire body takes on a violet glow, the head and the upperside of the fish darkens, and the belly turns yellow-orange. The dorsal fin becomes darkly striped with a red patch at the top of the first fin ray and the anal fin becomes red with dark borders. On either side of the tail line red longitudinal lines are visible. In an animal which flees a great deal, these colours disappear completely. Strongly disturbed bitterlings also show a typical colour pattern, becoming darker, all their scales appearing to have dark edges, and the tail line being black-violet.

During the reproductive period the males have two white wart-like structures just above the mouth, the so called pearl organs, which contrast strikingly with the dark head colours of fighting males. These structures resemble the pearl organs of the Japanese bitterling (*Acheilognathus intermedium* Tem. and Schl.) as described by Tozawa (1929).

c. The Behaviour of a Male towards a Female. Only males
which will defend an area around a mussel perform courtship movements in the presence of a female. Only ripe females ready to spawn
and characterized by the long ovipositor elicit full courtship behaviour in the male. At first a male will rush at the female when the
female enters a defended area. Sometimes there is some head butting
by the male, but usually the male quivers after the rush. *Quivering*
is a very rapid lateral undulating movement of the entire body with
high frequency and small amplitude. Finspreading does not occur.
After the initial quivering the male orients itself towards the mussel
in front of the female and quivers while swimming in the direction
of the mussel for a short distance. This combined movement of quivering and swimming I have called *leading*. If the female follows, the
male again leads towards the mussel. If the female does not follow,
the male stops, returns to the female and again leads the female.
Leading can be performed once, may be repeated and may be inter-
spersed with stopping, turning, etc. In leading, the tail is bent to one
side and the dorsal and anal fins are bent to the opposite side. The
tail is bent in such a way that the female (behind the male) is at the
convex side of the curve (Fig. 11). I have called this movement *tail*

FIG. 11.   Leading with tail bending.

bending. Tail bending is only performed when the female is behind
the male.

When the female arrives at the mussel after leading, the male takes
a head-down posture. A skimming movement may then be performed
if the female is close to and behind the male. Very often this skimming
is accompanied by sperm ejection, which combination is the fertilization movement and is hereafter called *skimming +*. The sperm is
sprayed over the siphons of the mussel and is visible as a small greyish

cloud (Fig. 5). After performing a skimming movement in the presence of the female, the male posts itself beside the mussel and quivers continuously.

Now the female also may perform a head-down posture. If the female leaves the mussel the male stops its continuous quivering and tries to lead the female again towards the mussel. If the female performs the head-down posture for a long time, the male also has a tendency to perform a head-down posture followed by skimming+, while the tendency to quiver decreases. The male may eject sperm many times before egg laying occurs. After egg laying by the female there is much skimming and skimming+ of the male and the female is chased way fiercely. The first skimming+ movements after egg laying are characterized by the large amounts of sperm that are ejected.

There is no intensification of the colouration in the male—as described for encounters between fighting males—during courtship behaviour (quivering, leading etc.) or during aggressive behaviour towards the female.

   d. The Behaviour of the Female towards Males or Females. During dioestrus, when the ovipositors are short (1–2 A.U.; 1 A.U. = 1 anal fin unit; 1 A.U. is 1/8 part of the length of the first anal fin ray; Duyvené de Wit, 1939), the females show schooling behaviour or, if alone, have a strong tendency to flee or to hide among the vegetation. During proöestrus, when the ovipositors reach a length of about 4–8 A.U., females behave much as they do during dioestrus, except that reactions to the mussel do occur. In oestrus the ovipositors rhythmically change in length from 4–8 to 15–20 A.U. Females with long ovipositors (10–20 A.U.) may be ready to spawn. In a very few cases I observed spawning of females having ovipositors of 2–10 A.U.

Whether or not a ripe female actively goes in search of a territorial male is unknown to me, but a ripe female tends to *follow* a leading male more or less rapidly. The female swims behind the leading male in a horizontal position; I did not observe the inclination pose as described by Meltzer (1947). After leading and skimming of the male, the female, if it has followed up to the mussel, performs a *head-down posture* greatly resembling that of the male. Usually, however, the head-down posture of the female is steeper than that of the male (Fig. 12 A, B).

If the siphons of the mussel are closed, the head-down posture of the female is prolonged. If the siphons are only slightly open, touching movements occur which often are performed in a plane perpendic-

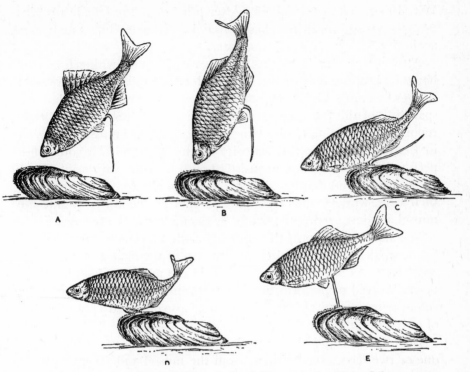

F<small>IG</small>. 12. Spawning of the female. (A) Head-down posture, (B) head-down posture with erection of the basis of the ovipositor, (C) touching, (D) pressing the eggs through the ovipositor and (E) leaving the mussel.

ular to the median plane of the mussel. If the siphons of the mussel are fully open, the female performs the touching movement in the median plane of the mussel and may perform the complete egg laying movement, hereafter called *touching +*. Immediately before touching and touching + the thick proximal part of the ovipositor is erected while the thinner distal part remains slack (Fig. 12 B). Then, in touching +, the female performs the rapid movement and places the erected part of the ovipositor into the exhalent siphon (Fig. 12 C). Immediately thereafter 1–4 eggs are pressed rapidly through the ovipositor tube, which becomes stiffened by the fluid (urine according to Duyvené de Wit, 1955) which is ejected and forces the eggs through the tube. This stiffening causes the slack ovipositor to penetrate deeply into the gill cavity of the mussel (Fig. 12 D) and makes it possible to deposit eggs there. Touching + is completed within one second. Having deposited the eggs the female rises and pulls its ovipositor, now slack, out of the mussel (Fig. 12 E). The egg laying apparatus has been described in more detail by Sorge (1932), Kristensen 1952), Duyvené de

Wit (1955) and Verster (1955). After touching+ the female remains near the mussel until it is chased away by the male. The female may again deposit eggs 5–10 minutes later.

After a ripe female has been prevented from spawning for many hours by keeping it separated from males and mussels, it may deposit its eggs in a mussel in absence of the male. On one occasion I observed spawning of the female even in absence of a mussel. Holčík (1959) reports the spawning of bitterlings in the absence of mussels in a pool in Central Bohemia; the majority of the eggs and the young fish perished. These data are inconsistent with the observations of Bresse (1950) who found that females which are not allowed to spawn resorb their eggs, while I observed that eggs that are deposited beside the mussel are devoured immediately by the male and the female.

Females may perform the same agonistic movements as described for the males. These agonistic movements of the female do not occur very often and are less intensive than in the males; females have not been observed to perform turning beats and they do not assume the colour patterns typical of fighting males. I also observed a few instances of quivering by a female.

During two reproductive periods I collected about 80 bitterlings one or two days after hatching from the mussel and I kept them in tanks not containing other bitterlings or mussels. After a year, when they were full-grown, these "isolated" bitterlings performed all re- productive movements of the sepecies in a normal way when mussels were placed in their tanks.

· ·

REFERENCES

ANDREW, R. J., 1957: The aggressive and courtship behaviour of certain Emberi- zines. Behaviour, 10, 255–308.

ARONSON, L. R., 1958: Hormones and reproductive behavior: some phylogenetic considerations. In: A. Gorbman, Comparative endocrinology. Wiley and Sons, Inc., New York, 98–121.

AUBERT, H., 1856: Beiträge zur Entwicklungsgeschichte der Fische. Z. wiss. Zool., 7, 345–65.

BAERENDS, G. P., 1941: Fortpflanzungsverhalten und Orientierung der Grabwespe *Ammophila campestris* Jur. Tijdschr. v. Entomol., 84, 68–275.

BAERENDS, G. P., 1956: Aufbau des tierischen Verhaltens. Kükenthal's Handb. Zoologie, 10, 3, 1–32.

BAERENDS, G. P., 1958 a: Comparative methods and the concept of homology in the study of behaviour. Arch. Néerl. Zool., 13, suppl. 1, 401–18.

BAERENDS, G. P., 1958 b: The contribution of ethology to the study of the causa- tion of behaviour. Act. Physiol. Pharmacol. Néerl., 7, 466–99.

BAERENDS, G. P., 1959: The ethological analysis of incubation behaviour. Ibis, 101, 357–68.

BAERENDS, G. P., 1960: Het organisme in zijn gemeenschap: aard en herkomst der communicatiemiddelen bij dieren. Werken Rectoraat R.U.-Gent, 3, 64–85.

BAERENDS, G. P. and J. M. BAERENDS–VAN ROON, 1950: An introduction to the ethology of Cichlid fishes. Behaviour, suppl. 1, 1–242.

BAERENDS, G. P. and J. M. BAERENDS–VAN ROON, 1960: Ueber die Schnappbewegung des Fischreihers (*Ardea cinerea* L.). Ardea, 48, 136–50.

BAERENDS, G. P., R. BROUWER and H. T. WATERBOLK, 1955: Ethological studies on *Lebistes reticulatus*. 1. An analysis of the male courtship pattern. Behaviour, 8, 249–335.

BASTOCK, M., D. MORRIS and M. MOYNIHAN, 1953: Some comments on conflict and thwarting in animals. Behaviour, 6, 66–84.

BEACH, F. A., 1958: Evolutionary aspects of psychoendocrinology. In: A. Roe and G. G. Simpson, Behavior and evolution. Yale Univers. Press, New Haven, 81–103.

BOESEMAN, M. J., J. VAN DER DRIFT, J. M. VAN ROON, N. TINBERGEN and J. J. TER PELKWIJK, 1938: De bittervoorns en hun mossels. De Levende Natuur, 43, 129–36.

BOL, A. C. A., 1959: A consummatory situation. The effect of eggs on the sexual behaviour of the male three-spined stickle-back (*Gasterosteus aculeatus* L.). Experientia, 15, 115.

BRADDOCK, J. C., 1945: Some aspects of the dominance-subordination relationship in the fish *Platypoecilus maculatus*. Phys. Zool., 18, 176–95.

BRANTNER, G., 1956: Die Unabhängigkeit des morphologischen Farbwechsels vom physiologischen Farbwechsel bei der Entstehung des Hochzeitkleides des männlichen Bitterlings. Zeitschr. vergl. Phys., 38, 324–33.

BRESSE, G., 1946: La reproduction des Bouvières. Bull. franc. pisciculture, 141, 177–87.

BRESSE, G., 1950: Role des moules d'eau douce dans la reproduction des Bouvières. Bull. franc. pisciculture, 159, 47–52.

BRETSCHNEIDER, L. H. and J. J. DUYVENÉ DE WIT, 1947: Sexual endocrinology of non-mammalian vertebrates. Elsevier Pub. Co., Inc., Amsterdam.

CRAIG, W., 1918: Appetites and aversions as constituents of instincts. Biol. Bull. Mar. Biol. Lab. Woods Hole, 34, 91–108.

DIAMOND, S., 1959: Information and error. Basic books, Inc. New York.

DÖLLINGER, I., 1818–1820: Denkschr. Akad. Wissensch. München, 7, 169.

DUYVENÉ DE WIT, J. J., 1939: Onderzoekingen over de sexueel-endocrine organisatie van *Rhodeus amarus* ♀ en de betekenis van de legbuistest voor de endocrinologie in het algemeen. Thesis, Utrecht.

DUYVENÉ DE WIT, J. J., 1955: Some results of investigations into the european bitterling, *Rhodeus amarus* Bloch. Jap. Journ. Ichtyology, 4, 94–104.

FABRICIUS, E., 1959: Hur mörten leker, Zoologisk Revy, 21, 17–26.

FRUCHTER, B., 1954: Introduction to factor analysis. D. van Nostrand Co., New York.

GREENBERG, B., 1947: Some relations between territory, social hierarchy and leadership in the green sunfish (*Lepomis cyanellus*). Phys. Zool., 20, 267–99.

HAYES, J. S., W. M. S. RUSSEL, C. HAYES and A. KOHSEN, 1954: The mechanism of an instinctive control system: a hypothesis. Behaviour, 6, 66–85.

HENRYSSON, S., 1957: Applicability of factor analysis in the behavioural sciences. Almqvist and Wiksell, Stockholm.

HINDE, R. A., 1952: The behaviour of the Great Tit (*Parus major*) and some other related species. Behaviour, suppl. 2, 1–201.

HINDE, R. A., 1953 *a*: The conflict between drives in the courtship and copulation of the chaffinch. Behaviour, 5, 1–31.

HINDE, R. A., 1953 *b:* Appetitive behaviour, consummatory act and the hierarchical organisation of behaviour—with special reference to the Great Tit (*Parus major*). Behaviour, 5, 189–225.

HINDE, R. A., 1954: Changes in responsiveness to a constant stimulus. Brit. J. Anim. Beh., 2, 41–55.

HINDE, R. A., 1955: A comparative study of the courtship of certain finches (Fringillidae). Ibis, 97, 706–45.

HINDE, R. A., 1956: Ethological models and the concept of 'drive.' Brit. J. Philos. Sci., 6, 321–31.

HINDE, R. A., 1958: The nest building behaviour of domesticated canaries. Proc. Zool. Soc. Lond., 131, 1–48.

HINDE, R. A., 1959: Unitary drives. Anim. Beh., 7, 130–142.

HOLČíK, J., 1959: Quantitative age and sex composition of population of european bitterling (*Rhodeus sericeus amarus*) in the back water (natural pool) and in the open water (drainage canal). Biologia, Bratislava, 14, 652–64.

HOLČíK, J., 1960: Age and growth of the european bitterling. Rozpravy ceskoslovenské akademie ved, Sesit 10, 1–111.

HOLST, E. VON and H. MITTELSTÄDT, 1950: Das Reafferenzprinzip. Wechselwirkungen zwischen Zentralnervensystem und Peripherie. Naturwiss., 37, 464–76.

HOLST, E. VON and U. VON SAINT PAUL, 1960: Vom Wirkungsgefüge der Triebe. Naturwiss., 47, 409–22.

IERSEL, J. J. A. VAN, 1953: An analysis of the parental behaviour of the male three-spined stickleback. Behaviour, suppl. 3, 1–159.

IERSEL, J. J. A. VAN, 1958: Some aspects of territorial behaviour of the male three-spined stickleback. Arch. Néerl. Zool., 13, suppl. 1, 381–401.

IERSEL, J. J. A. VAN, 1959: Ambivalent gedrag. E. J. Brill, Leiden.

IERSEL, J. J. A. VAN and A. C. A. BOL, 1958: Preening of two tern species. A study of displacement activities. Behaviour, 13, 1–88.

KALLENBERG, H., 1958: Observations in a stream tank of territoriality and competition in juvenile salmon and trout (*Salmo salar* L. and *S. trutta* L.). Rept. Inst. Freshw. Res. Drottningholm, 39, 55–99.

KORTLANDT, A., 1959: An attempt at clarifying some controversial notions in animal psychology and ethology. Arch. Néerl. Zool., 13, 196–230.

KRAUSS, F., 1858: Mitteilungen über den Bitterling. Würtemberg. Jahreshefte, 14, 115–23.

KRISTENSEN, I., 1952: Hoe krijgt het wijfje van de bittervoorn (*Rhodeus amarus*) haar legbuis in de mossel. De Levende Natuur, 55, 1–5.

KUSTER, H. C., 1843: Ueber die Artunterscheidung der Najaden. Isis, 565–86.

LIND, H., 1959: The activation of an instinct caused by a "transitional action." Behaviour, 14, 123–35.

LORENZ, K., 1937: Ueber die Bildung des Instinktbegriffes. Naturwiss., 25, 289–300.

LORENZ, K., 1950: The comparative method in studying innate behaviour patterns. Symp. Soc. Exp. Biol., 4, 221–69.

LORENZ, K., 1951: Ueber die Entstehung auslösender "Zeremonien." Die Vogelwarte, 16, 9–13.

MARLER, P., 1956: The behaviour of the chaffinch. Behaviour, suppl. 5, 1–184.

MARLER, P., 1957: Studies of fighting in chaffinches. (4). Appetitive and consummatory behaviour. Brit. J. Anim. Beh. 5, 29–38.

MASLOWSKI, A., 1863: Ueber den Fischembryo in den Kiemen von *Anodonta*. Bull. Soc. Imp. Nat. Moscou, 36, 269–79.

McDOUGALL, W., 1928: An outline of psychology. Methuen & Co., London.

MELTZER, J., 1947: The oestrus of *Rhodeus amarus* Bl. Proc. Kon. Ned. Akad. Wetensch., **6**, 1–11.

MILLER, N. E., 1957: Experiments on motivation. Science, **126**, 1271–79.

MORRIS, D., 1955: The causation of pseudofemale and pseudomale behaviour: a further comment. Behaviour, **8**, 46–57.

MORRIS, D., 1956 *a:* The function and causation of courtship ceremonies in animals (with special reference to fish). L'instinct dans le comportement des animaux et de l'homme. Masson et Cie, Paris, 261–86.

MORRIS, D., 1956 *b:* The feather postures of birds and the problem of the origin of social signals. Behaviour, **9**, 75–113.

MORRIS, D. 1957: "Typical intensity" and its relation to the problem of ritualisation. Behaviour, **11**, 1–12.

NEWMAN, M. A., 1956: Social behaviour and interspecific competition in two trout species. Phys. Zool., **29**, 64–81.

NICHOLLS, J. T., 1943: The fresh-water fishes of China. The Am. Mus. Nat. Hist. Centr. Asia, **9**.

NOLL, F. C., 1877: Gewohnheiten und Eierlegen des Bitterlings. Der Zool. Garten, **18**, 351–62.

OLT, A., 1893: Lebenweise und Entwicklung des Bitterlings. Z. wiss. Zool., **55**, 543–76.

PICKFORD, G. E. and J. W. ATZ, 1957: The physiology of the pituitary gland of fishes. New York.

PRECHTL, H. F. R., 1956: Neurophysiologische Mechanismen des formstarren Verhaltens. Behaviour, **9**, 243–319.

QUENOUILLE, M. H., 1952: Associated measurements. Butterworth, London.

SCOTT, J. P. and E. FREDERICSON, 1951: The cause of fighting in mice and rats. Phys. Zool., **24**, 273–309.

SEVENSTER, P., 1949: Modderbaarsjes. De Levende Natuur, **52**, 160–69 and 184–89.

SIEBOLD, C. T. E. VON, 1863: Die Süsswasserfische von Mitteleuropa. Leipzig.

SORGE, H., 1932: Anatomische Untersuchungen am Bitterling. Sitz. Ber. Ges. Naturfr. Berlin, **8**, 86–124.

TAVOLGA, W. N., 1956 *a:* Pre-spawning behaviour in the Gobiid fish, *Bathygobius soporator*. Behaviour, **9**, 53–75.

TAVOLGA, W. N., 1956 *b:* Visual, chemical and sound stimuli as cues in the sex discriminatory behaviour of the Gobiid fish, *Bathygobius sporator*. Zoologica (N.Y.), **41**, 49–65.

THORPE, W. H., 1951: The definition of some terms used in animal behaviour studies. Bull. Anim. Beh., **9**, 34–40.

THORPE, W. H., 1956: Learning and instinct in animals. Methuen, London.

THURSTONE, L. L., 1956: Factor analysis. In: M. H. Marx, Psychological theory. Macmillan, New York.

TINBERGEN, N., 1942: An objectivistic study of the innate behaviour of animals. Bibl. Biother., **1**, 39–98.

TINBERGEN, N., 1951: The study of instinct. Oxford, Clarendon press.

TINBERGEN, N., 1952: "Derived" activities; their causation, biological significance, origin and emancipation during evolution. Quart. Rev. Biol. **27**, 1–31.

TINBERGEN, N., 1953: The Herring Gull's world. Collins, London.

TINBERGEN, N., 1959: Comparative studies of the behaviour of Gulls (Laridae): a progress report. Behaviour, **15**, 1–71.

TOZAWA, T., 1929: Experiments on the development of the nuptial coloration and pearl organs of the Japanese bitterling (*Acheilognathus intermedium*). Fol. Anat. Japon., **7**, 407–17.

* TUGENDHAT, B., 1960: The normal feeding behaviour of the three-spined stickleback (*Gasterosteus aculeatus* L.). Behaviour, 15, 284–318.

UMRATH, K., 1957: Ueber den physiologischen und den morphologischen Farbwechsel des Bitterlings, *Rhodeus amarus*. Zeitschr. vergl. Phys., 40, 321–28.

VERHOEVEN, B. and G. J. VAN OORDT, 1955: The influence of light and temperature on the sexual cycle of the bitterling, *Rhodeus amarus*. Proc. Kon. Ned. Akad. Wetensch., Ser. C., 58, 628–34.

VERSTER, A. J. M., 1955: Ethological observations on the bitterling (*Rhodeus amarus* Bl.) with special reference to pseudomale and pseudofemale behaviour. Unpublished Thesis, Bloemfontein.

VOGT, C., 1849: Notes sur quelques habitants des Moules. Ann. Scienc. Natur., Ser. 13, 12, 198–204.

WICKLER, W., 1957: Das Verhalten von *Nannostomus beckfordi aripiragensis* Meinken. Beaufortia, 6, 203–20.

WIEPKEMA, P. R., 1957: Het spel van de bittervoorns. De Levende Natuur, 60, 169–78.

WUNDER, W., 1931: Experimentelle Erzeugung des Hochzeitkleides beim Bitterling (*Rhodeus amarus*) durch Einspritzung von Hormonen. Zeitschr. vergl. Phys., 13, 696–709.

WUNDER, W., 1934: Gattenwahlversuche bei Stichlingen und Bitterlingen. Zool. Anz. Suppl., 7, 152–58.

A STUDY OF THE BEHAVIOUR OF THE CHACMA BABOON,

PAPIO URSINUS

by
NIELS BOLWIG [1]
*Department of Zoology, University of the
Witwatersrand, Johannesburg*

I. INTRODUCTION

This study of the Chacma baboon was begun early in 1955 when Prof. R. A. Dart and Mr. L. K. Marshall drew my attention to the surprising superficiality of the available knowledge of these animals. The study has been carried out in two phases: one on two tame baboons, Joe and Jenny, the other on a number of wild troops in the Waterberg, and particularly in the Kruger National Park. The total number of troops observed has been 16.

A. Joe and Jenny

Joe and Jenny were presented to me on October 4th, 1955, by the Institute for Poliomyelitis Research, Johannesburg. Joe was at that time four months old, Jenny six months. Both came, as far as is known, from the Skeerpoort west of Pretoria, and had been taken from their mothers before being weaned. They had been kept together in a small cage in a room in which other monkeys and baboons were also kept. Joe appeared to have been treated roughly, perhaps by employees who cleaned the cage. He was extremely nervous and had adopted Jenny as a mother-substitute. Jenny, on her part seemed very maternal and held him firmly in her arms protecting him. At the time of arrival

---

[1] The present study of baboons would probably never have been undertaken if Professor Raymond Dart at the University of the Witwatersrand had not drawn my attention to some of the problems. I am greatly indebted to him for his support and for the inspiring discussions we have had. I also wish to thank the Institute for Poliomyelitis Research for presenting me with the two baboons used for my observations and the University of the Witwatersrand for its financial support.

Finally my sincere thanks for the assistance granted by the National Parks Board, particularly to the Board's Director, Mr. R. Knobel; also Col. Rowland Jones, Dr. de V. Pienaar and other members of its staff.

Joe still had his black fur while Jenny had almost entirely lost this. Both baboons were housed in a small rabbit cage in my home until a proper cage could be built in the garden. Here it was soon revealed that Jenny was extremely possessive, always keeping Joe away from anybody approaching the two of them.

Concerning food, however, Jenny grasped everything she could lay hands on, leaving for him only what she could not manage. Both baboons refused meat of any sort but greedily ate insects, bread, vegetables and fruit.

On November 13th the baboons were temporarily transferred to a bigger wire cage in the garden, big enough for them to be able to play about and jump between branches placed there. The long imprisonment in too small a cage had, however, made them uncertain in jumping and Joe particularly seemed afraid of making big jumps. After a few days both animals became as sure-footed as any young baboon I have observed in the Zoo.

On December 3rd both baboons were transferred to a large cage in my garden, 9'6" x 6'6". The cage is a strong steel construction with iron grill in front and with roof and sides covered with corrugated iron. The floor is of cement and from floor to roof is a part of a tree top with very thick branches. At the time of transfer to the final cage, Joe had lost all his juvenile black coat except for a little on the crown of his head.

The study of Joe and Jenny has been supplemented with observations on other captive baboons and monkeys, in the Medical School of the University of the Witwatersrand, at the National Zoo in Pretoria, the Zoo in Johannesburg, and on animals kept in captivity elsewhere. Most animals observed, other than Joe and Jenny, have shown very little of interest because they have been too concerned with begging for food or their behaviour has become distorted by the treatment they have received. This, of course, is particularly the case in Zoos where the public are allowed to tease the captives.

Naturally I, too, have found it impossible to avoid influencing the behaviour of my animals; but the peaceful atmosphere under which they are growing up has left them healthy, happy and better balanced and thus, I believe, more capable of showing their innate characters.

B. The Study of Wild Baboons

Most observations on wild baboons were made during visits to the Kruger National Park. Here alone 13 troops have been observed. Thanks to the experience gained from Joe and Jenny, it has been possible to obtain results more quickly from the wild baboons than would otherwise have been expected. It must, however, be stressed that the behaviour of captive baboons often is so distorted that it can be difficult to deduct anything and that the experience gained from them cannot always easily be transferred to wild animals.

The technique employed was as far as possible to write down every observation however insignificant it might appear, or to record the behaviour on a 16 mm cine film. In both cases the records were carefully examined and analysed afterwards. The cine film proved, in this connection, extremely valuable.

The best observations were made on or near rubbish heaps outside the camps in the Kruger National Park. Here the baboons were so accustomed to the native servants emptying their buckets, that it was possible to come very close to otherwise timid animals. After some time the animals became so confident that they approached almost to within arms-reach, making it possible to take photographs without a teleobjective.

II. THE STRUCTURE AND THE ACTIVITIES OF A TROOP

A troop of baboons can possess a considerable territory (up to 6 miles in diameter) which may overlap that of a neighbouring troop. Where two troops have overlapping territories the weaker usually withdraws at the approach of the stronger group. Such retreats were observed at Pretoriuskop and Skukuza in the Kruger National Park. From various reports I have received from people with permanent residence in areas inhabited by baboons it seems highly likely that violent fights between the troops occur from time to time.

Each troop is built up of a number of adult males, a considerably greater number of females, and juveniles of all ages. The number of the latter usually amounts to two or three times that of the adults. Unfortunately no exact figures can be given because the troops observed were inhabiting dense bush where counting was impossible and the time spent with each troop was not long enough to make it possible to recognise every individual. The structure of a troop of baboons seems more permanent than that of *Cercopithecus ascanius* Schmidt: (Haddow, 1952 and Buxton, 1952) and single males appear to be rare.

All troops observed had a typical patriarchal hierarchy. The hierarchy mainly showed itself in the order in which the animals fed and mated, the stronger animals always having first choice. The extent to which a male would allow the presence of other baboons when eating or allow other weaker males to cover a female, depends on the individual's temper and its gastric or sexual hunger. On one occasion an amiable old superior male allowed the other five mature males of the troop to cover the same female in turn, after he had satisfied himself and subsequently turned to food. I have frequently observed more than one male feed in company with a female in oestrus.

An ideal family life such as described by Marais seems not to exist, nor is there any reason to think that the formation of permanent family groups is a frequent feature. I have, however, on occasions seen small groups of females surrounding the same male for more than an hour. Once a family group consisting of a male, and three females,—one of them in oestrus—was followed and observed for more than two hours. After that all trace of them was lost in the dense bush. Often a male and a female in oestrus could be seen squatting together usually apart from the rest of the troop. When the female got up and walked off the male usually followed close behind her. It will be seen from these observations that there are great individual differences in the sexual associations and that no rules can be given.

Among the females a hierarchial order is less obvious. Females in oestrus are, however, often of a quicker temper than those in anoestrus and are therefore often avoided on the feeding ground by the other females. The result is that the females in oestrus have a first choice of food among the females.

There are great individual differences in the attitude towards juveniles, but the females usually take greater interest in the juveniles than do the males.

Young baboons are very playful and their parental instinct is developed amazingly early. It is a common sight to see very young individuals carry babies either on their backs or hanging under their bodies.

Idle males usually squat on the ground or on rocks, tree trunks or other elevated points, preferably behind a bush (Fig. 1), a stone, or some other object (Fig. 2). Regular scratching and yawning can be observed. Males squatting in this fashion act as sentinels and warn the troop by their loud barks when danger approaches. These sentinels have been described by Fitzsimons (1919, 1924). When the troop is on the move there seems to be a tendency for some of the males to form a rear guard although no definite marching order has ever been observed. In one troop at Lower Sabie the supreme male was always seen to walk behind the troop when crossing a narrow bridge. He looked back alternately over right and left shoulder. Various attempts by my native helper to drive troops through the bush while I watched from

FIG. 1.   Sentry behind branches.

the distance, seemed to confirm the observations that there is a tend-

FIG. 2.   Sentry on termite hill.

ency for one or more males to drop behind the troop. No clear picture was, however, formed of this behaviour.

Grooming is a common feature when the troop is resting. Females groom juveniles, other females or males. Males groom very rarely.

Although the baboons have no fixed sleeping quarters, they have certain places they prefer,—usually tall trees or steep rocks.

The daily routine is more or less fixed, starting with eating in the morning, resting in the afternoon and eating again for a short while in the evening, before the troop retires to its sleeping quarters.

III. TYPES OF BEHAVIOUR

The various types of behaviour were studied in detail partly on Joe and Jenny, partly on wild baboons, and attempts were made to analyse them thereby hoping to arrive at a deeper understanding of their activities and the ways in which the animals make themselves understood.

A. Sounds

Any sound uttered by a baboon expresses emotion.

a. Grunts. Deep grunts can be uttered rhythmically, the faster the rhythm the greater the state of agitation. When at their quickest they are uttered not only during the expiration, but also during the intake of air, sometimes finally merging into a roar or growling shriek. Judging from observations in the Kruger National Park, the grunt may have the biological function of notifying other baboons of an individual's presence and whereabouts. It succeeds in holding the family and the troop together and warning off other individuals whose presence is undesired. Thus it may attain a function analogous to bird song.

b. Barks. A male baboon, seeing something at a safe distance but which it considers to be frightening, emits a bark similar to that of a dog. Its voice, however, carries much further than that of a dog and the bark serves as a threat to the intruder as well as a warning to the troop. Two days after the arrival of my baboons, the four month old male, Joe, uttered this warning bark at the sight of my dog (Airedale crossbreed).

c. Screech. This sound signifies that the animal is highly agitated. The type of agitation is not indicated. When screeching, the teeth are bared, the mouth is half open.

d. Growling screech. In the Kruger National Park the adult males were often heard uttering this screech when fighting or chasing one another.

e. Coughing shout or screech. This expression of joy and delight varies according to the excitement behind it. Its range extends from a quick grunt or an intermittent, almost coughing sound, to a loud intermittent shout. It never attains quite the same shrillness as an angry or frightened screech. The mouth is relaxed and wide open, the teeth are bared, and the eyebrows usually lifted. More often than not the animal is very active. This is the most expressive and varied type of sound emitted, and together with the accompanying facial mimic it informs the experienced keeper of the mood of the animal, whether simply amused or full of joy over the keeper's presence. In wild animals the accompanying mime is far less developed than in captive baboons, and in the Kruger National Park I have witnessed what signifies cordial laughter on very few occasions while, in the case of my two captive baboons, the female, Jenny, has the most expressive "laughter" (Fig. 3).

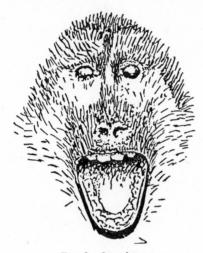

Fig. 3.   Laughter.

f. Deep soft oo-oo. This sound is usually uttered with rounded lips or at least with a somewhat contracted *musculus orbicularis oris,* so that the teeth are covered. The face is otherwise relaxed and the ears may be standing out from the head. I have observed Joe produce this sound on a few occasions when he has been separated from Jenny, and in the Kruger National Park I often watched juveniles producing it while anxiously awaiting their turn to eat. The sound indicates fretting and the facial expression is similar to that of fretting chimpanzees as described by Darwin (1872).

B. Aggressive Behaviour

a. Threat (Figs. 4 and 5). The animal usually starts by looking straight at its opponent. Its ears may be slightly forward and its fur is raised, particularly on its neck, shoulders and back. Usually the animal stands on all four legs. Its arms become rigid and straight, its hind legs are firmly planted on the ground, and its head is lifted. The whole

Fig. 4. Threat.

Fig. 5. Threat.

posture gives an impression of self assurance. If the animal moves, it does so in a rigid way, often in sudden jerks. It may stamp the ground with one hand, usually the right, similarly to the obstinately defiant stamps made by a buck with its front legs when disturbed. This stamping may merge into a jerky rubbing of the ground. In this case the hands are usually thrust forward, slightly from the side towards the midline, often in a grasping manner as if the animal literally wished to "rub the floor" with its opponent. In some cases of threat, the males retract the upper lip, slightly baring their canines into a snarl. This attitude I have never observed in the less aggressive females.

Darwin (1872) thought that snarling did not occur in monkeys. Due to the relatively large size of the canine muscle in baboons, snarling is possible in these animals. This is, for example, in contrast to *Cercopithecus aethiops,* the South African blue monkey, in which the canine muscle is so weak that snarling may be impossible or difficult to recognise. Joe has, on occasions when threatening me, retracted his upper lip more than his lower one, the wrinkles on his nose indicating a contraction of the canine and malaris muscles. A young male baboon in the Kruger National Park once threatened me by baring only the canine on the side of its mouth that was facing me.

b. Attack. The animal suddenly darts forwards making great use of its arms in setting off. Its pace is swift and smooth, but its movements give an impression of being deliberate and well calculated. The head is lifted, ears and hair raised, as during the preceding threat.

Usually the opponent flees and escapes, but if overtaken the back of its head and its shoulders are tortured by the attacker. In cases where the attacked animal is much smaller than the attacker, it is often tackled differently. The attacker grasps its opponent with one hand, (usually the right) and quickly rubs it against the ground (Fig. 6).

Fig. 6. Angry male, "rubbing the ground" with a youngster.

These movements much resemble those performed during threat, and have undoubtedly given rise to them.

C. Fighting

A remarkable feature is the way in which baboons join in fights once they have begun. Group fighting always starts with a quarrel between two baboons. In the following battle one of the baboons is defeated and screams vociferously. This screaming is the signal for a sympathetic baboon nearby to join in. In nature this is usually a mature male. Zuckerman (1932) has admirably described what now happens among captive baboons. The newcomer always takes the part of the defeated baboon and soon the winner becomes defeated. This is the signal for more baboons to join in but this time on the opposite side. Thus the battle increases with baboons alternately joining one or the other side depending on the momentary luck of the battle.

In nature a battle such as that described by Zuckerman seems to be very rare. What usually happens is that the interfering male chases the victorious party. Both baboons soon get tired, and part, and nothing further happens. Fights always draw the attention of other baboons who watch them with the greatest interest.

The habit of coming to the rescue of a defeated individual seems biologically important, because the interference usually prevents the victor from doing serious harm to the defeated party.

Joe and Jenny, in spite of their youth, had this instinct for coming to the rescue highly developed at the time I got them. When, a few days after their arrival, I wanted to put a strap on Joe, he screamed with terror and struggled all he could. This upset Jenny who broke out of her cage, and soon I was struggling with two screaming, biting, baboons. Some time later, when I had to rescue Jenny who had tried to escape from her cage, and had got stuck, it was Joe who attacked. Luckily it is a comparatively rare event for me to be attacked by Joe and Jenny together, but if one of the baboons takes fright at something and screams, it may lead to attack by the other baboon. For a long time the scuffle often began with one baboon pinching the other from behind in play or out of jealousy. The hurt baboon then thought I was the culprit and screamed with fear and anger. The actual culprit, seeing the frightened companion looking straight at me, would then turn its attention to me and attack, preferably from behind. The best thing to do in such circumstances is to ignore both animals and continue one's work, preferably with one's back to the wall! Under no circumstances can one afford to give the impression of being the cause of the commotion.

Very interesting were two occasions when Joe attacked due to a minor misunderstanding and Jenny came to my rescue. A similarly interesting case was described by Felce (1948). On that occasion an escaped chimpanzee came to the "rescue" of a young zoo-keeper who screamed with fright when he met the animal in a passage behind the cages.

. . . .

G. Rubbing of Food

Rubbing of food against the ground or against the forearm before stuffing it into the mouth, is a type of behaviour frequently displayed by eating baboons. The reason for this behaviour is obscure. It looks

Fig. 10. Displacement scratching.

as if the animal tries to clean the food. The reaction can sometimes be excited in Joe and Jenny, by bringing strangers or other animals to their cage at feeding time, or by giving them plenty of articles of attractive food, so that sudden choosing is imposed upon them. In the latter case they may pick up one bit of food after the other, rub it and put it down again. It is possible that this behaviour indicates, or at least can indicate anxiety.

H. Sexual Behaviour

a. The female in oestrus. During the period of oestrus the females often become somewhat short tempered and the males pay them greater attention. This naturally places them higher in the hierarchy. Often males allow such females to eat in their company before they permit any other females or youngsters to approach.

The relationship between males and a female in oestrus vary greatly. If there is a shortage of females in oestrus, a male may take full possession of such a female and follow her wherever she goes. The female too, may be attracted to a certain male and I have on very few occasions observed a female in oestrus follow a certain male over a period of up to a couple of hours. Sometimes, however, there is no bond developed between a male and a female in oestrus and the female can then be passed on from male to male, each of which covers her in turn. A similar communal sexual relationship exists in howler monkeys (Carpenter, 1934).

The red swollen genitalia of a female in oestrus usually attracts the attention of other females and youngsters who may examine her genitalia with fingers, nose and tongue.

As is also the case in other mammals, the female in oestrus may occasionally exhibit male behaviour and mount another female in male fashion. The behaviour is similar to that of a mounting male.

b. Mating behaviour. Mating is always initiated by the female stopping in front of a male, usually after he has been following close behind her for some time. The female usually lifts her tail slightly and bends it to one side, thereby making her anal-genital region more visible and accessible to the male. While presenting this way she looks over her shoulder towards the male and smacks her lips (Fig. 11).

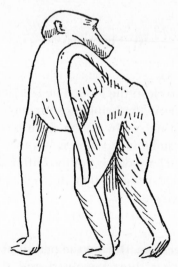

FIG. 11.   Presenting.

The male now approaches the female while smacking his lips vigorously. He then stands half upright on his hindlegs, grips the pelvic region of the female with both hands and mounts. If the female is so tall that he cannot reach, he will climb her calves and stand there during the act of copulation. While the act lasts, the lipsmacking becomes more and more vigorous until the teeth become completely bared and slightly parted. At this stage the animals grunt quickly with increasing strength. After parting the female's grunts usually merge into a short intermittent roar. Often she becomes greatly agitated and circles on the spot as if in great pain.

c. Masturbation. Males without females are often seen seeking sexual satisfaction by playing with their erected peni. An old sexually starved male was seen in the Kruger National Park to perform onanism. The ejaculation was subsequently picked up and the fingers licked.

d. Inverse sexual behaviour and homosexuality. These types of behaviour are very common among both captive and wild baboons. At an age of eleven months Jenny, who was playing with a Pekingese puppy, who she loved and mothered, once showed the reaction of mounting the puppy in male fashion, performing rhythmic movements of the pelvis.

To what extent Joe's presenting is to be regarded as pseudo-female behaviour is uncertain, but homosexual behaviour among juvenile and young male and female baboons is seen also in the wild stage. Zuckerman (1932) has given an elaborate description of this phenomenon in baboons.

Also females in oestrus may exhibit inverse sexual behaviour.

e. Presenting. This action has been described in detail under mating behaviour. It can be exhibited by males as well as by females, but in nature it is a comparatively rare action by males. Usually females present when passing in front of a male. It may or may not be accompanied by lipsmacking. Sometimes the male stretches out a hand and touches the female's hindquarters. Presenting to young ones even when on their mother's lap, has been noticed on some occasions. It also forms part of the posture of an animal when frightened or threatened by a superior individual.

f. Lipsmacking. Lipsmacking is a complicated type of action during which the lips are moved, rapidly exposing and covering the teeth in a quick succession, while the tongue is moved in and out. These movements produce an audible smacking sound. It is also known from other old-world monkeys. In all monkeys it is a friendly gesture, probably with a sexual background. It precedes copulation and lasts throughout the act. Joe and Jenny have displayed this behaviour from their infancy when I approach their cage. As Jenny's presenting to me decreased, almost disappearing before the age of two, lipsmacking also decreased to a corresponding degree. It is, however, maintained when she grooms me. Joe, on the other hand, has increased his presenting and lipsmacking when he sees me.

On visiting other captive baboons and monkeys I have tried to imitate this lipsmacking and have frequently succeeded in persuading the animals to present to me. Most convincing was the instance when I came across a young mature blue vervet monkey (*Cercopithecus aethiops*), at the Medical School. On my arrival the monkey, who was in solitary confinement, was in a rage. The African keepers were unable to approach it without its screaming and threatening them. When I performed my version of lipsmacking it suddenly changed its attitude, and approached the wire separating us, in a state of great excitement. It grasped my fingers and hand with all its force and made efforts to rub its erected highly-coloured penis against my arm. Soon it also began to lick and groom my hand. A similar but less pronounced friendly attitude was demonstrated by two monkeys of the same type in a neighbouring cage. Other monkeys in the collection merely calmed down in response to my lipsmacking approach.

In contrast with these observations are those made in the Kruger National Park. On no occasion did I elicit any friendly response to my lipsmacking.

I. Grooming

Grooming is a behaviour that is difficult to explain. It is a definite female behaviour. Out of 80 cases of grooming noted it was found that in 27 cases a female groomed a female, in 33 cases a female groomed a male and in only 7 cases did a male groom a female. In 6 of the cases in which a male groomed a female, it was done briefly in an absent-minded way. Of the remaining 13 cases of grooming, 5 were females grooming youngsters, 4 youngsters grooming females, and 3 youngsters grooming youngsters and 1 female grooming herself. There seemed to be a tendency for younger females to groom the older females longer and more frequently than the other way round.

Grooming is often initiated by the one individual presenting to the other. Particularly evolved and rigid is the ceremony linked with the grooming of an adult male. This ceremony is initiated by the female which presents. Often the presenting is accompanied by lipsmacking by either or both parties. The male stretches out his hand towards the female's hindquarters, thereby indicating the wish for a closer contact. Then he strokes her sacral and genital regions. Usually he does not groom properly, rather caresses the area round her tail and her genitalia in a manner that appears absentminded.

. . . .

SUMMARY

i. In this paper an attempt has been made to describe the behaviour of the Chacma, and to make an analysis thereof. The observations were made on two young captive baboons, Joe and Jenny, as well as on wild ones.

ii. There is a hierarchical organisation of the troop which mainly shows itself in feeding and mating. Among the females the hierarchical order is less obvious than among the males. It seems as if females in oestrus are of higher rank than those in anoestrus. The male-female association is often very casual and the formation of permanent family groups are rather the exception than the rule. Idle males act as sentinels.

iii. A. All sounds emitted express emotion. Various sounds and their emotional motivations are described.

B. In the typical threat posture the animal stands facing the opponent with lifted head, stiff arms and hairs on shoulder and back raised. It looks straight at the opponent. Often it snarls and its movements are rigid and jerking. It may rub the ground with its hand or stamp with it. It then suddenly darts forward in attack.

C. The opponent is pursued and, if caught up with, is bitten, usually in backhead and shoulder, or, if smaller rubbed against the ground. Other baboons come to the rescue of the defeated individual. In nature this leads to a wild chase. In captivity it may end up in some mass fighting.

D. Baboons have great respect for authority.

E. In the retreating submissive behaviour the animal crouches and moves with its side or tail towards the aggressor. The teeth may be bared in horror and the aggressor is watched evasively over the shoulder while the retreating animal presents its hindquarters.

F. Yawning and scratching are commonly noticed in sentinels. They are considered as displacement activities, signifying nervous tension.

G. When eating the baboons frequently rub their food against their fore-arm. It may signify nervous tension.

H. Sexual behaviour has given rise to many other activities.
a. Great interest is often shown in females in oestrus, the genitalia of whom are often examined by other females and juveniles.
b. Mating is initiated by lipsmacking and presenting from the female.
c. Masturbation and onanism is common in inferior males without a female.
d. Inverse and homosexual behaviour is common in captivity.
e. Presenting is a friendly and inviting gesture with a sexual origin.
f. Lipsmacking is a very much used friendly and inviting gesture, probably with a sexual origin.

I. Grooming is a typical female activity. It is impossible to explain its significance. The concentration with which the act is performed seems to indicate some physiological background.

J. The various types of behaviour have been analysed and their elements and significance listed.

K. In cases of opposing emotional motivations the elements of behaviour are combined in characteristic ways which are interpreted by the onlooking baboons.

L. Female baboons are usually fond of very young individuals. The mothers usually look very well after their babies during their first few weeks, but the interest gradually fades after the young ones have been weaned and begin to stray about. They show great interest in each others' babies.

The maternal instinct is developed already at an age of six months or less.

The attitude of the male towards the young varies from complete intolerance to great affection.

M. The young individual always knows its guardian and seeks its protection in case of danger.

N. In play, the young baboon includes almost all the activities of the adult. Fighting, biting and mating are some of the main features. The various types of bites are described. The play copulation includes the full ritual exhibited by adults during their mating. It is surprising to find that the innate ritual is fully developed in youngsters only a few months of age.

O. Any object can be of value to a baboon. Its value depends on the interest shown in it by other individuals.

P. Baboons are primarily vegetarians, but they love in addition to their diet of insects and probably birds' eggs. Occasionally they turn carnivorous.

Q. Much food is dug up from the ground or collected under stones. The turning of stones is an innate behaviour which is performed at a very young age.

R. Baboons seem to have an innate fear of snakes or other cylindrical bodies which can bend and wriggle.

Towards other animals which do not serve as food they normally show indifference. On occasions however, the juveniles take pleasure in teasing other animals. Cases where kudu and lions were teased are described. In the latter case the mature males attempted to maintain order among the juveniles trying to prevent them from approaching too close. This action seems to indicate that the rescue responses can not be explained as a simple reflectory response.

REFERENCES

BUXTON, A. P. (1952). Observations on the diurnal behaviour of the redtail monkey (*Cercopithecus ascanius schmidti*) in a small forest in Uganda.—J. Anim. Ecol. 21, pp. 25–28.

CARPENTER, C. R. (1934). A field study of the behaviour and social relations of howling monkeys.—Comp. Psychol. Mon. 10; 2, pp. 1–168.

CHANCE, M. R. A. (1956). Social structure of a colony of *Macaca mulatta*.—Brit. J. Anim. Behav. 4, pp. 1–13.

DART, R. A. (1957). The osteodontokeratic culture of *Australopithecus prometeus*. —Transv. Mus. Mem. 10, 105 p.

DARWIN, C. (1872). Expression of the emotions.—London.

——, (1889). The descent of man.—London.

FELCE, W. (1948). Apes.—London.

FITZSIMONS, F. W. (1919). The natural history of South Africa, Mammals I.

——, (1924). The monkey folk of South Africa.—London.

HADDOW, A. J. (1952). Field and laboratory studies on an African monkey, *Cercopithecus ascianus schmidti* Matschie.—Proc. Zool. Soc. London 122, pp. 297–394.

MARAIS, E. N. (1939). My friends the baboons.—London.

SHILLER, P. H. (1952). Innate constituents of complex responses in primates.— Psychol. Rev., pp. 177–91.

ZUCKERMAN, S. (1932). The social life of monkeys and Apes.—London.

CHAPTER 6

INTERNAL FACTORS AND INNATE BEHAVIOR

The most complete theoretical and descriptive statements regarding innate behavior are given by Professors Tinbergen and Lorenz. In their views, as in the views of others who have considered innate behavior (Beach, 1948), it is clear that a number of internal factors are involved in such behavior. The problem of the present chapter will be to investigate some relationships between internal factors and innate behavior. Particular attention will be given to hormonal and neural factors.

Theories of the Relationship between Internal Factors and Innate Behavior

Three theories that attempt to specify the relationship between internal factors and innate behavior will be discussed. The theories are stated briefly because of their tentative nature based on the incompleteness of the physiological and psychological data across a variety of species and phyla.

Theory of Structural and Sensory Changes. The view of the present writers is that internal factors affect innate behavior in one or both of the following ways. They affect external structures and/or motor patterns, some of which are secondary sex characteristics. These effects alter the animal's sign stimulus value for the other animals involved in the sequence of innate behaviors. Such changes then alter details of the entire sequence of innate patterns such as mating, care of the young, and fighting. The second effect of internal factors is on the sensitivity of structures of the animal so that sensitivity to stimuli and subsequent responses are changed. One example is the change in the sensitivity of the *glans penis* of the male rat that is associated with hormonal changes; another example is the decrease in visual sensitivity that occurs in an animal following removal of the occipital area of the neo-cortex. These hypotheses are consistent with a number of the specific findings that will be discussed in this chapter. However, the hypotheses are meant to deal with behavior and not with physiological mechanisms.

Theory of Internal Arousal and Consummatory Mechanisms. This name is applied to the theory of Beach (1948, 1958b) that is primarily a physiological theory that evolved from his studies of sexual behavior. Beach distinguishes between internal changes associated with *arousal mechanisms* and those associated with *consummatory mechanisms.* The *arousal mechanism* is a conceptual scheme that has such properties as: being organized and functional in young animals, showing individual differences in reactivity that "cannot be interpreted as a consequence of hormonal variation because similar individual differences are seen in males which have been castrated on the day of birth" (Beach, 1958b, p. 279), being responsive to external stimulation such as an appropriate mate, and being modifiable by experience.

The *consummatory mechanism,* another conceptual system, is assumed to be activated when the arousal mechanism reaches some threshold level. The consummatory mechanism for sexual behavior, for example, is assumed to be functionally organized at a neural level in pre-pubertal animals and the motor patterns associated with the consummatory mechanism are assumed to be relatively stereotyped and unalterable by experience, particularly for species of the lower phylogenetic levels. It is further assumed that the consummatory mechanism for primates, such as chimpanzees, is incompletely organized prior to specific consummatory experience.

Hormonal and neural factors are assumed to participate in both the arousal and consummatory systems but their participation differs from species to species and between the sexes. These views are consistent with the data that suggest differential effects of hormonal and neural changes between species and between the sexes of the same species.

Theory of Hierarchical Organization of Neural Centers. Tinbergen has developed a detailed theory of the relations between internal factors and innate behavior (1951, p. 123). The theory like both of those previously described, considers that innate behavior involves internal and external factors. However, it is more similar to Beach's theory since it postulates a neural and hormonal model of innate behavior. The Tinbergen model suggests a hierarchical organization of neural centers, each of which has its own afferent and efferent connections. Each center is associated with a particular component of an instinctive response. The energy or impulses from a particular neural center are assumed to flow into motor pathways and into lower centers due to the action of the appropriate sign stimulus, the releaser, that removes the block from the neural center and allows the impulses to be activated. This is called the action of the *innate releasing mechanism*. Hormones are assumed to act on the highest centers by facilitating the action of the releasing stimulus, but the hormones do not provide the energy or motivation for innate behavior, they simply allow the behaviors to be run off.

The development of this theoretical model by Tinbergen was closely shared with Lorenz (Lorenz and Tinbergen, 1957) and both of these theorists have cautioned against taking it too literally. The model is particularly useful in organizing some research findings regarding the apparent spontaneity of innate behavior, the fixed sequential aspects of many instinctive behaviors, and the role of the sign stimulus in instinctive behavior.

The General Relationship between Internal Factors and Behavior

Behavior involves an intimate interplay between the responding organism and a stimulus. As pointed out in Chapter 5, the stimulus, especially for instinctive responses, may be the response of another organism. Thus, any factor that affects sensitivity to a class of stimuli or affects the stimuli themselves, that is, the organism as a stimulus, must necessarily affect behavior. In additon, internal factors affect structures and the functions of these structures, some of which are secondary sex characteristics. Thus, two major consequences for behavior follow from these general considerations: (*a*) perceptual or motor responses of the organism may change with structural changes; (*b*) insofar as these response changes represent social signals, sign stimuli, for another organism, the changes will affect the interactions of the organisms that are involved. Such interactions between individuals are particularly important in reproductive and aggressive behaviors and these two behavior classes are the principle ones for which internal factors have been found to have effects.

We are suggesting that internal factors, particularly hormonal and neural, *participate in behavior* but *do not produce behavior*. This view is consistent with Tinbergen's statement (1951, p. 74), that such factors are associated with "increasing the excitability of the sensory-motor mechanism especially involved in the instinctive activity." The present view is antithetical to the view that internal factors directly produce or drive behavior. "Drive" interpretations are considered to be imputations on the data that arise from an inability or failure to determine the changes in structures, the functions of the structures, or the sign stimulus functions that are associated with the internal changes.

Some Cautions. The generality of any specific finding about relationships between internal factors and innate behavior is limited by a number of considerations. Among these are the following: (*a*) different species may respond differently to similar internal changes; (*b*) individual differences within a species to similar internal changes may be large; (*c*) past experience may modify innate responses in such a way as to override the effects of internal factors; and (*d*) a number of hormonal changes may be produced by behavior changes rather than the converse. For example, the removal of the gonads does not prevent reproductive behavior for some male insects (Haskell, 1960 **) but it does prevent it for some male birds (Eisener, 1960), and as noted by Beach (1958b, p. 272), there are always a few individuals who fail to display the expected behavioral change associated with some particular hormonal change.

Hormonal Factors and Innate Behavior: A Survey of Methods

Hormones are secreted by endocrine glands that are located in various parts of the body. In animal forms these secretions are carried by the blood. Thus, any particular hormone can have widespread effects due to its wide distribution. Hormonal processes have been identified in higher plants; many invertebrates, especially insects; and all vertebrates, including humans.

The endocrine glands in vertebrates that are generally recognized are: hypophysis or pituitary, thyroid, parathyroid, adrenal, islands of Langerhans in the pancreas, mucosa of the gastro-intestinal tract, the gonads (testes of males and ovaries of females), and the fetal component of the placenta in prenatal organisms. A number of these glands, such as the pituitary and the adrenals, are divided into functionally and structurally different parts each of which secretes different hormones.

Neural secretions of a hormonal type have recently been identified in both invertebrates and vertebrates. Although these secretions appear to be related to fundamental processes, such as the physiology of regeneration and reproduction, they have not yet been related to behavior. Gorbman and Bern (1962) present a detailed study of comparative aspects of endocrinology and discuss neuro-secretions of invertebrates and vertebrates. Since the majority of hormonal systems have very indirect or limited effects on behavior, the primary emphasis in the present section will be on gonadal and pituitary hormones.

One method used to investigate hormonal factors and behavior involves *removal of the endocrine glands* and assessment of behavior for the groups among which the endocrines have been removed. The study by Tavolga (1955 **) illustrates this method in the investigation of reproductive behavior of fish, and the study by Haskell (1960 **) illustrates it with insects. It will be noted that in these studies control groups were subjected to an operation similar to the one used with the experimental groups, but the endocrines were not removed from the control groups.

A second method that is frequently used in conjunction with the first involves *replacement treatment* with hormones. In this method the hormone that is assumed to be depleted by removal of a gland is replaced by injecting it directly into the organism's system. In some cases pellets containing the hormone are placed under the organism's skin so that the hormone is slowly absorbed. Replacement treatment is usually used as a cross-check for observations of behavior changes following removal of the gland. That is, if removing an endocrine and the depletion of its hormones lead to a behavior change, replacement of the particular hormone associated with the gland should lead to behaviors associated with the normal, intact animal. This method is illustrated by Martins and Thales (1948 **).

A third method used to study the effects of hormonal factors on behavior involves *supplemental treatment* with hormones. In this case, the intact animal is given extra doses of hormones and observations of premature occurrences of behavior patterns or exaggerated behaviors are taken as evidence that the hormone is involved in the behavioral process. As an example of this method, one group of young dogs described by Martins and Thales (1948 **) was given supplemental hormone treatment and premature occurrences of adult micturition patterns were observed.

The results of experiments involving hormones and behavior must be viewed against the background information regarding endocrines before interpretations about specific hormonal changes and their effects on behavior can be postulated. For example, the hormonal systems of the entire body are interrelated so that a change in one system may change a second system, and this second system may be the one that is associated with the observed behavior change. This is particularly important when detailed analyses of hormones and reproductive behaviors are made. Particular difficulties in interpretation arise when studies of effects of removal of endocrine glands are conducted with those glands that secrete a large number of different hormones. This is one reason that the method of replacement treatment is frequently used in conjunction with the method of endocrine removal. Another complication arises from the fact that the chemical functions of some hormones are changed when the hormones reach their site of action. So, for example, some gonadal hormones start as male hormones and then function chemically like female hormones in certain parts of the body. In addition, some hormones are secreted from a number of structures, for example, estrogen is secreted by ovaries, placental tissue, and the corpus luteum.

Hormones and Reproductive Behavior

Among the most direct relationships between hormones and behavior are those found for reproductive behaviors (Beach, 1958a&b; Young, 1951). Even these relationships are very complex and contingent on such variables as the evolutionary level of the species, the sex and the age of the animal, and its prior experience with reproductive behavior. Gonadal hormones, estrogens associated with females and androgens associated with males, are most directly concerned with courting and copulation. Other endocrine systems are involved in other aspects of reproductive behavior such as nest building and care of the young. These endocrine systems involve the anterior pituitary, the thyroid, and the adrenal glands. The relationships between these systems and behavior will be discussed in a later section.

Gonadal Hormones and Reproductive Behavior of Invertebrates. As noted by Beach (1958a) data regarding behavior and endocrinology is much less complete for invertebrate species than for vertebrate species. However, the gross anatomy of species of a number of invertebrate phyla indicate the presence of gonads which are thought to be related to reproductive behavior for species in these phyla. For example, planaria, the familiar genus of flatworms, engage in sexual reproduction involving differentiated males and females. Segmented worms, such as the earthworm, are typically bisexual with each animal containing organs and endocrine systems of both the male and the female. However, experimental study of the relations between these endocrine systems and reproductive behavior have not been undertaken with either of these groups of animals.

Studies of the reproductive behavior of some insects and the relations of gonadal hormones to these behaviors reveal a rather complex picture as indicated in the study by Haskell (1960 **). Haskell found that species-specific courting, stridulation, and copulation of male grasshoppers were not affected by removal of the testes and accessory glands, whereas the receptive behavior of females was inhibited within twenty-four hours by removal of their ovaries and accessory glands. As Haskell notes, similar differential effects of gonad removal have been noted for other insects, such as crickets, in the order *Orthoptera*.

Relations between innate reproductive behaviors and hormonal factors among insects such as bees, ants, and wasps in the order *Hymenoptera* are not predicted in a simple way from the mammalian model of behavior and hormones. The high degree of division of labor, the caste system of some *Hymenoptera*, has associated structural changes involving most parts of the animals' bodies including their gonads and accessory glands. The queens among these species have large ovaries and sperm sacs into which sperm are stored from the repeated matings that occur during the "marriage flight." Workers and soldier ants seem to be degenerate females that have atrophied ovaries, but occasionally these individuals lay unfertilized eggs that produce males upon hatching. The males are responsive to the behavior of the queen and copulate with her during the marriage flight, but the role of their gonads has not been clearly established.

Gonadal Hormones and Reproductive Behavior of Vertebrates. Relationships between innate reproductive behaviors and gonadal hormones are incompletely investigated for lower vertebrates such as amphibians and reptiles. Courting and copulation of the male skink, a lizard-like reptile (Reynolds, 1943), and of the male chameleons (Noble and Greenberg, 1940) are eliminated by the removal of the testes. Conversely, copulation can be induced in chameleons if pellets of testosterone were implanted in the skin of these castrated males or in the skin of immature males or females. Data regarding amphibians, such as frogs, toads, and salamanders, also indicate that removal of the testes of the male stops courting and copulation. However, some early studies cited by Beach (1958a) indicate that removal of the testes of amphibians *during the mating season* rather than before it does not interfere with copulation. One interpretation of these data is that the inhibition of courting and copulation by castration leads to the disappearance of the secondary sex characteristics including the stimulating responses that are necessary for successful copulation. However, individuals that are castrated during the reproductive season have the secondary sex characteristics that are necessary as sign stimuli for mating behavior.

The data regarding gonadal hormones and reproductive behaviors of fish indicate a weak relationship between the secretions from the testes and courting and copulatory behavior. The study by Tavolga

(1955 **) indicates that gonadectomy (removal of the gonads) does not
prevent courtship or spawning in Gobiis. Similar results have been
found for Jewel fish (*Hemichromis bimaculatus*) by Noble and Cumpf
(1936). Thus, as reported for insects, sexual responses of males of these
species are not controlled by gonadal hormones. Rather, these responses seem to be controlled by the responses of the receptive female
and the general sexual maturity of the male.

Many studies of reproductive behavior of birds have dealt with investigations of effects of hormonal factors. However, as noted by
Eisener (1960) in a review of more than two hundred fifty research
papers, generalizations about the relationships between endocrine
process and behavior of birds are dangerous because the most systematic data have been collected from two atypical species. These are the
domestic fowl that has unusual reproductive behavior and the pigeon
that is unusual because of its milk-producing crop.

The behaviors of birds that have been most frequently studied in
relation to hormonal factors are: courting, copulation, nest building,
and care of the young. Gonadal and gonadotropic hormones (those
secreted from the pituitary which interact with gonadal hormones)
have been implicated in these relationships. Warren and Hinde
(1959 **), using a simple method for measuring nest building of birds,
found that injections of ovarian hormones led male and female canaries to build nests during the nonbreeding season. Other changes in
behavior and secondary sex characteristics have been studied using
castrated male birds. So, for example, castration of male domestic fowl
and gulls led to the reduction or elimination of mating calls of both
species and led to reduction in the size of the combs and wattles (secondary sex characteristics) of domestic fowl. Replacement therapy
with androgens was associated with return of the characteristic male
structures and the recurrence of courting responses (Collias, 1950;
Phillips and McKinney, 1962 *).

Reproduction involves a prolonged, mutual interaction especially
among birds, and this interaction is based on vocalizations, movements
and displays, sign stimuli. Thus, any change in these sign stimuli that
are also secondary sex characteristics, would be expected to lead to a
change in reproductive behavior. So, for example, the failure of the
male to show male responses would be associated with the absence
of female responses and ultimate failure or reduction in reproductive
behavior. These conclusions follow from the theory of structural and
sensory change that was proposed to explain some of the effects of hor-

mones on behavior. Other data to which the theory is applied are considered in the section dealing with effects of pituitary hormones.

PHILLIPS, R. E. AND MCKINNEY, F. The role of testosterone in the displays of some ducks. *Anim. Behav.*, 1962, 10, 244–46.

Ducklings of three species were given daily injections of testosterone propionate and control groups were given injections of oil. Males and females of Pintail (*Anas ocuta*), Mallard (*Anas platyrhyncos*), and Redhead (*Aythyo americana*) were used. The courtship displays, including postures, movements, and calls of adult males, were observed in the treated male ducklings of the three species. No such responses were observed among the treated females or control birds. Courting responses occurred particularly if a bait female were presented. Castration of the male Mallards when they were mature led to a greater decrease in courting among control castrates than among those previously injected. Replacement therapy led to recovery of the courting postures, movements, and calls. While these results do not identify the target structures associated with hormonal effects, they do illustrate some specific effects of hormones on secondary sex characteristics of a behavorial sort. Such changes would be involved in producing changes in reproductive behavior as a function of hormone treatment.

The study of gonadal hormones and reproductive behaviors of mammals has been concentrated on laboratory and domesticated species including: rats, dogs, cats, and infrahuman primates (Beach, 1948; Beach, 1958a&b). Relationships between testosterone and the male reproductive responses have been investigated by the method of gonadal removal, hormone replacement, and hormone supplement. For a number of species the responses of mounting, erection, and ejaculation can be eliminated and made to return in adult males, or forced from prepuberal animals by appropriate procedures with male hormones.

However, some data argue against the simple interpretation that these behaviors arise in a direct way from hormones. For example, prepuberal males normally show components of mating behavior, including mounting and erection but not ejaculation. Castrated mammals, castrated immediately after birth, also show these responses (Beach, 1958b). However, prenatal administration of hormones affected subsequent mating (Phoenix, *et al.*, 1959 *). In addition, individual differences in mating responses are found among normal animals, among castrated animals, and among those receiving replacement therapy (Rosenblatt, 1958 *). Although the facts about individual differences have not been adequately incorporated into theories, such individual differences may be related to the persistent finding that prior experience with mating can offset or in other ways alter hormonal effects. That is, a biologically intact male can be conditioned to avoid mating by pairing approach to the receptive female with a strong noxious stimulus (Beach, *et al.,* 1956). Conversely, reluctant male dogs and cats can be conditioned to approach receptive females after which they mate promptly and frequently (Beach and Zitrin, 1945).

PHOENIX, C. H., GOY, R. W., GERALL, A. A. AND YOUNG, W. C. Organizing action of prenatally administered testosterone proprionate on the tissues mediating mating behavior in the female guinea pig. *Endocrinology,* 1959, **65,** 369–82.

A number of female guinea pigs were treated with doses of testosterone during most of their periods of pregnancy. The sexual behavior of the offspring of these females was compared with that of the offspring of normal females. The female offspring were tested for responses of lordosis (the typical female mating response) and mounting (the typical male mating response). The offspring of treated mothers showed less lordosis than normals and following treatment with testosterone these offspring showed more mounting. The suppression of lordosis persisted for more than 12 months. It was concluded that the testosterone injected into the pregnant females permanently altered the biological organization and behavior of their female offspring (for example, some of the female offspring were hermaphroditic).

ROSENBLATT, J. S. AND ARONSON, L. R. The influence of experience on the behavioral effects of androgen in prepuberally castrated male cats. *Anim. Behav.,* 1958, 171–82.

Thirteen male kittens were castrated when four months old (prepuberal) and when they were adults they were tested for sexual responses to receptive females. Almost no sexual responses occurred on these tests. All of the males then received prolonged replacement treatment with androgenic hormones during which time half of them had a number of sexual experiences and the others did not. Following recovery from hormone treatments, all of the males were again tested for sexual responses to receptive females. The males that had had sexual experience showed appropriate sexual responses while the others did not. These results indicate that hormones may be necessary to initiate mature sexual behavior but sexual experience is necessary to maintain it. In addition, it can then be maintained in higher vertebrates in the absence of appropriate hormones.

Mating behavior of infrahuman primates is almost independent of gonadal hormones. Prepuberal male monkeys show the total complex of mating responses with the exception of ejaculation. Castration does not prevent the development of sexual responses even if castration occurs before puberty or does castration eliminate sexual activity with the exception of ejaculation in adult males (Beach, 1948). However, as Beach points out (1958b, p. 276) in discussing the behavior of the castrated primates: "sexual excitability may remain high for an indefinite period and copulation may continue but mating performance is often perfunctory and lethargic. . . ." That is, some general effects of castration sometimes occur among infrahuman primates. One interpretation of the lethargy is that structural changes associated with castration, such as were found on the *glans penis* of the rat (Beach and Levenson, 1950) may occur for the primate and these changes may lead to reduced sensitivity and indifferent responsiveness.

CLARK, G. Prepubertal castration in the male chimpanzee with some effects of replacement therapy. *Growth*, 1945, **9**, 327–39.

Growth and sexual behavior of a male chimpanzee that had been castrated when 22 months old were studied until the animal was more than 12 years old. It was found that its growth, such as weight gaining, was more typical of the female than the male chimpanzee. However, the development of its sexual behavior was similar to that of the normal male as was the development of the *glans penis*. Brief periods of treatment with testosterone after puberty did not affect the growth or behavior. These data suggest that hormones have little relationship to sexual behavior of male infrahuman primates.

It is clear that mating behavior is sufficiently complex among higher animals that sexual responsiveness of individuals may differ as a function of differences in stimuli that elicit the behavior and as a function of differences in the responses of mates that act as salient stimuli for mating behavior. Thus, removal or replacement of any single biological product would be expected to have only a modest effect on mating responses, even if such responses are biologically essential. The theoretical task for the psychologist becomes one of identifying the factors associated with reproductive behavior (e.g. stimuli, past history, structural and functional changes) and specifying the relevance of these variables both within and between species.

Pituitary Hormones and Reproductive Behavior. The pituitary is found in all vertebrates and functional relationships between hormones from the pituitary and gonadal hormones are documented for all classes of vertebrates (Beach, 1958b). For example, some pituitary secretions control the production of estrogens and androgens. In addition, a reciprocal relationship exists such that excessive production of gonadal hormones inhibits further production of gonadotropic hormones from the pituitary. Detailed discussions of the relationships among the hormonal systems, especially as they apply to reproductive behavior are given by Beach (1948), Dodd (1955), and Eisener, (1960).

HUMPHRIES, A. A. JR. Observations on the mating behavior of normal and pituitary implanted *Triturus viridescens*. Physiol. Zool., 1955, **28**, 73–79.

The mating of normal salamanders (*Amphibia*) was found to involve a sequence of innate stimulus–response elements. The male oriented to a glandular secretion from the female and moved toward the extended cloaca of the female. The orientation of the male elicited undulating movements of the body of the female. The male then clasped the female, the first element of the copulatory response. If a sperm mass was not deposited by the male, the courting sequence was repeated.

Females that had received supplementary pituitary implants were more active in soliciting males and themselves clasped males or other females.

However, the supplementary pituitary implants activated these responses only after ovulation had occurred. In other words, the exaggerated and inappropriate mating responses occurred only after the physiological reproductive cycle had begun.

Removal of the pituitary leads to atrophy of the gonad and replacement therapy leads to its reactivation. Thus, removal of the pituitary removes gonadal hormones. Humphries (1956 *) studied the effect of supplemental pituitary hormones on reproductive behavior of the females of a species of salamander. He found that the treated females were more active in their solicitation of males than untreated females, but he could not identify why this happened. Supplementary treatment with anterior pituitary of chicks of domestic fowl leads them to crow at nine days of age and show treading (the copulatory response) at 13 days of age (Domin and Vandyke, 1932). These results indicate that secondary sexual characteristics, both structures and response patterns are affected directly or indirectly by pituitary (gonadotropic) hormones. These results can account for some of the effects on behavior of treatment with pituitary hormones.

In the discussion of cautions relevant to hormones and behavior it was noted that a body of evidence is accumulating that indicates that *aspects of reproductive behavior affect the production of hormones.* The specific data to which that discussion referred involves the finding that some behaviors associated with reproduction lead to an increase in the production of prolactin, which is another pituitary hormone found in mammals and in birds that have milk crops (Lehrman, 1958 *). Prolactin has long been implicated as a hormone that is a factor in some aspects of reproductive behavior but it was assumed that the hormone controlled the behavior. Evidence that behavior controls the secretion of this hormone indicates that some responses that occur early in the reproductive sequence control later responses through the indirect means of affecting hormonal output. In addition hormones, like prolactin affect structures such as the milk crop of the pigeon that serve as sign stimuli for mutual responses between the mating animals or between the individual and its young.

LEHRMAN, D. S.   Effect of female sex hormones on incubation behavior in the Ring Dove. *J. comp. physiol. Psychol.,* 1958, 51, 142–45.

Sixty-nine mating pairs of ring doves (*Strystophelia risoria*) were used to investigate the relationships between incubation behaviors and the hormones estrogen, progesterone, and prolactin. Incubation behavior was measured in terms of the persistence of the birds in remaining on eggs in the nest. Hormones were given to some birds, and their behavior and subsequent levels of prolactin secretion were compared with control birds. Contrary to the expected view, it was found that stimulation from the birds' behavior (nesting) and its mate (courting) affect the secretion of estrogen and progesterone, and these hormones then affect subsequent behavior. Prolactin injections alone did not lead to incubation behaviors.

Hormones and Other Innate Behaviors

The two classes of responses that will be discussed in this section are micturition and fighting. For some species these responses can be considered as secondary sex characteristics, that is, they differentiate males from females. For example, the responses involved in micturition clearly and reliably differentiates males from females both for domestic and wild species of dogs (*Canidae*). Similarly, the responses involved in fighting differentiate males from females for many species of domestic and wild birds, although the differentiation is less complete than for micturition.

Gonadal hormones, particularly androgens, appear to be important factors associated with both of these classes of responses. The study by Martins and Thales (1948 **) shows the relationship between gonadal hormones and the micturition pattern of dogs. The data from this study support and extend that obtained by Berg (1944 *) who had shown a correlation between the presence of testosterone and the development of leg-lifting that is associated with micturition of mature male dogs. While the results of both studies clearly implicate testosterone as a necessary factor in the development of the pattern, the mechanism for the relationship is not clear. That is, controlled experiments using replacement therapy and supplemental hormone treatment with spayed females suggest that the response of leg-lifting must occur early in the dog's life if it is to be brought out by subsequent treatments. If it does not occur, as for example with older females that are spayed after puberty and then given testosterone treatment, the testosterone treatment is not sufficient to lead to male micturition responses. On the other hand, females given testosterone treatment while immature, show the characteristic male micturition response. It has also been found that the male micturition response does not depend on supporting stimuli such as visual or olfactory cues, although the frequency of the response can be increased by appropriate external stimuli. It should be noted that urine and feces also function as sign stimuli associated with mating and the marking of territorial for a number of species of mammals.

BERG, I. A. Development of behavior: The micturition pattern in the dog. *J. exp. Psychol.*, 1944, 34, 343–68.

The micturition pattern of dogs, characterized by leg-lifting for mature males and squatting for females, was studied with a total of 22 dogs of various breeds. The dogs were studied from several months of age through maturity. Prior to sexual maturity, both males and females squat but the male pattern could be elicited in male pups at 8 weeks of age by repeated treatment with testosterone. In the normal male pups the adult pattern develops in discrete stages characterized as cephalocaudal change and mass to specific change. This development occurs from the 19th to the 43rd week. Female pups never show leg-lifting in association with urination even after injections of testosterone. However, injections of estrogen and presentation of fearful stimuli led adult males to squat. It is concluded the male pattern is innate and controlled by male hormones which act on the more elementary pattern of squatting.

The data regarding the relationship between fighting and hormones present a picture that is in some respects similar and in some respects different from that found for micturition of dogs. As indicated by Beaman (1947 *) fighting by male mice is facilitated or reduced by appropriate treatment with gonadal hormones. Similar observations have been reported for birds, particularly domestic fowl (see Chapter 8 for a discussion of this topic). Since females also fight, the effect of androgen treatment on mature females is to increase the frequency and vigor of their fighting (Allee and Foreman, 1955). Thus, unlike the micturition pattern of the dog that is shown only by mature male dogs or others that are specially treated, fighting is shown to some extent by both males and females and is increased in frequency and vigor by hormonal treatment of either sex.

Beaman, E. A. The effect of the male hormone on the aggressive behavior of mice. *Physiol. Zool.*, 1947, **20**, 373–405.

The fighting behavior of males to two strains of mice was studied under a variety of conditions: Both strains of mice, C57 Black and Bagg albino, were observed under normal conditions, when castrated and after replacement treatment with androgenic hormones. It was found that patterns of fighting were very similar for both strains although the C57 Blacks fought more frequently. For both strains castration led to a marked decrease in frequency of attacks and fights and implants of testosterone led to a recovery of attacking and fighting behavior.

The specific mechanisms that are involved in the association between fighting and hormones for birds and mice have not been identified. Nor have they been identified in the micturition pattern of dogs. Scott (1958) postulates that hormones lower the fighting threshold for mice and birds and Martin and Thales (1948 **) suggest that gonadal hormones organize neural patterns associated with the male micturition pattern. Neither of these views has sufficient supporting evidence but each is held by some researchers (Beach, 1958b; Tinbergen, 1951).

One interpretation that we suggest to account for the changes in fighting shown by animals that are treated with gonadal hormones involves two related ideas. The first idea is that the hormones affect the animal's secondary sex characteristics, such as its voice, posture, and structures such as the comb and spurs of domestic fowl. The other idea is that fighting involves two animals and is initiated by the movements of one or both of the animals. Thus, it is suggested that the effects of hormones are on the secondary sex characteristics, sign stimuli, which are then directly involved in the initiation or continuation of fighting between members of the same species. A relationship between hormones, particularly androgens, and secondary sex characteristics is known for such animals as mice, birds, and primates (Collias, 1950; Witschi, 1961). In addition, the functions of the movements of one animal as a sign stimulus for the attack or retreat by another are known for many species (see Chapter 8). Experiments with mice (Scott & Fredrickson, 1951) and the study by Ratner (1961, as reported in Chapter 8) indicate the importance of success or failure in fighting on the subsequent fighting behavior of the animal. In summary it is suggested that secondary sex characteristics lead to the initiation of more fights and a success or failure in fighting lead to continued fighting or inability to fight. Thus, the effects of the hormones are indirect.

Although this interpretation of the effects of hormones on behavior does not deal with the physiological problem of determining the details of the process by which hormones act on *target structures* and their functions, the interpretation is consistent with the findings of the previously discussed experiments. It can also be used to explain the results of some other experiments that have investigated the relationship between hormones and fighting for infrahuman primates. Specifically, this interpretation resolves some apparently difficult problems proposed by Bindra (1959) in his analysis of the relations between hormones and fighting of chimpanzees. Research, including a study by Birch and Clark (1950 *), indicate that if supplemental hormone treatment or replacement treatment is given to chimpanzees it leads to a swelling or reddening of the sex skin (a sign stimulus involved in the behavior of this species). This change is then associated with an increase in fighting behavior. On the other hand, when the hormonal treatments do not lead to swelling of the sex skin, no change in fighting is observed. While these data cannot be satisfactorily explained using the theory that hormones affect thresholds of response or arousal levels, they can be explained by considering the relationship between the reddening of the sex skin as a sign stimulus and the response of other chimpanzees to this sign stimulus.

BIRCH, H. G. AND CLARK, G. Hormonal modification of social behavior:

IV. The mechanism of estrogen-induced dominance in chimpanzees. *J. comp. physiol. Psychol.*, 1950, **43**, 181–93.

The dominance relationships between two previously castrated (ovarectomized) female chimps was studied before, during, and after hormone treatment. Dominance was measured in terms of which animal got a single piece of food when it was placed between them. Before hormone treatments chimp L dominated chimp N on all test trials. Treatment of N with estrogenic hormones shifted the dominance so that N was eventually dominant on all trials. The frequency of domination by N was almost perfectly correlated with the reddening and swelling of N's sex skin. After N's recovery from the hormone treatments, L regained her dominance on the food tests. The results of this study clearly show the importance of secondary sex characteristics on dominance behavior.

Micturition and fighting are only two classes of innate behaviors that are affected by hormonal factors. The study of hoarding by hamsters (Smith, *et al.*, 1954) illustrates another such relationships.

SMITH, W. I., KRAWCZUN, A. J., WISEHAUPT, N. J. AND ROSS, S. Hoarding behavior of adrenalectomized hamsters. *J. comp. physiol. Psychol.*, 1954, **47**, 154–56.

A total of 60 mature golden hamsters were put on food deprivation schedules prior to being tested for hoarding. They were then all tested for amount of hoarding of food. Following the hoarding tests two groups were adrenalectomized, one group received the operation but the adrenals were not removed and one group served as a normal control group. All of the animals were then tested again for hoarding. The adrenalectomized groups hoarded more than 30% less than the control groups which did not differ from their earlier levels of hoarding. The change was interpreted in terms of a reduction in activity level for the experimental groups.

Neural Factors in Innate Behavior

Research dealing with the relationships between neural factors and behavior is particularly difficult to understand for a number of reasons. One source of difficulty involves the widely different terminologies that are used by different researchers in referring to neural processes and structures. Thus, the task of knowing what is being talked about is often beyond a general reader. Brady (1958) acknowledges the problem and attempts to trace some of the shifts in this terminology. He points out, for example, that the neural correlates identified as being associated with emotional behavior have been called variously: Rhinencephalon, Visceral brain, limbic system, and paleocortex. In an effort to establish standard terminology for our discussion a brief analysis of some anatomical questions will be dealt with.

Anatomical Considerations. We will use a classification based on the division of the vertebrate brain into a number of gross spatial areas proceeding from the anterior (front) portions to the posterior portions. The divisions as noted in Figure 6–1 and Table 6–1 are:

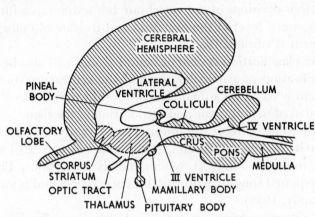

FIG. 6-1. A schematic drawing of the main divisions of the brain. The telencephalon consists of the cerebral hemispheres, olfactory lobe (or bulb), and corpus striatum. The diencephalon is made up of the thalamus, hypothalamus (not labeled), optic tract, pituitary body, pineal body, and mammillary bodies. The mesencephalon consists of colliculi and crus. The cerebellum and pons make up the metencephalon, and the medulla is the myelencephalon. This drawing gives a general scheme of the structure of the brain in all the higher vertebrates. (*After J. D. Lickley. The nervous system. New York: Longmans, 1919, p. 20*)

telencephalon, diencephalon, mesencephalon, metencephalon, and *myelencephalon.* The *forebrain* (prosencephalon) includes the mesencephalon and the *hindbrain* includes the metencephalon and myelencephalon. The relative prominence and degree of differentiation

TABLE 6-1

DIVISIONS OF THE VERTEBRATE BRAIN

Main Divisions	Cephalic Area	Some Important Structures
Forebrain (prosencephalon)	Telencephalon	Cerebral Cortex Olfactory Centers Basal Ganglia
	Diencephalon	Thalamus Hypothalamus Pituitary Gland
Midbrain	Mesencephalon	Tectum Superior Colliculus Inferior Colliculus Tegmentum
Hindbrain	Metencephalon	Cerebellum Pons
	Myelencephalon	Medulla

of the various divisions of the vertebrate brain differ as a function of
the phylogenetic level of the organism and its state of embryological
development (Pribram, 1958).

Another classification system of neural tissues will also be used for
the identification of particular parts of the central nervous system.
This system is based on a dual classification in terms of evolutionary
development of neural tissue and the location of the tissue going from
the outside to the core of the brain. The *neo-cortex,* comprising the
cerebrum in higher vertebrates, is the external cortex. The *paleo-*
cortex includes the olfactory system and its projections. The paleocortex is equated roughly with the rhinencephalon, and is an internal
cortex (Brady, 1958).

The brain and nervous system of invertebrates differ in a number
of ways from those of vertebrates. Figure 6–2 shows a diagram of
the brain of an ant. The two major areas of the invertebrate brain
as shown in Figure 6–2 are the *supra-oesophygeal ganglion* and
the *sub-oesophygeal ganglion.* These areas are also called the supra
and sub-pharyngeal ganglia. The two areas are connected by neurones
that are not shown in Figure 6–2. The large, posterior portion of the

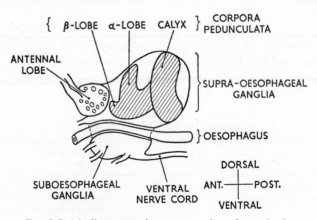

FIG. 6–2. A diagrammatic representation of a sagittal section through the ant's brain, showing the anatomical relationships of the different lobes and ganglia.

supra-oesophygeal ganglia is called the *corpora-pedunculata* and is
only present in higher invertebrates such as insects. In general, the
supra-oesophogeal ganglion is thought to be involved in integrated
behaviors, but the data on this point are not clear. For example, removing this ganglion in the worm and octopus interferes with behavior if test trials are widely spaced in time but not if the trials are

closely spaced in time (Evans, 1963; Stein, 1962; Wells and Wells, 1957). In general, as Vowles points out (1961, p. 27) the study of localization of functions for invertebrates and especially insects has just started. It is the view of the present writers that localization of brain function would be less likely among invertebrates than vertebrates, but this remains to be seen.

Neural Factors and Innate Behavior of Invertebrates. Some degree of encephalization is present in flatworms, such as the planaria and segmented worms, such as the earthworm. Removal of portions of this cerebral tissue in the earthworm leads to systematic changes in the innate tactic responses of the animal. The "decerebrate worm" moves forward in bright light whereas the normal worm moves backward (Ratner, 1962). Crustaceans and some Arthropods respond in a similar way to removal of cerebral tissue (Prosser, 1959). The approach to and mounting of the female by the male mantis requires intact neural tissue, but once the male clasps the female, copulation can be completed following removal or deactivation of the dorsal area of the mantis' brain, the *corpora pedunculata* (Roeder, 1935). The caterpillar of the Cecropia moth spins a malformed cocoon following removal of portions of the *corpora pedunculata*. The degree of malformation or incompleteness of the cocoon is related to the amount of tissue that is removed (Van der Kloot and Williams, 1954). These facts are presented to give some idea of the kinds of research that have been conducted with invertebrates in investigations of the functions of their neural tissue. However, general interpretations of the relationships between neural tissue and behavior are not yet available.

Neural Factors and Innate Behaviors of Vertebrates. Several facts regarding instinctive behavior have led researchers and theorists to focus on the relationship between neural factors and such behavior. One fact involves the spontaneity of instinctive behaviors; the other involves the species-specific responses associated with this behavior. Tinbergen, (1951, p. 67) reviewed the physiological evidence for spontaneous activity of neural tissue for a number of invertebrate species and lower vertebrates and he concluded that the spontaneity of behavior is consistent with the findings of spontaneous neural activity. In addition, neural models of patterns of spontaneous activity have been proposed to account for the findings regarding regular rhythms or cycles of behavior such as the twelve-hour activity cycle that characterize so many species of animals (Harker, 1958).

The contribution of neural factors to the species-specific characteristic of instinctive behavior has been investigated by several methods.

One of them involves *the method of brain stimulation* in which electrical current is applied to particular areas within the brain of the experimental animal. Areas of the diencephalon and particularly the hypothalamus have been stimulated in cats and fish and both appetitive and consummatory elements of instinctive responses have been observed when such stimulation occurs. For example, stimulation of one area of the diencephalon of the cat elicited species-specific fighting and sleeping, including the appetitive component for searching for an appropriate place to sleep (Tinbergen, 1951, p. 108). Reports of similar work with birds also indicate that a variety of elements of complex instinctive responses such as, mating, fighting, and escape, can be elicited by brain stimulation applied to small areas of the brain (Holst and St. Paul, 1963). However, other theorists, such as Brun (1951, p. 23), point out that these areas should be considered only as parts of the entire neural system that is involved in complex behaviors and they should not be considered as specific loci of such behaviors. He emphasized that impulses into the diencephalon activate other parts of the brain such as the metencephalon and even the spinal cord.

The *method of tissue removal* (ablation) has also been used for investigations of neural factors and innate behavior. The studies by Hale (1956 *) and Noble (1941) show the effects of forebrain lesions on reproductive and fighting behavior for a variety of species of fish. Studies of effects of removal of neural tissue on reproductive behavior of mammals implicate the telencephalon, diencephalon, and neocortex as being involved in such reproductive behavior (Beach, 1958, b). However, it is also clear from these sudies that removal of massive amounts of tissue is necessary to lead to a cessation of copulation for such animals as rats, cats, and infrahuman primates. Removal of the anterior hypothalamus in the diencephalon of male rats reduces but does not eliminate copulation. Ablation of the nuclei of the telencephalon of cats changes but does not eliminate mating. After the operation, previously inappropriate objects such as chickens, dogs, and monkeys elicit mounting and attempts to copulate (Schreiver and Kling, 1953).

HALE, E. B. Effects of forebrain lesions on the aggressive behavior of the green sunfish, *Lepomis cyanellus. Physiol. Zool.,* 1956, 29, 107–27.

The fighting behavior of the normal green sunfish involves actions identified as: threat display, weaving (a pattern of swimming), nipping, and driving (pushing fish that are lower in the dominance hierarchy). Pairs or groups of fish with extensive or complete removal of the forebrain showed much less fighting than normal pairs or groups. However, operated fish in tanks with normals showed more fighting than operated fish alone. This may happen because the normals make more responses that elicit fighting than operated fish make. In general, it was found that the operated fish (complete or partial ablation of the forebrain) showed fighting when particularly compelling salient stimuli, such as the movement of a normal fish, occured. That is, persistent visual and tactile stimulation was necessary. When such stimulation occurred the actions of the operated fish were not distinguishable from the actions of the normal fish.

The effects of removal of neo-cortical tissue on mating of mammals are a function of the amount of tissue that is removed, the phylogenetic level of the animal and its sex. Removal of large portions of the neo-cortex of male rats and rabbits does not lead to cessation of the responses of pursuing, mounting, and copulating with females, although complete removal of the neo-cortex does lead to the cessation of these behaviors. Removal of portions of the occipital cortex of the male cat interferes with pursuit and mounting but copulation can be achieved if the male is placed on the female. Thus, it seems that for male mammals the higher the animal is on the phylogenetic scale the greater the effect of removal of neo-cortical tissue. The findings with females are different. Female rats, rabbits, cats, and dogs that have had the entire neo-cortex removed (decortication) continue to be receptive with sexually active males. In other words, receptive sexual behavior of females is virtually independent of cortical participation at all phylogenetic levels.

Other Internal Factors in Innate Behavior

A number of other internal or biological factors have been investigated in terms of their relationships with components of innate behavior. Among these are deprivation programs, radiation treatments, and electro-convulsive shock. The effects on consummatory behavior of deprivation of such products as food, water, or a mate are discussed in Chapter 9. But an example of the effects of such variables of the behavior of invertebrates is provided in the study by Lees (1948 *). In this study the effects of food deprivation and satiation on tactic responses of the sheep tick are illustrated.

LEES, A. D. The sensory physiology of the sheep tick. *J. exp. Biol.,* 1948, **25,** 145–207.

The effects of a number of physiological conditions including dehydration (dessication) and food deprivation were studied in the sheep tick, *Ixodes ricinus* G. These conditions were studied in relation to kinetic and tactic responses. Hungry ticks oriented toward a warm object, while satiated ones oriented away from it. The response to temperature was increased when the warm object was wrapped in fresh sheep wool. The reactions to temperature were klinotactic. Similar responses to humidity were also found as a function of the degree of dessication, the water balance, of the animals. Hungry ticks

made food-getting responses to vibration of the rod on which they were clinging, much as they might if a stalk of grass were moved by the presence of
an animal from which they could get blood.

The effects of irradiation on behavior and biological processes
have been of concern recently and research regarding this factor
has been summarized by Furchtgott (1963). The study by Furchtgott
et al. (1959 *) indicates that radiation of fetal animals (pigs and rats)
reduces reproductive behavior in these animals when they have become mature. However, the mechanism or process that is affected by
prenatal radiation is not established.

FURCHTGOTT, E., MURPHEE, R. L., PACE, H. B. AND DEES, J. W. Mating
activity in fetally irradiated male swine and rats. *Psychol. Rep.,* 1959, 5,
545–48.

Female pigs and rats were irradiated for a number of days during their
pregnancy. The sexual behavior of the male offspring of the irradiated
animals was then compared with the sexual behavior of normal males of the
same species. Frequency and latency of mounting receptive females were
used as measures of sexual behavior. The prenatally irradiated male pigs
showed significantly less mounting than the control animals. The behavior
of the prenatally irradiated rats was similar but did not differ significantly
from the controls. The results were interpreted in terms of a generalized
effect of prenatal irradiation on behavior. That is, the experimental animals
seemed more "fearful" and less active although weight of their testes did not
differ from that of control animals.

Another condition that has been widely investigated is that of
electro-convulsive shock. Since such shock is used under some conditions in treatment of behavior disturbances of humans, the general
study of its effects is of importance. Beach *et al.* (1955 *) find that
copulation and ejaculation are affected in rats that received a series of
such shock treatments. An interpretation of these results is not being
made because of their complexity.

BEACH, F. A., GOLDSTEIN, A. C. AND JACOBY, G. A. JR. Effects of electro-
convulsive shock on sexual behavior in male rats. *J. comp. physiol. Psychol.,*
1955, 48, 173–79.

An exploratory study of the effects of electro-convulsive shock (ECS) on
mating on the male rat was conducted using 14 adult rats of mixed laboratory
strains. Measures of latency, frequency, and duration of mounting and copulation by the males with females were obtained. The males then received ECS
on each day for 12 days. Three tests of mounting and copulation were made
during this period. Then mating tests were made for a number of days after
the last period of ECS. Comparisons of behavior before ECS with that during ECS indicated increased latency of response to the females and increased
frequency of copulation. Performance returned to the preshock levels on
tests after the last period of ECS.

STRIDULATION AND ASSOCIATED BEHAVIOUR IN CERTAIN
ORTHOPTERA. 3. THE INFLUENCE OF THE GONADS

By P. T. HASKELL

Anti-Locust Research Centre, London

INTRODUCTION

The previous papers in this series (Haskell, 1957, 1958) described the stridulation and associated behaviour of males and females of four related grasshopper species; this work raised many new problems, the most interesting of which are connected with the sexual behaviour of the insects. For example, great interest attaches to the development of the "responsive state" in females (Haskell, 1958) in which the insect orientates to and moves towards a singing male, and the inhibition of this state by copulation and oviposition. Although the weight of evidence in insects (see Hanström, 1939) seems to be against any active controlling influence of the gonads, it was felt that these organs may play some role in the various behaviour patterns involved in courtship and copulation in the present grasshoppers and this paper describes experiments designed to investigate this speculation.

Materials and Methods

The species used were *Omocestus viridulus, Chorthippus brunneus* and *Chorthippus parallelus;* these were collected in the field at Imperial College Field Station, Berkshire, England, and reared under conditions described previously (Haskell, 1957, 1958). The apparatus for recording and analysing stridulation and for observing behaviour associated with it has also been described previously (Haskell, 1957). Each insect was individually marked, and was weighed daily; this enabled a general check on condition to be made, especially in relation to surgical operations and in the case of females allowed information on the oviposition cycle to be obtained. The definitions of stridulation and associated behaviour used by Haskell (1957) are retained in the present paper.

The Effect of the Gonads on Stridulation in Males

The experiments involved the extirpation of the gonads and associated glands in males; this was carried out, both in nymphs and adults, by making a small slit in the side of the abdomen about the level of the 6th segment and extracting the organs with fine, sharpened forceps, the wound being afterwards sealed with wax. Practice led to the perfection of this technique so that it was possible in most cases to remove not only the testes but the accessory glands with one movement of the forceps. Control for removal was made by killing the insects at the conclusion of the experiment and completely dissecting the abdomen to check for traces of sexual or accessory organs. Needless to say, mortality was high but sufficient numbers survived to enable a number of experiments to be carried out.

The castrated males were kept together in a breeding cage isolated from females; they were placed one by one in an observation cage (Haskell, 1957) and observed for spontaneous stridulation, response to playback of recorded stridulation, response to imitations of stridulation and response to and behaviour with females in the responsive state. Many insects, although not killed at once by the operation, died within a few days; it was found in general that those surviving for three days lived for the normal life span although a proportion of nymphs surviving the operation subsequently died on moulting to adults. Because of the numbers involved and the time necessary for behavioural observations, only those insects which lived seven days or longer could be tested for responses with females.

As controls for this experiment, insects of the equivalent instar or adult age were collected in the field and a slit made in their abdomen of the same size and in the same position as in the castrates. Table I summarizes the results of this experiment; figures in this table do not include males which, on death and final dissection, were found to have portions of their testes and/or accessory glands still present in the abdomen. It will be seen that as far as spontaneous stridulation and behaviour with females was concerned, castration produced no very apparent effect. The song pattern and duration of both normal and courtship songs in castrated males was on the whole normal, regardless of whether the insects were castrated as adults or as nymphs; a few aberrations did occur but were of such a nature, as for example short duration of song, or small reduction of pulse repetition frequency, as to be explicable in terms of shock rather than any definite psysiological change. The very fact that some of the castrated males sang normally

TABLE I

Effect of Removal of Gonads on Stridulation and Associated Behavior in Various
Stages of *C. parallelus* and *O. viridulus* Males.

	C. parallelus			O. viridulus
	3rd instar	4th instar	Adults	Adults
Number castrated	22	39	55	22
Number surviving	9	17	35	12
Number and % of survivors singing spontaneously	None	4(28.4%) out of 14	23(71.8%) out of 32	7(58.3%) out of 12
Number and % of controls singing spontaneously under similar conditions as above	2(20%) out of 10	3(25%) out of 12	21(84%) out of 25	7(70%) out of 10
Number and % of survivors observed in courtship and/or copulation	—	2 (see text)	10(52.6%) out of 19	4(44.4%) out of 9
Number and % of controls observed in courtship and/or copulation under similar conditions as above	—	—	8(66.6%) out of 12	3(50%) out of 6

and carried out courtship and copulation behaviour shows that the presence of the gonads does not exercise control of these behaviour patterns.

It was notable, however, that although on the whole courtship and copulation behaviour followed the patterns previously described, the activity of castrated males was reduced and the courtship behaviour was often enfeebled and much prolonged. This particularly applied to the duration of copulation; several pairs consisting of a normal female mated with a castrated male remained together for periods of from 2–10 hours, contrasting with the usual 1/2–2 hours of normal insects. This prolongation of copulation was almost certainly not due to the lack of any substance derived from the testes, since several implantations of living gonads were made into castrated males without altering the general behaviour. Rather is the cause of the prolongation to be looked for in the failure to produce and empty a spermatophore and this aspect is discussed later. In those castrated males which lived for their normal life span, there was no progressive enfeeblement, either in stridulation or in courtship behaviour. As far as nymphal behaviour is concerned, often in the fourth instar these stridulate and attempt to mate with females, and this was observed on two occasions with castrated fourth instar *C. parallelus*. Although there was no very marked species difference in response to castration, the males of *O. viridulus,* despite their larger size, seemed more enfeebled than those of *C. parallelus*.

Effect of Gonads on Stridulation and Associated Behaviour in Females

Since the onset of the "responsive state" in female Acrididae is associated with maturation (Haskell, 1958; Renner, 1952) experiments relating to the influence of the gonads on this behaviour pattern were carried out. Two methods for assessing the influence of the ovaries and accessory glands were envisaged; the first was extirpation, the surgical and control techniques being the same as described above for males. The second method attempted was biochemical and depended on an observation made by Carlisle and Butler (1956) that ovarian growth in the honeybee was stopped by injections of crustacean eye-stalk gland hormone. Ovarian inhibiting hormone from prawns was prepared in a variety of ways, in solution in ethyl oleate and as an emulsion in water using sodium lauryl sulphate as the dispersing agent and was injected into nymphal and adult females. Doses injected ranged from one to five eyestalk equivalents; since one eyestalk equivalent inhibits for one week the ovaries of a prawn of weight 2–5 gm., it was felt that the doses used should be effective, if active, in grasshoppers of weight of about 0.3 gm. However, no inhibitory action of any sort was detected; out of 15 fourth instar female *C. brunneus* and the same number of *C. parallelus* nymphs injected, 8 and 10 respectively moulted to adults and subsequently laid eggs. Out of 25 adult females of each species treated, 15 *C. brunneus* and 12 *C. parallelus* subsequently laid viable egg-pods. Histological examination of ovarian tissue from experimental females showed no abnormalities.

Behaviour experiments had therefore to be confined to females whose ovaries had been extirpated; this was done, as with males, both in the third and fourth instar and with adults. However, mortality after extirpation in the nymphal stages was extremely high and since those surviving the operation lived only a few days, very few surviving the final moult, experiments with nymphs were abandoned. Mortality in adults was also fairly high but sufficient survived for several experiments.

Fourteen *C. parallelus* virgin adult females, already in the "responsive state," had their ovaries and accessory glands extirpated; they were tested with singing males every day for six days after the operation and the results are summarized in Table II. It will be seen that in three cases (Insects 3, 7, 11) the responsive state disappeared within 24 hours, in seven cases (Insects 1, 2, 4, 5, 8, 9, 14) it persisted for 48 hours and was then lost, and in the remaining four cases (Insects 6, 10, 12,

TABLE II
EFFECT OF EXTIRPATION OF OVARIES FROM VIRGIN ADULT FEMALES OF
C. parallelus.

Insect	Time in days					
	1	2	3	4	5	6
1	+ Op	+	−	−	−	−
2	+ Op	+	−	−	−	−
3	+ Op	−	−	−	−	−
4	+ Op	+	−	−	−	−
5	+ Op	+	−	−	−	−
. 6	+ Op	+	+	+	+	−
7	+ Op	−	−	−	−	−
8	+ Op	+	−	−	−	−
9	+ Op	+	−	−	−	−
10	+ Op	+	+	+	+	+
11	+ Op	−	−	−	−	−
12	+ Op	+	+	−	−	−
13	+ Op	+	+	+	−	−
14	+ Op	+	−	−	−	−
15	+ control	+	+	+	−	+ov
16	+ control	+	+	+	+	+
17	+ control	+	−ov	−	+	+
18	+ control	+	−	−	+	+
19	+ control	+	+	+	−ov	−
20	+ control	+	+	+	+	+

Key: + responsive state; − loss of response state; Op when ovaries removed; ov insect oviposited.

13) it persisted for more than 48 hours. However, in Insect No. 6, the subsequent control dissection showed that the insect had retained a portion of ovariole tissue. Of the six control insects two (No. 16, 20) remained responsive for the rest of the experiment, three more (15, 17, 19) remained positive except when interrupted by oviposition and one (18) became unresponsive for unknown reasons for two days in the middle of the experiments.

In a further series of experiments with virgin adult *parallelus* females in the responsive state, the ventral nerve cord was cut between the 4th and 5th or 5th and 6th abdominal ganglia; out of eight insects which survived this operation for five days or more only two lost the responsive state, the remaining six actively responding to singing males.

The trend of these results was such as to suggest a non-nervous factor controlling the onset of the responsive state; the following experiment was therefore performed to find out if a factor was present in the blood affecting this behaviour pattern. Ten virgin adult *C. parallelus* females were castrated as before and their response behaviour checked daily; eight survived the operation for more than four days and as soon as they had lost the responsive state four were injected in the cervical membrane region with 2 cu. mm. of saline isotonic with their haemolymph. The remaining four were injected with 2 cu. mm. of haemolymph taken from a virgin adult *parallelus* female, with ovaries, which was in the responsive state. The results are summarized in Table III; it will be seen that although the surviving controls were uniformly negative in response, all the three surviving experimental animals showed a return to the responsive state for some period before death.

Inhibition of the Responsive State after Copulation

The responsive state in several grasshoppers is inhibited for periods of 2–24 hours by approaching oviposition and also by complete copulation (Haskell, 1958; Renner, 1952). Renner showed in *Euthystira brachyptera* that most probably the specific event causing inhibition after copulation was the filling of the receptaculum seminis of the female with sperm from the spermatophore. The question arises as to whether the cause of inhibition is a mechanical effect mediated by the nervous system, perhaps resulting from the mechanical stimulation of proprioceptors in the end-organ of the receptaculum consequent

TABLE III

INJECTION EXPERIMENTS WITH CASTRATED ADULT FEMALE *C. parallelus*.

		Time in days after operation				
Insect	Treatment	1	2	3	4	5
1	Injected 2 cu. mm. isotonic saline	−	−	−	−	Dead
2	"	Dead				
3	"	Dead				
4	"	−	−	−	−	Dead
5	Injected 2 cu. mm. haemo-lymph of female in re-sponsive state	−	+	+	−	Dead
6	"	+	+	−	−	Dead
7	"	−	+	−	−	Dead
8	"	Dead				

Key: + responsive state; − responsive state lost.

on its filling with seminal fluid, or a hormonal one, resulting either directly from the seminal fluid or as a result of its stimulation of the tissue of the receptaculum. This organ is innervated from the last abdominal ganglion and it is therefore reasonable to suppose that any nervous inhibition centering on it will be transmitted to higher centres by way of the ventral nerve cord. To test this supposition, seven *C. parallelus* females in the responsive state were allowed to copulate to completion with males; after 24 hours they were tested for responsiveness with singing males and were all negative. Their ventral nerve cord was then cut in the region of the 6th abdominal ganglion and the wound sealed with wax. Three died within 24 hours but four survived for three days during which time no response to singing males was observed. On dissection after death, the nerve cord was found to be severed in all four insects and sperms were found in their receptacula.

An attempt was made to stimulate the receptaculum mechanically by injecting into it through a thin flexible glass tube and micrometer syringe 2 cu. mm. of isotonic saline; the injection was done successfully with four responsive *parallelus* females, but in no case was the responsive state inhibited. Attempts were also made to remove the receptaculum seminis but the operation was always followed by a moribund state so that copulation never took place in the experimental animals. Experiments in which mating pairs were parted at various times after the onset of copulation, the female then being tested for responsiveness and subsequently dissected, showed that responsiveness was never lost after copulation unless sperms were present in the receptaculum. In two cases it seemed that insertion of the neck of the spermatophore had begun and had been accompanied by the passage of some fluid, but no sperms were found in the receptaculum and the responsiveness of the females had not been terminated.

DISCUSSION

The experiments on the influence of gonads on stridulation in the present paper are the more interesting in that the effects in males and females are so different. In males there is no effect; stridulation and copulation behaviour seemed to be unaffected; this was also noted by Regen (1909) in the case of castrated male *Gryllus campestris*. The observations of Husain and Baweja (1936) on the behaviour of desexualized adults of *Schistocerca gregaria* showed no alteration of courtship or mating behaviour, except that the duration of copulation was unduly prolonged. This was also noted during the present work; since copulation is normally terminated shortly after emptying of the spermatophore (Boldyrev, 1929), it seems likely that stimuli resulting from the transfer of sperm lead to the breaking-off of mating and the absence of a spermatophore occasioned by castration could induce abnormally long periods of copulation. However this may be, the important point is that in males the major elements of the stridulation/courtship pattern were not altered by castration; in females the case is otherwise.

Consideration of the data of Table II, although rather sparse for this type of experiment, strongly suggests that castrated females in the responsive state lose this condition between 24–48 hours after the operation. The comparatively slow onset of inhibition argues against this being mediated by nervous control and the related experiments on cutting the ventral nerve cord support this conclusion. The blood injection experiments (Table III) could clearly not stand by themselves but taken in conjunction with the previous two experiments support the hypothesis that some blood-borne chemical factor is responsible for onset of the responsive state in female *C. parallelus*. The work of Renner (1952) with castrated females of the grasshopper *Euthystira brachyptera* tends to the same conclusion; here also the insects underwent changes in their response pattern, the timing again suggesting hormonal control.

The inhibition of the responsive state by copulation has been demonstrated by Regen (1923) for crickets and by Renner (1952) and Haskell (1958) for grasshoppers; Renner's work suggested the filling of the receptaculum seminis with sperm as the causal stimulus and the present work supports this conclusion with the further implication that the inhibition is due to a chemical factor and is not directly mediated by the central nervous system. The two observations on responsive *C. parallelus* females which had been interrupted after partial copulation and in which fluid but no sperm was present in the receptaculum, suggests that it is in the seminal fluid itself that the controlling chemical factor will be found.

There is a widely held view (see Hanström, 1939, for many references) that the gonads of insects play little or no part in the development of secondary sex characteristics; morphologically speaking this is almost certainly true, as the frequent occurrence of gynandromorphs suggests and the present work does not suggest otherwise. However, much evidence is now available (see Engelmann, 1957) suggesting that the *function* of the reproductive system is controlled in many respects by hormones. For example, in Orthoptera the corpora allata control egg development and maturation and possibly an intragonadal hormone controls ovulation, and the work of Engelmann (1957) has demonstrated the presence of intra-organ hormone cycles involving the reproductive system.

It seems possible that some such system exists in some acridid grasshoppers and the present work, in agreement with that of Renner (1952), suggests that this is the case. The operation of this system affects sexual behaviour and since this must be basically controlled by higher nervous centres the ultimate point of action of the hormone or hormones involved must be on such centres, although perhaps indirectly. Speculative systems capable of explaining the present observed changes in sexual behaviour in grasshoppers could be erected but in view of the sparse information on copulation and fertilization mechanisms in Orthoptera this would be premature; the preliminary work herein described may, however, stimulate further work along the lines that the female gonads operate as one regulatory centre in a "hormone chain." The fact that crustacean eye-stalk hormone had no effect on grasshopper ovaries, although capable of inhibiting growth of the ovaries of honeybees (Carlisle and Butler, 1956), is perhaps an indication that different orders of insects have evolved somewhat different hormone systems, at least biochemically.

SUMMARY

1. Extirpation of testes and accessory glands in males of the acridid grasshoppers *C. parallelus* and *O. viridulus* did not alter their stridulation nor the behaviour associated with it; however, time spent in copulation was considerably increased and it is suggested that this may be due to the fact that in normal males the emptying of the spermatophore is the stimulus for the cessation of copulation.

2. Injections of crustacean eyestalk hormone, found to inhibit ovarian development in honeybees, was without effect on ovarian tissue in the grasshoppers used.

3. Removal of ovaries and accessory glands in female *C. parallelus* in the "responsive state" resulted in the disappearance of this condition in from 24–48 hours. The responsive state was reinduced in several castrated females by injection of blood from females in the responsive state.

4. The responsive state was not terminated by cutting the ventral nerve cord in the abdominal region in normal females.

5. Inhibition of the responsive state in females by copulation only

occurs after the passage of sperm into the receptaculum seminis; this inhibition is not mediated by the central nervous system, consequent on mechanical stimulation of the receptaculum seminis, and is probably due to some chemical factor associated with the sperm.

ACKNOWLEDGMENTS

This work was carried out as part of a vacation research project on grasshopper behaviour financed by the Anti-Locust Research Centre, and thanks are due to Professor O. W. Richards for permission to work at Imperial College Field Station and for supplying laboratory facilities there. I am indebted to Dr. D. B. Carlisle, Plymouth Marine Laboratory, for providing extracts of crustacean eyestalk hormone. I must thank the following for their assistance in the experimental and behaviour observations: Miss D. M. Lamont, Miss A. Long, Mr. R. F. Sturrock, Mr. D. W. Tarry and Mr. E. Donahaye and particularly Mrs. M. Siddorn for supervising much of the laboratory work.

REFERENCES

BOLDYREV, V. F. (1929). Spermatophore fertilization in the Migratory Locust (*Locusta migratoria* L.). *Izv. prikl. Ent., Leningrad,* 4, 189–218.

CARLISLE, D. B. and BUTLER, C. G. (1956). The "queen-substance" of honeybees and the ovary-inhibiting hormone of crustaceans. *Nature, Lond.,* 177, 276–77.

ENGELMANN, F. (1957). Die Steuerung der Ovarfunktion bei der ovoviviparen Schabe *Leucophaea maderae* (Fabr.). *J. insect Physiol.,* 1, 257–78.

HANSTRÖM, B. (1939). *Hormones in invertebrates.* Oxford: Clarendon Press.

HASKELL, P. T. (1957). Stridulation and associated behaviour in certain Orthoptera. 1. Analysis of the stridulation of, and behaviour between, males. *Brit. J. anim. Behav.,* 5, 139–48.

HASKELL, P. T. (1958). Stridulation and associated behaviour in certain Orthoptera. 2. Stridulation of females and their behaviour with males. *Anim. Behav.,* 6, 27–42.

HUSAIN, M. A. and BAWEJA, K. D. (1936). Studies on *Schistocerca gregaria* Forsk. IV. Colour changes and sexual behaviour in desexualised *Schistocerca gregaria* adults. *Ind. J. agric. Sci.,* 6, 586–90.

REGEN, J. (1909). Kastration und ihre Folgeerscheinungen bei *Gryllus campestris* L. ♂. I. Mitteilung. *Zool. Anz.,* 34, 477–78.

REGAN, J. (1923). Über die Orientierung des Weibchens von *Liogryllus campestris* L. nach dem Stridulationsschall des Männchens. Ein Beitrag zur Physiologie des tympanalen Sinnesorgans. *S.B. Akad. Wiss. Wien* Abt. I, 132, 81–88.

RENNER, M. (1952). Analyse der Kopulationsbereitschaft des Weibchens der Feldheuschrecke *Euthystira brachyptera* Ocsk. in ihrer Abhängigkeit vom Zustand des Geschlechtsapparates. *Z. Tierpsychol.* 9, 122–54.

EFFECTS OF GONADECTOMY AND HYPOPHYSECTOMY ON PRESPAWNING BEHAVIOR IN MALES OF THE GOBIID FISH, BATHYGOBIUS SOPORATOR[1]

WILLIAM N. TAVOLGA [2]

Department of Animal Behavior, American Museum of Natural History, New York

As in other vertebrates, the endocrine secretions of the gonads of teleosts are known to affect morphological characteristics. "Nuptial" or breeding colors, gonopodia of viviparous poeciliids, the ovipositor of the bitterling, and many other structures associated with reproduction have been described as being under the direct control of gonadal hormones. In some cases the gonadotrophic function of the pituitary has been included as a direct or indirect factor in the development of these secondary and accessory sexual characteristics. Most of the reports on the teleost fishes have dealt with the effects of hormone administration, and a few have utilized the techniques of gonadectomy and hypophysectomy.

Despite the fact that the spawning behavior of a large variety of teleostean species has been described, the data available on the relationships of the endocrine glands with reproductive activities are sparse, inadequate, and contradictory. The present report is a corollary to a descriptive study of the spawning behavior in the gobiid fish, *Bathygobius soporator* (Cuvier and Valenciennes) (Tavolga, 1954). These data represent an approach to the investigation of the internal mechanisms involved in sex discrimination and courtship behavior in this species.

[1] The author is indebted to the staff and facilities of Marine Studios, Marineland, Florida, for their co-operation and generous aid. Mr. F. G. Wood, Jr., curator of the Marineland Research Laboratory, was especially hospitable and helpful. Dr. Lester R. Aronson and Dr. Theodore C. Schneirla, of the American Museum of Natural History, were kind enough to offer their comments and criticisms on the manuscript.

[2] Public Health Service Research Fellow of the National Institute of Mental Health.

SOURCE AND MAINTENANCE OF MATERIAL

The specimens used in this work were collected from tide pools and shallows along the Intracoastal Waterway in the vicinity of Marineland, Florida. The animals were all collected and the operations and observations were made during the summer months of July and August, at which time the spawning season for this species is at its height. Additional observations, reported in a separate section, were made during the months of February and March.

Individuals used in the castration and hypophysectomy experiments were all sexually mature males, ranging from 85 to 90 mm. in standard length. Additional animals used as stimulus objects were males, 80–90 mm., and females, 55–65 mm. in standard length. The females were checked each day to determine the stage of their ovarian cycle, i.e., whether they were gravid. Since the cycle in this species during the summer months is about 7–10 days, females at any stage were usually available when needed.

The large males used as resident test animals (operated or controls) were isolated in 5-gallon aquaria, and the rest were kept as stock in 10-gallon tanks. All aquaria were supplied with running, filtered sea water, and the animals were fed daily on minced shrimp.

The resident animals were each provided with shelters consisting of unglazed flooring tiles (approximately $4'' \times 4'' \times \frac{1}{2}''$), one of which was inclined against the front glass of the aquarium. The triangular shelter thus formed was readily used by the gobies for hiding and spawning.

SUMMARY OF REPRODUCTIVE BEHAVIOR IN *BATHYGOBIUS*

Males of this species are territorial, and they defend an area immediately around a shelter. Combat with intruding males is characterized by an intense darkening of the coloration, together with gaping, quivering, butting, tail-slapping, and biting.

In the presence of a gravid female, the color phase of the male changes to a light-tan body color with a blackened chin and throat. The female is approached with rapidly fanning and gasping movements on the part of the male. If spawning is imminent, the female will enter the nest, and oviposition will begin. During the "courtship" behavior, the male darts back into the nest at irregular intervals, and, while inside, he strokes or rubs his anal-urogenital region over the nest surfaces. After the female enters the nest, the male assumes a dark color phase which is retained through most of the spawning period.

Small males and nongravid females who intrude upon a territory-holding male are approached and nipped at by the resident. The latter usually nips and chases the intruder about the tank, but no characteristic color change on the part of the resident is present.

In spawning, the female extrudes adherent eggs onto the inner surface of the nest, while the male moves his urogenital papilla through the eggs as he releases sperm. After spawning, the male fans and guards the spawn for an incubation period of 4–5 days, until the larvae hatch. A more detailed description of normal spawning behavior is given in an earlier report (Tavolga, 1954).

METHODS OF TESTING REACTIONS OF RESIDENT MALES

The resident males were tested in their reactions toward other gobies by introducing animals into the aquarium with the resident. The actions and color changes of the resident were recorded for a 5-minute test period. The intruder was then removed. The tests on each individual had to be spaced about 24 hours apart, because of a persistence of response among resident animals, especially after a vigorous combat or courtship. In this way, any overlapping of response was avoided.

In making the observations, records were taken on the initial reaction-complex of the resident male toward the intruder and then on the subsequent behavior of the resident. The initial reaction-complex consists of an approach to the intruder, preceded or followed by a color change. The approach is usually a rapid dart but, at times, may consist of a slow swimming. The color change, if present, is either a darkening toward combat coloration or a lightening toward the courtship pattern.

The subsequent behavior of the resident may become consolidated into combat, courtship, or neither of these. Combat takes place only between large males, although tendencies toward this behavior can occasionally be observed between small males and between females. Courtship behavior of a resident male occurs with varying degrees of intensity and vigor. A strong, prolonged courtship, usually directed toward gravid females, will last through the entire observation period. This behavior includes the fanning and gasping movements, as well as frequent returns to the nest, rubbing and cleaning its surfaces. A short, weak courtship reaction, as defined here, comprises courting movements that are intermittent. In these cases the behavior of the resident changes to nipping and chasing or to quiescence within a few seconds or a minute. The nipping and chasing behavior, as well as the quiescence, is considered as "neutral," in that there is no accompanying color change toward the dark combat type or the light courtship phase.

CASTRATION TECHNIQUES

Males of *Bathygobius* grow to a larger size and possess longer posterior dorsal and anal fin rays than females do. The most reliable sex-differentiating characteristic, however, is the structure of the urogenital papilla. In the male this organ is conical and pigmented, whereas in the female it is truncate, less pigmented, and possesses two small brushes of epidermal papillae at its tip.

The testes are about half the length of the body cavity. They are tapered anteriorly and flattened in cross-section. In a large male each testis is about 15–20 mm. long and 3–4 mm. broad. It is attached by a broad connection at its posterior end to the base of a sperm reservoir. These sperm reservoirs of gobiid fishes have been referred to as seminal vesicles (Young and Fox, 1937), *glandes génitales annexes* (Champy, 1941; Coujard, 1941), and *Samenblasen* Eggert, 1931). Each seminal vesicle is almost as long as the testis and tapers to a fine point anteriorly. The vesicles lie free in the body cavity and are fused together at their posterior ends, where they form the ejaculatory duct leading into the urogenital papilla. The testes are easily identified by virtue of their shape, attachment to the dorsal peritoneum, and the presence of a broad, dark-red (in life) stripe along their ventral surface. This stripe comprises the "testicular gland," which lies along the hilum of the testis and envelops the spermatic duct (Eggert, 1931; Champy, 1941).

The genital system of males collected in the summer (Fig. 1, *A*) is always replete with motile, viable spermatozoa. Histological sections show that all stages of spermatogenesis are present in the testis and that the spermatic ducts and seminal vesicles are turgid with sperm.

Twenty-five large males were selected, and prior observation indicated that they were normal in so far as courtship and combat behavior were concerned. Five of these animals were used as sham-operated controls. Two of the remaining twenty did not survive the operation; thus eighteen castrated males were obtained.

The animals were anesthetized in 0.1 per cent MS-222 (tricaine methanesulfonate, Sandoz Pharmaceuticals) in sea water for 1 or 2 minutes until swimming movements ceased and respiration became slowed. They were then kept in a 0.05 per cent solution of the anesthetic for the 8 or 10 minutes required for the operation. Brief transfers to the higher concentration were occasionally necessary when an animal showed signs of premature revival.

A ¼-inch incision was made through the posterior portion of the abdominal wall parallel to and about $\frac{1}{16}$ inch to one side of the ventral mid-line. The incision was kept open with hemostats, and then a pair of fine eye forceps was used to reach in, push aside the viscera, and grasp the anterior end of the testis. Iridectomy scissors were used to cut the testis away from the dorsal peritoneum and sever its attachment to the seminal vesicle as closely as possible. The testis was then lifted out, and a single stich with cotton thread closed the incision. The same operation was repeated on the other side of the ventral mid-line for the removal of the second testis.

Healing appeared to be well in progress in 48 hours, and the stitches sloughed off in 3–4 days. Surface scars were barely noticeable after 20 days. Subsequent dissection of the castrates, about 50 days after the operation, revealed that twelve of the eighteen animals had regenerated testicular tissue. Six of the 18, however, showed no macroscopically identifiable testicular regeneration. The regeneration, in the cases where it took place, resulted in the formation of

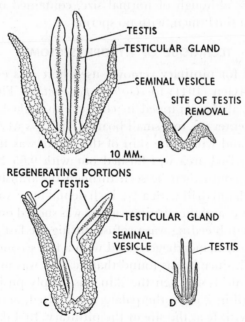

Fig. 1.—Genital systems of normal and operated males of *Bathygobius*. *A*, genital system of normal 72-mm. male collected in August. *B*, genital system of 74-mm. male that had been completely castrated for 50 days. *C*, genital system of 78-mm. male that had been castrated for 50 days, but possesses portions of regenerating testicular tissue. *D*, genital system of normal 68-mm. male collected in February.

asymmetrical masses of testicular tissue, sometimes arising from the point of juncture with the seminal vesicles and sometimes independent of this point. The reddish testicular gland was present on all the regenerated masses. The seminal vesicles were normal in appearance and size in these animals (Fig. 1, C). In the six males which showed no regeneration the seminal vesicles were shrunken, twisted, and reduced to less than half normal length (Fig. 1, B).

Histological examination of the genital systems of the operated animals was carried out by routine sectioning procedures, i.e., Bouin's picro-formol fixative and haematoxylin-eosin stain. There was a complete absence of testicular tissue attached to the genital system in the six nonregenerating males. The testicular tissue of the regenerating animals appeared normal in general structure and possessed all stages of spermatogenesis, ducts filled with mature sperm, and testicular gland tissue. In nine of these males, the regenerated testes had reestablished connections with the seminal vesicles, so that the latter contained large quantities of sperm. In the remaining three, the seminal vesicles, although of normal size, contained only an acidophilic colloid in the lumen, with no sperm.

TECHNIQUE OF HYPOPHYSECTOMY

The method for pituitary removal used here was essentially that described by Vivien (1941) for *Gobius paganellus*. The animal was anesthetized as above, wrapped in cheesecloth soaked in sea water, and strapped, venter up, to a small board. The jaws were retracted by means of cord and wire. The skin of the palate was incised and retracted. The incised area was flushed out with 0.65 NaCl, and the pituitary gland could then be seen through the translucent floor of the cranium. A hand drill with a $\frac{1}{16}$-inch dental burr was used to bore through the bone, and the pituitary gland was sucked out with a small pipette. Although bleeding was profuse during the last stage, clotting was rapid, and the hemorrhage ceased with a few seconds. The palate was not sutured, since it was found that healing was more rapid and there was less infection when the skin was simply pushed back over the wound. Within 2 days, the palate was knitted, and only a small blood clot was visible at the site of the pituitary. In 4 days, no vestige of the operation was macroscropically visible.

Six males were successfully hypophysectomized and survived the operation. After 30 days, they were sacrificed, and the heads were sectioned—in each case the hypophysectomy was complete. The genital systems of these males were considerably reduced in size, approaching the condition illustrated in Figure 1, *D*, for males collected in February and March.

BEHAVIOR OF CASTRATES 24 HOURS AFTER OPERATION

Immediately after reviving from the anesthetic and for about 24 hours afterward, castrated males were quiescent, remaining in one spot, usually in a shelter, for long periods of time. Their breathing rate appeared to be slowed, and they showed no interest in food. Their coloration was the usual two-bar pattern. Sham-operated controls, however, returned to normal activity within a few minutes after revival, and they exhibited active feeding as well as courtship and combat reactions. These sham-operated animals were indistinguishable from nonoperated controls and were grouped with the latter in all subsequent observations.

On the day following the operation, gravid females were introduced into the tanks with each of the eighteen castrates. In eight cases the male showed no reaction to the presence of another animal in his tank. In three cases the female was prodded by the observer into the shelter occupied by the castrate, and the male darkened slightly and huddled into the far corner of the shelter. In seven cases, the castrated male reacted to the gravid female by darkening slightly and exhibiting some tendencies toward fighting, i.e., throat puffing and nudging. This abortive combat behavior did not last for more than 1–1½ minutes in any case.

BEHAVIOR OF CASTRATES 3–10 DAYS AFTER OPERATION

The reactions of the males at this stage of castration were fully tested over a period of 7 days. In general, the castrated males exhibited normal behavior in isolation; they fed regularly, reacted quickly to intruders, and showed occasional spontaneous digging and fanning within the nest. There were no behavioral differences between individuals which could be correlated with the later information on regeneration of testicular tissue. The following data, then, are not separable into the two groups corresponding to this regeneration or lack of it.

The reactions of the castrates to introduced gobies comprised an immediate change to courtship coloration, accompanied by vigorous and prolonged courting movements. This courtship reaction took place not only toward gravid females but toward nongravid females and males as well. In two cases males exhibited a transient courtship reaction toward a large *Fundulus* when it was placed in the aquarium.

In one case, a courtship coloration was exhibited toward the hand of the observer when it was dipped into the tank.

The courting behavior of the castrates showed certain differences from that of normal males. The body coloration during courtship is normally lightened to a pale tan or buff color (Pl. 1, *B*), whereas the color of the castrates became distinctly lighter, e.g., a cream or milk-white (Pl. 1, *C*). The blackened chin area characteristic of the courtship color phase was amaller and less sharply delimited in the castrates. The vigorous fanning movements of courtship were spasmodic in the castrates, and the gasping and snapping movements were more frequent than in the controls.

Gravid females responded to the courtship and followed the males into the nests. In three cases, females were left in the tanks with castrate males and permitted to spawn. The spawning behavior of the males appeared to be normal. They exhibited darkening after the female entered the nest, as well as nest-rubbing, erection of the uro-genital papilla, and, later, fertilizing movements. The eggs deposited by the female were, of course, infertile, but the male brooded them by fanning in the normal fashion. Infertile eggs were brooded for up to 48 hours after spawning, after which time they began to decay. Nongravid females retreated in the face of a courting approach by the castrate. Introduced males never showed any combat behavior toward the castrated, resident males.

The reactions of the castrated males toward introduced animals were observed in a series of 90 trials. Each male was given 5 trials on 5 successive days (one trial per day). The types of introduced animals were alternated as follows: (1) gravid female, (2) male, (3) nongravid female, (4) male, (5) gravid female. Two kinds of initial responses by the resident castrated males were observed: (1) an approach to the introduced animal and (2) a change of coloration toward the courtship phase. In the first type the approach was followed, in all cases but one, by a color change toward the courtship type and by extensive courting behavior. In the second type the coloration change was followed by an approach to the intruder and subsequent prolonged courtship. Table 1 summarizes the results of the 90 observations. It was evident that the castrated animals exhibited a courtship reaction toward all types of introduced animals.

In normal animals the initial approach response may be followed by nipping and chasing behavior toward nongravid females and small males or by a change to the darkened combat coloration toward large males. Occasionally, normal males exhibit an initial response consisting of a color change followed by an approach. This is particularly frequent toward gravid females, in which case the color changes to the courtship type. Less frequently, the color pattern darkens toward the combat type when the intruder is a male. The latter response was completely absent among the castrates. Table 2 presents a comparison between the intact males and the castrates in terms of their initial responses toward introduced animals. It will be noted that, in a significantly larger number of cases, the castrates exhibited a courtship coloration prior to their approach to the intruder and prior to any activity on the part of the intruder. The absence of any tendency toward combat behavior on the part of the castrates is also noteworthy.

An attempt was made to measure courtship quantitatively, comparing intact with castrated animals. The "vigor" of the courting movements, i.e., amplitude and frequency of the tail fanning, could not be measured except possibly by means of high-speed cinematographic equipment, and differences in these respects between normal and operated animals were not perceptible to the observer. Two measurements of courtship duration were used. Since the courting

TABLE 1

TABULATION OF REACTIONS OF 3–10-DAY CASTRATED MALES TOWARD INTRODUCED ANIMALS

	Type of Introduced Animal				
Initial Reactions of Resident Males	*Gravid Female*	*Male*	*Nongravid Female*	*Male*	*Gravid Female*
Approach, followed by courting behavior	3	5	7	0	5
Courting coloration and movements, followed by an approach..............	15	13	10	18	13
Approach, followed by nipping and chasing	0	0	1	0	0

TABLE 2

COMPARISON OF INITIAL RESPONSES OF INTACT AND CASTRATED
MALES TOWARD INTRODUCED ANIMALS

Type of Resident Animal	*Type of Introduced Animal*	*Initial Response an Approach*	*Initial Response a Color Change*	
			Darkening	*Lightening*
Intact male	Gravid female	33	0	17
	Nongravid female	46	0	4
	Male	20	5	0
Castrated male	Gravid female	8	0	28
	Nongravid female	8	0	10
	Male	5	0	31

activity was found to be discontinuous, i.e., composed of spells of strong waving, the duration of each of the courting spells was recorded. In addition, the total time spent by the male in courting movements was recorded in terms of percentage of observation of testing time. The testing periods were 5 minutes each, and these data were recorded from the last three sets of tests listed in Table 1. Subsequently, as tank space became available, normal males were similarly tested. The results are presented in Table 3, in terms of extremes and means (with standard error of the mean). It should be noted that these figures represent variously skewed distributions, since a courting spell was often continuous over the full observation period, i.e., representing an artificial, observer's maximum. Similarly, a record of 100 per cent courtship represents a continuous courting spell for 5-minutes—again not a true maximum.

TABLE 3

Comparison of Courtship Response between Intact and Castrated Males

Type of Resident Male	Type of Introduced Animal	Duration of Courting Spells (Seconds)		Percentage Courtship of 5-Minute Observation	
		Range	Mean ($\pm o_M$)	Range	Mean ($\pm o_M$)
Intact male	Gravid female	5–300	56.5$\pm$11.9	30–100	78.9$\pm$7.1
	Nongravid female	5– 20	11.6$\pm$ 5.3	0– 13.4	4.3$\pm$4.9
	Male	0	0	0	0
Castrated male	Gravid female	5–300	103.8$\pm$14.7	10–100	88.6$\pm$4.8
	Nongravid female	10–300	92.2$\pm$13.8	28–100	83.2$\pm$5.5
	Male	10–300	88.5$\pm$12.2	25–100	79.8$\pm$4.2

Table 3 shows that normal males differed sharply in their reactions toward gravid and nongravid females and toward males. Courtship, if any, toward nongravid females was sporadic and of short duration, and reactions toward males usually included darkening and combat. Castrated animals, however, exhibited a considerable amount of courtship toward all three types of introduced animals. The differences in the figures in Table 3 on the reactions of the castrates are not significant.

In addition, it appears that the courtship response of the castrates toward gravid females was greater as measured here than that of normal males, but this difference is of doubtful statistical validity— D/σ_d is 2.5 in the case of the duration of courtship spells and 1.2 in the case of percentage courtship.

BEHAVIOR OF CASTRATES 15–50 DAYS AFTER OPERATION

Approximately 30 days after castration, the tests of the reactions of the operated animals indicated the separation of these fish into two groups. Twelve individuals began to show signs of return to normal behavior in their reactions toward introduced males. As mentioned earlier, dissection of the castrates after 50 days showed that regeneration of the testes had taken place in most of them. Since some regeneration was expected, the data on each individual were kept separate, and the observations on the two groups, viz., regenerating and nonregenerating, are compared later.

As stated previously, the two groups were not separable on the basis of their behavior during the period 3–10 days after the operation. The operated animals were again tested in their reactions toward males and toward gravid and nongravid females at periods of 15–25, 30–40, and 40–50 days after castration, and their reactions were broadly classified as neutral, combat, short courtship, and prolonged courtship, as defined earlier in this report.

Table 4 shows the changes in the reactions of the operated animals toward introduced males. In the six nonregenerating individuals, the reactions continued to be predominantly courtship, whereas the regenerating group showed a return to combat behavior after 30 days and a sharp reduction of courtship behavior after 40 days.

Table 5 shows that the courtship response in the regenerating animals become reduced. This was significantly so after 30 days, with

TABLE 4

REACTIONS OF OPERATED MALES TOWARD INTRODUCED MALES,
SHOWING EFFECTS OF TESTICULAR REGENERATION

Days after Operation	Type of Reaction toward Introduced Males	Males without Testicular Regeneration	Males with Regenerating Testes
15–25	Neutral	2	9
	Courtship	28	51
	Combat	0	0
30–40	Neutral	3	11
	Courtship	27	24
	Combat	0	25
40–50	Neutral	3	4
	Courtship	27	10
	Combat	0	46

TABLE 5

EXTENT OF COURTSHIP OF OPERATED MALES TOWARD INTRODUCED
MALES, AS AFFECTED BY TESTICULAR REGENERATION

Days after Operation	Approximate Duration of Courtship Reaction	Males without Testicular Regeneration	Males with Regenerating Testes
15–25	Short	7	24
	Prolonged	21	27
30–40	Short	5	19
	Prolonged	22	5
40–50	Short	3	5
	Prolonged	24	5

TABLE 6

EXTENT OF COURTSHIP OF OPERATED MALES TOWARD INTRODUCED
NONGRAVID FEMALES, AS AFFECTED BY TESTICULAR REGENERATION

Days after Operation	Approximate Duration of Courtship Reaction	Males without Testicular Regeneration	Males with Regenerating Testes
15–25	Short	1	10
	Prolonged	9	15
30–40	Short	4	13
	Prolonged	7	8
40–50	Short	1	17
	Prolonged	10	3

TABLE 7

EXTENT OF COURTSHIP OF OPERATED MALES TOWARD INTRODUCED
GRAVID FEMALES, AS AFFECTED BY TESTICULAR REGENERATION

Days after Operation	Approximate Duration of Courtship Reaction	Males without Testicular Regeneration	Males with Regenerating Testes
15–25	Short	4	8
	Prolonged	11	27
30–40	Short	1	11
	Prolonged	14	24
40–50	Short	0	5
	Prolonged	14	30

the chi-square test indicating *P*-values of less than 0.05. The differences for the 15–25-day period are of a low and doubtful order of significance.

The extent of courtship of the operated animals toward nongravid and gravid females was recorded. Tables 6 and 7 present a comparison between the two groups of operated males at different periods after castration. A distinct decline was present in the extent of courtship of regenerating animals toward introduced nongravid females, but the differences are statistically significant only for the period after 40 days (*P* is less than 0.01). No significant differences were present in the reactions of these males toward gravid females, i.e., prolonged courtship predominated heavily.

In Table 8, the data on the operated animals after 40 days are presented regrouped and compared to a series of observations on 25 normal males. Each of the controls was tested once with a male as the intruder and twice each with a gravid and a nongravid female.

TABLE 8

REACTIONS OF EXPERIMENTAL AND CONTROL RESIDENT
MALES COMPARED

	Neutral	Courtship		Combat
		Short	Prolonged	
		Reactions toward Introduced Males		
Nonregenerating*	3	3	24	0
Regenerating†	4	5	5	46
Control‡	0	3	0	22
		Reactions toward Introduced Nongravid Females		
Nonregenerating*	1	1	10	0
Regenerating†	6	17	3	0
Control‡	31	18	0	0
		Reactions toward Introduced Gravid Females		
Nonregenerating*	1	0	14	0
Regenerating†	2	5	30	0
Control‡	0	0	50	0

* Six males tested 40–50 days after castration and possessing no testicular regeneration.
† Twelve males tested 40–50 days after castration and possessing testicular regeneration.
‡ Twenty-five control males.

The similarity between the regenerating animals and the controls is distinct, particularly in regard to their reactions toward males and nongravid females. The males whose testes showed no regeneration continued to display strong courting activity toward any introduced goby.

OBSERVATIONS IN FEBRUARY AND MARCH

All the previous data are based upon observations and collections made in July and August, i.e., during the spawning season of this species. A group of about thirty mature *Bathygobius* was collected and observed during the months of February and March. These animals were maintained in a large 20-gallon aquarium, which was supplied with many empty oyster shells and rocks, used as shelters by the gobies.

Although no specific records were kept on the behavior of any one individual, it was noted that members of both sexes were territorial and moved into hiding places. Both males and females exhibited a great deal of nipping and chasing. Males displayed the characteristic dark colors and movements of combat behavior toward one another. It appeared that the males did most of the fighting, although this may only have seemed so to the observer because of the more distinctive colors of combating males. Female combats were shorter in duration, and the animals did not exhibit so complete a darkened color phase as did the males. Occasional nest-cleaning movements were also observed. In general, these animals behaved similarly to those collected during the spawning season—but with one prominent difference: no courtship behavior was ever observed.

The genital systems of these animals were examined both macroscopically and microscopically. The females were all found to have small, white ovaries with immature oöcytes. This is quite unlike the ovaries of summer females, which contain mature or maturing, yellow-colored, yolk-filled eggs. The male genital system (Fig. 6–3, *D*) was reduced in size. The testes, with their testicular gland tissue, were about 10–15 mm. long in 70–75-mm. males, with the seminal vesicles thin and shrunken. The latter were only about half the length of the testes. Histological examination showed that the testes contained spermatocytes, but very few spermatids or mature sperm were present either in the sperm ducts or the seminal vesicles.

Although these data are of a preliminary nature, they are included here because of their significance in the interpretations given later.

BEHAVIOR OF HYPOPHYSECTOMIZED MALES

The six hypophysectomized males were observed and periodically tested in their reactions to other gobies throughout the 30 days following the operation. Their general behavior was quiescent, and they exhibited little or no tendency toward territorial behavior. Shelters were rarely utilized, and, as frequently as not, these animals rested in the central region of the tank floor. This behavior was in sharp contrast to that of normal or castrated gobies, which usually remain in their shelters or in the rear corners of the aquarium.

The reactions of the hypophysectomized males toward other gobies were consistently negative, with very few exceptions. During the course of over 60 trials in which gobies of both sexes were introduced into tanks containing the operated males, on four occasions the resident male showed a slight darkening and nudged the intruder. This behavior was interpreted as an incipient combat. In no case did these males show any courtship behavior, even toward gravid females. The coloration of the operated males was distinctive only in a pale-gray tone to the ground color.

DISCUSSION

Within the limits of the testing method, the direct conclusions that can be drawn from the evidence here presented are as follows:

1. Castration in *Bathgobius* male abolishes a combat response toward introduced males.

2. Courtship response toward females is not reduced in the castrates, and they court other males, gravid females, and nongravid females in a similar manner.

3. The courtship response of normal males toward gravid females is of longer duration than toward nongravid females. The duration of courtship of castrated males is similar toward other males and toward gravid and nongravid females.

4. Regeneration of the testes in incompletely castrated animals results in the restoration of a normal combat response toward introduced males and the reappearance of quantitative differences in the courtship response toward gravid and nongravid females.

5. Hypophysectomy abolishes both courtship and combat responses toward introduced animals and appears to impair the territorial behavior of males.

As reviewed by Beach (1948), in Amphibia, reptiles, birds, and most mammals, male sex behavior is directly correlated with testicular endocrine function, and castration always results in the abolition of, or at least considerable reduction in, the male sexual drive. This is less true in the primates, where prior experience plays a more prominent role.

In fishes, the relationship of the gonads to sex behavior is not well known, and the evidence is, as yet, fragmentary and inconclusive. Males of the stickleback (*Gasterosteus*—Bock, 1928; Ikeda, 1933) and Japanese bitterling (*Acheilognathus*—Tozawa, 1929) have been reported as losing all spawning and nesting behavior after castration. There was also a loss of "nuptial" colors. Jones and King (1952) found that castrate male salmon (*Salmo salar*) showed no territorial or spawning behavior.

The dependence of secondary male characteristics upon testicular hormones in the teleosts has been demonstrated by castration experiments in the bowfin (*Amia calva*—Zahl and Davis, 1932), the bitterling (*Rhodeus amarus*—Glaser and Haempel, 1931), the elritze (*Phoxinus laevis*—Kopeć, 1927), and certain poeciliid fishes such as *Gambusia* (St. Amant, 1941), the swordtail (*Xiphophorus hellerii*—Van Oordt and Van der Maas, 1926), and the guppy (*Lebistes reticulatus*—Hopper, 1949a, b, 1951). Similar evidence has been obtained by hormone administration techniques for male bitterlings (*Acheilognathus* and *Rhodeus*—Wunder, 1931; Saito, 1936; Duyvené de Wit, 1940), male poeciliids (*Gambusia*—Turner, 1941, 1942; *Xiphophorus*—Regnier, 1938; Sangster, 1948), male *Fundulus* (Burger, 1942), and the female gobiid fish *Chloea* (Kinoshita, 1938). It may be presumed that in these cases the reproductive behavior would be similarly controlled by testicular hormone. This is not entirely true in the case of the mouth-breeding cichlid, *Tilapia macrocephala,* in which Aronson (1951) found that although castrated males lost their characteristic yellow opercular colors, they built normal nests.

In contrast with the foregoing, Noble and Kumpf (1936) reported in abstract that castrated male jewel fish (*Hemichromis bimaculatus*) and Siamese fighting fish (*Betta splendens*) exhibited normal courtship, nesting, and spawning behavior. No loss of "nuptial" colors occurred in *Hemichromis* after castration.

None of these reports presented any analysis of the behavior pattern of castrated or treated animals by means of which quantitative or small qualitative differences in behavior could be detected. In particular, the prespawning behavior was not studied. It is difficult, then, to generalize from these seemingly contradictory reports, since neither the methods nor the data are mutually comparable and the species of teleosts investigated have been widely divergent phylogenetically, eologically, and behaviorally.

Ever since the early work of Houssay (1931) and others, the anterior pituitary (gonadotrophic activity) has been utilized in both experimental and commercial applications as a stimulus to ovulation in many species of fishes (Pereira and Cardoso, 1934; Gerbilsky, 1938*a, b;* Khan, 1938; Morosowa, 1938; Hasler, Meyer, and Field, 1940). The techniques and interpretations are fundamentally similar to the methods of induction of ovulation in amphibians, as widely practiced by experimental embryologists (Rugh, 1948). In some cases the stimulation of spawning behavior in teleosts has also been affected by pituitary treatment (Von Ihering, 1935; Koch and Schneuring, 1936; Von Ihering and De Azevedo, 1937; De Azevedo, Dias, and Vieira, 1938; Hasler, Meyer, and Field, 1939). The gonadotrophic function of the anterior pituitary of fishes, then, is evidently very similar to that of other vertebrates.

Hypophysectomy has been reported for only a few species of fishes, and its effects have been studied primarily in relation to the chromatophore-controlling intermediate lobe. In general, however, growth and sexual maturity are arrested (Pickford, 1953), and, specifically, Vivien (1938, 1939, 1941) described the regression of the gonads and accessory glands after hypophysectomy in a European gobiid fish, *G. paganellus*. Pituitary implantation restored normal gonad condition and spawning. Similar results have been obtained in *Fundulus* by Matthews (1939), Burger (1941), and Pickford (1953). Pickford (1952) reported evidence that strongly indicated the control of male sex behavior in *Fundulus* by pituitary action via some mechanism exclusive of a gonadotrophic effect on the testes. The luteinizing hormone fraction was tentatively identified as the specific factor involved.

What, then, is the role of testicular hormones in the behavior of the male *Bathygobius?* It is evident that castration does not impair courtship or spawning behavior. The castrates act as though they do not "perceive" the differences between males, gravid females, and nongravid females or else are unable to respond to these various stimuli except in one fashion—courtship. In this sense, the testicular hormones act to make possible a discriminatory response on the part of the resident male.

One way in which the mechanism can be interpreted is that the hormone affects the threshold of the visual, chemical, and, possibly, auditory sense organs. The alteration of these thresholds may render them less sensitive to a male (or nongravid female) stimulus object or, possibly, result in hypersensitivity, assuming that the differences between stimulus animal types are quantitative. In any case, a further analysis of the stimulus object is in order, with comparisons of male and female, gravid and nongravid. Such an analysis should be oriented to demonstrate precisely to what, in the male goby's perceptual world, he is responding.

SUMMARY

1. Males of the gobiid fish, *B. soporator,* isolated in small tanks, respond to temporarily introduced gobies in the following manner:
   a) Introduced males are attacked.
   b) Gravid females are courted.
   c) Nongravid females are also courted, but the courting behavior is of shorter duration.
2. Castration of males, when tested as above, results in:
   a) Absence of combat behavior toward introduced males.
   b) Courtship response toward gravid females not impaired.
   c) Equal duration of courtship response toward males, gravid females, and nongravid females.
3. Regeneration of the testes in some of the castrates results in a restoration of the combat response toward introduced males and the reappearance of quantitative differences in courtship response toward gravid and nongravid females.
4. Castrated males show a reduction in the size of the seminal vesicle.
5. Animals collected outside the spawning season possess reduced testes and seminal vesicles. These animals show normal combat behavior.
6. Hypophysectomy results in the cessation of both combat and courtship behavior and probably impairs the territorial behavior of males.

LITERATURE CITED

ARONSON, L. R. 1951. Factors influencing the spawning frequency in the female cichlid fish *Tilapia macrocephala.* Amer. Mus. Novitates, No. 1484, pp. 1–26.

AZEVEDO, P. DE, DIAS, M. V., and VIEIRA, B. B. 1938. Biologia do saguirú. Mem. Inst. Oswaldo Cruz., 33:481–554.

BEACH, F. A. 1948. Hormones and behavior. New York: Paul B.Hoeber.

BOCK, F. 1928. Kastration und sekundäre Geschlechtsmerkmale bei Teleostiern. Zeitschr. f. wissensch. Zool., 130:455–68.

BURGER, J. W. 1941. Some experiments on the effects of hypophysectomy and pituitary implantations on the male *Fundulus heteroclitus.* Biol. Bull., **80:** 31–36.

————. 1942. Some effects of androgens on the adult male *Fundulus. Ibid.,* **82:** 233–42.

CHAMPY, C. 1941. Sur l'existence d'une glande testiculaire et d'une glande génitale annexe chez les gobies. Compt. rend. Soc. de biol., **135:**571.

COUJARD, R. 1941. Sur l'existence d'une glande testiculaire et d'une glande génitale annexe chez les gobies. Compt. rend. Soc. de biol., **135:**560–71.

DUYVENÉ DE WIT, J. J. 1940. A quantitative and qualitative test for steroid hormones based on the ovipositor reaction of the female bitterling (*Rhodeus amarus* Bloch). Jour. Endocrinol., **2:**141–56.

EGGERT, B. 1931. Die Geschlechtesorgane der Gobiiformes und Blenniiformes. Zeitschr. f. wissensch. Zool., **139:**249–558.

GERBILSKY, N. L. 1938a. L'Influence de l'agent gonodotrope de l'hypophyse sur l'état de la fraieson chez l'*Acipenser stellatus.* Compt. rend. (Doklady) Acad. Sci. U.R.S.S., **19:**333–36.

————. 1938b. Effet des injections crânniennes de suspension d'hypophyse chez les téléostéens. *Ibid.,* pp. 327–31.

GLASER, E., and HAEMPEL, O. 1931. Das experimentelle hervorgerufen Hochzeitkleid des kastrierten Fisches als Stigma einer Test- und Standardisierungsmethode des männlichen Sexualhormone. Pflüger's Arch. f. d. ges. Physiol., **229:**1–14.

HASLER, A. D., MEYER, R. K., and FIELD, H. M. 1939. Premature spawning induced in trout by pituitary glands of carp. Endocrinology, **25:**978–83.

————. 1940. The use of hormones for the conservation of muskellunge, *Esox masquinongy immaculatus* Garrard. Copeia, 1940, pp. 43–46.

HOPPER, A. F., JR. 1949a. Development and regeneration of the anal fin of normal and castrate males and females of *Lebistes reticulatus.* Jour. Exper. Zoöl., **110:**299–320.

————. 1949b. The effect of ethynyl testosterone on the intact and regenerating anal fins of normal and castrated females and normal males of *Lebistes reticulatus. Ibid.,* **111:**393–414.

————. 1951. The effects of ethynyl testosterone and progynon on the regeneration of the gonopodium of normal castrated males of *Lebistes recticulatus.* Papers Michigan Acad. Sci. Arts and Letters, **35:**109–20.

HOUSSAY, B. A. 1931. Action sexuelle de l'hypophyse sur les poissons et les reptiles. Compt. rend. Soc. de biol., **106:**377–78.

IHERING, R. VON. 1935. Die Wirkung von Hypophyseninjektion auf den Laichakt von Fischen. Zool. Anz., **111:**273–79.

IHERING, R. VON, and AZEVEDO, P. DE. 1937. Über die Wirkung des Säugetier-Hypophysenhormons auf den Laichakt der Fische, Zool. Anz., **120:**71–75.

IKEDA, K. 1933. Effect of castration on the secondary sexual characters of anadromous three-spined stickleback, *Gasterosleus aculeatus aculeatus* (L.). Jap. Jour. Zoöl., **5:**135–37.

JONES, J. W., and KING, G. M. 1952. The spawning of the male salmon parr (*Salmo salar* Linn. juv.). Proc. Zoöl. Soc. London, **122:**615–19.

KHAN, H. 1938. Ovulation in fish. Effect of administration of extract of anterior lobe of pituitary gland. Current Sci. Bangalore, **7:**233–34.

KINOSHITA, Y. 1938. On the secondary sexual characters, with special remarks on the influence of hormone preparations upon the nuptial coloration in *Chloea sarchynnis* Jordan and Snyder, Jour. Sci. Hiroshima Univ., ser. B, div. 1, **6:** 5–22.

KOCH, W., and SCHNEURING, L. 1936. Die Wirkung von Hypophysenvorderlappenhormon auf den Laichakt von Fischen. Zool. Anz., 116:62–64.

KOPEĆ, S. 1927. Experiments on the dependence of the nuptial hue on the gonads in fish. Biol. gen., 3:259–80.

MATTHEWS, S. A. 1939. The relationship between the pituitary gland and the gonads in *Fundulus*. Biol. Bull., 76: 240–55.

MOROSOWA, T. E. 1938. Die Wirkung des Prolans und des unsterilisierten Harns schwangerer auf die Reifung der Geschlechtsprodukts des Barsches (in Russian with German summary). Zool. Zhur., 15:169–74.

NOBLE, G. K., and KUMPF, K. F. 1936. The sexual behavior and secondary sexual characteristics of gonadectomized fish. Anat. Rec., suppl., 67:113 (abstr.).

OORDT, G. J. VAN, and VAN DER MAAS, C. J. J. 1926. Castration and implantation of gonads in *Xiphophorus helleri* Heckel. Proc. kon. Akad. wetensch. Amsterdam, 29:1172–75.

PEREIRA, J. J., and CARDOSO, D. M. 1934. Hypophyse et ovulation chez les poissons. Compt. rend. Soc. de biol., 116:1133–34.

PICKFORD, G. E. 1952. Induction of a spawning reflex in hypophysectomized killifish. Nature, 170:807–8.

————. 1953. A study of the hypophysectomized male killifish, *Fundulus heteroclitus* (Linn.). Bull. Bingham Oceanog. Coll., 14:5–41.

REGNIER, M.-T. 1938. Action de quelques hormones sur les caractères sexuels secondaires de *Xiphophorus helleri* Heckel. Trav. Stat. zool. Wimereux, 13:615–24.

RUGH, R. 1948. Experimental embryology: a manual of techniques and procedures. Minneapolis: Burgess Pub. Co.

ST. AMANT, L. 1941. The effect of castration and treatment with ethynyl testosterone on the development of the gonopodium of *Gambusia affinis*. Anat. Rec., suppl., 79:53–54 (abstr.).

SAITO, T. 1936. Note on the influence of the sex hormone preparations upon the nuptial coloration of the fin and the protrusion of oviduct in *Acheilognathus intermedium*. Zoöl. Mag. Japan, 48:503–5.

SANGSTER, W. 1948. A study of the quantitative effects of ethynyl testosterone upon the sword and gonopodium of *Xiphophorus hellerii*. Physiol. Zoöl., 21:134–47.

TAVOLGA, W. N. 1954. Reproductive behavior in the gobiid fish, *Bathygobius soporator*. Bull. Amer. Mus. Nat. Hist., 103:427–60.

TOZAWA, T. 1929. Experiments on the development of the nuptial and pearl organs of the Japanese bitterling. Folia anat. Japon., 7:407–17.

TURNER, C. L. 1941. Gonopodial characteristics produced in the anal fins of females of *Gambusia, affinis affinis* by treatment with ethinyl testosterone. Biol. Bull., 80:371–83.

————. 1942. A quantitative study of the effects of different concentrations of ethynyl testosterone and methyl testosterone in the production of gonopodia in females of *Gambusia affinis*. Physiol. Zoöl., 15:263–80.

VIVIEN, J.-H. 1938. Sur les effets de l'hypophysectomie chez un téléostéen marin, *Gobius paganellus* L. Compt. rend. Acad. de sci., 207:1452–55.

————. 1939. Rôle de l'hypophyse dans le déterminisme du cycle génitale femelle d'un téléostéen *Gobius paganellus* L. *Ibid.*, 208:948–49.

————. 1941. Contribution à l'étude de la physiologie hypophysaire dans ses relations avec l'appareil génital, la thyroïde et les corps suprarénaux chez les poissons sélaciens et téléostéens *Scylliorhinus canicula* et *Gobius paganellus*. Bull. biol. France et Belg., 75:257–309.

WUNDER, W. 1931. Experimentelle Erzeugung des Hochzeitkleides beim Bitterling

(*Rhodeus amarus*) durch Einspritzung von Hormon. Zeitschr. f. vergl. Physiol., 13:693–708.

YOUNG, R. T., and FOX, D. L. 1937. The seminal vesicles of the goby, with preliminary chemical and physiological studies of the vesicular fluid. Proc. U.S. Nat. Acad. Sci., 23:461–67.

ZAHL, P., and DAVIS, D. D. 1932. Effects of gonadectomy on the secondary sexual characters in the ganoid fish, *Amia calva* Linnaeus. Jour. Exper. Zoöl., 63:291–308.

THE EFFECT OF OESTROGEN AND PROGESTERONE ON THE

NEST-BUILDING OF DOMESTICATED CANARIES

By ROSLYN P. WARREN and R. A. HINDE
Madingley Field Station, Cambridge University
Department of Zoology

INTRODUCTION

Nest-building in female birds occurs during the seasonal recrudescence of the gonads and reproductive tract. This suggests that it depends on ovarian hormones, but there is little direct evidence about the precise ones involved. Until recently studies involving oestrogen treatment of non-breeding females had demonstrated morphological changes, but no effects on nest-building had been reported. Lehrman (1958), however, noticed building behaviour in Ring Doves (*Streptopelia risoria*) after oestrogen treatment. It seemed, therefore, that the earlier negative results in other species could have been due to insufficient dosages or periods of administration. Further, since a combination of exogenous oestrogen and progesterone may be more efficient in inducing oviduct growth in chickens (Brant and Nalbandov, 1956) and doves (Lehrman and Brody, 1957), it may also be effective for nest-building.

PROCEDURE

The canaries, of the Border variety, were paired and placed in metal cages (described in Dunnett and Hinde, 1957) and supplied with a standard plastic canary nest-pan. The experiments were started in October, after the moult, and at intervals thereafter through November, December and January.

Each pair was watched on at least seven days before the first hormone injection, and usually daily for at least two weeks afterwards. Building material—grass and feathers in small wire-netting baskets—was supplied for the duration of each watch; all material was then removed. Each watch lasted 12 minutes, and detailed records of building behaviour were taken as described previously (Hinde and Warren,

1959); in particular, the number of times each bird carried material, and the number of times it placed material in the nest-pan were recorded.

The injections were given in the pectoral musculature three times weekly. Hormones used were aqueous suspensions of oestradiol benzoate (Oestroform Aqueous B.D.H.) and progesterone (Lutoform, B.D.H.). The dosages of oestradiol were 0.1–0.15 mg. (1 mg./ml.); 0.25–0.3 mg. (2 mg./ml.) and 0.5 mg. (5 mg./ml.). The dosage of progesterone was 0.125 mg. (5 mg./ml.). Control animals were injected with 0.1 ml. of Frog Ringer solution. A total of 76 females and 6 males were injected; they were distributed between groups as shown in the next section.

RESULTS

The results are shown in Tables I and II. Ten birds which died within the first 10 days after the injections started, and 5 birds which were never seen to carry material, are not included in the tables. The remaining birds in each group were divided as follows:

Category 0. Birds which were seen to carry material, but not to place it in the nest-pan. For these, the mean number of carrying bouts per watch are given.

Category +. Birds which were seen to place material in the nest-pan. For these, the mean numbers of carrying bouts and of placings per watch are given.

(i) *Controls.* (Table I). Seven females, after 7 daily pre-injection tests, were given 0.1 ml. Frog Ringer solution 3 times per week. In two cases the injections were continued for three weeks, and in the other five for over four weeks. These control birds were started at intervals throughout the period in which the hormone experiments were conducted. No control bird was seen to place material, and carrying was rare.

(ii) *0.1–0.15 mg. oestrogen.* (9 females, Table I). This dose level produced a small but definite increase in carrying but had no definite effect on placing.

Of 4 birds which did not place throughout the experiment, 2 were seen to carry before the injections and all 4 afterwards. The maximum number of carryings in any test after injection was 6. Two of these birds were injected for a fortnight, and two for three weeks.

Of 5 birds which were seen to place, 4 were seen to carry, and 1 to place, before the injections, and all placed after the injections. Thus the pre-injection performance of these birds was better than that of

TABLE I

MEAN NUMBER OF CARRYING (C) AND PLACING (PI) BOUTS PER WATCH SHOWN BY BIRDS INJECTED WITH OESTROGENS

Sex	Treatment	Placed (+) or Carried Only (0)	No. of Birds	Bouts of Carrying (C) or Placing (PI)	−7/−6	−5/−4	−3/−2	−1/0	1/2	3/4	5/6	7/8	15
♀	Control Frog Ringer	0	7[1]	C	0·07	0·07	0·28	0	0·16	0·22	0·08	0	0
	0·1–0·15 mg. oestrogen	0	4[2]	C	0	0·6	0·28	0·37	2·3	2·0	2·0	2·4	1·5
	0·25–0·3 mg. oestrogen	+	5[3]	C	(0)	(0)	0·5	0·87	1·0	(0·25)	1·4	(1·0)	2·2
				PI	(0)	(0)	0·1	0·25	0·25	(0·25)	0	0	0·2
		0	2[4]	C	0	0	0	0	(1)	0·5	0·5	1·0	1·5
	0·5 mg. oestrogen	+	5[5]	C	0	0	0·2	0·3	0·8	1·4	0	1·8	2·8
				PI	0	0	0	0	0	0	0	0·7	2·2
		0	5[6]	C	0	0	0	0·2	1·4	1·6	1·1	–	–
♂	0·5 mg. oestrogen	+	17[7]	C	0·23	0·53	0·72	0·91	1·7	3·6	2·7	2·7	2·0
				PI	0	0	0·02	0	0·8	2·0	2·1	2·5	2·0
		0	4[8]	C	1·0	1·5	0	0·4	1·0	0·2	0·2	0	–
		+	2[9]	C	0	0	0	0	0	0·5	2·5	3·8	–
				PI	0	0	0	0	0	0·5	0·75	2·0	–

1. Each figure based on 9–14 watches
2. " " " 5– 8 "
3. " " " 8– 9 "
4. " " " 2– 4 "
5. " " " 5–10 "

6. Each figure based on 6–10 watches
7. " " " 22–36 "
8. " " " 4– 8 "
9. " " " 2– 4 "

except figures in parenthesis, based on 4 watches

except for days 5–8 (15–19 watches)

the 4 birds which never placed. The maximum number of carrying bouts per test was 7, and of placings 1.

(iii) *0.25–0.3 mg. oestrogen*. (7 females, Table I). On average, the effect of this dose level was little greater than that of the previous one, but one bird built vigorously after treatment.

Two birds did not place throughout the experiment; these did not carry before injection but did after. Five birds were seen to place: 3 of these did not carry before injection, but all did afterwards. None of these birds was seen to place until a week after the first injection; after a fortnight, the mean number of placings was 2.2, but one bird carried 9 times and placed 7 times on Day +15, and carried 14 times and placed 14 times on Day 19.

(iv) *0.5 mg. oestrogen*. (37 females, Table I). Although this dose level was toxic to some individuals, it induced vigorous building in others.

Ten birds died during the first 10 days after injections started. Five others were never seen to carry, and are not included in Table I. Five birds carried but did not place; 4 of these did not carry before injections but all carried after, the maximum number of carrying bouts in any test being 9. Of 17 birds which were seen to place, 14 carried and 1 placed before the injections. Thus the pre-injection performance was better than that of the birds which did not place after injection. There was a marked increase in building behaviour after the injections started, and all 17 birds placed; the maximum number of carrying bouts and placings was 15.

(v) *0.15 mg. oestrogen + 0.125 mg. progesterone*. (Table II). The addition of progesterone to low levels of oestrogen produced no definite effect on nest-building.

Five females were treated with 0.15 mg. oestrogen thrice weekly for 3 weeks or longer, and then given 0.15 mg. oestrogen + 0.125 mg. progesterone thrice weekly. Three of these birds did not place either with oestrogen alone, or with oestrogen and progesterone. Two birds were seen to place both before and after the oestrogen and progesterone injections: there was no clear evidence that the slightly higher mean number of carrying bouts with progesterone was due to this hormone. Taking all five birds together, there was no increase in carrying after progesterone treatment.

(vi) *0.5 mg. oestrogen + 0.125 mg. progesterone*. (Table II). The addition of progesterone to high levels of oestrogen also produced no definite effect.

Six females were treated with 0.5 mg. oestrogen + 0.125 mg. pro-

TABLE II

Mean Number of Carrying (C) or Placing (P1) Bouts per Watch Shown by Birds Injected with Oestrogen and Progesterone (or Progesterone only) after Oestrogen Treatment

Treatment	Pre-treatment	Placed (+) or Carried Only (0)	No. of Birds	Bouts of Carrying (C) or Placing (P1)	-7/-6	-5/-4	-3/-2	-1/0	1/2	3/4	5/6	7/8	9/10	15/16
								Day w.r.t. Start of Treatment						
0·15 mg. oestrogen and 0·125 mg. progesterone	0·15 mg. oestrogen	0	3¹	C	2·5	1·4	0·5	1·5	1·2	0	0·8	0·8	—	0
		+	2¹	C	0·5	1·0	1·5	1·7	2·5	3·3	0·5	2·3	—	2·0
				P1	0	0	0·3	0	0	0	0	0·7	—	0
0·5 mg. oestrogen and 0·125 mg. progesterone	0·5 mg. oestrogen for 1 wk.	+	4²	C	—	0·7	2·2	3·5	3·5	—	3·1	6·3	7·1	9·0
	0·5 mg. oestrogen for 18+days	+	2³	P1	—	0	1·5	3·0	3·3	—	2·6	4·8	6·5	9·0
				C	—	7·5	5·5	6·7	9·0	(1·5)	7·3	5·5	10·0	—
0·125 mg. progesterone only	0·5 mg. oestrogen +0·125 mg. progesterone	+	5⁴	P1	—	7·5	5·5	6·3	8·0	(1·5)	7·0	5·5	10·0	—
				C	3·9	5·6	7·6	5·9	3·4	0·9	1·2	0·04	—	—
	progesterone			P1	3·7	4·6	7·0	4·6	3·0	0·02	0·3	0	—	—

1. Each figure based on 2–5 watches
2. „ „ „ 4–8 „
3. „ „ „ 2–4 „
4. „ „ „ 5–10 „

gesterone after previous oestrogen treatment. Four of these had had one week's pre-treatment with oestrogen, the other 2 had been on oestrogen for 18 days and 40 days respectively. All 6 placed while on oestrogen alone. The 4 birds which had one week's pre-treatment with oestrogen showed a gradual increase in building behaviour during the period on oestrogen, but no marked further increase during the first week on progesterone. They did show a high mean number of carryings and placings after this point, but similar scores were obtained with birds which were kept on 0.5 mg. oestrogen alone for the same period (see, for example, the pre-progesterone period of the 2 birds which had been on oestrogen for 18+ days). The 2 birds which had a prolonged pre-treatment on oestrogen also provided no clear evidence that progesterone either increased or inhibited building.

(vii) 0.125 *mg. progesterone only.* (Table II). Progesterone alone did not maintain the building behaviour previously induced by oestrogen.

Five females were treated with oestrogen and progesterone as in (vi) and then given 0.125 mg. progesterone only thrice weekly. All these were placing on oestrogen + progesterone; the building behaviour fell off rapidly when the oestrogen was stopped. There was no placing on or after Day +6.

(viii) *Males treated with* 0.5 *mg. oestrogen.* (6 males, Table I). High doses of oestrogen caused an increase in building in some males.

Six males were given 0.5 mg. oestrogen thrice weekly. Four did not place throughout the experiment, and showed no increase in the frequency of carrying as a result of the treatment. Two others did not carry or place before the injections, but began to do so 6 days after the injections started.

SURVIVAL

Although injections of 0.5 mg. oestrogen were effective in inducing nest-building, they also had a toxic effect on some individuals. Of 37 birds injected, 10 died in the first 10 days after injections started, and others later. None of the control animals, and none of those injected with 0.1–0.15 mg. or with 0.25–0.3 mg. died in the three weeks after injections started. Thus the margin between the effective dose and the lethal dose is rather small.

DISCUSSION

The results presented above indicate that large doses of oestrogen can induce nest-building behaviour in canaries during the nonbreeding season. Progesterone alone, in the dosage used, does not. The building behaviour of many of the females treated with 0.5 mg. oestrogen included all the building movements used in nest construction and was at least qualitatively similar to that shown in the natural breeding season. Although there was no precise correlation between pre-and post-injection behaviour, the hormone was usually more effective in birds which had shown some building before treatment.

Little previous work on the effects of oestrogens on avian behaviour has been reported. They are known to induce sexual responses in domestic fowl (reviews in Beach, 1947; Collias, 1950), but Emlen and Lorenz (1942) found no indications of sexual behaviour in Valley Quail (*Lophartyx californica*) after implants of stilboestrol pellets, and Noble and Wurm (1940) claimed that, in the Black-crowned Night Heron (*Nycticorax nycticorax*), "no phase of the female behaviour is due to oestrogens." Shoemaker (1939) used oestrone on female canaries, and did not observe any effect on behaviour. Sexual behaviour was not studied in the present experiment, but it is usually associated with nest-building and it is likely that both are influenced by the same hormones. There are thus some apparent discrepancies in the evidence—oestrogens induce sexual behaviour in hens but appear not to do so in Quail or Herons, and the effect on the nest-building of canaries in this paper is not paralleled in the other studies. These may be considered as follows:

(*a*) *The behaviour studied.* The authors cited above were concerned primarily with female sexual behaviour. This is influenced by the previous behaviour of the male, and thus any failure to detect an effect of oestrogens on sexual behaviour could be due to a deficiency in the males. Nest-building can be elicited reliably from canaries in the appropriate conditions, but functionally comparable behaviour in Quail and domestic hens is relatively inconspicuous.

(*b*) *Dose levels.* The dosages effective in the present study were high, and near the lethal level. Low dosages were relatively ineffective. We have no means of knowing whether the amount of oestrogen injected is greater than that normally secreted by the ovary, but the hormones used were synthetic products manufactured for use in mammals, and there may be chemical differences between avian and mammalian oestrogens. It is also possible that, during the off-season, there is a refractoriness of the sensory-neuro-muscular mechanisms to oestrogens comparable to the suggested refractoriness of the pituitary and gonads (e.g. Marshall, 1954).

(c) *Species differences.* Some of the apparent discrepancies could be due to differences in the species used. However, the results of this study indicate that if the dose level is high enough, oestrogens do influence reproductive behaviour in canaries.

Since the smaller doses of oestrogen had only a limited effect on nest-building, and the larger doses were toxic to some individuals, combinations of oestrogen and progesterone were tried. Although oestrogen tends to inhibit some aspects of parental behaviour in mammals, it induces mammalian oestrous more predictably when given in combination with progesterone (e.g. Boling *et al.*, 1938; Ring, 1944). Further, although birds have no corpus luteum, progesterone has been demonstrated in the blood of hens (Fraps, Hooker and Forbes, 1948); and Lehrman (1958) has shown that the oviducts of Ring Doves enlarge more when oestrogen is given in combination with progesterone than when it is administered alone.

In the doses used in this experiment, progesterone did not produce any appreciable augmentation of the action of oestrogen—nor, on the other hand, did it suppress it. It is known, however, that the effects of oestrogen and progesterone on reproductive morphology depend on the relative as well as the absolute amounts of each; and indeed opposite effects may be induced by varying the dosage (Mason, 1952). It is therefore still possible that progesterone would be found to play a role in other dosage combinations.

SUMMARY

1. Female canaries were injected with various levels of oestrogen and of oestrogen in combination with progesterone.

2. Doses of oestrogen from 0.1 to 0.3 mg. thrice weekly had a negligible effect on building behaviour. Doses of 0.5 mg. thrice weekly were toxic to some individuals, but produced active nest-building in others.

3. No enhancement or inhibition of the effect of oestrogen by progesterone was found in the dose combinations used. Progesterone alone did not maintain building behaviour previously induced by oestrogen.

4. Doses of 0.5 mg. oestrogen induced nest-building in some males.

ACKNOWLEDGMENTS

This study was supported by a grant from the United States Air Force Biosciences Division.

REFERENCES

BEACH, F. A. (1947). *Hormones and behaviour.* New York: Hoeber.

BOLING, J. L., YOUNG, W. C. AND DEMPSEY, E. W. (1938). Miscellaneous experiments on the oestrogen-progesterone induction of heat in the spayed guinea pig. *Endocrinology,* 2, 182–87.

BRANT, J. W. A. AND NALBANDOV, A. V. (1956). Role of sex hormone in albumen secretion by the oviduct of chickens. *Poult. Sci.,* 35, 692–700.

COLLIAS, N. E. (1950). *Hormones and behaviour, with special reference to birds and the mechanisms of hormone action.* In Symposium on Steroid Hormones, Ed. E. S. Gordon, Univ. of Wisconsin.

DUNNETT, G. E. AND HINDE, R. A. (1957). Chapter on Canaries in *U.F.A.W. Handbook of Laboratory Animals.* London: U.F.A.W.

EMLEN, J. T. AND LORENZ, F. W. (1942). Pairing responses of free-living Valley Quail to sex hormone implants. *Auk,* 59, 369–76.

FRAPS, R. M., HOOKER, C. W. AND FORBES, T. L. (1948). Progesterone in blood plasma of the ovulating hen. *Science,* 108, 86–87.

HINDE, R. A. AND WARREN, ROSLYN P. (1959). The effect of nest-building on later reproductive behaviour in the domesticated canary. *Anim. Behav.,* 7, 35–41.

LEHRMAN, D. S. (1958). Effect of female sex hormone on incubation behaviour in the ring dove (*Streptopelia risoria*). *J. comp. physiol. Psychol.,* 51, 142–45.

LEHRMAN, D. S. AND BRODY, P. (1957). Oviduct response to estrogen and progesterone in the Ring Dove. (*Streptopelia risoria*). *Proc. Soc. exp. Biol.* (N.Y.), 95, 373–75.

MASON, R. C. (1952). Synergistic and antagonistic effects of progesterone in combination with estrogens on oviduct weight. *Endocrinology,* 51, 570–72.

MARSHALL, A. J. (1954). *Bower Birds.* London: Oxford University Press.

NOBLE, G. K. AND WURM, M. (1940). The effect of testosterone propionate on the Black-Crowned Night Heron. *Endocrinology,* 26, 837–50.

RING, G. R. (1944). The estrogen-progesterone induction of sexual receptivity in the spayed female mouse. *Endocrinology,* 34, 269–75.

SHOEMAKER, H. H. (1939). Effect of testosterone propionate on behaviour of female canary. *Proc. Soc. exp. Biol.* (N.Y.), 41, 299–302.

HORMONAL REGULATION OF THE MICTURITION BEHAVIOR

OF THE DOG

THALES MARTINS[1] and J. R. VALLE
Instituto Oswaldo Cruz, Rio de Janeiro, and
Instituto Butantan, São Paulo, Brazil

It is known that the body posture of canines during urination differs in both sexes not only in the domestic species but also in wild *canidae,* as the wolf (5) and the Brazilian wolfdog, *Chrysocyon jubatus* (6).

The male does not show the conspicous modification of body posture until he is approaching sexual maturity, and this fact suggests the possibility that the sex difference in behavior during micturition may be controlled or at least affected by gonadal hormones. Viewed in this light the question is seen to be a complex one involving problems of endocrinology, physiology of micturition, experimental psychology, behavior and ecology.

As previously reported, spayed females show no post operational change in the micturition pattern, and castration of males over 4 months old does not always prevent the appearance of the masculine posture during micturition in adulthood (7). In males castrated very early in life the infantile posture is maintained, but, the adult pattern can be produced by testosterone treatment (8). Bitches treated with testosterone from the first days of life exhibit the male posture when urinating. Furthermore, when estradiol was administered to 4 castrated males, it evoked the adult masculine response in 2 animals (9, 10, 11).

The present report presents new findings as well as additional data which support and extend our earlier studies.

MATERIAL AND METHODS

A total of 55 dogs born in our laboratories and including males and females have been observed for periods of 8 to 72 months. The

---
[1] Fellow of the J. S. Guggenheim Foundation.

majority of animals was studied for more than 11 months. Almost all were small or middle sized fox-terriers of pure or cross breed. One Dobermann was employed. The animals were kept in large outdoor cages and behavior was observed under free conditions in large yards. Control and hormonally treated animals were taken from the same litter, and thus littermates were studied under different hormonal conditions. Several groups were used as shown in Tables 1 and 2. Here they will be briefly described.

TABLE 1

MICTURITION BEHAVIOR OF DOGS AND BITCHES UNDER VARIOUS HORMONAL CONDITIONS

Groups	Total in Each Group	Age at Castration	Treatment [2]	Number of Cases Showing Pattern of Behavior [3] at End of Experiment				
				I	A	IA	F	FA
		days						
Normal males	5	—	—					
Castrated males	11	28–113	—	8	5			
" "	2	38–52	Arachis oil	2	1	2		
" "	4	52–107	Estradiol benz.	2	2			
" "	4	54–118	Testost. prop.	3	1			
Normal females	7	—	—				7	
Castrated "	5	30–43	—				5	
" "	5	39–111	Testost. prop.				5	
Normal "	4	—	Testost. prop.				3	1[4]

[1] All animals included in this table were small or middle sized, weighing from 4 to 10 kgrs. See Table 2 also.

[2] Treatment began at the day of castration, and in the normal females when they were 50–120 day old.

[3] I: infantile male; A: adult male; IA: infantile and adult male types alternately and with less frequent micturition; F: female posture; FA: female posture and sometimes adult male type.

[4] This bitch eventually exhibited the adult male type; her mother was treated with testosterone propionate just before fertilization.

Normal males: Six animals were under observation up to 53 months.

Castrated males: Twelve dogs were castrated when 28 to 64 days old and one was operated on the 112th day of life. Two members of this group were treated with control injections of sesame or arachis oil.

New born male treated with testosterone propionate: One animal received 5 to 25 mg. of the hormone subcutaneously, 4 or 5 times a week. The last dose was given in the form of a pellet weighing 75 mg. and implanted when he was 32 days old.

Castrated males treated with testosterone propionate: Three animals were castrated when 54, 58 and 60 days and one when 118 days old. Hormonal treatment began the day of castration. In some cases the androgen was injected 3 times a week and in others it was also implanted at 20–30 day intervals. Two dogs received a total of 81 and 141 mg. of the hormone respectively; the period of treatment of the other 2 animals of this group is recorded in table 3.

Castrated males treated with estradiol benzoate: Four animals were castrated when 52–107 days old and the hormone was injected from 2 to 4 times per week beginning the day of castration. A total of 27–32 mg. had been given by the time the animals were 8–11 months old. Two puppies in this group were treated from

TABLE 2

MICTURITION BEHAVIOR OF DOGS AND BITCHES TREATED SINCE
THE THIRD DAY OF AGE WITH SEX HORMONES[1]

Animal	Sex and Condition	Age at Castration Days	Treatment	Pattern of Behavior	Remarks
F1	Normal male	—	Test. prop.	Adult male behavior from the 39th day of age.	Treatment until 32 days old; adult male type was maintained through the observation period up to 362 days of age.
F2	Castrated male	23	Estrad. benz.	Adult male behavior from the 61st day of age.	Treatment discontinued when 85 days old; adult male behavior was maintained as in F1.
F3	Normal male	—	Sesame oil	Adult male behavior from 173 days old.	Behavior maintained as above.
F4	Spayed female	73	Test. prop.	Adult male behavior from the 65th day of age.	Hormonal treatment until 131 days old and behavior maintained as above.[2]
S1	Castrated male	12	Estrad. benz.	Adult male behavior from the 95th day of age.	Died with urinary disorders when 103 days old.
S4	Spayed female	12	Test. prop.	Adult male behavior from the 70th day of age.	The male adult type was maintained through the period of observation; 100 days under treatment
S3	Normal female	—	—	Feminine behavior from 21 days old.	Feminine type through the observation period of 212 days.

[1] These animals were not included in Table 1. F and S are littermates respectively.
[2] The absorption of the hormonal pellet (75 mgs. by the 63rd day of age) as judged by palpation was complete at the end of 3 months. It seems that the persistence of the male behavior even 299 days after the implantation was not dependent on absorption of hormonal residues.

TABLE 3

SUMMARY OF THE MONTHLY OBSERVATION OF THE MICTURITION BEHAVIOR OF TWO
TESTOSTERONE TREATED CASTRATED DOGS AND ONE CASTRATED CONTROL

Dogs	Born	Age at Castration days	From Nov. '44 to Apr. '45	Months 1945 M	J	Jl	A	S	O	N	D	1946 J	F	M	A
39A	Nov. 6. '44	58	I	I	I	I	*I*	*I*	*I*	*I*	IA	A	A	A	A
43	Nov. 11. 44	54	I	I	I	I	*I*	*I*	*I*	*I*		A	A	IA	IA
44	Nov. 11. 44	54	I	I	I	I	I	I	I	I		I	I	I	I

[1] I—infantile male behavior; A—adult male behavior; IA—alternately infantile and adult male behavior.
[2] Dogs 39A and 43 received a total of 400 mgrs. of testosterone propionate in pellets or injections; the period of the treatment is italicized. Dogs 43 and 44 are littermates.

the third day of life. F2, castrated when 23 days old, received 4 to 6 weekly injections of 25–50 μg. until the 5th week when the body weight had reached 2.1 kg. Then the dosage was increased to 100 and 160 μg. S1 castrated at 12 days, was treated like F2 but received higher doses of 150 and 200 μg.

Normal females: Seven animals were under observation from birth, for periods varying from 6 to 39 months.

Spayed females: Five animals castrated when 30–43 days old were observed to 6–15 months of age. One of these females received control injections of arachis oil.

Normal females treated with testosterone propionate: Hormonal treatment of 4 animals began at 50–120 days of age. Implants and injections of the hormone during the subsequent 4–12 months amounted to a total of 100–240 mg. in different individuals. One puppy was treated from the third day of age with 4 or 5 weekly injections of 5–25 mg. She was implanted with a 75 mg. pellet on the 48th and again on the 63rd day of age and was castrated when 73 days old.

Spayed females treated with testosterone propionate: Six bitches were observed in this group. Four were spayed at 39–64 days of age one when 111 days old. For 6–11 months after operation they received 2 or 3 weekly injections totalling 285–340 mg. of the hormone. During the same period 125 mg. divided in 6 implants for each animal were also administered. The sixth animal, a puppy S4, was spayed when 12 days old and treated from the third day of life with 3 to 5 weekly injections of 5–25 mg. In addition a 75 mg. pellet was implanted when the dog was 35 days old.

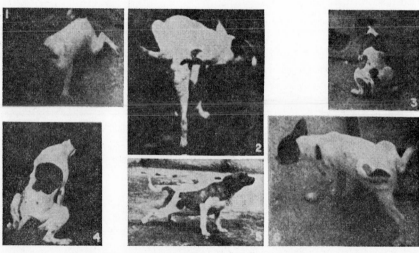

Fɪɢ. 1.   Normal infantile male dog, F3, control, photographed when 89 days old. Infantile male type at micturition; the shifting to the adult pattern was observed by the 175th day of age.

Fɪɢ. 2.   Adult normal dog, R1. Adult male type of micturition against a wall.

Fɪɢ. 3.   Infantile female dog 3 months old at micturition.

Fɪɢ. 4.   Normal bitch. The same posture at micturition of the infantile female of Figure 3.

Fɪɢ. 5.   Castrated male dog, n.2. The infantile type of behavior at micturition was maintained up to 26 months. Photographed when 15 months old.

Fɪɢ. 6.   Normal male dog, F1, treated with testosterone propionate from the third day of age. Beginning of the male posture at micturition when 39 days old. Picture taken by the 58th day of age.

New born puppies of either sex do not maintain a definite or constant position while urinating; they begin to show a characteristic posture only at 3 to 5 weeks of age.

Infantile male pattern (Figs. 1 and 5): There is abduction, a slight extension and sometimes a little flexion of the hind legs. When these are extended a slight projection of the trunk is also frequently observed. When flexion occurs it is much less pronounced than in the infantile female thus affording a sharp difference between the sexes even before maturity.

Adult male pattern (Fig. 2): One of the hind legs is lifted with flexion and abduction of the thigh. While the other leg remains in extension the trunk undergoes a torsion towards the opposite side. The result is a lateral emission of urine. Shifting from the infantile to the adult pattern occurs when the dog attains the puberal development. The one Dobermann which we observed exhibited the characteristic adult male posture by the 10th month but in all other males this pattern appeared between 5 and 8 months of age. Sometimes the infantile pattern temporarily reappears in adult dogs. This reversion is apt to occur when the animal is frightened or is maintained in too confined quarters. In normal circumstances, however, the male posture appears with great frequency, sometimes being shown repeatedly in a few minutes. When micturition occurs repeatedly at short intervals the amount of voided urine decreases in a few drops or even to zero. This means that the stimulus to micturition may still be present even when the bladder is empty. Obviously optic and olfactory stimuli must be involved. The dog always sniffs the target before assuming the adult male posture, the performance, as a rule, being against conspicuous vertical objects like trees, posts, corners and walls.

Learning or imitation are not necessary since isolated animals show the complete behavior as soon as sufficiently mature.

Female pattern (Figs. 3 and 4): The pattern for infantile and adult females is the same. It appears on the 3rd or 4th week and remains unchanged throughout life. Its characteristic feature is a strong flexion and abduction of the hind legs accompanied by a pronounced lowering of the hindquarters. The visual and olfactory elements of the surroundings have not the same importance as in males; olfactory exploration before urination may be omitted. The frequency of micturition also differs in males and females. For instance, while the bitch urinates once an hour the dog tends to urinate 10 times or more during the same period.

It is said by some owners that the male posture may be very rarely exhibited by old bitches.

Castrated males (Fig. 5): Eight males castrated at 28–64 days of age and one castrated at 112 days maintained the infantile pattern throughout the postoperative observation period. One dog castrated when 61 days old shifted to the adult pattern; and 2 others operated at comparable ages showed alternation of the infantile and the adult patterns. Three of the 12 castrates were observed up to 8 months and the others from 11 to 26 months. Although exhibiting the infantile micturition pattern some of them showed mating behavior with mounting and rhythmic movements of the pelvis.

New born male treated with testosterone propionate (Fig. 6): This male, F1, was seen lifting his leg for the first time on the 39th day of life. For a short period the adult and infantile postures were used interchangeably but from the 46th day only the adult male pattern was present. Henceforth it continued for the whole period of observation lasting 280 days. From its first appearance the adult pattern comprised all features including body posture and scenting of objects.

Castrated males treated with testosterone propionate: Two animals castrated at 60 and 118 days of age and treated thereafter with male hormone shifted in proper time to the adult pattern. One such animal, however, occasionally reverted to the infantile posture. Observation of 2 other males, castrated when 54 and 58 days old, was more decisive. They received no androgen until the 9th month of age at which time they were still exhibiting the infantile behavior at micturition. In these two cases the adult pattern appeared after 4 or 5 months of treatment. Following the withdrawal of the hormone the adult male pattern was maintained by one dog whereas the other at times exhibited the immature response (Table 3). In the meantime 2 castrated controls injected with pure oil maintained the infantile pattern throughout the experiment.

Castrated males treated with estradiol benzoate: Four animals were castrated when 52–107 days old and treated thereafter. Two maintained the infantile pattern and two showed the adult behavior. In this particular case estradiol seems to have a similar action to testosterone, and this fact was emphasized by the results of experiments on 2 new born puppies (Table 2). One of them, F2, began lifting the hind leg by the 61st and the other, S1, by the 95th day of age. A littermate control, F3, did not behave thus until 173 days. In fact, none of the normal males under observation exhibited the adult pattern before 150 days of age.

Despite the withdrawal of estrogen at 83 days after birth, F2 showed adult behavior at micturition throughout the 280 days of observation.

Spayed females: Although operated when 30–43 days old, spayed females showed no change from the normal female pattern during 15 months of observation.

Normal females treated with testosterone propionate: No change was observed in 3 of 4 bitches treated from 50th day of age. The fourth animal, R3, eventually exhibited the male posture and it is worth mention that her mother was also treated with the male hormone up to the time of insemination. The treatment of R3 did not prevent mating and fertilization but the single offspring did not survive.

Spayed females treated with testosterone propionate: No alteration of the female pattern was shown by 5 spayed bitches treated from the 39th to the 111th day of age.

New born females treated with testosterone propionate: Results in both puppies were concordant and conclusive. At the 34th day of age F4 urinated very frequently and usually did so near some vertical objects. The female posture was employed but there were repeated attempts to direct the urine toward conspicuous objects. When the bitch was 65 days old, lifting of the leg was observed and henceforth the complete male pattern including sniffing was exhibited frequently. Occasionally she reverted to the female posture but this usually occurred just when she had been set free and was voiding a copious amount of urine. Afterwards the female would exhibit the adult male pattern, repeatedly, often emitting only a few drops of urine. It is worth mentioning that this puppy was spayed when 73 days old and consequently the shift to the adult male behavior occurred prior to spaying. Despite the cessation of hormone treatment when she was 131 days old, the bitch continued to show male behavior during micturition until the end of the observation period which lasted 280 days. Sometimes she also adopted the male mating pattern. Although she was kept in a room with her male littermates this female was quite aggressive and assumed priority in feeding and in choice of sleeping places.

The female S4 began exhibiting the adult male micturition pattern at 70 days old and continued to do so through the observation period of 100 days. Her behavior was substantially the same as that of F4 described above.

Although not directly related to the subject of this paper other effects of the hormones administered, especially on puppies, deserve mention here. An acceleration of the behavioristic and somatic development was noticed in both sexes particularly on males after androgenic treatment. The aggressiveness and the dominance of the injected animals have already been mentioned. The position of the ears may be taken as another index. After 10 days of testosterone or estradiol injections they were held erect while in a male littermate control this position of the ears was not seen until 210 days of age. Palpation showed that the ear cartilage, particularly in the animals receiving testosterone, was thicker and in addition there seemed to be some action on the tonus of the ear musculature.

After a few weeks of treatment it was easy to recognize the males receiving estradiol. There was a protrusion of the anal region with edema, swelling of the perineal glands and rectal enlargement leading to interference with defecation. Another feature of the estradiol treatment was the enormous longitudinal outgrowth of the skin which became loose and folded. This effect was less marked as hormone administration continued but it did not completely disappear after hormone withdrawal. Also the fur lacked the luster and thickness seen in the normal and the testosterone treated animals; as judged by the observation on shaved areas, the rate of hair growth was considerably decreased.

No hematological studies were made on the puppies injected from the third day of life, but the anemizing effect of estradiol in the other 4 cases has previously been described (14). It was also found that castrated males treated with estradiol showed increased excitability of the vas deferens (15).

All normal and spayed females treated with the male hormone exhibited a hypertrophied clitoris possessing a bulb similar to the canine penis. This change persisted after cessation of the hormone treatment. Size and color changes of the clitoris of the new born puppies were noticeable in the second week of treatment.

DISCUSSION

Present results seem to substantiate the conclusion that the canine micturition pattern depends on sex hormones acting on reflex arcs of a very early differentiation. It may be considered a functional sex character.

Only one other study has dealt with this behavior from the hormonal point of view. Berg (4) reported the induction of adult male behavior in an immature male treated with testosterone. He also found that castration of 2 male puppies, 7 and 11 weeks old, prevented the shift to the adult pattern, although this pattern could be induced by testosterone injections. In 2 intact adult bitches testosterone treatment did not alter the female micturition pattern. This is understandable since our experiments have shown the weak reactivity of the bitches even when spayed at an early age and treated for a long time. His results on 2 normal adult males treated with estradiol benzoate and theelin are ambiguous. Daily injection of 10,000 I.U. for 8 days increased the frequency of micturition in one case; and resumption of the treatment after 4 weeks with 1,000 I.U. every other day induced reversion to the puppy pattern. Another animal stopped leg elevation after the 5th injection of 2,000 I.U. but returned to the normal behavior after the cessation of treatment.

The suggested interpretation that this action of estrogens was a result of testis depression seems questionable. Such an effect would probably require a much longer treatment. Moreover, as was shown in the present work, castration of young or adult dogs may have no influence on the appearance or maintenance of the adult male behavior. Furthermore our results with estradiol-treated castrates showed that several individuals shifted to the adult pattern, a few cases doing so very prematurely. This seems to prove that the female hormone has the same action on the male as testosterone.

Berg's observations that the behavior at micturition does not depend upon learning or upon trial and error are supported by our findings. We also share his opinion that the development of behavior in the male follows a course of cephalocaudal differentiation. Apart from this direction in the developmental sequence we think that, after the behavior is established, the order of physiological events, as to their manifestation, is also a cephalocaudal one. In the male the inciting stimuli are olfactory and optic. Since the olfactory and visual systems seem to be involved it would be interesting to investigate the effects of sectioning the optic and olfactory nerves and in addition to study the effects of decortication. The literature is somewhat confusing because the infantile male pattern apparently has often been mistaken for the female posture.

Concerning the mechanism of hormonal action it is necessary to determine whether, during the embryonic differentiation or early in the postnatal period, the hormones act as organizers inducing certain connections amongst special nervous centers; or whether they are only activators of genetically predetermined arcs and thus modify the thresholds of excitability. The functional effects here described indicate that the hormone possesses a selective action, a certain neurotropy which, during the developmental period, might well exert an organizing action, stimulating the development of specific centers or connections. However such interpretations are at present merely speculative.

The hormonal regulation of the micturition pattern shows some analogies to mating behavior. Experiments on other mammals, especially rats (1, 2, 3, 12), have demonstrated that the sexual repertoire in males and in females includes the mating patterns of both sexes, the responses depending on the type of hormone present and on external stimuli. Our results with bitches correspond fairly well to this general scheme. In males, however, it was not possible to induce the female pattern of micturition by estradiol injections. Instead this treatment induced precocious male behavior. Nevertheless it is possible that the male possesses the organization for the female pattern but that the feminine mechanisms exhibit a higher threshold of reactivity. Lethal anemia and urinary disorders due to high dosage of estradiol are technical complications which make it difficult to check this point. Experiments on ovary graftings are in progress, and this may make possible a slow and continuous absorption of estrogens without any harmful effects.

It seems fairly clear that sexual differences in behavior at micturition do not depend upon differences in stimuli from the urogenital zone. Male castrates treated with doses of estradiol which profoundly altered genital anatomy continued to show the adult male behavior; and the majority of the testosterone-treated females with virilized genitalia maintained the female pattern while urinating.

Careful observation of the dog and the bitch during micturition indicates differences in symmetry of bodily response. The position of the lifted leg in the adult male is essentially the same as that exhibited by both legs in the normal female; the rest of the dog's posture is merely equilibrium reaction. As the postures of the infantile male and of the female are symmetrical it could be said that the male hormone, at a certain level at least, produces an asymmetry of body reactions.

It must be emphasized that the adult dog's micturition pattern is not solely a matter of bodily posture. For the infantile male or the female the less frequent and always copious micturition seems to function merely to empty the bladder. In the adult male, however, micturition proper is only one link of a chain of events. The male possesses a tendency not only to urinate, but to do so upon certain spots or targets. The physiological significance of this fact, and the possibility that micturition represents an important aspect of the ecology of the animal should be investigated.

According to v. Uexküll (13) the dog's habits of urination serve to mark his ecological territory by means of odoriferous signs. Without adopting his teleological viewpoint the hypothesis seems admissible if one keeps in mind that the usefulness is not the cause but the consequence of the pattern of behavior.

In conclusion, the canine micturition pattern is a good example of an hormonal action on behavior. Testosterone is able to modify the body posture and the functional as well as the ecologic feature of an elementary physiological act.

SUMMARY

There are three patterns of canine micturition posture which characterize the sex. In the male the infantile type of standing position with slight flexion or extension of the hind limbs is changed to the adult one of leg elevation at the age of 5 to 8 months in the small and middle sized breeds. Both types differ from the female pattern which during infancy and adulthood consists of squatting with the hind legs.

Castration of males over four months old does not prevent the shift to the adult pattern in most cases. Early castration, however, leads to the maintenance of the infantile urinary behavior throughout adult life.

The adult male pattern was induced in dogs castrated early in life by injections or implants of testosterone propionate. One normal new born puppy treated with this hormone from the third day of life began leg elevation when 39 days old, whereas a littermate control did not do so until 173 days of age.

Among 6 castrates treated with estradiol benzoate, 4 exhibited male behavior. Two of these animals shifted very early, when 61 and 95 days old.

In 5 spayed and untreated females no changes were observed. After administration of testosterone propionate to 4 normal and 5 spayed bitches 1 occasionally exhibited the male pattern. No masculinization of the micturition pattern was induced in the remaining even though the clitoris showed marked hypertrophy and the females displayed male mating behavior. However, in 2 new born bitches, which were treated from the third day of life, the complete male pattern at micturition began at the early ages of 65 and 70 days.

The urinary posture of the dog is therefore a functional secondary sex character regulated by gonadal hormones. In the female and in the infantile or castrated male, micturition depends on the degree of bladder distention. In normal adult males or testosterone treated castrated males and females, however, the micturition posture is assumed with great frequency even when the bladder is empty, and depends on environmental stimuli. Micturition in this case, as a consequence of testosterone action, has possibly other functions in the ecology of the animal.

BIBLIOGRAPHY

1. BEACH, F. A.: Copulatory behavior in prepuberally castrated male rats and its modification by estrogen administration. *Endocrinology*, 1942, **31**, 679–83.
2. ———: in *Recent Progress in Hormone Research*. New York: Ac. Press Inc., **1**, 1947.
3. BEACH, F. A. and RASQUIN, P.: Masculine copulatory behavior in intact and castrate female rats. *Endocrinology*, 1942, **31**, 393–409.
4. BERG, I. A.: Development of behavior: the micturition pattern in the dog. *J. experimental Psychology*, 1944, **34**, 343–68.
5. COLBERT, E. H.: The origin of the dog. *Nat. Hist.*, 1939, **43**, 90–95.
6. MAGALHÃES, A. C.: *Ensaio sobre a fauna brasileira*. São Paulo, 1939.
7. MARTINS, TH., VALLE, J. R., and PORTO, A.: Efeitos do tratamento prolongado de cadelas com o propionato de testosterona. *Mem. Instituto Butantan*, 1942, **16**, 237–39.
8. MARTINS, TH., and VALLE, J. R.: A atitude do cão na micção e os hormonios sexuais. *Mem. Instituto Oswaldo Cruz*, 1946, **44**, 343–61.
9. ———: A atitude do cão na micção c os hormonios sexuais. *Rev. Brasil. de Med.*, 1947, **4**, 85–89.
10. ———: L'attitude de miction du chien et les hormones sexuelles. Experiences sur des mâles. *C. Rend. de la Soc. de Biol.*, 1947, **141**, 620–22.
11. ———: Experiences sur des femelles. *C. Rend. de la Soc. de Biol.*, 1947, **141**, 623–25.
12. STONE, C. P.: Sex drive, in: *Sex and Internal Secretions*. Edited by Allen, Danforth and Doisy. Baltimore: Williams & Wilkins, 1939.
13. VON UEXKÜLL, J.: *apud Buytendijk F. J. J., The mind of the dog*. Cambridge: Cambridge Univ. Press, 1936.
14. VALLE, J. R. and PRADO, J. L.: Ação anemiante em cães de benzoato de estradiol: *Mem. do Instituto Butantan*, 1946, **19**, 199–204.
15. VALLE, J. R. and PORTO, A.: Gonadal hormones and the contractility in vitro of the vas deferens of the dog. *Endocrinology*, 1947, **40**, 308–13.

CHAPTER 7

BEHAVIORIAL CONSEQUENCES
OF EARLY BEHAVIOR: EARLY EXPERIENCE

An idea that is both a truism and a peg for a great deal of current research is that experiences early in an animal's life have far-reaching effects on its behavior later in life. Theory and research regarding the effects of early experience have abounded since the beginning of this century and are now proceeding at an increasing pace.

Approaches to the Study of Early Experience

Research on the effects of early experience has covered a wide range of variables, species, and behavior patterns and has grown from a variety of theoretical and experimental problems. The theories and observations of Sigmund Freud emphasized the importance of early experience on later behavior of humans; ethologists, such as O. Heinroth, K. Lorenz, and W. H. Thorpe, identified and studied effects of specific early experiences on the later behavior of animals; psychologists, such as L. Carmichael, studied maturation under conditions of extreme environmental deprivation; D. O. Hebb studied effects of amounts of stimulation early in life on later perception and problem solving; and R. Spitz and J. P. Scott have focused on analysis of behavior development in terms of early experiences during critical periods.

The present chapter focuses on the following three approaches to the study of the effects of early experience on later behavior: (a) enrichment or supernormal stimulation; (b) deprivation or subnormal stimulation; (c) alteration in typical stimulation. These three approaches will be examined in terms of effects on learning, perception, social behavior, and temperamental characteristics. Then some theories regarding the effects of early experience will be described. General surveys of the variable of early experience are available in the writings of Beach and Jaynes (1954), King (1958), and Thompson and Schaeffer (1961).

Enrichment or Supernormal Stimulation

The studies by Gibson and Walk (1956**) and King and Eleftheriou (1959**) illustrate methods, results, and theories relating to the effects of early enrichment or supernormal stimulation on later behavior. In the Gibson and Walk study stimuli which were to be used later in a discrimination learning situation were present in the living cages for one group of animals and were withheld from the otherwise identical living cages of the control group. The group which had these stimuli added to their environment learned faster and to a higher level than those which did not have this enriched environment. Such studies of the effect of supernormal stimulation on later learning and perception have particular bearing on Hebb's theory of behavior development (1955). However, the generality of the effect of enrichment has not been tested below higher vertebrates such as rats, dogs, and primates.

The study by King and Eleftheriou (1959**) illustrates another way of investigating the problem of the effect of supernormal stimulation on later behavior. In this study, *diffuse supernormal stimulation* (electric shock and handling, also called gentling) was provided to one group of animals and the later behavior of this group was compared with the later behavior of a group raised under normal conditions of stimulation. Even though the effects of specific and diffuse supernormal stimulation cannot be considered as identical, due in part to the different procedures used for their study (King, 1958), positive consequences of both types of early experiences have been found. While the results of some research such as that by McMichael (1961*) indicate little effect of supernormal stimulation, the majority of the reported studies, as the study by King and Eleftheriou (1958**), by Levine and Lewis (1959*), and Denenburg and Karas (1959*), indicate that such stimulation does facilitate or improve the organism's reactions in situations that involve learning, problem solving, stress, and exploration.

Deprivation or Subnormal Stimulation

The second approach to the study of the effects of early experience has been to raise young animals under conditions which deprive them of some of the stimuli which are typically present in their normal environment. Interest in research on the effects of such deprivation (subnormal stimulation) stems from a variety of sources: (*a*) concern about the effects of institutional care of infants where stimulus deprivation may occur, (*b*) theories of behavior that focus on the importance of innate behavior patterns that presumably do not require prior elicitation for the later behavior to occur, (*c*) extending theories to effects of subnormal stimulation that are used to explain the effects of early supernormal stimulation. As viewed from theories that emphasize perceptual or motor learning, subnormal stimulation is assumed to interfere with later behavior, while for theories that emphasize innate behavior such consequences are not assumed. These differential expectations have led to more investigation of effects of subnormal stimulation than supernormal stimulation.

The studies by Thompson and Heron (1954**) with dogs, by Padilla (1935) with birds, Melzack (1952*) with dogs, Harlow (1958*) with monkeys, Griffith (1961*) with rats, and Ganz and Riesen (1962*) with monkeys suggest the breadth of inquiry about subnormal stimulation and the range of species for which the condition has been found to have effects. Laboratory study of subnormal stimulation during the early life of the organism has taken a variety of forms. For example, animals have been raised with subnormal amounts of social contact, sucking, parental contact, and pattern vision. The effects of these procedures have then been related to activities such as social behavior, food-taking, sexual behavior, fear, learning, discrimination, and problem solving.

Several cautions should be noted about interpreting studies using subnormal stimulation: (*a*) The degree of subnormality of stimulation is judged in terms of departure from normal stimulation where normal is defined as typical for the laboratory animal. This may not be normal stimulation for the species. (*b*) Total deprivation is rarely used. (*c*) Subnormal stimulation is usually established to block or prevent responses that normally occur. However, eliminating or reducing stimulation may not block responses to other previously inappropriate stimuli, so the experimental condition may not do what the experimenter expects it to do. (*d*) Subnormal stimulation, such as is associated with raising animals in darkness, may lead to permanent damage or deterioration in the receptor system so that later behavior may be impaired due to structure damage and not to behavior change alone. Disregard of these cautions make it difficult to interpret some of the results of studies of subnormal stimulation and weaken their impact in terms of differentiating between the theories of effects of early experience.

Alteration in Typical Stimulation

A third approach to the investigation of the effects of early experience on later behavior has involved raising young animals under *conditions of stimulation that are different from the conditions under which they are typically raised*. This approach to the study of early experience is primarily aimed at identifying the specific early experiences or stimuli that affect the later behavior of the animal.

The study by Denniston (1959**) with squirrels illustrates one of the methods used in this approach. In Denniston's study the group of squirrels that was socialized by humans in the laboratory were able to be conditioned more rapidly and to a higher level than a group that was socialized in the natural environment. In studies such as Denniston's, socialization, frequently called taming, is not considered to involve supernormal or subnormal stimulation, rather it is considered to involve an alteration of stimulation. Some of the studies of effects of taming or substitution of human socializing for natural socializing have been loosely conceived and have used very small numbers of animals. However, the results have been provocative. Examples of such studies are Lorenz's work with jackdaws (1952), Adamson's (1960) study of a family of lions, and Hayes and Hayes (1951) study of a chimpanzee raised in their home. Such altered stimulation has been found to affect learning, sexual behavior, social preference, and fear.

From the discussion of imprinting in Chapter 5, it will be remembered that imprinting involves the relationship between young animals, particularly birds, and their parents. The response of following the parent is one manifestation of imprinting and is used as an index of the process for purposes of research. Thus, studies of imprinting, using objects other than the parent, can be considered to involve the study of the effect of alteration of typical stimulation on later behavior. The study of Ramsey and Hess (1954**), on imprinting in ducks illustrates the use of the method of alteration in typical stimulation. Similar studies with other species of birds are reported by Hinde, *et al.* (1956) and Jaynes (1956). In both sets of experiments it was found that imprinting with an artificial stimulus generalizes from the artificial stimulus to stimuli that are similar to it. It is interesting to note that such generalization does not seem to occur with imprinting on the natural parent.

A related line of investigation using alteration of stimulation is seen in the study of bird song by Thorpe (1958*). Thorpe investigated the question of whether the later song patterns of a bird are affected by the song patterns they hear when they are young. The extremes of the effects of such altered stimulation on song patterns are represented by the domestic canary that is prized for the flexibility of its song, and the cuckoo that inhabits the nests of other species but is not affected by the songs of the host birds. Marler (1959) summarizes the results of a number of related studies of bird songs. Kuo (1960*) altered the early social histories of animals of a number of species by having them live together and studied the effects of this on later food competition and social behavior.

Results of Studies on the Effects of Early Experience

The effects of supernormal, subnormal, and altered stimulation will now be considered specifically with regard to the processes of perception, temperament, learning, and social behavior. It should be noted that these behavior processes are not independent from each other so that a condition of early experience that affects perception may affect learning, if the learning is dependent on perception. Similarly, any condition which affects temperament may also affect social behavior. In addition, the absence of detailed knowledge about the behavior and behavior development of normal animals limits the understanding of the effects of these abnormal conditions of stimulation.

Effects on Perception. The typical approach to the study of the effects of early experience on perception has involved the method of subnormal stimulation. Riesen (1961) discusses the fact that physiological changes sometimes occur in the animals' receptors during the period of subnormal stimulation. Such deterioration of the receptor seems to proceed more rapidly the higher the species of the vertebrate, comparing the cat with the monkey, for example. In addition, the deterioration reverses less readily the higher the species of the vertebrate following release from subnormal stimulation. However, even when such deterioration occurs the details of changes in perception cannot be predicted entirely from the changes in the physiology of the receptors .

Because of the possibility of deterioration of the receptors under subnormal stimulation and because of the complexity of the relationship between deterioration and the species being studied, special procedures have been used to produce subnormal stimulation when vision is involved. In this case translucent shields are placed over the heads of the young animals. These prevent pattern vision but do not produce total darkness and the resulting deterioration of the receptor.

The results of studies using these shields suggest that early deprivation leads to disturbances in perceived movement of a stimulus, disturbances in discrimination between lateral movement and movement toward the face, changes in the shape of the generalization gradient toward increased steepness for the deprived animals and disturbance of form discrimination, if the forms to be discriminated do not have repeated patterns. The experimental animals used in these studies have included primates, cats, rats, and birds.

MELZACK, R. AND SCOTT, T. H.   The effect of early experience on response to pain. *J. comp. physiol. Psychol.*, 1957, **50**, 155–61.

Ten Scottish terriers were raised in restricted environments providing subnormal stimulation "from puppyhood to maturity" (the exact duration is not specified). Control animals were raised as pets in homes. All dogs were tested with three types of painful stimuli: shock, burn, and pinprick. The restricted dogs required many shocks to learn to avoid the shock apparatus and they ran aimlessly around the test area. They stayed near the experimenter and the flaming match after having been burned, while the control animals quickly moved away. Similar behaviors occurred after the experimenter had pricked the restricted and control dogs. It was concluded that the extreme subnormal stimulation led the restricted dogs to be unable to perceive and respond appropriately to usually painful stimuli.

GANZ, L. AND RIESEN, A. H.   Stimulus generalization to hue in the dark reared Macaque. *J. comp. physiol. Psychol.*, 1962, 55, 92–99.

The effects of subnormal visual stimulation on the characteristics of the stimulus generalization gradient were investigated with two groups of infant monkeys. Two species were used: *Macaca rhesus* and *Macaca radiata*. Animals in one group were raised from birth until 10 weeks of age in dark boxes. The others were raised in similar boxes that were illuminated. At 10 weeks of age each of the animals was tested for stimulus generalization to different hues (colors) after having learned a key-pressing response to a particular hue. The generalization gradients were decremental in both groups, as is usually found. However, they were "steeper and concave upward in the Hue-Naïve Group (subnormal stimulation, relatively shallow and linear in the Experienced Group."

Little if any work on the effects of early experience on perception has been undertaken with lower vertebrates or invertebrates, although many species of such animals have highly evolved receptor systems and might lend themselves to such experimentation. For example, the frog, salamander, and octopus have highly evolved neural and receptor systems, and they are familiar experimental animals.

The majority of the experimental studies of the effects of early experience on perception have used subnormal visual stimulation. However, subnormal tactile stimulation has been studied by Nissen, *et al.* (1951). A chimpanzee was maintained for more than two years with its lower legs and arms in cardboard tubes. When the restraints were removed, a variety of the animal's manipulative responses were impaired and it had great difficulty in learning to discriminate between tactile stimulation to the right hand versus the left hand, when visual cues were controlled.

Effects on Temperament. Effects of early experience have been investigated using a variety of dependent variables which for present purposes are labeled as indexes of temperament. Specifically, these dependent variables have included immobility or freezing reactions (fear), defecation and urination (emotionality), activity (emotionality), and tolerance for intense stimulation (reaction to stress). Effects of early experience on temperament have been studied using all three experimental approaches.

Portions of the study by King and Eleftheriou (1959**) illustrate the method and measures that are frequently used for studies of temperament. In this study, two groups of wild mice were raised with supernormal stimulation and their behavior was compared at a later time with two control groups. The investigators found that emotionality and reactions to stress depended both on the characteristics of the early experience and the species of the mouse. The fact that different subspecies of mice react differently to similar early experiences makes it difficult to generalize interpretations of the effects of early experiences on temperament. But some concensus has been reached and is discussed below.

DENENBERG, V. H. AND KARAS, G. G. Effects of differential handling upon weight gain and mortality in the rat and mouse. *Science,* 1959, 130, 629–30.

Laboratory rats and mice were given differential supernormal stimulation before weaning. One group of rats was handled daily from 1–10 days of age, one group from 11–20 days of age, one group from 1–20 days of age, and one group was a nonhandled control group. Groups of mice were treated similarly. The groups were compared in adulthood in terms of body weight and mortality and response to food and water deprivation. For both species, animals that were handled the most weighed the most. Response to food and water deprivation (assumed to be related to stress) showed conflicting results. Handled mice died earlier than control mice, while the opposite was true for the rats.

LEVINE, S. AND LEWIS, G. W. Critical periods for the effects of infantile experience on the maturation of the stress response. *Science,* 1959, 129, 42–43.

Groups of albino rats were handled (gentled) at different ages in infancy and then tested at 14 days of age for reaction to stress. The stress situation was a cold environment and measurement was made of the change in adrenal ascorbic acid after stress. It was found that handling between 6 and 13 days of age reduced the change in the adrenal responses as compared with nonhandled control rats and rats handled at other ages. It was concluded that a critical period existed during which handling affected this physiological response to stress.

McMICHAEL, R. E. The effects of preweaning shock and gentling on later resistence to stress. *J. comp. physiol. Psychol.,* 1961, 54, 416–21.

A total of 81 male albino rats were divided at birth into three groups. On every day from birth through weaning one group was handled (gentled), one group was shocked, and one group kept under the usual conditions with the female. At 47 days of age, shortly before maturity, each rat was given a number of tests for reaction to stress and then a number of physiological measurements were made. The groups did *not* differ on any test for reaction to stress, such as reaction to deprivation of food and water, or reaction to being immobilized. The groups did differ in body weight. The gentled group was heavier than the two other groups throughout the experiment.

Laboratory varieties of rats and mice have been the favorite experimental subjects for the study of effects of supernormal stimulation on temperament. There is considerable agreement that supernormal stimulation resulting from handling or from electric shock reduces emotionality as measured by reduced urination and defecation, increases activity, and reduces reaction to stress as indicated by greater weight gaining and reduced mortality. Studies by Levine and Lewis (1959*), Bovard (1958), and Denenberg and Karas (1959*) report positive findings relating to these points, while the study by Mc-Michael (1961*) reports negative findings except for the measure of weight gain. The effects of supernormal stimulation *during prenatal life* of rodents suggests that such stimulation reduces emotionality during postnatal life (Thompson and Sontag, 1956*).

Studies of the effects of alteration of typical stimulation on temperament indicate that socializing by humans reduces fear reactions as measured by freezing or prolonged immobility. Thorpe (1956, pp. 351–76) describes a number of studies of the effects of taming by foster parents on later behavior of wild birds, and Ratner and Thompson (1960*) report such a study with domestic fowl. The findings are consistent with the everyday practices used in training animals. That is, taming reduces emotionality. However, it is repeated that the effect of a specific early experience on temperament depends both on the experience and the species being studied.

RATNER, S. C. AND THOMPSON, W. R. Effects of age and experience on immobility reactions (fear) of domestic fowl. *Anim. Behav.*, 1960, **8**, 186–91.

Three hundred chicks (domestic fowl) were tested from two through 66 days of age for immobility responses to handling by a predator (a human). A test consisted of grabbing and holding the bird down for 15–30 seconds and then observing the occurrence and duration of immobility responses, also called animal hypnosis. One group of birds was tested repeatedly; the other group was tested only once and not touched prior to the test. Immobility reactions were found to be virtually absent in chicks until they were seven to ten days of age after which numbers of birds responding and durations of immobility increased markedly. Some chicks remained immobile more than 45 minutes. The response of birds tested repeatedly gradually diminished until older birds were no longer responding to handling by the "predator."

THOMPSON, W. D. JR. AND SONTAG, L. W. Behavioral effects in the offspring of rats subjected to audiogenic seizures during the gestation period. *J. comp. physiol. Psychol.,* 1956, 49, 454–56.

Twelve female albino rats that were pregnant and susceptible to audiogenic seizures were divided into two groups. From the fifth through the eighteenth day of their gestation period the females in one group were subjected to audiogenic seizures; those in the other group served as control animals. The young from the females of both groups were treated the same and at 80 days of age were all tested for learning in a water maze (considered to be a stress situation). The young of females subjected to seizures learned significantly more slowly than the young of control females. However, the young of the two groups of females did not differ in weight, number of siblings, or activity levels.

Effects on Learning. Supernormal stimulation, such as that reported by Gibson and Walk (1956**), has been found to enhance instrumental and other more complex learning tasks. Supernormal stimulation associated with shock and handling also enhances avoidance conditioning, as does alteration in stimulation from taming (King and Eleftheriou, 1959**; Denniston, 1959**). While it is possible that taming represents an example of supernormal stimulation rather than alteration in stimulation, observations of the treatment of the young by the natural parent suggests that the human foster parent does not provide more stimulation than is provided by the natural parent. A great deal is provided in both cases. Rather, it seems that early experience with the human and the laboratory situation allow interfering responses to adapt in the tame animals, while the responses do not adapt for the untamed animal until long after it is brought into the laboratory situation.

Subnormal stimulation has been found to impair or interfere with later learning. The study by Thompson and Heron (1954**) using dogs illustrates this with a complex learning task, and the study by Melzack (1962*) illustrates impairment from subnormal stimulation on a simple black-white discrimination task.

MELZACK, R. Effects of early perceptual restriction on simple visual discrimination. *Science,* 1962, 137, 978–79.

The learning of three young dogs (Beagles) raised under normal conditions was compared with the learning of two of their litter-mates raised under conditions of subnormal stimulation. Specifically, the experimental animals were maintained in cages that restricted pattern vision but not light from three weeks of age until nine months of age. Then all of the dogs were tested on simple black-white discrimination and reversal of this discrimination (see Chapter 11). Control tests indicated the groups did not differ in brightness perception, but the restricted dogs took much longer to learn the simple discrimination and much longer to learn the reversal. That is, the subnormal visual environment impaired discrimination of brightness and subsequent learning based on this discrimination.

SCHALLER, G. B. AND EMLEN, J. T.   The development of visual discrimination patterns in the crouching reactions of nestling Grackles. *Auk*, 1961, **78**, 125–37.

Nestlings in 21 nests of common Grackles (*Quiscalus versicolor*) were observed and tested for their responses to mechanical stimuli (jarring the nest) and visual stimuli, including stuffed grackles, owls, and other birds. Nestlings made two responses: gaping and crouching. Crouching first occurred at about 4 days of age to mechanical stimuli only. It occurred to visual stimuli at about 8 days of age, which is 2 days after the visual system has become functional. Isolating the young immediately after the visual system was functional delayed the occurrence of crouching to visual stimuli. It was concluded that the nestlings had to learn to use visual stimuli for crouching based on the visual discrimination of stimuli associated with reward (parents) and other objects.

Effects on Social Behavior, Especially Imprinting. Social behaviors are the responses of one animal that involve another member of the species as the stimulus for the response. While these behaviors are described in detail in Chapter 8, for present purposes they include reactions of the young to the parent or parent object, reactions of the parent to the young, reactions to a mate, and reactions to an aggressor.

The largest body of data on the relationship between early experience and later social behavior has been developed around the concept of *imprinting* and the associated concept of *critical period.*

The idea that is implied by the concept of imprinting can be traced to observations made by Spalding and reported in 1873. The name imprinting was given by Heinroth to a type of learning shown by young birds in response to objects that were around them when they were young (Thorpe, 1961, p. 167). Specifically, Heinroth reported that young geese raised from hatching by humans followed these humans as they would their natural parents. Other observations suggested that the relationship between the bird and the imprinted object extended to social behaviors, especially mating, later in life. The concept of critical period is related to the process of imprinting in that imprinting is assumed to occur only during a fixed and relatively short period in the animal's development. The presentation of a large, moving object at times other than the critical period will not lead to imprinting. Ramsey and Hess (1954**) attempted to determine the duration of the critical period for imprinting of ducklings. They found maximum imprinting when the ducklings were 13–15 hours of age and sharply decreasing imprinting at younger and older ages.

Although there is controversy about imprinting at the theoretical level, the fundamental observations have been verified time and again, (Ramsay and Hess, 1954**; Hess, 1957*; James, 1959* and 1960*; Harlow 1958*). The short-term effects of imprinting are that the young animal approaches and follows the imprinted object, the parent, in the natural situation. The long-term effects of this early experience are that the animal, when mature, directs social and sexual behaviors toward the object with the characteristics of the original imprinted object (Lorenz, 1937).

HARLOW, H. F.   The nature of love. *Amer. Psychol.*, 1958, **13**, 673–85.

This paper reports some of the conditions of the parent object that lead to affectional behavior (attachment) and some consequences of this behavior for infant monkeys. Texture of the mother object was identified as one of the important variables affecting this behavior. Thus, infant monkeys were raised with wire mother surrogates and cloth mother surrogates, both of which supplied milk. The infants spent much more time with the cloth than the wire mothers, fed more from the cloth mothers, went to the cloth mothers if threatening stimuli were presented, and looked at cloth mothers more than at wire mothers in visual exploration tests. Other monkeys that had been raised with natural mothers spent more time with cloth mothers when both kinds were given to them at about 250 days of age.

HESS, E.   Effects of meprobamate on imprinting in waterfowl. *N. Y. Acad. Sci.*, 1957, **67**, 724–33.

The effects of four variables on the degree of imprinting of mallard ducks were studied. The variables were: age when imprinting occurred, distance traveled during imprinting, time spent in the imprinting situation with distance constant, and effects of tranquilizing drugs during imprinting and tests for imprinting. A critical period for age of susceptibility to imprinting was found between 12 and 17 hours of age. Degree of imprinting increased as distance traveled during imprinting (amount of effort expended) increased. Time spent in the imprinting experience from 2 to 30 minutes did not affect degree of imprinting if effort were kept constant. Tranquilized ducklings did not imprint, but normally imprinted ducklings given tranquilizer for tests did show following responses (imprinting).

JAMES, H.   Social inhibition of the domestic chicks response to visual flicker. *Anim. Behav.*, 1960, **8**, 223–24.

Two groups of Barred Rock chicks (domestic fowl) were imprinted from 2 through 7 days of age using a flickering light as the imprinting stimulus. Imprinting was measured in terms of the closeness of the animals to the light. Birds in one group were kept isolated from other birds during the time from 2 through 7 days of age; the birds in the other group were kept all together. It was found that the isolated birds showed a higher degree of imprinting than the birds that were kept together. It was concluded that the birds that were kept together had imprinted on each other and this interfered with imprinting on the flickering light.

JAMES, H.   Flicker: an unconditioned stimulus for imprinting. *Can. J. Psychol.*, 1959, **13**, 59–67.

Imprinting was studied in two experiments with Barred Plymouth Rock chicks. Imprinting was measured in terms of the distance the chick traveled to approach a flickering light. Three rates of flicker were used: ¼ second on–¼ second off, 1 second on–1 second off, 5 seconds on–5 seconds off. All three rates were found to be equally effective in eliciting approach and chicks

made "pleasure calls" when near the flickering lights. In the second experiment a small ball was hung near the flickering lights for one group of
chicks. Six days later, after the critical period for imprinting, chicks were
tested for approach to the ball. The group that had had the ball near the
lights approached showed imprinting on the previously neutral object. Control chicks did not approach the ball.

Research on imprinting has taken a number of directions. Some
studies suggest that almost any stimulus configuration that is detectable by the young animal and involves *varying input stimulation*
(VIP) may be an adequate stimulus for imprinting (Marr, 1963). The
VIPs may be changes in movement, brightness, proprioception, olfactory stimulation or auditory stimulation. However, large differences in degree of imprinting to comparable stimuli have been found
within species and between species (Hess, 1959), and these differences
remain to be explained. Considerable ingenuity has been used in
establishing the generality of imprinting for species other than birds.
It has been observed and studied in insects, fish, deer, dogs, and
primates (Hess, 1959). These data suggest that imprinting is a relatively general phenomenon both with regard to the range of species
that may imprint and the classes of behavior that seem to be affected
by imprinting.

The results of studies of the effects of *subnormal stimulation on
later social behavior* present some problem in interpretation. Some
studies suggest that subnormal stimulation impairs later social behavior; other studies suggest that subnormal stimulation has only
temporary effects on later behavior. The effects of subnormal stimulation on later behavior seem to depend on the species that is studied.
In general, social behavior is affected by subnormal stimulation for
those species and those behavior patterns that normally develop in
the chronic presence of the parent animal. Thus, animals that have
long periods of parent-young relations seem to be more affected by
subnormal stimulation than animals that have very brief periods of
parent-young relations. So, for example, species of birds that leave
the nest and show some independence very shortly after hatching seem
to be little affected by subnormal stimulation. However, those species
that have prolonged contact between the parent and young are affected by subnormal stimulation, if the studies of their songs can be
generalized (Thorpe, 1958 *).

Kuo, Zing Yang. Studies on the basic factors in animal fighting: VII Inter-
species coexistence in mammals. *J. Genet. Psychol.*, 1960, 97, 211–25.

This study was designed to find out if some usual aggressive interspecies
and intraspecies social responses could be inhibited by appropriate early
training. Different animals were raised together under careful supervision

and their behavior in test situations was compared with the behavior of animals that had been raised in the usual ways. Dogs, cats, rabbits, rats, canaries, and cockatoos were used in the study. The important aspects of supervision consisted bringing the different species together at early ages, keeping them together, adapting and punishing attacks on other animals, and adapting quick-escape responses. Those animals in the supervised groups showed group eating, the absence of a dominance hierarchy, and tolerance for strange animals introduced into the cage. Control animals showed the typical aggressive responses in similar test situations.

THORPE, W. H.   The learning of song patterns by birds, with a special reference to the song of the chaffinch. *Fringilla coelebs. Ibis,* 1958, **100,** 535–70.

The songs of a number of species of birds are described and illustrated with samples of spectographic recordings. However, the main emphasis of the study was on the development of the song of the chaffinch. A number of these birds were raised in complete visual and auditory isolation from the fifth day after hatching. These birds produced simple songs that had some features of the normal wild birds' song, such as the duration and number of "notes," but lacked the other aspects of such songs. If isolation continued, the song was modified very little, but if the isolated birds were put with others before 13 months of age their song was modified by the songs of the chaffinch in their community. This interaction is called "counter-singing."

Theories of the Effects of Early Experience on Later Behavior

Four theoretical positions that are concerned with interpretation of the results of studies of the effects of early experience will be discussed. While these theories are not mutually exclusive or exhaustive of possible theories, they suggest approaches that are characteristic of attempts to explain the results of studies of the effects of early experience. For present purposes, the theoretical positions will be labeled in terms of the principle processes that are assumed to account for the effects of early experience. These processes are: (*a*) learning, (*b*) perception, (*c*) physiology, and (*d*) critical periods. At the present time each theoretical position is assumed to explain all or almost all of the results of the effects of early experience. However, each of the theoretical positions may be appropriate for some particular set of results, such as learning or perception, and none may be appropriate for all of the results regarding the effects of early experience on later behavior.

Learning.   General acceptance of the fact that learning affects subsequent behavior makes the learning interpretation of the effects of early experience relatively obvious. The questions become why should *early learning* exert special effects on *later learning* and exactly how the effects are expressed for the behaviors that have been studied.

The answers to these questions are not contained in the formal statements of any learning theory, but Beach and Jaynes (1954) and

Thompson and Shaefer (1961) have considered the problems. These writers suggest that early learning has special and prolonged effects because it interferes with learning of new responses and because it generalizes broadly to a wide range of stimulus situations due to the undifferentiated nature of the young organism's behavior and perception. Thus, a fear reaction associated with an early traumatic experience is considered to generalize very broadly and to lead to a generally fearful animal. Such learning is assumed to account for the differences in temperament among animals given traumatic experiences as compared with normal control animals.

The learning interpretation of the effect of early experience is particularly useful for studies that find effects of supernormal and altered stimulus conditions. That is, the theory suggests that the animals learn responses to these stimuli that are presented early in their lives and these learned responses interfere with or generalize to situations later in life.

Perception. Hebb (1949) and his associates emphasize two concepts that are used in the explanation of the effects of early experience. One is the concept of *perceptual elements* that are assumed to develop from the early perceptual experience of the animal and serve to organize later perceptions. The other is the concept of *arousal* that depends on diffuse or generalized stimulation and sensitizes or alerts the animal. Early experiences are assumed to lead to specific states of arousal that facilitate or interfere with the establishment of perceptual elements. Insofar as these perceptual elements are important in later behavior, then early experience has affected it.

Many of the results of the effects of early subnormal and supernormal stimulation early in life are interpreted as being due to differences in arousal level and associated occurrences or lack of occurrences of formation of perceptual elements. For example, the animal raised under conditions of subnormal stimulation has a low level of arousal that then reduces his interactions with his already impoverished environment. In addition, the animal has very few perceptual elements and would be expected to show poor learning and poor perceptual performance later in life. The study by Melzak (1962 *) illustrates the type of study in which the perceptual theory of early experience has been applied.

Physiology. Several physiological explanations have been proposed to account for the effects of early experience on later behavior. Hebb (1949; 1955) has a neurological theory that is closely related to his perceptual theory. The physiological theory is based on the finding of two types of sensory pathways in the central nervous system. One type of pathway is assumed to transmit relatively specific patterns of impulses from the receptor through the thalmus to the sensory projection area, direct projection system. The other type, associated with the reticular formation, transmits impulses from the receptor to many points in the cortex, the diffuse projection system. Hebb (1955) speculates that early experiences energize the arousal system and organize perceptual elements.

Hormonal theories constitute the other type of physiological theory dealing with the effects of early experience. These theories, such as the theory of Bovard (1958), are often interlaced with neurological theories. The central thesis of Bovard's theory is that early experience affects the threshold for response to stress by changing the activity of the posterior hypothalamus. This neural change is assumed to modify the responses of the sympathetic-adrenal medulla and pituitary-adrenal cortex. Thus, supernormal stimulation from early handling is assumed to inhibit the activity of the posterior hypothalamus which allows greater activity of the anterior hypothalamus and its associated parasympathetic centers.

Bovard (1958) and Levine (1962) both analyze the effects of early experience in terms of complex interactions between neurological processes and hormones such as ACTH (adrenalcorticotropic hormone), STH (somatotropic hormone), and ADH (antidiuretic hormone). However, details of the relationships between behavior, behavior development and the neuro-endocrine process are incompletely known, and in some respects paradoxical.

Critical Period. The critical period theory involves the idea that specific stages or periods of life occur during which the animal is particularly sensitive to behavior changes that affect a large number of behaviors later in life. This theory, familiar in the work of embryologists and psychoanalysts, has been applied to the effects of early experience in animals by Lorenz (1937) and Scott and Martsen (1950).

Imprinting is an important example of an early experience whose effects are analyzed in terms of critical periods. The critical period for imprinting ducks, for example, is reported (Hess, 1959) to extend from hatching to approximately two and one-half days of age with a maximum sensitivity to imprinting at about twelve hours of age. That is, only during this period of a duck's life can imprinting occur. If it occurs, it then affects the behavior of the duck immediately and throughout maturity.

Several other ideas are implicit in the critical period theory. One is that behaviors that develop during the critical period are relatively irreversible. Another is that the critical period represents a time of increased sensitivity or receptivity with particular stimulus-response associations. A third is that structural or functional physiological changes are associated with the beginning and the end of the critical periods. Scott and Martsen (1950) have developed in detail the idea of the association of structure change and behavior change in their description of critical periods in the development of dogs. For example, the opening of the dog's eyes is assumed to be associated with the onset of the second or socialized period in the animal's life. The critical period theory of the effect of early experience is usually related to theories of instinctive behavior, such as those of K. Lorenz and N. Tinbergen. As such, the critical period theory emphasizes behaviors that occur in the natural development of species and relates these behaviors to basic behavioral functions such as care of the young, survival of the young, reproduction, and aggression. Thus, in terms of these theories imprinting is *necessarily* related to later behavioral functions.

Summary

The effects of early experience are assessed by comparing the behavior of a normal group of animals with a group that has received subnormal, supernormal, or altered stimulation. The assessment of the effect is then made at some time after the groups have been exposed to different kinds or amounts of stimulation. Subnormal stimulation seems to reduce responsiveness to some classes of stimuli and increase responsiveness to others. For example, subnormal stimulation leads animals to show more fear but to learn more slowly than normal groups. In general, supernormal stimulation can be described as having similar effects, namely reducing responsiveness to some classes of stimuli and increasing it to others as compared with normal groups. Altered stimulation leads to similar consequences. That is, stimuli that elicit little or no response for the normal animal elicit elaborate responses for the altered group, while other stimuli that are effective with the normal animal elicit very little from the altered group. For example, a moving box can elicit following and courting responses for animals imprinted on it. Conversely, the human or laboratory situation will elicit strong responses for the normal, untamed animal but will elicit very weak responses for the animal socialized in the situation.

Innate behaviors including responses to the parent, courting, copulation, and other social responses were ordinarily thought to be independent of specific early experiences, but investigations using subnormal and altered stimulation indicate that these behaviors can be modified. For example, the song that is characteristic of the species may not occur unless early experience with the full song is provided. Learned behaviors, including perceptual and motor learning, are found to be particularly responsive to different kinds of early experience.

In general, the question of the effects on behavior of early experience can be thought of in terms of three questions: (*a*) What stimulus-response (S–R) elements are more likely to occur as a function of the early experience? (*b*) What S–R elements are less likely to occur? (*c*) How do these occurrences or nonoccurrences interact especially in terms of the behaviors required in the test situation? Insofar as early experience alters behavior during a critical period or alters biological development, then the early experience would be expected to lead to relatively permanent effects on behavior. A behavioral description of each kind of early experience and its effect is presented below.

Subnormal stimulation. In this case the animal does not encounter classes of stimuli that the normal animal does. Thus, few discriminations are made, little habituation occurs, and motor and receptor development may be retarded. In a test situation at a later age there is a great probability the animal will encounter novel, fear-producing stimuli and will not discriminate among them since they all elicit strong fear responses including freezing, defecation, and urination. Sign stimuli for innate responses generally elicit both approach and other responses in a normal animal. If the other responses, such as avoidance, are very strong, as they would be for animals raised under subnormal stimulation, then the sign stimulus will lead to inappropriate behavior. Insofar as the stimulus is another animal, then social behavior will be disrupted.

Supernormal stimulation. In this case, the animal encounters a great variety of stimuli. It habituates fear responses to these which increases the chances of approaching them, and it develops responses to complex stimuli. On tests at a later age there is little probability of the animal encountering a completely novel and fear-producing stimulus. The animal can respond based on prior discriminations with few interfering fear responses. Tests of temperament show reduced fear and tests of learning show facilitation as compared with normal groups.

Altered stimulation. One class of stimuli is substituted for another that normally occurs in the life of the animal. The most frequent substitution is an inanimate parent object for the natural parent. The inanimate object elicits responses on tests like those elicited in the normal animal by the natural parent. However, the responses to the inanimate object generalize more broadly than they do for the normal animal and its natural parent.

THE EFFECTS OF RESTRICTING EARLY EXPERIENCE ON
THE PROBLEM-SOLVING CAPACITY OF DOGS[1]

WILLIAM R. THOMPSON and WOODBURN HERON
McGill University

In psychological research on the nature-nurture problem, extensive work has been done on the degree to which inherited endowment can be influenced by environment. On the human side, many studies have dealt with the effects of improved environment on IQ (9, 14, 16, 18). On the whole, these have failed to demonstrate decisively any gains in performance on intelligence tests which were administered during or shortly after the period of enriched experience. Newman, Freeman, and Holzinger, in their classic study of twins separated at an early age and reared apart (12), found in some cases differences in intelligence as great as 24 IQ points. But in other pairs, also raised in very different environments, they found almost no differences. Similarly, studies such as those of some Iowa investigators (18), purporting to show losses in IQ scores due to an impoverished environment, have been by no means definitive. The rather remarkable claims made by Skeels and Dye, for example, have been challenged by Goodenough and Terman (18) on the grounds that their study involved a highly biased sample. Thus the human data have failed to supply any clear-cut answer to the problem.

Animal experimentation on the same question has given more conclusive results. A number of authors (1, 4, 5, 8, 17) have found that adult rats, whose early experience has been restricted, do worse on tests of learning ability and intelligence than those who have had an enriched early environment. In the case of the dog, a higher genus capable of more complex behaviour, wide effects have been observed to result from limitation of early perceptual experience (2, 15). The first of these studies by Clarke *et al.* showed that performance on intelligence tests was definitely poorer in three dogs raised in restriction; the results also indicated that restriction affected other aspects of be-

---

[1] This research was supported by a grant-in-aid from the Rockefeller Foundation.

haviour. Although these results were based on small numbers, they agree closely with the rat experiments referred to above. Since the dog is much closer to man than the rat in the range and complexity of its behaviour, it would seem of considerable importance to check and extend the findings of Clarke *et al.* on this genus. Some light might thus be shed on the apparent discrepancy between the human and animal data.

Accordingly, the present experiment is an attempt to examine the effects of restricting the early experience of dogs on their problem-solving ability later in life.

THE EXPERIMENT

Animals

Twenty-six pure-bred Scottish terriers, all descendants of one litter of the Bar Harbor strain, were used. Sixteen were males, and ten were females. Rearing conditions were as follows: a litter was split at the time of weaning as evenly as possible into a control and an experimental group. The control subjects, 13 in all, were raised as pets, either in homes or in the laboratory, up to the age of eight months, so as to give them as rich an early environment as possible. After this period, they were kept in metal dog cages 24 by 32 by 72 inches, and exercised outside daily when weather permitted. The 13 subjects in the experimental group were reared till they were from seven to ten months old under three degrees of restriction; severe, moderate, and slight.

The two severely restricted subjects were raised in complete isolation in specially constructed boxes with solid walls, 30 by 40 by 60 inches.[2] These boxes were divided in the centre by a sliding metal door into two separate compartments, so that one side could be cleaned while the dog occupied the other side. One side was always kept dark, the other lighted by an overhead bulb inside the compartment. Since the dog spent alternate days in each section, it received light on every other day. Air was circulated through the boxes by means of a fan. A small panel in the top of the boxes permitted observation.

The eight moderately restricted subjects were raised for from eight to ten months in ordinary metal dog cages. The wire-mesh fronts of these cages were covered with cardboard, but the tops were left uncovered, so that the subjects received light but were unable to see

---

[2] These boxes were designed and constructed by Mr. Ronald Melzack.

anything outside their cages except the ceiling. Two or three dogs were kept together in one cage. They had contacts with human beings for about ten minutes daily, while their cages were being cleaned.

The three slightly restricted subjects were raised for seven months in similar cages, the fronts and tops of which were left uncovered. Consequently, these subjects received a considerable amount of perceptual experience, although only of the environment immediately outside their cages. They also had occasional contact with human beings and were brought into the adjoining room for grooming or medication about once a month.

At the end of the period of restriction, the experimental subjects were kept under the same conditions as the normal subjects. They were allowed to exercise outside and had frequent contact with human beings. There was no detectable difference between the two groups in health and vigour, although the mean weight of the normal subjects (15.6 lb.) was greater than that of the restricted (14.7 lb.).

It should be mentioned at this point that, although the total number of dogs involved in the whole study was 26, the number used in any particular experiment always fell short of this. This was due largely to shortage of space for housing the animals and the consequent necessity of staggering the testing over a period of several years. Deaths and pregnancies were additional factors which reduced the total number available at any particular time. . . .

General Behaviour of the Restricted Dogs

Restriction had gross effects which were plainly observable in the experimental animals as soon as they were removed from their rearing cages. In contrast to the reports of Clarke *et al.,* all the present animals were hyperactive after they emerged. They galloped actively about the room, often jumping at the walls. In addition, they showed a marked tendency to chase their tails, and even when remaining in one spot displayed a peculiar "marking time" behaviour, evinced by rapid movements of the legs and head. In other respects, the previous observations (2) of the restricted animals' behaviour were confirmed. The present subjects displayed a marked tendency to lick at the experimenters' hands, and would become very excited when they did so. At the same time, they showed some tendency to withdraw when the experimenter approached, this withdrawal usually being accompanied by bursts of hyperactivity. These types of behaviour appear to be fairly permanent, and can be noticed in animals which have been removed from restriction for over a year.

In addition, it was observed that the restricted animals at first showed marked disturbances in sensory-motor co-ordination. They had great difficulty in negotiating stairs, and would often skid and fall if they attempted to turn corners rapidly, In addition, they showed some tendency to bump into objects, the experimenters, or other dogs. These types of behaviour, however, disappeared within a few months.

Motivational and Emotional Behaviour

In the measurement of problem-solving ability, the motivation and emotionality of subjects may often affect their scores. To allow for this possibility in the present experiment, a few simple tests of these traits were given to seven normal and eight restricted subjects, and a comparison made between them.

The first of these involved a measurement of the amount of food eaten by each subject in four three-minute sessions. Each dog was put in a small enclosure in an experimental room and allowed to eat freely for three minutes from a dish containing 300 gm. of Purina dog checkers. The subject was then given its full daily ration of food and returned to its cage. Over the four sessions, the mean amounts of food eaten by the normal and restricted subjects were respectively 74.6 gm. and 99.4 gm. These do not differ significantly.

The second test of hunger motivation was similar to one described in the Bar Harbor Dog Testing Manual (10). Subjects were required to run to food down a long corridor, approximately 9 by 90 feet. The number of seconds to get to food in two daily sessions of five trials each was used as a measure. It was found that the restricted dogs took longer than normals in both sessions, though the differences are again not significant. In Session I, the means were 7.6 seconds for normals, 11.5 seconds for restricted, and in Session II, the corresponding means were 7.4 seconds and 9.7 seconds. However, it should be mentioned that timing was commenced only when the subject had actually started out toward the food. Some restricted subjects were very slow in this respect and sometimes had to be aided by being faced in the right direction by one experimenter and being called by the other experimenter who stood next to the goal box. None of the normal subjects behaved in this manner. Usually they had to be restrained until the experimenters were ready for them to start. This fact may not necessarily indicate a difference in motivation, however; rather it may indicate a difference in intellectual capacity to maintain attention on a specific problem. Thus, at least on the basis of these two tests, there is no reason to suppose that hunger motivation was stronger or weaker in the normal than in the restricted subjects.

Since emotionality in the two groups will be the subject of a forthcoming paper, it will not be dealt with in detail here. During the intelligence tests no systematic differences in emotionality could be detected. Some dogs in each group were more timid than others and more difficult to train. But this was by no means confined to either normals or restricted. The same applies to motivation, no differences between the groups in strength of food drive being observed during the tests.

In view of the above findings as to the normal and restricted subjects, we feel justified in attributing the differences that appeared between them in the tests of problem-solving ability to differences in intelligence or problem-solving capacity.

PRELIMINARY TESTS OF INTELLIGENCE

Four short tests, two orientation and two barrier tests, were used initially to give some preliminary indication of the kind and magnitude of intellectual differences between the two groups of dogs. All these tests were given in an experimental room, the testing area being approximately 8 by 10 feet. Seventeen dogs were used in all tests except the first in which 18 were used. Of these, eight were normal, three slightly restricted, five moderately restricted and two extremely restricted. At the time of testing, their ages ranged from 7½ to 12 months, and none had been exposed previously to problem solving. All tests involved a food incentive and 24-hour deprivation. All tests were conducted in the afternoon.

Orientation Test I

Procedure. The situation is diagrammed in Figure 1. The four corners of the testing area are labelled A, B, C, D. Each subject was started by one experimenter at corner D and trained for ten trials to run to food at A, approximately eight feet away. All subjects easily acquired this habit, usually in less than the full number of trials given. Then, in full sight of the subject, the food pan was switched 90° to corner C, so that, whereas it had previously been on the subject's right side, it was now on its left. The attention of the subject was drawn to the new position by banging the pan on the floor and holding the food out for it to see. Five trials were then given from starting corner D to C. After this, the pan was changed to corner B, diagonally opposite D, and five more trials given. Then another trial was given from D to C, two trials from D to A, and one final trial from B as starting point to A. There were thus 10 training trials, and 14 test trials. An error was scored when, in any test run, the subject did not follow a direct path to the food. The total of possible errors was thus 14. Minor deviations from the direct path were not counted as errors.

Results. The mean number of correct runs for normal subjects was 13.7, and for all restricted subjects, 5.9. There was no overlap between the groups and the difference is highly significant ($t = 8.86$, $p < .001$). The first few trials immediately after the ten training trials gave the most dramatic results. Without exception, restricted subjects continued to go to corner A before going to C, even though they had been shown that the food was at C and could see it there. These errors could not have been due to sensory defects, since in the training trials these dogs were able to locate the food quite easily. It is clear from the means given that the normal subjects had no difficulty in this test. Only one dog out of the seven made any errors at all, and it made only two.

Orientation Test II

Procedure. The situation is essentially the same as diagrammed in Figure 1. A starting box was placed in the middle of the testing area,

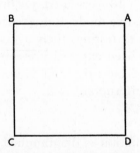

Fig. 1. The testing area used in the two orientation tests.

its entrance facing wall AB. For training purposes, food was located in the corner at point A diagonally to the right of the entrance of the starting box. Ten trials were given to the animals in this position. The starting box was then rotated so that its entrance faced, in turn, wall BC, wall AD, and wall CD, one trial being given in each of these positions. It was then rotated back to the first position for three trials, and finally, with the box in the same position, the food was moved to corner B, diagonally front and left of the entrance. For this last trial, the subject was taken to the food and allowed to sniff at it before being put into the starting box. Scoring was in terms of correct runs. An error was a run to a corner of the room other than the one in which the food pan was located.

Results. The mean number of correct runs on the eight trials was: for normal subjects 5.14, for restricted 2.70. The difference is significant ($t = 4.70$, $p < .001$). One of the slightly restricted subjects bettered the performance of one of the normal subjects and equalled that of three others. The one normal which did poorly was one of the two which had returned to the laboratory before reaching eight months of age. As in the previous tests, restricted subjects tended to perseverate in their responses, and to orient in relation to the starting box rather than in relation to the total situation.

Barrier Test I

Procedure. The situation is presented in Figure 2. The starting box was placed at point marked S, next to one wall of the testing area.

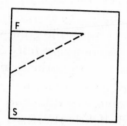

Fig. 2. The testing area used in the two barrier tests.

Food was placed in a pan approximately six feet in front of the box at F. Each subject was given five trial runs to food under these conditions. Then a chicken-wire barrier, 5 feet in length and 4 feet high, was introduced immediately in front of the food. An error zone was marked with chalk extending from one end of the barrier to a point on the wall two feet from the other end. Ten trials were given to each subject; scores were the number of runs which did not involve an entry into the error zone.

Results. Mean scores for normal and restricted subjects were respectively 6.75 and 2.40. The difference is significant ($t = 6.13$, $p < .001$). Restricted subjects tended to have more difficulty in breaking the previously established habit of running straight to food and consequently entered the error zone much more frequently than normal subjects.

Barrier Test II

Procedure. In this test, the wire barrier was placed at right angles against a wall on one side of the testing area as before, and an extra piece of mesh, two feet long, was added to the protruding end of the barrier. This piece was arranged so that it was parallel to the wall. The whole constituted an enclosure which was open at the rear. Food was placed outside the enclosure at the mid-point of the mesh barrier. Each subject was taken to the food and allowed to sniff at it, then placed in the enclosure. To solve the problem, the animal had to turn its back on the food, exit through the rear of the enclosure, and run around the barrier to the goal. The time which it took the subject to do this was used for scoring purposes. Five trials were given to each dog.

Results. Mean times in seconds from start to food, for the five trials, were 29.4 seconds for normal subjects, and 72.10 seconds for restricted subjects. The difference is significant ($t = 2.26$, $p < .05$). Only one case of overlap between the groups occurred.

In summary, the four preliminary tests clearly indicated that restricted subjects were inferior to normals in mental ability. If comparisons are made only between normal and restricted litter-mates, the results are exactly the same. No differences appeared between the severely, moderately, and slightly restricted groups.

DELAYED REACTION

Procedure

Five normal and seven moderately restricted dogs were used in this experiment. One normal and two restricted subjects were two years of age at the time of testing. All others were approximately one and a half years old. All except one normal (litter A1) and two restricted (litter C1) had previously had the preliminary tests. These three exceptions had been run on the open-field maze (see below).

The experimental situation is diagrammed in Figure 3. The two food boxes (in front of parts marked G) were made of unpainted plywood. They measured 10 by 10 inches. Their doors were suspended from a crossbar, and so balanced that they would open at a touch and then remain open. On these doors were lucite frames into which stimulus cards could be inserted. In the present experiment, white

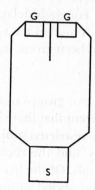

FIG. 3. Ground plan of the apparatus for testing delayed reaction.

cards were used on both doors. The starting box, marked S, measured 30 by 20 by 18 inches and was located eight feet from the food boxes. Subjects could be released from the starting box by lifting two sliding panels, one lucite, the other wood. When subjects in either group showed any tendency to make a choice too quickly, the plywood door was lifted before the lucite one, so that the subject had an opportunity to choose the correct side before leaving the box. Beaverboard barriers, two feet high, were placed at the sides, as shown in Figure 3.

All subjects were put on a 24-hour food-deprivation schedule, and were fed their full daily ration of food immediately after testing. Each was taken in turn to the experimental room and allowed to watch the experimenter placing food in one of the goal boxes. To make sure the animals were attending, they were also permitted to try to get at the food, though restrained from eating any of it. They were then taken immediately back to the starting box. For the preliminary training trials, the subject was shown the position of the food, and then placed in the starting box. The door of this was then immediately opened (zero delay) and the subject allowed to make its choice. The position of the food was varied randomly, unless the subject developed a preference for one side, in which case the other side was reinforced more frequently. The wrong goal box was closed, and the subject was allowed to correct its errors. Ten trials a day were given, until the subject had reached a criterion of ten correct choices in ten trials. Each dog that achieved the criterion was then tested with the following delay periods (commencing from the moment of its insertion into the starting box): 5, 10, 15, 20, 25, 30, 40, 50, 60, 70, 80, 90, 105, 120, 135, 150, 180, 240, 300 seconds. For each delay period, the criterion was five out of five correct runs. A total of ten trials a day was given. After a maximum of 300 trials had been given, testing was stopped.

Results

The performance of the two groups of dogs is summarized in Table I. It is immediately apparent that there is no overlap at all between them. Six out of seven of the restricted subjects were unable to achieve criterion even at zero delay, and the remaining one reached only a 25-second delay with 300 trials. Of the five normal subjects, the worst one reached a 50-second delay period within 255 trials, while the three best reached four- and five-minute delays in less than 250 trials. There was every indication that they could have exceeded this performance if more trials had been given, but since their superiority was already plainly established, there seemed little point in continuing. The oldest subject in the normal group was the best, but in the restricted group, the two older subjects were no better than the younger ones.

A comparison between the four normal and five restricted litter-mates (litters A2 and B) that had run the preliminary tests first and the delayed-reaction test second shows exactly the same results. The other normal dog (litter A1) qnd the two restricted (litter C1) had the same father, and their mothers were sisters. They were also run in the same order (maze followed by delayed-reaction), and can therefore be legitimately compared. There was no overlap between them. Thus there is little doubt of the marked differences between the normal and restricted dogs.

TABLE I

THE NUMBER OF TRIALS REQUIRED BY NORMAL AND RESTRICTED
DOGS TO REACH DELAY PERIODS OF VARYING LENGTHS

	Normal			Restricted	
Litter	Delay Period Reached (Sec.)	Trials Required	Litter	Delay Period Reached (Sec.)	Trials Required
A1	300	230	A2	25	300
A2	50	255	A2	0	300
B	240	185	B	0	300
B	240	220	B	0	300
B	135	235	B	0	300
			C1	0	300
			C1	0	300
Median	240	230		0	300

OPEN-FIELD MAZE[3]

Procedure

This test was based on the one described by Hebb and Williams (6) for testing the intelligence of rats, and later standardized by Rabinovitch and Rosvold (13).

Eleven normal and eight moderately restricted dogs were used in the experiment. Ages ranged from one to one and a half years at the time of testing. Results for six of the dogs have already been summarized in a previous paper (2), but are included here in more detail.

Nine of the subjects (four normal, five restricted) had been run previously on the preliminary tests and the delayed-reaction test, in that order. In the normal group, two subjects of litter C1, two of litter F, and one of litter A1 had had none of the tests. One subject of litter C1, and one of litter C2 had taken only the preliminary tests. In the restricted group, three subjects of litter C1 had had none of the tests. It will be noted that, on the average, the restricted group had had more experience with tests than the normals.

The maze consisted of an outdoor wire enclosure, 17 by 17 feet, and approximately 2½ feet high. It was divided into 49 square units. The adjustable barriers, also of wire, varied in length from one to six units and were arranged in various combinations, each combination forming a particular problem. Eighteen such problems were devised, each having a certain number of error zones representing deviations from the correct path. A sample problem is diagrammed in Figure 4. Barriers are marked by solid lines, error zones by broken lines.

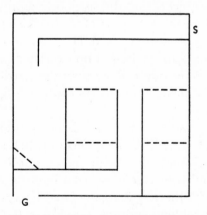

Fig. 4. Open-field maze, problem No. 11.

[*] Thanks are due to Mrs. Muriel Stern who assisted in part of this test.

Before formal testing commenced, a series of simple practice problems was given to the subjects, one a day, until they ran without hesitation from the starting gate to food at the other end of the maze. For most subjects this took three to five days. No difference could be detected between the normal and restricted subjects in the rate at which they adapted to the maze. The main series of 18 problems was then given at the rate of one per day, six trials per problem. Error and time scores were taken.

The specific procedure was as follows: each dog was put on a 24-hour deprivation schedule and tested in the afternoons, weather permitting. Two experimenters were necessary, one to let the subject in through the starting gate, the other to feed it at the goal (one bite of food was allowed at the end of each trial) and send it back to the starting point. All subjects readily learned to run round the side of the maze back to the start after each trial. If a subject made more than 20 errors on a trial, it was guided by one experimenter through the correct path. At the end of six trials, each subject was given the remainder of its daily ration of food in an enclosure near the maze, while the next subject was being tested.

Results

On the average, restricted subjects made more errors on all 18 problems except Nos. 10 and 17, on which the two groups were equal. The most difficult problem was No. 13 which some subjects, both normal and restricted, found impossible to solve. The means of the two groups are significantly different ($t = 3.37$, $p < .01$), and there were only two normal subjects that did as poorly as any of the restricted subjects. One of these was a pregnant female which had some difficulty in running and quickly became tired. However, total scores of the subjects from problems 8 to 18 showed no overlap at all, indicating that the normal subjects improved more than the restricted subjects from one problem to the next. Time scores of the two groups were about equal.

In this test it is possible to compare six normals and eight restricted of three litters (A2, B, C1), the members of which participated in the experiments in the same order. With these factors held constant, there was found to be only one case of overlap in error scores (in litter B).

The reliability of the test was calculated by a rank correlation of odd against even problems and was found to be 0.67 ($p < .01$). Application of the Brown-Spearman formula raised this to 0.80. Consequently, the maze can be regarded as a reliable test.

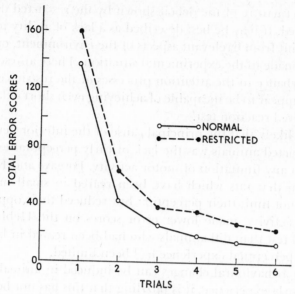

FIG. 5. Intra-problem learning curve of normal and restricted dogs on the maze test.

Although normal subjects were superior to restricted subjects in maze learning, the course of learning of the two groups during any one problem was similar. This is shown in Figure 5. The points of the curves were obtained by averaging error scores on each trial over problems 1 to 18. There is some tendency for the curves to converge gradually from the first three trials. The restricted subjects made more errors on each trial, but especially on the first few trials on a problem.

There was no indication of the development of learning sets during the course of testing. This is probably owing to the fact that only 18 problems were used and that these were graded roughly in order of difficulty, with the easiest first and the hardest last.

In summary, it may be stated that restricted subjects showed a definite inferiority in maze learning as compared to normal subjects, particularly in the first few trials of each problem, and improved at a slower rate from problem to problem.

DISCUSSION

The results clearly demonstrate that the limitation of early experience has adverse effects on the problem-solving ability of the adult dog. These effects appear to be fairly permanent, since they are detectable in animals which have been removed from restriction for over a year.

The exact nature of the deficit shown by the restricted dogs is not easily defined. It may be best described as a lack of ability to discriminate relevant from irrelevant aspects of the environment, or to adapt to changes made in the experimental situation. There also seems to be some disturbance in the attention processes of the restricted animals, since they appear to be incapable of achieving even short delay periods on the delayed-reaction test.

It seems likely that the principal cause of the inferior performance of the restricted animals was the lack of early perceptual experience, rather than any limitation of motor activity. Forgays and Forgays (4) have shown that rats which have been reared in small mesh cages, which did not limit their perception but reduced their opportunities for motor activity, made lower error scores on the Hebb-Williams closed-field test than did animals who had been reared in large cages, but whose perceptual experience had been limited.

If major behavioural changes can be induced in animals by altering their early experience, it is puzzling that this has not been clearly demonstrated in human beings. There would appear to be three main reasons: first, except in a few rather ambiguous case studies (3, 7, 11), there has not usually been a great contrast between the environments of the experimental and control groups. It is doubtful, for example, whether nursery-school experience is much more intellectually stimulating than the home, though it may be of benefit socially and emotionally. Secondly, enriched experience might have greater effects if commenced at an earlier age than it ordinarily is. Thus Wolf (17) found that restricting the early experience of rats by sealing their eyes and ears induced deficits later on only if it was done during the nursing period. If introduced later than 25 days, it had little or no effect. Thirdly, testing for possible differences between nursery-school subjects and controls is usually carried out during the nursery-school period or soon afterwards. This may well be too soon for any effects induced to manifest themselves. There may be no point in looking for effects immediately after the nursery-school period, but a great deal of point in looking for them when the children concerned have reached maturity. Indeed, all the animal experimentation seems to suggest that this is so. This appears to be one case where the comparative method is immediately useful in interpreting and clarifying data obtained from human subjects.

SUMMARY

The purpose of the experiment was to examine the effects of restricting early experience on the problem-solving ability of dogs at maturity.

Thirteen Scottish terriors were raised for the first seven to ten months of life with their perceptual experience restricted in varying degrees. Their 13 litter-mates, serving as normal controls, were raised as pets in homes or in the laboratory. On the basis of several tests, it was concluded that the two groups did not differ in motivation or emotionality in such a way as might bias their performance on the tests of learning ability.

Four preliminary tests of problem-solving capacity (two orientation and two barrier tests) were given to subjects, followed by a test of delayed reaction and an open-field maze test. On all these tests, restricted subjects proved strikingly inferior to normal subjects.

It was concluded that restriction of early perceptual experience has a definite and fairly permanent retarding effect on dog intelligence, a result in agreement with previous animal experimentation. Such an effect probably depends more on experience with the environment than on practice in solving problems. On the basis of the comparative work, several reasons were suggested for the failure of human experimentation on the subject to yield incisive results.

REFERENCES

1. BINGHAM, W. E., and GRIFFITHS, W. J. The effect of different environments during infancy on adult behavior in the rat. *J. comp. physiol. Psychol.*, 1952, 45, 307–12.
2. CLARKE, R. S., HERON, W., FETHERSTONHAUGH, M. L., FORGAYS, D. C., and HEBB, D. O. Individual differences in dogs: preliminary reports on the effects of early experience. *Canad. J. Psychol.*, 1951, 5, 150–56.
3. DAVIS, K. Extreme social isolation of a child. *Amer. J. Sociol.*, 1940, 45, 554–65.
4. FORGAYS, D. G., and FORGAYS, J. W. The nature of the effect of free-environmental experience in the rat. *J. comp. physiol. Psychol.*, 1952, 45, 322–28.
5. HEBB, D. O. The effects of early experience on problem solving at maturity. *Amer. Psychologist*, 1947, 2, 306–7.
6. HEBB, D. O., and WILLIAMS, K. A method of rating animal intelligence. *J. genet. Psychol.*, 1946, 34, 59–65.
7. HILL, J. C., and ROBINSON, B. A case of retarded mental development associated with restricted movement in infancy. *Brit. J. med. Psychol.*, 1929, 9, 268–77.
8. HYMOVITCH, B. The effects of experimental variations on problem solving in the rat. *J. comp. physiol. Psychol.*, 1952, 45, 313–21.
9. JONES, H. E. Environmental influences on mental development. In L. Carmichael (Ed.), *Manual of child psychology*. New York: Wiley, 1946, pp. 332–69.
10. *Manual of dog testing techniques.* Bar Harbor, Me.: Jackson Memorial Laboratory, 1950.

11. MASON, M. L. Learning to speak after six and a half years of silence. *J. Speech Disorders*, 1942, **7**, 295–304.
12. NEWMAN, H. H., FREEMAN, F. N., and HOLZINGER, K. J. *Twins: a study of heredity and environment.* Chicago: Univer. of Chicago Press, 1937.
13. RABINOVITCH, M. S., and ROSVOLD, H. E. A closed-field intelligence test for rats. *Canad. J. Psychol.*, 1951, **5**, 122–28.
14. STERN, C. *Principles of human genetics.* San Francisco: W. H. Freeman, 1949.
15. THOMPSON, W. R., and HERON, W. Exploratory activity in normal and restricted dogs. *J. comp. physiol. Psychol.*, in press.
16. WELLMAN, BETH L. IQ changes in preschool and nonpreschool groups during preschool years: a summary of the literature. *J. Psychol.*, 1945, **20**, 347–68.
17. WOLF, A. The dynamics of the selective inhibition of specific functions in neurosis: a preliminary report. *Psychosom. Med.*, 1943, **5**, 27–38.
18. *Yearbook: National Society for the Study of Education*, 1940, **39**, (I, II).

THE EFFECT OF PROLONGED EXPOSURE TO VISUALLY
PRESENTED PATTERNS ON LEARNING
TO DISCRIMINATE THEM

ELEANOR J. GIBSON and RICHARD D. WALK

Cornell University

Recent literature on the development of discrimination has shown an increasing trend toward acceptance of empiricistic explanations (2, 9). That ability to discriminate visually presented patterns develops with the experience and environmental reinforcement of the growing animal may be the case, but the evidence for this view is still inconclusive. Early studies by Lashley and Russell (11) and by Hebb (8) on the rat favored a nativistic interpretation of the differentiation of visual qualities, but later comparable studies with the chimpanzee and pigeon (13, 14) apparently favored an empiricistic explanation. Recent experiments by students of Hebb (5, 6, 10) have employed an "enrichment" technique, with results which appear to favor a learning hypothesis. These studies attempted to provide a generally "rich" environment and used as criteria tests of a rather general type. If opportunity to view a varied and patterned environment is important in the differentiation of visual qualities, we do not know how general or how specific the relevant experience must be.

The experiment to be reported proposed to investigate the dependence of visual form discrimination in adult rats on a specific variation in visual stimulation during growth. To this end, an experimental group of animals was raised from birth in cages which exhibited on the walls circles and triangles identical in form with ones later to be discriminated. The control group was raised under the same standard conditions but without opportunity to see these forms before the discrimination learning began. If the opportunity to view specific forms favors development of the ability to differentiate them in a later discrimination learning problem, the experimental animals should learn faster and show a higher proportion of Ss reaching the criterion than the control group.

METHOD

Rearing

The Ss were albino rats reared from birth in identical 1/2-in. wire-mesh cages measuring 15 by 13 by 9 in. The cages were placed next to each other in a small, softly lighted empty room. Each cage was surrounded by white cardboard walls on three sides, several inches from the wire mesh, and a blank wall of the room on the fourth side, 4 ft. from the mesh. At the top 7 ft. from the mesh was the ceiling of the room. Visible within the cage were only the cage mates, a water bottle on one wall, and food.

On the walls of the cages of the experimental animals were fastened four black metal forms, two equilateral triangles and two circles. The circles were 3 in. in diameter and the triangles were 3 1/2 in. on a side. These patterns were changed in position occasionally to assure a random relationship to food and water. All during the experiment, stimulus patterns were left on the sides of the cages of experimental group animals.

A total of four groups was used, two experimental and two control. These will be numbered as follows: E_1 (experimental, litter 1), E_2 (experimental, litter 2), C_1 (control, litter 1), and C_2 (control, litter 2). Litters E_1 $(n = 8)$ and C_1 $(n = 2)$ were the first born. These litters were born five days apart and, because of the long interval between litters, not split. E_2 $(n = 10)$ and C_2 $(n = 9)$ were born within a day of each other, and litters were split when the pups were one or two days old. The young were weaned at four weeks of age, and at eight weeks sexes were divided so that males and females were in separate cages. The experiment was begun when the animals were approximatly 90 days old.

Apparatus

The apparatus was a modification of one described by Grice (7). Two V-shaped discrimination compartments were joined together and a false floor constructed, as described in Baker and Lawrence (1). The two stimulus patterns were side by side at the 10-in.-wide end of both choice chambers. The 4 3/8-in. by 4 3/8-in. metal stimulus holders slid into grooves between the 1 3/4-in. center partition and the side of the apparatus. Masonite doors fitted into grooves 1/4 in. in front of the stimulus holders. The apparatus was painted a flat black, and each section was covered by glass. A 25-w. bulb mounted 25 in. above the floor furnished the only illumination. The stimulus holders were first painted a flat white, and a black circle and triangle were painted on the white background. The circle was 2 3/4 in. in diameter and the equilateral triangle 3 in. on a side. The stimulus holders had 1 1/8-in. square doors in them, and the animal obtained food by pushing open the door in the center. There were four separate stimulus holders, one with the circle and one with the triangle, for each discrimination box.

Training Procedure

Pretraining. Animals were placed on a 24-hr. feeding cycle for approximately one week prior to the start of experimentation. They were given three to four days' training in obtaining a small quantity of wet mash from the stimulus holders by pushing open the door in the center. The stimulus holders were painted flat black for this pretraining. The door on only one side of the discrimination box was raised at a time. As soon as the animal obtained the food from the food cup, E lowered the door in front of the stimulus holder. The door between the two discrimination boxes was then opened for the next trial, and the animal secured food by pushing its nose against the black stimulus holder at the opposite end. The animal ate ten times from the cup in the holder in the following order: RLLRRLLRRL.

Discrimination training. During discrimination training both Masonite doors on the choice side of the apparatus were raised, exposing the two stimulus patterns side by side. Both stimulus holders were baited. As soon as the animal pushed against one stimulus door, the Masonite door in front of the opposite stimulus was closed. If the choice was correct, the animal was allowed to eat the wet mash in the food cup. After 60 sec., the door between the two compartments was opened and the animal proceeded to the opposite end, where the next choice was made. If it was incorrect, a modified correction procedure was followed. Both doors in front of the stimulus holders were closed. After 60 sec. the animal was allowed to make a choice in the opposite discrimination box. Animals were allowed up to three errors per trial. Following the third error the door in front of the correct stimulus figure remained open, and the animal was allowed to eat from it. This procedure meant that the animal ate equally often on each side of the apparatus. Ten trials were given each day with a maximum of three errors per trial.

The positive stimulus was presented in the following order: RLRRLLRLLR; LRLLRRLRRL; RRLLRRLRLL; LLRRLLRLRR. The order was repeated every four days. For half the animals in each group the circle was the positive stimulus, and for half the triangle. Animals were run until they attained a criterion of 18 out of 20 correct responses, with the last ten consecutive responses correct (one day's run), or until they were run in the experiment for 15 days (150 trials). After the experimental session animals were allowed to eat food pellets for 1 hr. The hunger drive was a function of approximately $22\frac{1}{2}$ hr. deprivation. Each of the two Es ran one-half of the experimental and one-half of the control animals.

RESULTS

The number of days of discrimination training and the errors (initial and repetitive) are presented in Table 1 for both groups of animals. In the table are indicated the sex and litter of each animal. The second litters (LE_2 and LC_2), it will be remembered, were split at birth and thus provide a somewhat better controlled population. It is obvious from the table that there is a difference between experimental and control groups. Out of the control group, only 1 animal reached the criterion during 15 days of training. But 15 of the 18 experimental group animals did. By the chi-square test, this difference is significant at better than the .001 level of confidence. If we calculate the chi square for animals of the split-litter groups only, using Fisher's exact test (4), the significance of the difference is between .002 and .001. The errors, both initial and repetitive, reflect the same trend.

A further check on differences in the population studied is possible by testing males against females. When this comparison is made, the chances are exactly 50 in 100 that there is any difference between sex groups.

TABLE 1

NUMBER OF DAYS TRAINED AND ERRORS FOR THE
EXPERIMENTAL AND CONTROL GROUPS

| | Experimental Group | | | | Control Group | | |
| | No. Days Run | Initial Errors | Repetitive Errors | | No. Days Run | Initial Errors | Repetitive Errors |
Animal				Animal			
LE₁ 30 ♂	12*	39	44	LC₁ 2 ♂	14*	25	11
LE₁ 31 ♂	7*	22	34	LC₁ 20 ♀	15	68	52
LE₁ 32 ♂	11*	28	19	LC₂ 4 ♀	15	50	44
LE₁ 33 ♂	5*	11	9	LC₂ 6 ♀	15	59	30
LE₁ 35 ♀	15	32	21	LC₂ 7 ♀	15	67	18
LE₁ 37 ♂	14*	40	41	LC₂ 12 ♀	15	60	28
LE₁ 40 ♂	7*	24	29	LC₂ 15 ♀	15	80	80
LE₁ 41 ♂	8*	24	24	LC₂ 11 ♂	15	66	72
LE₂ 44 ♀	7*	23	28	LC₂ 5 ♂	15	68	80
LE₂ 47 ♀	10*	25	16	LC₂ 13 ♂	15	74	117
LE₂ 62 ♀	15	70	73	LC₂ 14 ♂	15	84	92
LE₂ 63 ♀	9*	23	16				
LE₂ 64 ♀	12*	39	50				
LE₂ 43 ♂	15	57	51				
LE₂ 45 ♂	13*	28	12				
LE₂ 46 ♂	10*	25	16				
LE₂ 60 ♂	9*	30	23				
LE₂ 61 ♂	10*	37	34				
Mean	10.50	32.06	30.00		14.91	63.73	56.73

* Indicates that animal reached criterion; the criterion day's trials are included in number of days run.

Figure 1 shows the learning curve for experimental and control groups. Percentage of correct responses is plotted against days of training. The animals that reached the criterion are included in the percentages on the assumption that they would continue at their final level of performance. The curves show that the groups begin to diverge by the third or fourth day of training and diverge increasingly thereafter until the tenth day, when a majority of the experimental group has learned.

DISCUSSION

The results presented show conclusively a difference in ease of learning a circle-triangle discrimination between the group reared with these forms exhibited on the cage walls and the control group. Since the control group had the same conditions of training (and pretraining), the same living conditions, and, in our second litters, the same heredity, the difference must be attributed to some advantage arising from the opportunity to look at the forms. This advantage could be something specific which happens early in the animals' de-

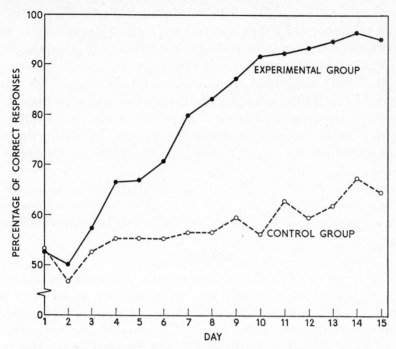

Fig. 1. Learning curves, in percentage of correct responses per day, for the experimental and control groups.

velopment, analogous with "imprinting" (12) or with Hebb's postulated development of reverberating neural circuits (9). On the other hand, a learning theorist who favors "hypotheses" as a factor in learning a discrimination might suggest that seeing the forms on the cage walls favors formation of the correct hypothesis. Since the forms were left on the walls during the learning period, it is not possible to conclude that early experience in viewing the forms is the basis of the effect. Suitable controls are at present being run to clarify this point.

Since research in discrimination learning has centered round the continuity hypothesis in recent years, it might be asked whether the present results tend to confirm or deny this hypothesis. The animals in the experimental group profited, in the discrimination task, from an opportunity to view the two forms without any differential reinforcement of them. Nondifferential reinforcement in viewing these could have occurred, since the animals ate and drank in their presence. Spence's 1936 article (15) suggests that some degree of positive excitatory potential, irrespective of differential reinforcement, would be consistent with faster learning when differential reinforcement is introduced. On the other hand, the values selected for his analysis are purely arbitrary, so it cannot be concluded that effective nondifferential reinforcement either confirms or refutes his statement of the hypothesis. Bitterman and Elam (3) concluded that perceptual differentiation occurs in the course of sheer experience with test stimuli, despite lack of differential reinforcement. But this conclusion is beclouded by their further finding that there is a general retarding effect of nondifferential reinforcement. The present results seem to demonstrate clearly the positive transfer from experience in viewing the test stimuli, without the complications introduced by specific application of reinforcement.

Further research on the problem described will investigate whether there is an optimal or critical time for the visual experience, and the relative specificity of the resulting facilitation of discrimination learning.

SUMMARY

This experiment sought to determine the effect of early and continued exposure to certain forms, presented visually, on the ease with which an adult animal learns to discriminate them. Two groups of animals were raised from birth in well-illuminated cages surrounded by white cardboard. Animals of the experimental group also had mounted on the walls of their cages black circles and triangles, from birth throughout the duration of the experiment. When the animals were approximately 90 days old, both experimental and control groups learned a circle-triangle discrimination. Animals of the experimental group reached the criterion significantly faster and made fewer errors than the control group. It was concluded that visual experience with the forms to be discriminated, even in the absence of differential reinforcement, facilitated the discrimination learning.

REFERENCES

1. BAKER, R. A., and LAWRENCE, D. H. The differential effects of simultaneous and successive stimuli presentation on transposition. *J. comp. physiol. Psychol.*, 1951, 44, 378–82.
2. BEACH, F. A., and JAYNES, J. Effects of early experience upon the behavior of animals. *Psychol. Bull.*, 1954, 51, 239–63.
3. BITTERMAN, M. E., and ELAM, C. B. Discrimination following varying amounts of nondifferential reinforcement. *Amer. J. Psychol.*, 1954, 67, 133–37.
4. FISHER, R. A. *Statistical methods for research workers.* (11th Ed.) New York: Hafner, 1950.
5. FORGAYS, D. G., and FORGAYS, JANET W. The nature of the effect of free-environmental experience in the rat. *J. comp. physiol. Psychol.*, 1952, 45, 322–28.
6. FORGUS, R. H. The effect of early perceptual learning on the behavioral organization of adult rats. *J. comp. physiol. Psychol.*, 1954, 47, 331–36.

7. GRICE, G. R. The acquisition of a visual discrimination habit following response to a single stimulus. *J. exp. Psychol.,* 1948, **38,** 633–42.
8. HEBB, D. O. The innate organization of visual activity. I. Perception of figures by rats reared in total darkness. *J. genet. Psychol.,* 1937, **51,** 101–26.
9. HEBB, D. O. *The organization of behavior.* New York: Wiley, 1949.
10. HYMOVITCH, B. The effects of experimental variations on problem solving in the rat. *J. comp. physiol. Psychol.,* 1952, **45,** 313–21.
11. LASHLEY, K. S., and RUSSELL, J. T. The mechanism of vision. XI. A preliminary test of innate organization. *J. genet. Psychol.,* 1934, **45,** 136–44.
12. LORENZ, K. Der Kumpan in der Umwelt des Vogels. *J. Orn. Lpz.,* 1935, **83,** 137–213.
13. RIESEN, A. H. The development of visual perception in man and chimpanzees. *Science,* 1947, **106,** 107–8.
14. SIEGEL, A. I. Deprivation of visual form definition in the ring dove. I. Discriminatory learning. *J. comp. physiol. Psychol.,* 1953, **46,** 115–19.
15. SPENCE, K. W. The nature of discrimination learning in animals. *Psychol. Rev.,* 1936, **43,** 427–49.

A LABORATORY APPROACH TO THE STUDY

OF IMPRINTING[1]

By A. OGDEN RAMSAY and ECKHARD H. HESS

According to Lorenz (1937), imprinting differs from other forms of acquired behavior in that: (1) it occurs very rapidly; (2) it occurs only in a very limited part of the animal's life; and (3) it is irreversible, or, at least, it is difficult to extinguish. Although imprinting was for some time thought to be found exclusively in birds, it now seems that it may be a more universal type of behavior. Suggestions from the literature point to the possibility that it may exist in such diverse forms as insects, fishes, and mammals (Thorpe, 1950). The characteristics of imprinting listed above make it an extremely important subject in the study of behavior. This is emphasized by Thorpe (1950) who wrote, "It needs and would repay full and precise experimental investigation more almost than any other aspect of animal behaviour." For this reason we decided to begin a careful analysis of the problem. The experiments to be described represent attempts to develop laboratory techniques to study the following problems:

(1) What is the critical age for imprinting to occur?

(2) What characteristics are necessary in the imprinting object if it is to release the reaction of following?

(3) How long must young birds be exposed to the imprinting object, if imprinting is to be complete and irreversible?

PROCEDURE

The Mallard ducklings (*Anas platyrhynchos*) used in these experiments were hatched from eggs incubated in a forced-air incubator. Two days before hatching, the eggs were transferred to a still-air incubator fitted with glass doors and shutters. This latter incubator was kept very humid, as the ducklings had to be removed and isolated as they hatched. Each duckling was given a number, and this number, as well as the day and hour of hatching, was noted on the cardboard

[1] This experiment was supported in part by The Abbott Memorial Fund of the University of Chicago.

box in which the duckling was placed. This information was also re-corded in the permanent records. The box containing the duckling was then placed in a third incubator, used as a brooder until imprint-ing and testing was completed, and only then was the duckling placed in daylight and given food and water.

During school hours and during the night, it was not feasible to watch the hatching incubator constantly. At these times the incubator was examined every 1–2 hours and the age of the duckling was esti-mated by the degree of dryness of the duckling.

For the experiments, papier-mâché Mallard duck decoys were se-cured. These models were then fitted with off-center wheels that caused them to waddle when moved. The models also contained loud-speakers that could be attached to tape-recorders. The latter were fitted with circular tapes which allowed the same pattern of sound to be presented repeatedly. Some of the models had articulated heads that moved on springs with the motion of the decoy. In addition, a male model was fitted with a heating element and a felt apron so that the duckling could go under the decoy for warmth.

The imprinting runs, as well as the test runs, were made in a 1.5 × 1.5 × 12 ft. runway. This was covered on the bottom and sides with monk's cloth and provided with a hinged cover of screen wire. It rested on legs 3 feet above the floor. Fifteen watt bulbs were present overhead at either end and in the center. The remainder of the room was kept dark whenever the eggs were hatching, or when the imprint-ing or testing of ducklings was in progress.

In the standard imprinting trials, the optimum male model, fitted with a heating element and a felt apron, was provided with an arbi-trarily chosen series of calls, best represented as *GOCK, gock, gock, gock, gock.* Two main methods of imprinting were used. In the first series, the duckling was kept with the model 10 minutes, and al-though the movement of the model was accommodated to that of the individual duckling, it was kept in motion as much as possible for the entire period. The duckling usually traveled 150 to 250 feet in the time allotted. In the second series, the duckling was kept with the imprinting object for 30 minutes and the model was moved a short distance every 5 minutes for a total of 12 feet.

Five to 70 hours after imprinting, each duckling was given the fol-lowing 4 tests, which we estimated to be in order of increasing dif-ficulty. These tests are graphically presented in Figure 1. The time of response and the character of the call note (*i.e.,* whether pleasure tone or distress note) of the duckling were recorded.

In the test situation a female model was used as well as the imprint-

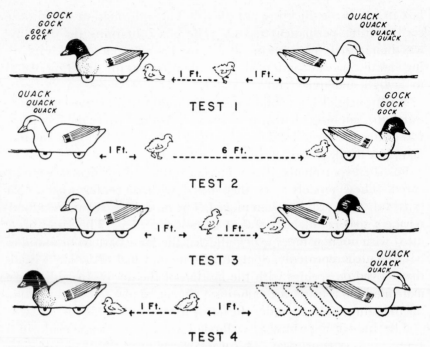

FIG. 1.   Diagram of procedures used to test amount of imprinting.

ing object or male model. The male model was connected to a tape recorder upon which was recorded the standard *gock,* and the female model was connected to a tape recorder which played the sound of a female Mallard calling her young. (In order to secure the latter record, a female Mallard with young was penned up, her young removed, and her call notes were recorded from a short distance.) In each test, as much as 2 minutes was allowed for a response.

Test 1.—In this test both models were motionless at first and both were calling. The duckling in a cardboard box was placed one foot from each model in the center of the runway. The box was then removed to release the duckling. After it has made a choice, the model chosen was moved slowly to the end of the runway to test the reaction of following in the duckling. Throughout the experiments the ducklings were never touched by hand but were picked up and released by means of the cardboard box mentioned.

Test 2.—This test was similar to Test 1 except the male model was now placed at the far end of the runway, 6 feet from the ducklings. This test was designed to determine if the duckling would respond to the imprinting object even though the female model was now closer and louder.

Test 3.—In the third test both models were kept silent and the ability of the duckling to make a response on the basis of visual cues alone was tested. The models and the ducklings were in the same starting position as in Test 1. After the duckling made a choice, the silent model was then moved to test the response of following.

Test 4.—In the last test the duckling was released from the center, as before, and the models were in the same starting position. However, in this test only the female was calling and when the duckling was released the female model was moved down the runway. Thus, to score a positive response, the duckling had to go to the male although confronted with a variety of conflicting stimuli.

If the duckling gave a positive response to the imprinting object (the male Mallard) in all tests, imprinting was regarded as complete. Such ducklings, when released, remained apart from parent female Mallards; the imprinting may, therefore, be regarded as irreversible. Only a few ducklings were difficult to score on a quantitative basis. For these few, a response was considered partial and scored as 0.5 if the duckling went in the direction of the imprinting object before the model was moved and remained there. Other qualitative differences in response were also noted. For instance, of the 92 ducklings tested in the standard series, a total of 35 chose the male model in Test 3 and only 8 of these gave a distress note, even though no sound was used in this test. In contrast, only 16 ducklings went to the female model in this test, and 10 of these gave a distress note.

CRITICAL PERIOD

Ninety-two ducklings were imprinted in the standard series, 54 by 10 minutes of following (Table 1), and 38 by the 30 minute method (Table 2). In both of these series 13–16 hours proved to be the best age for imprinting. Approximately 50 per cent of the 21 ducklings imprinted in this age-group were completely imprinted. Only 3 other ducks made perfect scores, and none imprinted before 12 hours of age or after 18 hours of age made perfect scores. Beyond 28 hours no imprinting occurred. In addition, 3 ducklings were exposed to the standard *gock* call continuously for over 24 hours before and up to the time of hatching. No imprinting occurred in these ducklings. In fact, 2 of the 3 responded to the recorded call of the female Mallard in preference to the call to which they had been exposed. The other duckling did not respond to either call.

Under the conditions of the experiment, therefore, the period 13–16 hours is definitely the period for maximum imprinting in Mallards. This is made obvious by the graphs which include all of the 92 animals imprinted in the standard series. Figure 2 shows the percentage of animals in each age group that made perfect imprinting scores. Figure 3 shows the percentage of positive responses made by these same ducklings in each age group. These results will be reported elsewhere (Hess and Ramsay).

Our results contradict the findings of Fabricius (1951a) who reported that ages before 12 hours are most favorable for imprinting in several species of ducks including Mallards. It may be that the tests we used were more sensitive than those used by Fabricius. We also wonder about the condition of his young birds: he reported that normal walking and running was not established until the ducklings were 16 to 28 hours old. All of our ducklings could walk and run many hours before that, although we recorded that 4 of the 8 ducklings imprinted before they were 2 hours old could not even crawl in a straight line at first but circled in a clockwise direction. Six ducklings, 3 to 4 hours old, imprinted by the 10 minute method, traveled an average distance of 75 feet in the time allowed. Maximum distance traveled was 250 feet, minimum 16 feet. Fabricius also reported (1951a) that fear responses first appeared in his Tufted Ducks (*Aytha fuligula*) and Eiders (*Somateria mollissima*) at 12 hours. Fear responses to the imprinting model did not appear in our Mallards until 24 hours. Eleven of the 14 ducklings imprinted in this age-group showed strong fear responses. Of over 100 other Mallard ducklings (imprinted earlier) only 3 (ages, 16, 20, and 16 hours) showed alarm. It seems significant that the only ducklings that showed any appreciable imprinting in the 21 to 24 hour group were the same individuals that showed no alarm.

SOCIAL FACILITATION IN IMPRINTING

Two groups of 2 animals each, well past the optimum imprinting age, were partially imprinted by being placed with 2 well imprinted ducklings and the imprinting object during the imprinting period. These all made much better scores than could be expected otherwise. Each of the 2 imprinted at 28 hours made a score of 3 positive responses. Each of the 2 ducklings imprinted at 38 hours made a score of 2 positive responses in the test period. Nice (1953) observed imprinting in a 6-day old Shoveller (*Spatula clypeata*), apparently through social facilitation. We plan further study to determine the effects of maturation of fear responses, and decline in tendency to respond to the imprinting object on imprinting as the duckling grows older.

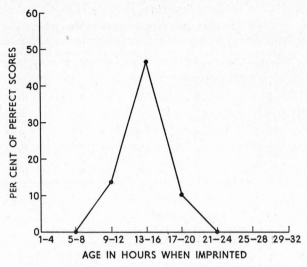

Fig. 2. Percentage of "perfect" scores for Mallards imprinted in various age groups.

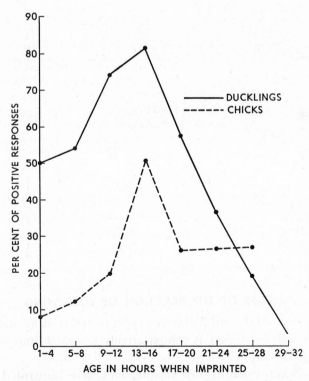

Fig. 3. Percentage of positive responses made by ducklings and chicks in test series.

TABLE 1
TESTS OF DUCKLINGS IMPRINTED FOR 10 MINUTES

No. of Ducklings	Age in Hours	Number of Positive Responses				
		Test 1	Test 2	Test 3	Test 4	Average
5	1– 4	5	4	3	0	2.4
8	5– 8	8	8	3	0	2.4
8	9–12	8	8	5	2	2.9
10	13–16	10	10	8.5	4	3.3
10	17–20	9	9	3	2	2.3
6	21–24	4	3	2	0	1.5
3	25–28	1	1	0	1	1.0
4	29–32	0	0.5	0	0	0.13

TABLE 2
TESTS OF DUCKLINGS IMPRINTED FOR 30 MINUTES

No. of Ducklings	Age in Hours	Number of Positive Responses				
		Test 1	Test 2	Test 3	Test 4	Average
8	1– 4	7	7	0	1	1.9
12	5– 8	10.5	10.5	3	0	2.0
7[1]	9–12	7	7	3	4.5	3.1
5	13–16	5	5	3	3	3.2
0	17–20	—	—	—	—	—
5	21–24	3	2	1	1	1.4
1	25–28	0	0	0	0	0

[1] Six of these 7 birds were 12 hours old when imprinted and very close to the age for maximum imprinting.

TABLE 3
TESTS OF CHICK IMPRINTED FOR 10 MINUTES

No. of Chicks	Age in Hours	Number of Positive Responses					
		Test 1	Test 2	Test 3	Test 4	Test 5	Average
5	1– 4	1	0	0	0	1	0.4
5	5– 8	1	0	0	0	2	0.6
3	9–12	0.5	0	0	0	2.5	1.0
4	13–16	3	2	1	0	4	2.5
3	17–20	0.5	0	1.5	0	2	1.3
3	21–24	2.5	0.5	0	0	1	1.3
3	25–28	1	1	0	0	2	1.3

RELEASE OF THE REACTION OF FOLLOWING

Experiments on this subject were exploratory in nature and no final conclusions can be drawn as comparatively few ducklings were used in each experiment.

Sound.—Seven ducklings of various ages were imprinted only on the recorded natural quack of a female Mallard calling her young. Of these, only 4 responded to the imprinting object at all in the test period. These 4 made fair scores in the tests (average score 2). The other 3 did not respond to either model. In contrast, of 38 Mallard ducklings similarly imprinted on the male model calling *gock,* only one failed to respond at all, and the group score averaged 2.3.

Twenty-four ducklings of various ages were carefully tested for inherent preferences. These ducklings were first tested with the models silent and then with the male model calling *gock* and the female model calling *quack.* The calls were then reversed in the models 2 or more times. At no time were the models moved and each duckling was allowed as much as 5 minutes to make a response. No talking occurred in the laboratory where the ducklings were kept until after they were tested. We could not eliminate talking outside the room.

None of the 24 ducklings made any move toward either the male or female models as long as the latter were silent. Fifteen showed no preference between the call notes. Of the 15, 10 made no move toward either sound, and 5 responded to each call once. Of the remainder of the 24, 8 chose the *gock* consistently and only one chose the *quack* repeatedly. Of 15 ducklings similarly tested for preferences between the recorded duck quack and a spoken simulated quack, 2 definitely chose the simulated quack and one the recorded quack. Thus, the ducklings showed no real preference.

Motion.—Four ducklings were kept with a motionless male model without heating element and with fixed head for 30 minutes. This model was giving the standard *gock* call. When the ducklings were tested, all gave positive scores on Tests 1, 2 and 3. However, only one was imprinted at the critical age, and again, this is the only duckling that gave a perfect score. If articulated motion, or motion within the organism, is one of the key stimuli in releasing the following reaction, as claimed by Fabricius (1951a), by the principle of heterogeneous summation, these ducklings should not have done nearly as well as they did. In our records it is recorded that 2 of these 4 ducklings followed poorly in their first following response when they were about 2 days old at the test period. It remains to be determined accurately whether any difference in this response is due to lack of exercise or practice by the duckling, or due to a lack of willingness to respond.

Three additional ducklings were imprinted by this same method on the non-moving, non-articulated male model, calling the standard gock for 30 minutes, and 3 others were imprinted by the same method on a small box fitted with a speaker. This box was approximately the same size as the male model, and the ducklings were all near the most favorable age for imprinting. When they were approximately 2 days old they were given the following tests: (1) male model and box both call the standard *gock*, (2) male model silent, box calls, and (3) male model calls, box silent.

In the test situation, those imprinted on the male model scored a total of 5.5 positive responses (and one negative). The ducklings imprinted on the box scored a total of 2.5 positive responses (and 2 negative). In other words, the ducklings imprinted on the male model were almost twice as strongly imprinted as those imprinted on the box. It also seems significant that 2 of the ducklings imprinted on the male model responded to the silent male even when the box was calling (Test 2), but none of those imprinted on the box responded to the silent box when the male model was calling (Test 3). These limited data seems to contradict Fabricius' (1951a) conclusion that ducklings have no inherent preference as to the form of the object.

FIELD STUDIES

Two groups of ducklings, kept with the male model during the entire imprinting period, remained with the male model and followed it in preference to parent female Mallards that tried to lead them away. These parent females had young of the same age as the experimental ducklings. During this experiment, as well as during the imprinting, the male model was calling *gock* intermittently. One day-old unimprinted duckling, used as a control, went by the male model calling *gock* and on to join the parent Mallard duck. One of these experimental groups that had been given less than 10 minutes practice during the imprinting runs in following a silent male model in the runway, went to a silent floating male model and followed it in spite of the female's attempt to lure them away. The second group with no practice in following a silent model went to the floating model, followed it briefly, and then left it to return to the more familiar model with wheels on nearby land.

These results are not surprising when we recall that young of various species will follow non-articulated, smoothly moving objects, such as balls and boxes drawn along a cable (Ramsay, 1951), and that Grey Lag-Geese (*Anser anser*) if caught at the critical age will follow boats (Lorenz, 1937).

A parent female Mallard duck, while resting quietly on land will sometimes spread her tail and move her folded wings slowly back and forth an inch or more from her body. In a previous experiment, 2 Mallards hatched by a Wood Duck (*Aix sponsa*) seemed to be attracted to a parent female Mallard which was displaying in this fashion but which, as far as we could observe, was not calling. This is an example of a *releaser* in the classical sense (Lorenz, 1937). It seems very likely, therefore, that Fabricius was dealing with 2 separate innate releasing mechanisms, and not with 2 key stimuli in the same releasing mechanism, when he stated that articulated motion, or motion within the organism, is one of the 2 key stimuli in the release of the reaction of following. As Tinbergben has emphasized (1951), unless the innate responses of the organism are carefully analyzed into separate components, it will appear that the animal is reacting to a complex of stimuli.

COMPARATIVE STUDIES

In contrast to these results with Mallard ducklings, 26 Cochin Bantam chicks, similarly treated as a group, showed comparatively little imprinting (see Table 3). None of the chicks chose the imprinting object in preference to the moving clucking female in Test 4, and only one chick responded to the male model in Tests 1, 2 and 3. In order to compare the chicks more adequately, an additional test followed Test 4. In Test 5 the female model was quiet and immobile and the male alone was calling. Even with the few animals tested, it is apparent that the critical age for imprinting in chicks corresponds closely to that for ducklings (Fig. 3).

Of 13 chicks tested for inherent preferences, all but 2 chose the recorded cluck of a mother hen in preference to the standard *gock*. It seems logical to asssume, therefore, that this very strong innate preference in chicks for the cluck resulted in these low scores and that by substituting another call that was not preferred, one might find that considerable imprinting had occurred. Since chicks are readily available in large groups as experimental animals, it would be worthwhile to devise suitable testing procedures for the study of imprinting in these animals.

SUMMARY

Ninety-two Mallard ducklings were imprinted on a male Mallard decoy speaking a rhythmical *GOCK, gock, gock, gock, gock,* through a loud-speaker installed in the decoy. In order to secure maximum imprinting, this model was provided with an articulated head, an internal heating element, and off-center wheels that produced a wad-dling motion. For testing, a female model with loudspeaker also was used.

From 5 to 70 hours after imprinting, each duckling was given the following 4 tests, which we estimate to be in order of increasing dif-ficulty:

(1) Both models motionless, both call; duckling 1 foot away from each.

(2) Female model louder and closer.

(3) Both models silent.

(4) Female model only calling and moving.

In the test situation the imprinting object, or male model, was used against the female model. The female was provided with the re-corded call notes of a female Mallard calling her young and the male was provided with the standard *gock*.

Thirteen to 16 hours proved to be the critical age for imprinting in Mallards. Approximately half of the ducklings imprinted in this age-group were completely imprinted and went to the imprinting ob-ject in all tests. Only 3 of the remaining ducklings gave perfect scores.

Three ducklings exposed to the standard *gock* call for 24 hours be-fore and up to the instant of hatching showed no imprinting on that sound.

Mallard ducklings were running normally in 3 to 4 hours. Fear responses did not appear until 24 hours.

Beyond 28 hours no imprinting occurred ordinarily and only one duckling showed any imprinting beyond 24 hours. Four older duck-lings (28 and 38 hours) were partially imprinted by association with well-imprinted ducklings during the imprinting runs.

Twenty-four ducklings were tested for inherent preferences. None responded to either the male or female model when it was still and silent. In addition, 15 showed no preference to either call note when they were simultaneously presented. Ten of the 15 gave no response and 5 responded once to each call. Eight ducklings showed a con-sistent preference for the *gock* and one responded repeatedly to the *quack*.

Four ducklings were imprinted on a motionless, non-articulated male model sounding the standard call. These four all made positive scores in Test 1, 2 and 3 and one, imprinted during the critical age, made a perfect score. Three additional ducklings imprinted by this method made scores over twice as good as another group of 3 ducklings imprinted on a box of the size of the model, giving the same call through an internal loudspeaker.

Five ducklings in two different groups were imprinted for 24 hours on a male model. These ducklings stayed with this male model in preference to live parent females with ducklings of their own age. One group of these, with some experience in following a silent model, followed a silent floating model although one of the parent female ducks tried to lure them away. The other group followed the floating model briefly and then returned to the similar model with wheels on shore but did not go to the live parent duck.

All but 2 of 13 bantam chicks tested for inherent preferences chose the recorded cluck of a mother hen in preference to the *gock*. None chose the *gock* in every test. Twenty-six bantam chicks were imprinted on the male model giving the standard call. These showed considerably less imprinting than Mallard ducklings. The critical age for imprinting chicks corresponds to that for ducklings.

LITERATURE CITED

FABRICIUS, E. 1951a. Zur Ethologie junger Anatiden. *Acta Zoologica Fennica*, 68:1–175. 1951b. Some experiments on imprinting phenomena in ducks. *Proc. Xth Int. Orn. Cong.*:375–79.

HESS, E. H. and RAMSAY, A. O. ms. The critical age for imprinting in Mallards.

LORENZ, K. 1937. The companion in the bird's world. *Auk,* 54:245–73.

NICE, M. M. 1953. Some experiences in imprinting ducklings. *Condor,* 55:33–37.

RAMSAY, A. O. 1951. Familial recognition in domestic birds. *Auk,* 68:1–16.

THORPE, W. H. 1950. The concepts of learning and their relation to those of instinct (pp. 387–408). *S.E.B. Symposia IV* Oxford Univ. Press.

TINBERGEN, N. 1951. The study of instinct. Oxford Univ. Press.

ESCAPE AND AVOIDANCE LEARNING AS A FUNCTION

OF EMOTIONALITY LEVEL IN THE

WYOMING GROUND SQUIRREL

Citellus richardsonii elegans

ROLLIN H. DENNISTON, II
University of Wyoming

The object of this study is to determine whether a significant difference might exist in the learning of escape and avoidance from electrical shock between thoroughly cage-conditioned and freshly caught Wyoming ground squirrels. The problem suggested itself following the reading of Spence's (1956) *Behaviour theory and conditioning,* Miller's (1948) *Fear as an acquirable drive,* and certain observations of wild animal behaviour in both field (1959–1956) and laboratory (1957 a and b). The consensus seems to be that anxious subjects (human) condition faster and to a significantly higher level than less anxious subjects. Rather different hypothetical constructs have been utilised in attempts to throw light on the situation, notably by Spence and Taylor (1953), Hilgard, *et al.* (1951) and Miller (*op. cit.*). Having at hand a group of newly-caught and apparently "emotional" ground squirrels and a standard stock of well cage-conditioned squirrels of the same species, we felt that data obtainable from them might throw some further light on the general problem of learning an instrumental response by emotional and less emotional subjects.

METHOD

Thirty-six adult male Wyoming ground squirrels were the subjects in these experiments. They were captured by the author from the same area of approximately a square mile near Laramie, Wyoming. Members of one group were captured no more than ten days before the beginning of the experimental work. This group was labelled "New." Its members showed many signs of "wildness" or "anxiety," such as high defecatory, urinary, and vocalisation rates and frequency,

404

both in and out of the immediate presence of the observer. These also reacted much more violently to handling than did the cage-conditioned group. Members of the second group had been confined to the laboratory colony for at least a year. These animals were much lower in anxiety-associated responses of the type cited above. This group was labelled "Old." Animals of both groups were mature and comparable in weights.

Although the author had had fifteen years' experience working with ground squirrels in the laboratory and felt that he knew that newly caught subjects were significantly more "emotional" than those adequately cage-conditioned, he had never run actual emotionality scores until undertaking the present series of experiments. Subjects were observed in their home cages in a series of five-minute check periods on successive days. A clean paper was introduced into the dropping tray at the beginning of each observation for fecal pellet counts and urination determination. If a subject vocalised in three of the five minutes, a positive score was recorded for this criterion.

The conditioning apparatus was a standard shocking grid 50 cm. $\times$ 30 cm., either half of which could be activated by an induced current to serve as the unconditioned stimulus (US). The conditioned stimulus (CS) was a 60-cycle buzzer. The grid covered the floor of a cage 30 cm. high, the two halves being separated by a fence 15 cm. high. The subjects were visible to E through a suitably illuminated one-way vision mirror.

All subjects were allowed to explore the conditioning apparatus for ten minutes on each of three days with buzzer and shock off, and were then given three sessions each of 3S. Sixteen subjects which persisted in responding to the CS by jumping the fence were eliminated from the experiment. Two animals either died or became seriously ill and were eliminated for that reason. Eighteen subjects were now exposed to the following regimen: two minutes adjustment to apparatus, 30 seconds CS, 30 seconds US. If the subject did not cross, he was placed on the other side, and all had the procedure repeated in the opposite direction. Fourteen daily pairs of trials were made for each S. Latencies of response to CS, US, and other incidental notes were made by E.

RESULTS

As far as defecation, urination and vocalisation may be accepted as criteria of "emotionality," the newly caught were significantly more emotional than the cage-conditioned subjects.

TABLE I
"Emotionality" Scores (Per Animal-Trial)

	N	Defecation	Urination %	Vocalisation %
Old	19	5·35±2·49	17·54	50·9
New	17	10·60±2·92	37·25	84·3
	t	9·47	2·23	3·55
	p	<·001	<·05	<·001

Response to US

Although not all subjects escaped from shock on even the last trial (78 per cent.—old and 67 per cent. new, see Fig. 1), all had shown

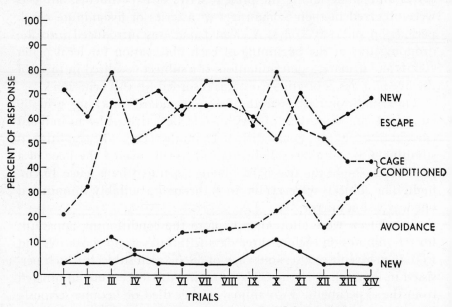

Fig. 1. Average escape and avoidance frequencies.

escape response to US during the series. There was no significant difference between old and new groups in incidence of escape response.

There was a significant difference in escape latencies. The new group responded much faster to US.

The new group showed a significantly lower level of learning avoidance response. On the last trial 36 per cent. of the old group responded to the CS, whereas none of the new group gave such a response. There was no significant difference in avoidance response latency between the two groups.

TABLE II

ESCAPE RESPONSE

	Incidence	%	Seconds Latency
Old	127/222	57·20	11·1 ± 1·38
New	156/246	63·41	5·4 ± 0·48
Difference	29	6·21	5·7
S.E.Δ		4·52	·128
P		<1·0	<·001

TABLE III

AVOIDANCE RESPONSE

	Incidence	%	Seconds Latency
Old	31/222	13·96	15·6
New	5/246	2·03	16·0
Difference	26	11·93±2·46	·4
P		<·002	

DISCUSSION

Although the new group of "anxious" subjects learned to respond to the shock with much shorter latency than the old, cage-conditioned group, the new group never learned to avoid the shock by responding to the warning buzzer. The old, less "anxious" group learned this avoidance response to CS quite satisfactorily. This better learning by "less emotional" subjects is, superficially at least, contrary to a large body of data which shows "high drive" subjects to be superior learners. Many of these data are summarised in Spence (1956, *op. cit.*). However, the same volume contains several suggestions which may help to explain our findings. The curve presented by Fig. 7 (p. 173) demonstrates a lessened rate of response under higher levels of aversive stimulation. The material included in Section 7, and especially the footnote on page 222 suggests that increased oscillation between competing responses may be expected to occur at high drive levels.

One possible reason for the difficulty in learning the avoidance response apparent in our "anxious" group was that members of this group tended to "freeze" into immobility as a response to novel environmental change. The response of freezing is obviously incompatible with avoidance response. Assuming that both the CS, or buzzer and the US, or shock were aversive, the US must further be assumed to be of such a nature, quantitatively or qualitatively, that the response tendency to it was sufficiently strong to overcome the incompatible $_sU_R$ of freezing. In Hullian (1952) symbolism $_sU_R$ signifies an unlearned stimulus-response connection, and $_sE_R$, a present reaction potential. So for the "anxious" group:

$$_sE_R \text{ (Escape)} > {_sU_R} \text{ (Freezing)} > {_sE_R} \text{ (Avoidance)}.$$

But for the "less anxious" group:

$$_sE_R \text{ (Escape)} > {_sE_R} \text{ (Avoidance)} > {_sU_R} \text{ (Freezing)}.$$

Although it may be true that the response tendency of an organism is in part the result of total drive level, and presumably there was a greater total drive in the anxious than the non-anxious group, the only measure we have of drive is response, and if the unlearned response tendency is incompatible with the learned response, apparently paradoxical differences in response between anxious and non-anxious groups may result. We believe it to be an over-simplification to interpret these data as over-motivation interfering with the learning of an expectancy. A superficial interpretation of these results might stop with the assumption that the newly caught group failed to learn avoidance because of giving the incompatible unlearned response of freezing. A more careful examination of the situation makes it apparent that the reason the new animals froze was because they were more anxious than the cage-conditioned subjects. In animal, and possibly in human subjects, under high anxiety there is at least one other response than avoidance possible to noxious stimuli, namely freezing. Unless this possibility is recognized chaos may result in attempting to interpret data from shock conditioning.

SUMMARY

An attempt was made to teach recently caught "anxious" wild rodents and thoroughly cage-conditioned subjects of the same species an avoidance response to a buzzer preceding shock. The less anxious cage-conditioned group learned the response more quickly and thoroughly than the more anxious group. Possibly this difference was, in part, due to the fact that newly caught animals tend to give the incompatible response of freezing to aversive but not actively noxious stimuli.

ACKNOWLEDGMENTS

1. This work was supported by National Institute of Mental Health Grant No. 969.

2. The author is indebted to Mrs. Mellee Luton-Fish for many of the observational data here reported.

REFERENCES

DENNISTON, R. H. (1949). Certain aspects of the development and behaviour of the Wyoming moose. *Anat. Rec.,* 105, p. 137.

DENNISTON, R. H. (1956). The behaviour, ecology, and population dynamics of the Wyoming or Rocky Mountain moose, *Alces alces shirasi. Zoologica,* 41, pp. 105–18.

DENNISTON, R. H. (1957a). Notes on breeding and size of young in the Richardson ground squirrel. *J. Mammal.,* 38, pp. 414–16.

DENNISTON, R. H. (1957b). Sexual behaviour and physiology cycle in an annual breeding wild rodent. *Anat. Rec.,* 128, p. 539.

HILGARD, E. R., JONES, L. W., and KAPLAN, S. J. (1951). Conditioned discrimination as related to anxiety. *J. exp. Psychol.,* 42, pp. 94-100.

HULL, C. L. (1952). *A behaviour system.* New Haven: Yale University Press.

MILLER, N. E. (1948). Studies of fear as an acquirable drive. *J. exp. Psychol.,* 38, pp. 89–101.

SPENCE, K. W. (1956). *Behaviour theory and conditioning.* New Haven: Yale University Press.

SPENCE, D. W. and TAYLOR, J. A. (1953). The relation of conditioned response strength to anxiety in normal, neurotic and psychotic subjects. *J. exp. Psychol.,* 45, pp. 265–72.

EFFECTS OF EARLY HANDLING

UPON ADULT BEHAVIOR IN TWO SUBSPECIES

OF DEERMICE, PEROMYSCUS MANICULATUS[1]

JOHN A. KING AND BASIL E. ELEFTHERIOU[2]

Roscoe B. Jackson Memorial Laboratory

Handled young rats have been found to show faster growth rates (Bernstein, 1957; McClelland, 1956; Ruegamer, Bernstein, and Benjamin, 1954; Weininger: 1954, 1956; Weininger, McClelland, and Arima, 1954), greater ability to withstand stress as an adult (Hammett, 1922; Weininger: 1954, 1956), greater adult activity (Hunt and Otis, 1955; Weininger, 1956), less adult emotionality (Hunt and Otis, 1955) and better learning (Bernstein, 1957; Levine, 1956; Levine, Chevalier, and Kouchin, 1956) than unhandled rats. This relationship between early handling and its effect upon the adult can be interpreted from three theoretical points of view (Levine, 1956): (*a*) That handling of the young rat may serve to enrich its perceptual environment and thus improve performance in learning situations is consistent with Hebb's theory (1949); (*b*) that early handling establishes a reinforcing relationship between the human experimenter and the animal subject (Bernstein, 1957); (*c*) that the handling is a "noxious stimulus" to which the rat adapts, thus enabling it to withstand adult stress-producing situations (Levine, 1956).

Since most experiments on early handling have used the white rat, which has been selected for docility, their results may depend upon a specially selected genotype. In order to avoid the possible effects of artificial selection for docility, wild deermice were chosen for this experiment. Deermice are native North American rodents of the

[1] This study was supported by Research Grant M–123 from the National Institute of Mental Health, U.S. Public Health Service.

[2] The authors wish to acknowledge the helpful criticism of the staff of the Division of Behavior Studies at the Roscoe B. Jackson Memorial Laboratory: J. P. Scott, J. L. Fuller, W. C. Stanley, and A. Christake. D. Anger of Upjohn Company aided in the construction of the conditioning apparatus. N. Shea and C. Shupp assisted in the analysis and preparation of the figures.

family Cricetidae, unlike the domestic rats and mice, which are in the family Muridae. Deermice have been bred in the laboratory, but they have never become particularly tame and they still maintain the characteristics of wild rodents. There are 63 subspecies of *Peromyscus maniculatus* (Miller and Kellogg, 1955), many of which differ in their adult behavior (Fig. 1). One subspecies, *gracilis*, is tractable and leisurely in movement, which allows it to be handled with considerable facility, while another subspecies, *bairdii*, tends to maintain its wild, timid, and jumpy characteristics regardless of its treatment (Foster, 1957; Horner, 1954; King, 1958). The innate behavioral characteristics of these two subspecies provide comparative material for the investigation of the effects of early handling on adult behavior.

The hypothesis to be tested is that early handling has a differential effect on animals of different genetic background. Specifically, we predicted that the treatment would have a greater effect with the naturally docile *gracilis* than with the wild *bairdii* and, regardless of treatment, *gracilis* would show less emotionality and fewer physiological effects during the testing procedure.

METHOD

Subjects

Two subspecies of deermice, *Peromyscus maniculatus bairdii* and *P. m. gracilis*, which had been bred in the laboratory from 8 to 12 generations, were used. A total of 80 mice began the experiment, 40 of each subspecies and 20 in each treatment. The death of two mice and the loss of data from two others made it necessary to reduce the number to 18 for each group in some calculations. Entire litters were selected at random for each type of treatment. Only litters containing 3 to 6 young were used. The litters were kept together with both parents in wooden

FIG. 1. Two subspecies of *Peromyscus maniculatus*. *P. m. bairdii*, on the left, is dark, has short ears, and short tail. Its natural habitat is the grasslands of the Midwest. *P. m. gracilis*, on the right, is large, light brown, with large ears and long tail. Its natural habitats are the northern mixed-hardwood forests of northern Wisconsin, Michigan, and New York.

boxes 6 in. by '6 in. by 12 in., with wood shavings, food, and water until they were weaned and isolated at 25 days of age.

Apparatus

The apparatus consisted of a handling machine, an activity alley, and an operant-conditioning box. The handling machine was constructed to simulate human handling by increasing the mouse's ambient temperature, by moving the mouse about, by increasing its perceptual experiences, and by compressing it as might be done in stroking. The machine consisted of a Plexiglas box 8 in. by 8 in. by 4 in. with ⅛-in. apertures on the sides to facilitate ventilation. The box was open at the top and fitted piston-like with an 8-in. by 8-in. lid, which remained stationary as the box moved up and down around it (Fig. 2). Both the lid and the bottom of the box were lined with 1-in.-thick foam rubber. The box was mounted on a wooden rod connected off center to a rotating wheel operated by a 50-rpm motor. The rotation of the wheel caused the box to move upward and downward with a 2½-in. displacement. The lid could be raised or lowered to previously calibrated points to adjust for the size of the mouse. A mouse was put in the box, the lid set at a minimum height inside the box to gently compress the mouse between the foam rubber each time the box was raised by the motor. A 75-w. reflector bulb was directed at the box from a distance of 1 ft. and served to heat the interior to 35° C.

The activity alley was constructed to measure the spontaneous exploratory behavior and activity over a 24-hr. period. The alley was 6 in. by 4 in. by 8 ft., constructed of wood, painted gray, and had a ¼-in.-mesh screen floor and top. One end had a 2-in. square opening, and the other end was covered with screen. The open end of the alley made it possible to connect a mouse's living cage to the alley without handling the mouse. A 2-in. by 4-in. passageway extended from the living cage to the alley. The amount of time spent in the alley was recorded on an electric clock, which was activated by the mouse's passing over a screen treadle located in this passageway and connected to a mercury switch. Partitions with a 2-sq.-in. opening separated the runway at 2-ft. intervals. The opening in each of the three partitions was provided with 1½-in. by 3-in. screen treadles resting on microswitches connected to counters in an adjacent room, where the activity was recorded. The room was lighted by a 25-w. bulb, located 1 ft. above the screen end of the activity alley (Calhoun, 1955).

The conditioning apparatus and shock-response schedule were adapted from Sidman (1953) and consisted of a 7-in. by 10-in. by 10-in. Plexiglas box mounted on a grid consisting of ⅛-in. stainless-steel rods, ¼-in. apart. At one end of the box a ³⁄₁₆-in. by ½-in. bar protruded through an aperture in the box and was connected to a microswitch. The frequency of responses (bar presses) and shocks were recorded on separate counters in an adjacent room. The source of current for the shock was the secondary of a 600-v. transformer with a 0.7-meg. potentiometer set to give 0.28-meg. resistance in parallel with the grid and the mouse. A stepping switch served as the "grid-confuser." The shock-response schedule was wired to deliver a 0.2-sec. shock every 10 sec. unless the bar was pressed, which delayed the shock each time for 25 sec. If the bar was held down, the shocks came at 10-sec. intervals after the initial 25-sec. delay from the bar press.

Eosinophil counts were made by drawing 0.5 cc. of blood from the ventral tail vein of the mouse into a white-blood-cell pipette and diluted with 0.6 cc. of phloxin stain prepared according to Spiers and Meyers (1949). The solution was placed in two chambers of a 0.2-mm.-deep Spiers and Meyers slide. Eosinophils were counted with a 440× magnification of a binocular microscope.

Adrenals were weighed to the nearest milligram on a torsion balance after they

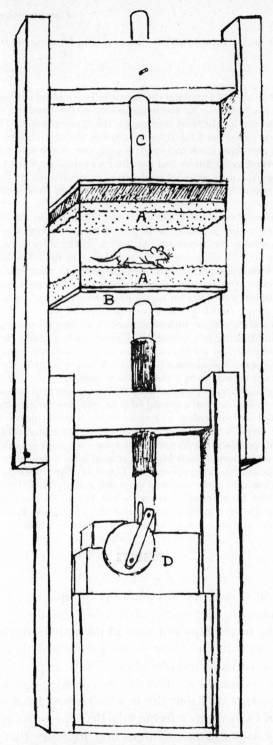

FIG. 2. Handling apparatus. A young mouse is placed between foam rubber pads (A) and then gently compressed by a 50-rpm motor (D).

were removed from the capsule and the surrounding fat tissue under a dissecting microscope.

Procedure

Treatment consisted of removing the infant mice from the mother with rubber-tipped forceps, placing them on the foam rubber of the handling box, adjusting the lid to the proper height, and turning on the 50-rpm motor. The mouse was moved and gently compressed for 10 min. each day for 23 days, from 3 days of age until 25 days of age. After each treatment period, the mouse was again picked up by forceps, returned to the litter, and the litter was then returned to the parents. At 25 days of age, the mice were weaned and isolated in separate cages. The control mice were weaned and isolated at the same age, but they were not handled until weaning.

Activity measures began when the mice were 70 to 88 (mean 79) days of age. One day prior to testing, the mice were placed in clean living cages which were kept in the room with the apparatus. At 9:30 A.M., the mice were placed at the open end of the activity alley and permitted to run in the alley during the next 24-hr. period. This long period was used in order to compensate for normal diurnal periodicity. After one day, during which the mice could run in the alley, they were transferred to a different cage and kept there until the following week. Since only one mouse could be tested each day, five or six mice accumulated before they were conditioned the following week. The interval between the activity test and the conditioning test varied by as much as five or six days each week. However, all the mice had a minimum interval of two days between the activity and conditioning tests. The amount of time each mouse spent in the alley and the number of times it crossed each treadle were recorded.

Conditioning measures began the week following the activity test. Five or six mice were tested each day for a period of 1 hr. per day for five days. The grids were sandpapered each morning and occasionally between mice, if the grid became unusually dirty. A record was made of the number of shocks received and the number of responses made by each mouse for each hour period.

Eosinophils were counted each Monday at least 1 hr. before the mice were first introduced to the conditioning apparatus. This was after a period of at least two days from the time they were removed from the activity alley. On Fridays, 1 hr. after a mouse had been removed from its last period in the conditioning apparatus, eosinophils were again counted and the mouse was killed. The mouse was then weighed, and its adrenals were removed and weighed.

RESULTS

Activity

The amount of activity was analyzed by square-root transformations of the number of crossings of the three treadles in the activity box and by the total amount of time in the activity runway. Table 1 shows the mean values of these scores for each of the four groups. The analysis of variance and probability levels are presented in Table 2. It can be seen from these tables that *bairdii* were significantly more active than *gracilis,* and that the treadle farthest from the nest box (location) was crossed more frequently than the other treadles. The significant location-treatment interaction indicates that the treated

TABLE 1

MEAN ACTIVITY LEVELS OVER 24-HR. PERIOD FOR FOUR GROUPS OF PEROMYSCUS

| Subspecies | Treatment | No. Treadle Crossings at Each Treadle | | | | Total Time Activity Box (Min.) |
		1	*2*	*3*	*Total*	
Bairdii	Treated	433.2	541.5	910.3	1,885.0	332.7
	Control	635.3	612.1	515.2	1,762.5	158.2
Gracilis	Treated	159.6	156.3	228.8	544.6	237.8
	Control	253.1	151.0	235.1	639.2	193.6
Total		1,481.2	1,460.9	1,889.4	4,831.3	922.3

TABLE 2

ANALYSIS OF VARIANCE OF ACTIVITY SCORES OVER 24 HOUR PERIOD

| Source | Treadle Crossings | | | Time in Box | | |
	df	*MS*	*F*	*df*	*MS*	*F*
Between						
Subspecies	1	3,527	7.32**	1	15.01	0.29
Treatment	1	720	1.49	1	416.66	8.10**
S × T	1	356	0.74	1	206.28	4.01*
Mice	72	482		72	51.45	
Within						
Locations	2	138	6.01**			
L × S	2	41	1.78			
L × T	2	111.5	4.85**			
L × M	144	22.97				
L × T × S	2	44.3	1.94			
Total	227			75		

* Signicant at the .05 level.
** Significant at the .01 level.

mice of both subspecies increased their activity at the farthest end of the activity runway, while the control mice decreased their activity away from the nest box. Total activity was correlated with the amount of time spent in the activity runway ($r = .60$, $p < .001$). The treated mice of both subspecies spent a significantly longer time in the activity runway during the 24-hr. test period than the control mice. The significant subspecies-treatment interaction indicates a subspecific difference in response to treatment. In this case, the effect of the treatment is more marked in *bairdii,* with a mean difference between treated and control of 174.5 min. ($t = 3.66$, $p < .01$), than in *gracilis,* with a mean difference of 44.2 min. ($t = .55$, $p > .50$). Correlations of shocks on the fifth day with activity at the third treadle were not significant for any of the groups.

Conditioning

An analysis of variance, including treatment, subspecies, and days, was performed on both the number of responses and the number of shocks. Although significant negative correlations between responses and shocks were obtained in the 20 computations (5 days $\times$ 4 groups), both shocks and responses were analyzed. The data were normalized by conversion to a stanine distribution. *Gracilis* made significantly more responses ($F = 33.17$, $p < .001$) and received fewer shocks ($F = 66.80$, $p < .001$) than *bairdii*. The significant subspecies-treatment interaction for both shocks ($F = 10.31$, $p < .001$) and responses ($F = 7.22$, $p < .001$) can be interpreted from Figures 3 and 4, which show that the treated *bairdii* performed less well than the control, while the treated *gracilis* performed better than the control *gracilis*. However, the interaction was significant only by virtue of combining both subspecies. The control and treated groups were not significantly different in either subspecies alone ($t = 1.67$, $p > .10$ for *bairdii* responses, and $t = 2.01$, $p > .05$ for *gracilis*). There was a sig-

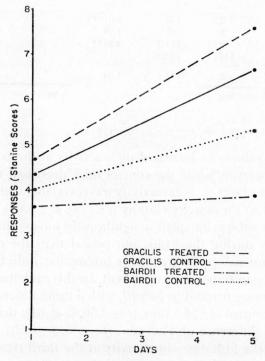

FIG. 3. Regressions curves for the responses of four groups of *Peromyscus* during five days in an operant-conditioning apparatus.

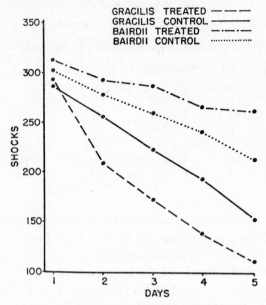

FIG. 4. Number of shocks received by four groups of *Peromyscus* during five days in an operant-conditioning apparatus.

nificant improvement in performance during the five days; most of this improvement was shown by *gracilis*, as indicated from the subspecies-day interaction of the responses. This differential improvement in the four groups is illustrated by the regression lines in Figure 3. Shocks were also significantly reduced during the five days, but the significant interaction of days-subspecies-treatment indicates that the reduction of shocks was specific for each group (Fig. 4).

Eosinophil Drop

The percentage of eosinophil drop during the five days of conditioning was used to measure the stress of the mice while in the conditioning apparatus. Although the mean percentage of drop was 0.63, an analysis of variance performed on the arc-sine transformation of the percentage drop reveals no significant differences between the four groups. Significant correlations were not obtained between the eosinophil drop and the number of shocks on the fifth day for any of the groups.

Adrenal and Body Weight

The adrenal weights at the termination of the experiment were used as a measure of chronic stress during the conditioning period. The adrenal weights were converted to milligrams per gram body

TABLE 3

MEAN ADRENAL WEIGHT AND BODY WEIGHT OF FOUR
GROUPS OF PEROMYSCUS

Subspecies	Treatment	Adrenal Wt. (mg/gm body wt.)	Body Wt. (gm.)
Bairdii	Treated	.27	16.4
	Control	.26	15.4
Gracilis	Treated	.36	18.4
	Control	.41	18.5

weight and subjected to an analysis of variance (Table 3). The adrenals of *gracilis* were significantly heavier than those of *bairdii* after the five days in the conditioning apparatus ($F = 49.58$, $p < .001$). In order to learn if the shocks of the apparatus had a differential effect on the two subspecies, ten nonshocked mice of each subspecies were sacrificed; the adrenal weights of *gracilis* were significantly greater ($t = 9.82$, $p < .001$) than those of bairdii. A significant subspecies-treatment interaction ($F = 12.02$, $p < .001$) indicates that the treatment had a differential effect on both subspecies. A product-moment correlation of the adrenal weight and number of shocks was negative ($r = -0.21$) but not significant ($p > .10$). There was a significant difference between the body weights of the two subspecies ($F = 19.3$, $p < .001$).

DISCUSSION

The purpose of the tests was to investigate subspecific and treatment differences in emotional and physiological responses of *Peromyscus* to novel and stressful situations. We predicted that *bairdii* would be more emotional and prone to stress than *gracilis,* and that the control mice would be more emotional than the treated mice, and that each subspecies would react differently to the treatment.

The subspecific difference in the measures used here in addition to the observations of other investigators working with these mice (Foster, 1957; Horner, 1954) fail to present any consistent conceptual framework regarding wildness or emotionality. The inverse correlation between activity and emotionality observed in other rodents (Hunt and Otis, 1955; Weininger, 1956) would suggest that the low activity scores of *gracilis* were indications of their emotionality, wildness, or timidity. On the other hand, if learning performance is negatively associated with wildness and emotionality (Levine, 1956; Levine, Chevalier, and Korchin, 1956), then the poor learning performance of *bairdii* would indicate that they were more emotional than gracilis. Another inconsistency is suggested by adrenal size, which tends to increase with stress (Weininger, 1956) or wildness (Richter, 1952). The large adrenals of *gracilis* would then suggest that they were wilder or more emotional than *bairdii*. Many of these inconsistencies can be resolved by reassessing the behavioral and physiological measures in the tests. For example, if the activity alley measured a mouse's attempt to escape rather than its exploratory behavior, and the learning apparatus primarily measured the operant level of freezing or leaping to shock (Foster, 1957) rather than learning, it might be concluded that *bairdii* was consistently more wild and emotional than *gracilis*. Likewise, the size of the adrenals could be discounted as a measure of stress in intersubspecific comparisons. Any such re-evaluation of these measures, however, would at best provide an arbitrary assessment of the character of each subspecies. In general, we can only conclude that these two subspecies do respond differently to the situations provided in this experiment.

The effect of the treatment is less confusing than the subspecific differences insofar as each subspecies reacted differentially to the same treatment. In activity and in the number of shocks and responses, the treated groups of both subspecies were at opposite extremes of the distribution of the scores, while the control groups were between the treated groups (Fig. 3 and 4). In adrenal weight, *gracilis* showed more of an effect of the treatment than *bairdii*. The significant interaction in most of these measures indicates that the treatment did have a differential effect on each subspecies.

When these results are interpreted from the three theoretical viewpoints of Hebb (1949), Levine (1956), and Bernstein (1957) mentioned in the introduction, the differential effect of the treatment on both subspecies requires an explanation. Hebb's hypothesis that handling increases perceptual experiences can explain the results if each subspecies perceived differently or responded differently to the same perceptual cues. This explanation has some merit, since *bairdii* open their eyes at 12 days of age, whereas *gracilis* open their eyes at 17 days of age (King, 1958). The perceptual environment during much of the treatment was quite different for both subspecies as indicated by the opening of the eyes and correlated neurological development. Levine's hypothesis that handling enables an animal to adapt to stress (1956) could explain the results on the basis that the innate capacities of each subspecies determine their method of adaptation to handling; one subspecies adapts by becoming more emotional (*bairdii*) while the other becomes less emotional (*gracilis*). Bernstein's suggestion that handling establishes a reinforcing relationship between the experimenter and the subject (1957) also explains the results if the innate characteristics of both subspecies are considered. These innate characteristics of the subject may determine whether its relationship to the experimenter or handling apparatus is positively or negatively reinforcing. In general, each theory offers an explanation for the results providing it incorporates the differential effect handling may have upon animals with various genotypes.

SUMMARY

The hypothesis tested was that early handling has a differential effect on animals of different genetic backgrounds, producing a greater effect on animals either naturally or artificially selected for docility than on animals inherently wild and untamable.

Two subspecies of deermice, *Peromyscus maniculatus gracilis* and *P. m. bairdii*, were selected for their genetic differences in wildness and emotionality. Each subspecies was divided into experimental and control groups of 20 mice. The experimental groups were placed in a mechanical handling apparatus 10 min. each day from 3 to 25 days of age, when they were weaned and isolated. At a mean of 79 days of age, the mice were tested for activity and learning, and were subsequently examined for adrenal weight, eosinophil drop, and body weight. On the basis of behavioral observations of the two subspecies, we predicted that *gracilis* would be more affected by early handling than *bairdii*.

1. *Bairdii* were more active than *gracilis*, and the treated mice of both subspecies spent more time in the activity apparatus than control mice.

2. *Gracilis* performed better in the conditioning apparatus than *bairdii*, and treated *gracilis* performed better than their controls, while the treated *bairdii* performed less well than their controls.

3. There were no significant differences in percentage of eosinophil drop.

4. The adrenals of *gracilis* are proportionally larger than those of *bairdii*, and the control *gracilis* adrenals weighed more than the treated *gracilis*.

The results were interpreted on the basis of subspecific differences and the applicability of the tests for measuring emotionality. The theories of Hebb, Levine, and Bernstein can explain the results, if the genetic differences of the two subspecies are incorporated. In general, the hypothesis that genetic differences contribute to the effect of early handling was supported.

REFERENCES

BERNSTEIN, L. The effects of variations in handling upon learning and retention. *J. comp. physiol. Psychol.*, 1957, 50, 162–67.

CALHOUN, J. B. A technique for investigating the distance parameter of home range. *J. Mammal.*, 1955, 36, 45–52.

FOSTER, D. A. A comparison of the prairie and forest races of the deermouse, *Peromyscus maniculatus*, with respect to certain measures of the behavior and temperament. Unpublished doctoral dissertation, Univer. of Michigan, 1957.

HAMMETT, F. S. Studies of the thyroid apparatus. I. The significance of the comparative mortality rates of parathyroidectomized wild Norway rats and excitable and nonexcitable albino rats. *Endocrinology*, 1922, 6, 221–29.

HEBB, D. O. *Organization of behavior.* New York: Wiley, 1949.

HORNER, B. E. Arboreal adaptation of *Peromyscus*, with special reference to use of the tail. *Cont. Lab. Vert. Biol.*, 1954, 61, 1–85.

HUNT, H. F., and OTIS, L. S. Restricted experience and "timidity" in the rat. *Amer. Psychologist*, 1955, 10, 432. (Abstract)

KING, J. A. Maternal behavior and behavioral development in two subspecies of *Peromyscus maniculatus*. *J. Mammal.*, 1958, 39, 177–90.

LEVINE, S. A further study of infantile handling and adult avoidance learning. *J. Pers.*, 1956, 25, 70–80.

LEVINE, S., CHEVALIER, J. A., and KORCHIN, S. J. The effects of early shock and handling on later avoidance conditioning. *J. Pers.*, 1956, 24, 475–93.

McCLELLAND, W. J. Differential handling and weight gain in the albino rat. *Canad. J. Psychol.*, 1956, 10, 19–22.

MILLER, G. S., and KELLOGG, R. *List of North American recent mammals.* Washington: Smithsonian Inst., U.S. Nat. Mus. Bull. 205, 1955.

RICHTER, C. P. Domestication of the Norway rat and its implication for the study of genetics in man. *Amer. J. hum. Genet.*, 1952, 4, 273–85.

RUEGAMER, W. R., BERNSTEIN, L., and BENJAMIN, J. D. Growth, food utilization and thyroid activity in the albino rat as a function of extra handling. *Science*, 1954, 120, 184.

SIDMAN, M. Two temporal parameters of the maintenance of avoidance behavior by the white rat. *J. comp. physiol. Psychol.*, 1953, 46, 253–61.

SPIERS, R. S., and MEYER, R. K. The effects of stress, adrenal and adrenocotricotrophic hormones on the circulating eosinophils of mice. *Endocrinology*, 1949, 45, 403–29.

WEININGER, O. Physiological damage under emotional stress as a function of early experience. *Science*, 1954, 119, 285–86.

WEININGER, O. The effects of early experience on behavior and growth characteristics. *J. comp. physiol. Psychol.*, 1956, 49, 1–9.

WEININGER, O., McCLELLAND, W. J., and ARIMA, R. K. Gentling and weight gain in the albino rat. *Canad. J. Psychol.*, 1954, 8, 147–51.

CHAPTER 8

BEHAVIOR OF ANIMALS IN GROUPS

INTRODUCTION

Many species of animals are observed to operate in groups. The problem of the present chapter is to examine some approaches to, some classifications of, and some methods for the study of the behavior of animals in groups. The material will be restricted to instances of behaviors of groups of animals of the same species. The discussion of interspecies behavior which has received experimental attention is treated in other chapters.

Study of the behavior of animals in groups has been called study of social behavior, animal sociology, and biosociology. When the topic is cast in these terms it seems at first glance to be limited to a few species at the pinnacles of evolutionary development, namely, social insects, such as bees, and social vertebrates, such as primates. However, observation of species other than the so-called "social species" reveals that no animal can be considered as a completely solitary animal. All species are found in groups under some circumstances, although the groups may be short-lived and small in numbers. It is important to note that, in the context of the present chapter, the concept of group is used in a descriptive manner to refer to a variety of types of collections of organisms of the same species. Consideration of group as a theoretical concept, as it might be used in social psychology, is beyond the province of this text.

Approaches to the Analysis of Behavior of Animals in Groups

Analysis of the behavior of animals in groups can be considered along a number of dimensions. These include size of the groups, degree of cooperation among individuals in the groups, functions of the behaviors of the individuals in the groups and identification of the stimuli and responses associated with the behaviors of individuals in the groups. Several of these approaches will be examined.

The Group as the Analytic Unit. The analysis of the behavior of groups in terms of the size of the group is of principal concern to ecologists. Allee (1931) has used the size of the group as an important condition that is related to his general principle of *automatic co-operation.* He observed and explained the deleterious effects of *underpopulation* on both the species and the individuals within the species in terms of the effects of group size and the principle of automatic cooperation. Allee's analysis is used in the discussion of cooperative groups. While his approach is more psychological than the approach which emphasizes only the size of the group, neither focuses directly on the behavior of the individual within the group and thus will be of secondary concern in the present chapter.

The Functional Analysis. The analysis of the behavior of animals in groups in terms of the functions of the behavior has been put forward most clearly and emphatically by the ethologists. To establish the functions of a behavior, the ethologist asks a number of related questions: What does the animal do? What does the behavior do to other members of the species? How is the behavior related to the survival of the individual and the species? Classes of behavior functions are identified and then detailed study of behaviors within the class are undertaken. Thus, Tinbergen (1953) suggests the following classes: mating, care of the young, family and adult group behavior, and fighting behavior. Other classifications of functions have also been proposed. Scott (1956) using somewhat different labels identifies the following functional categories: sexual, care-giving, care-soliciting, contagious, and agonistic (fighting). Both of these classification systems can be considered to provide categories for description of behavior. An example of the use of functional categories for the study of social behavior of a species is seen in the study of the ant (Wallis, 1962*). The functional approaches emphasizes social groups as opposed to mere aggregations of individuals. By social grouping is meant the situation in which the behavior of one individual directly affects the behavior of another—social behavior, in the vocabulary of the ethologist. Typical examples of social behaviors are care of the young and fighting.

WALLIS, D. I. Behaviour patterns of the ant, *Formica fusca. Anim. Behav.,* 1962, **10,** 105–11.

The behavior patterns shown by worker ants in 20 different colonies were observed and classified. The colonies were kept in plaster nests that were divided into a darkened chamber (the nesting chamber) and an illuminated chamber (the foraging area). Among the behaviors involving other individuals were: examining, licking, fighting, threatening, seizing, dragging, escape, food-sharing, and food-accepting. Behaviors involving the brood in the nest were: feeding, licking, and carrying.

Since behaviors associated with mating and care-giving functions have been discussed in Chapter 5, the present chapter will be concerned primarily with social behaviors other than reproduction that are present in adult groups. An example is fighting. It should be noted, however, that the behavior involved in different functions are frequently interrelated. For example, fighting often precedes mating as in some species of deer (Darling, 1937), fish (Tinbergen, 1951), and birds (Lack, 1943). In addition, the same movements that are involved in one behavior function may be involved in another.

The Stimulus-Response Analysis. Identification of the stimuli and responses involved in the behaviors of animals in groups has been of concern to ethologists and other investigators of the behavior of animals. The stimuli in this case are the stimulus features of one animal to which other animals respond. For example, the growl of one dog may be a stimulus for the response of another dog; the posture of one bird may be a stimulus for the response of another bird. An example of this S–R approach was previously presented in connection with the study of begging responses in the young gull in which stimuli from the parent bird elicited their response. A considerable amount of research has been conducted following this approach (Collias, 1950), and many types of stimuli associated with the activity of one animal that serve as elicitors of responses in another have been identified. We will use a combination of the functional and S–R approaches for classification and description of behavior of animals in groups.

Methods of Study of Group Behavior. Field, laboratory, and combinations of field and laboratory methods have been used for the study of social behavior of animals. The field method has been used primarily to obtain general description of social behavior and is illustrated in the study by Davis (1959**) on the territorial ranking of starlings, and the study by Carpenter (1934*) on the social relations of the howler monkey. Because of the difficulties of identifying and controlling individual animals in the field, laboratory-field methods have been more commonly used for the study of the behavior of the individual animal. The laboratory method and the laboratory-field method allow both the identification of individuals and the experimental control of specific independent variables that may affect behavior. The studies by Ratner (1961**) with domestic fowl and Shaw (1960**) with fish illustrate the use of these methods.

CARPENTER, C. R. A field study of the behavior and social relations of howler monkeys. (*Alouatta palliata*). *Comp. Psychol. Monogr.*, 1934, **10**, #2, 168 pages.

Several subspecies of howler monkeys (*Alouatta palliata*) were observed for eight months in their natural surroundings in Central America. The animals moved in groups with the mature males leading. The groups varied in size from 4 to 35 individuals with the larger groups containing subgroups of several families. The females cared for the young who stayed with the females after another infant was born. However, the relationship between mother and young usually decreased after weaning. Female howlers were generally peaceful and cooperative. Males were generally indifferent toward the young, but the males responded to predators and dominated in the groups. Males in the same group behaved peacefully and cooperatively. At least nine different vocal signals and specific responses to these were identified.

Social Stimuli and Their Characteristics

The Social Stimulus. Stimuli associated with one organism that serve as social stimuli for the responses of another cover the entire range of sensory modalities. These modalities include auditory, visual, tactual, olfactory, and gustatory. As has been suggested in Chapter 3, animals' responses to each other are used as evidence for the receptor systems which characterize the species. For example, the differential coloration of males and females in a species suggests both that the display of the colors is a social stimulus and that the species has color vision. Similarly, the use of songs by one bird when in the territory of another suggests that members of the responding species have receptor systems appropriate for this class of stimulation. An example of such a relationship that has been incompletely investigated is the so-called singing of earthworms (Warden, Jenkins and Warner, 1941). The "singing" sounds have been recorded but neither the social function nor the appropriate receptor systems has been identified.

Some of the stimuli that serve as social stimuli for the animals in groups are beyond the sensory capacity of the human observer. This is particularly evident for species living in water, and for species in which olfactory and gustatory modalities are highly evolved. For example, the female butterfly, like the sexually receptive female dog, exudes an odor to which the male responds, even though the male may be at a great distance from the female. The presence and social functions of such chemical stimuli are now clearly established for the fire ant (Wilson, 1962*).

WILSON, E. O. Chemical communication among workers of the fire ant, *Solenopsis saevissima* (Fr. Smith). 3: The experimental induction of social responses. *Anim. Behav.*, 1962, **10**, 159–64.

Previous research had suggested that several chemical substances were associated with behavior of the worker fire ants toward others of the species.

This study systematically investigated the functions of these social signals, releasers of social responses. Each substance was associated with specific behavior patterns including attraction of workers, mass foraging, alarm, grooming, and emigration. The substances were obtained from structures in the bodies of ants and then presented under controlled conditions to the test animal.

Chains of Social Stimuli and Responses. Examination of the behavior of animals in groups indicates that the response of one animal to a social stimulus may become itself a social stimulus for the response of the first animal, and so forth through a long chain of stimuli and responses. A now classic example of such a chain is taken from Tinbergen's analysis (1951) of the courting pattern of the stickleback fish. In this example, the male's zigzag dance is the stimulus for the response of approach by the female, the stimulus of an approaching female results in the male's response of swimming away, the stimulus of the swimming male results in the response of swimming after the male, and so forth through a chain which culminates in the response of fertilization of the eggs by the male. Comparable chains are characteristic of the mating behavior of the majority of vertebrates and higher invertebrates. Chains are also typical of other behaviors which have a social function.

Fighting and Cooperation

The activities of the individual animal in adult groups will be discussed in terms of three behavioral categories that involve fighting and cooperation. These categories are: dominance hierarchies (often called peck orders), territoriality (defense of a particular area), and cooperative groups (herds and schools). Dominance hierarchies and territoriality are characterized by fighting, while cooperative groups are not. It should be made clear that the use of words such as fighting and cooperation is not meant to convey the impression that the animal "intends" to act in this or that way, or that it is willingly seeking fights or cooperation. Rather the use is a convenience to avoid coining new words and to provide a general idea of the characteristic form of the behaviors. For each of these categories the form of the responses made by the individuals and some of the variables affecting the behavior of the individual will be discussed.

Dominance Hierarchies. Animals which live in groups frequently have complex social relations with each other that are not based in a simple way on mating or territorality. Among these relationships are dominance relationships that are found among a great variety of species of invertebrates and vertebrates. Dominance relationships ramify into many sectors of the animals' lives. For example, the rank of an individual bird in a dominance hierarchy affects its priority for selecting and eating food, and priority for selecting and using resting places. The behaviors that establish and maintain the dominance hierarchies typically involve aggressive contacts between members of the group. For two birds, for example, the animals fight, peck, threaten, and push each other until one of the pair consistently defers or submits when in the presence of the other. Thus, a dominance hierarchy involving two animals is created. This process may be repeated for most of the possible pairs in the group with the result that an entire hierarchy of dominating and submitting relationships develops. One procedure for measuring hierarchies for birds is illustrated by Ratner (1961**) and another procedure often used with mammals is described by Miller and Murphy (1956*).

MILLER, R. E. AND MURPHY, J. V. Social interactions of rhesus monkeys: I. Food-getting dominance as a dependent variable. *J. Soc. Psychol.,* 1956, 44, 249–55.

Dominance relationships among a group of ten monkeys *(Macaca rhesus)* were observed and measured using two methods. All possible pairs of monkeys were tested in a box, a pair at a time, to determine which individual took a small pile of raisins. The entire group was also observed to determine the dominance order in the living cage. Both methods yielded stable and similar dominance orders, but the pair tests did not reveal that within the cage two suborders had formed. One involved the three most dominant animals and the other involved the remaining animals.

The hierarchy that evolves is frequently found to be a linear one. A linear hierarchy, stated most simply, is one in which one animal dominates all others and is called the *alpha* animal. The second animal, *beta,* dominates all but the alpha animal. The third animal, *gamma,* dominates all but alpha and beta and so forth to the bottom of the hierarchy at which point is found an animal that submits to all others and may die prematurely from lack of adequate food, water, or shelter. Linear hierarchies have been found among cattle. In this case the hierarchy is called a "hook order" (Schein and Fohrman, 1955*).

SCHEIN, M. W. AND FOHRMAN, M. H. Social dominance relationships in a herd of dairy cattle. *Brit. J. Anim. Behav.,* 1955, 3, 45–55.

A total of 165 female cattle *(Bos taurus)* were observed from 3 months of age through maturity as they lived in different herds. Aggressive behaviors and dominance relationships were found within the herds. Aggressive behaviors involved active approaches, threats by lowering the head or pawing the ground, and hooking or pushing. A linear dominance or "hook order" was found. Significant positive correlations were found comparing status in the hook order with age and weight of the cattle. A strange cow was ignored if put into a large herd but was fought against if put with one other animal.

Under some conditions other hierarchical arrangements are found. The triangular or circular hierarchy may be considered as one in which the linear order is short-circuited. That is, the gamma animal, for example, may dominate the alpha animal, although gamma is clearly dominated by beta, and beta is clearly dominated by alpha. It should be noted that reports of triangular relationships may be based on inaccurate observation, short-term instability in the dominance hierarchy, or the fact that a linear dominance hierarchy simply is not yet clearly established for the group of animals being studied.

Variables Affecting Behavior of Animals in Hierarchies. A number of variables have been identified which affect the behavior and the status of the individual animal in the dominance hierarchy. These variables are: hormonal factors, the external stimulus situation, prior experience in dominance hierarchies, competing responses associated with other stimuli, individual differences, and gradual changes in responsiveness of the individual.

The hormonal factor most noticably associated with fighting and dominating is the male gonadal hormone, testosterone. Injection of testosterone into hens (Allee, *et al.*, 1939*) has been found to enhance the status of the hen in the dominance hierarchy, while castration of males has been found to lead to eventual loss of status in the hierarchy. Hinde (1960) has pointed out the rather remarkable comparative fact that the same substance, testosterone, similarly affects mammals, birds, and fish. Additional discussion and references regarding the relation of hormones to behavior is presented in Chapter 6.

ALLEE, W. C., COLLIAS, N. AND LUTHERMAN, C. Z. Modification of the social order among flocks of hens by injection of testosterone propionate. *Physiol. Zool.*, 1939, 12, 412–20.
        The effect of the male hormone testosterone propionate, was studied in four groups of female domestic fowl. Control birds received injections of oil. Hens that were low in the peck order and received the hormone became more aggressive and raised their status in the peck order. They held their elevated positions after the effects of the hormone had vanished. Young birds, pullets, did not change their status in the peck order but they became more aggressive in fights with strangers. Control birds were not affected.

NOBLE, G. K. AND BORNE, N. The effect of sex hormones on the social hierarchy of *Xiphorphorus helleri. Anat. Rec.*, 1940, 78, supp. 147.
        Male hormone, testosterone, was given by injection to one group of female swordtail fish (*Xiphorphorus helleri*) and by insertion of pellets into another group. Control groups did not receive hormones. Those fish that received hormones rose in their dominance hierarchies. The changes in social status were accompanied by changes in sexual characteristics from femaleness to maleness.

The *external stimulus situation,* as it affects dominance hierarchies can be divided into *salient stimulus* effects and general *environmental stimulus* effects. Controlled observation of animals in groups indicates the salient stimulus for an animal's response in a group is the specific animal to which it is responding. In other words, dominating or submitting behaviors are controlled to a large extent by the stimulus of the other animals in the group. Roosters, for example, do not ordinarily dominate hens but are indifferent to them. As suggested in the study by James (1956*), dogs of different breeds are selective in their dominance reactions to each other, a beagle is consistently submissive to terriers, but not to other beagles. Consistent differences in dominating behaviors are also found for species of fish (Kuo, 1960*).

JAMES, W. T.   Social organization among dogs of different temperaments, Terriers and Beagles reared together. *J. comp. physiol. Psychol.,* 1951, 44, 71–77.

Beagles and terrier pups were raised together and were then tested for dominance, breed preference, and mate selection. Terriers were consistently dominant over beagles as measured in a food competition situation; they preferred beagles and only terriers sired the females of both breeds. Beagles preferred other beagles and showed little or no dominating of other beagles, although they were submissive to the terriers.

KUO, ZING YANG.   Studies on the basic factors in animal fighting: V. Interspecies coexistence in fish. *J. Genet. Psychol.,* 1960, 97, 181–94.

The characteristics of the dominance relationships within and between seven species of fish were studied by observing the fish under controlled aquarium conditions. Several species, including gold fish and angel fish, did not establish dominance relations within the species or between species. Species of fighting fish, such as the Chinese fighting fish, Siamese fighting fish, and Red Swordtails quickly established dominance hierarchies within and between species. Isolation from the time of hatching until maturity did not inhibit fighting or subsequent dominance relations when the previously isolated fighting fish were assembled.

The effects of the salient stimulus on dominating and submitting behavior arise from both the innate and the learned properties of the stimulus. The innate eliciting properties of postures, displays, and vocalizations are known from the study of innate behavior of invertebrates and vertebrates (see Chapters 4 and 5). Frequently, the innate properties of a social stimulus elicit *competing responses,* such as fighting and mating. Thus, a rooster's reaction to the movements of a hen may be a mixture of mating and dominating responses with mating responses predominating. Responses that compete with dominating would also occur if a predator came among the social group.

Several lines of evidence indicate the importance of the variable of learning on responses of animals to the salient stimulus. The study by

Ratner (1960**) shows that learning to be submissive with one bird generalizes to other birds, and similar processes have been shown with mice. Mice become dominant or submissive when confronted by another mouse depending on the outcome of their prior fights. Along another line, Guhl (1953) has demonstrated that birds remember each other and respond in the previously established dominating or submissive ways even after long periods of separation. The fact that the animals recognize each other and respond in their previously learned ways leads to the relative stability that is found in the dominance hierarchies.

The effect of *general environmental stimuli* on dominating behavior is most clearly seen in cases in which one animal has had prior residence in an area or has established its territory in an area. In these cases the resident has a high probability of dominating others that enter its area. This process has been shown clearly with fish (Braddock, 1949*). The interesting thing about the effect of general environmental stimuli is that animal A may dominate B when in A's territory, but A may be dominated by B when in B's territory.

The variable of *individual differences* is operative in dominance hierarchies as in all other behaviors (Hinde, 1959). For example, equal doses of hormone do not have identical effects on all animals or do any of the other variables which have been identified have identical effects on all animals within the species. In addition, *gradual change in responsiveness* to other animals occurs as an animal grows from infancy to maturity (Bouvbjerg, 1956*; Nice, 1937; Ratner, 1961). Superimposed on the gradual changes from aging are gradual and cyclical changes associated with such conditions as hunger, mating, and migratory processes. For example, dominance relationships among chimpanzees have been reversed as a function of food deprivation (Nowliss, 1941*).

NOWLISS, V.   The relation of degree of hunger to competition interactions in champanzees. *J. Comp. Psychol.*, 1941, 32, 91–115.
   Pairs of chimpanzees were tested in a food-getting situation to determine which member of each pair was dominant and which was submissive. Dominance was judged in terms of which animal got the food. The submissive animal moved away from the food following attack, threat, or "vocal protest" of the dominant member. Then, in a series of experiments, the effects of prior feeding on dominance was measured. Three levels of prior feeding were used: 54 hours of deprivation, normal feeding, and satiation. Deprived submissive animals always got food from satiated dominant animals, but this reversed as soon as the dominant animals were deprived of food or were normally fed.

BOUVBJERG, R. V.   Some factors affecting aggressive behavior in crayfish. *Physiol. Zool.*, 1956, 29, 127–36.
   Crayfish (*Procambarus alleni Faxon*) were collected in Florida and cul-

tured in tanks in the laboratory for research purposes. This procedure provided supplies of males and females of different ages and sizes that had similar environments prior to the present experiment. The present experiment investigated the effects of age, size, sex, and presence of sensory receptors on fighting. The fighting of crayfish, like that of domestic fowl, involves threatening postures, strikes (like pecks), and fights. One animal may retreat from the one showing these responses or may respond with similar responses. The effects of the variables (age, etc.) were studied by observing the development of dominance hierarchies among small groups of animals. The size of the animals was directly related to occurrences and outcomes of fighting for both males and females. The larger the animal the more aggressive it was. In mixed sex groups the males dominated the females. Juvenile crayfish also showed fighting when only one quarter the size of adults but adults dominated them. Elimination of either visual stimuli or tactile stimuli by covering the eyes or clipping the antennae did not stop fighting but elimination of both classes of stimuli did. Some of these animals made fighting movements but others did not respond to them.

Territoriality. Studies of the fighting of an individual animal have indicated that this behavior often occurs in a particular area. Such fighting in defense of a particular area is called *territorial behavior* and represents a type of social organization among animals. The dominance hierarchy represents the case in which a large number of animals share an area, whereas territoriality represents the case in which animals subdivide an area into individual portions which the owner defends. Some species show territorial behavior during mating season and dominance hierarchies during the time when they live together in larger groups. However, it seems that territoriality is characteristic of more species than are dominance hierarchies. Territoriality is shown by deer, fish, beetles, birds, dogs, and mollusks.

Types of Territorial Behavior. Territorial behavior takes two rather distinct forms in terms of the area being defended. For some species defense occurs around a particular object regardless of the specific location of the object; for others, it occurs within a fixed geographic area. The defense of an object, *object oriented territory,* is most clear in cases when the object moves or can be moved. This is the case with a female who has been paired with a male. It has been found that the buck deer fights most frequently and most vigorously in the vicinity of the doe. A comparable finding has been made with male bitterling fish that defend the area around a mussel into which the female bitterling will deposit her eggs (Tinbergen, 1953, p. 60). If the mussel moves or is moved, the bitterling changes its defense to a new area where the mussel is located. Unlike the mussel as an object for defense, the nest or nesting areas used by many animals are relatively fixed in space. In these cases, *geographical territory,* the nest becomes the center of the area that comprises the territory. The study of the territorial behavior of starlings (Davis, 1959**) illustrates details of the behaviors of these birds in establishing territories. The generality of territorality is evident for the studies of ants (Headley, 1941), bees (Free, 1958*), geese (Jenkins, 1943*), and monkeys (Carpenter, 1943*).

FREE, J. B.   The defense of bumblebee colonies. *Behav.,* 1958, 12, 233–42.

    The methods for defending the hive and some of the variables affecting these behaviors were studied with six species of bees including *Bombus agrorum, Bombus terrestris,* and *Bombus lucorum.* Aliens were attacked at a strange hive or investigated by manipulations with the antennae. The scent of the strange hive on the alien was the stimulus eliciting attack. Large colonies were found to have "guard bees" just inside the hive entrance. The aggressive guards had larger ovaries than the workers in the hive. The fighting between queens was thought to arise from their highly developed ovaries.

JENKINS, D. W.   Territory as a result of despotism and social organization in geese. *Auk,* 1944, 61, 30–47.

    Three species of geese that were living in one area were systematically observed during an eight-month period. Peck rights and peck orders developed between the species and within the species but not within the family groups. The Blue Goose was dominant over the Lesser Snow and Canadian Goose. The dominating relationships were organized around territories. Different types of territories were found: *family territory* and *mated female territory* involved defense in the presence of the family or the mated female, whereas *nesting territory* was found only around the area of the nest.

Behavior in the Territory.   Various behaviors are shown by animals within their territories. One class involves the defense of the territory from encroachment of other members of the species. The defensive behaviors include ritualized threats, threatening advances, and fights. Specialized body structures and/or postures are frequently used by the defending animal in the threats that it makes. The male fence lizard, for example, displays a blue belly as a threat, and many birds posture to expose brightly colored feathers.

    Another class of behaviors involves the animal's signaling its presence in its territory or the boundries of its territory. For example, many mammals use scents either from special scent glands or from their urine or feces to signal the boundries of their territory. Other vertebrates signal by special vocalization, such as the song of male birds and the croaking of male frogs. Frequently, these signals function both as threats to other males of the species and as inducements to unattached females of the species.

    Animals of a number of species establish and maintain territories for a relatively long period of time. The primary factor that seems to operate in the establishment of a territory is *prior residence*. This factor operates in several ways. It is associated with an increased chance of winning in a fight when the animal is in its territory and it is associated with an increased chance of reclaiming the territory for those individuals that come into the area on some periodic schedules, such as is true of the migrating birds. Study of the song sparrow, for example, indicated that some males were never defeated in fights on their own territory and such individuals returned to the same territories for a number of years (Nice, 1943).

BRADDOCK, J. C. The effect of residence on the dominance in fish, *Platypoecilus maculatus. Physiol. Zool.,* 1949, **22**, 151–69.

Each of 80 males was maintained in isolation for two days and each was then put into an aquarium with another male that had been living there. In half of the cases the "resident" male was considerably larger than the "intruder" and in half it was smaller. The larger residents were dominant in almost all cases but even the smaller residents were dominant in some cases. That is, prior residence overcame the size factor to some degree. Comparable results were found with females of the same species.

Cooperative Groups

Several students in animal behavior have emphasized the generality and importance of cooperative behavior among animals (Allee, 1931; Scott, 1958; Tinbergen, 1953). As previously stated, the term cooperative behavior is not intended to refer to intentional cooperation, but is used to be descriptive of the interactions of groups of adult animals, parent and young, and males and females of the same species.

Groups of Animals. Most vertebrates and invertebrates function in groups at some time in their life cycles. Although the study of these behaviors has typically emphasized ecological and other biological factors, some research has focused on the more psychological aspects of the event, such as the behavior of the individual in the group and the identification of variables associated with bringing the individual into the group.

KEENLEYSIDE, M. H. Some aspects of the schooling behavior of fish. *Behav.,* 1955, **8**, 183–248.

Blinded and normal individuals of six species of fish were tested on factors related to schooling. Using olfactory cues, blinded individuals stayed near their own species but did not join the schools. Normal individuals joined larger schools and schools of their species. Food deprivation led to dispersal of schools, while threatening stimuli led to aggregating for one species. Readiness for reproduction led males to leave the schools and establish territories.

From the studies by Shaw (1960**) and Keenleyside (1955*) it appears that the schooling of fish can be considered as innate behavior that occurs in response to visual or chemical stimuli associated with the members of the species or, if members of the same species are not present, with members of related species. In addition, the collection of individual animals into groups is generally considered to be more than a case of mere proximity among individuals. When individuals collect into groups a number of consequences can follow: (*a*) it facilitates finding and using large supplies of food, such as is true among bees; (*b*) it functions for the detection and defense against enemies (bees, geese, and antelope, for example, use sentinels when other individuals are feeding); (*c*) it enhances survival of the individual when the group is under severe environmental conditions. For example, Allee reports (1951, Chapter 4) that fish and worms survive larger doses of poison per individual when in a group than when isolated.

The consequences of group living can also be negative or at least quite complicated. Calhoun (1963) studied the wild Norway rat in its natural (backyard and alley) habitat. He found that hoarding (storing food) is discouraged in a group situation because the animal that stores food is attacked or punished. Groups or "gangs" of nondominant rats acted together like social outcasts and their behavior was deleterious to any female in the area. These females had small and poor litters whose condition was attributed to the stress of excessive mating. Calhoun (1962) has also found deterioration of group behaviors including mating, care of the young, and nest building among laboratory rats that became overcrowded in a small portion of their living space. Calhoun interpreted these data in terms of learning and frustration (blocking) of learned responses. Specifically, he hypothesized that the rats became social feeders which led them to eat frequently but only for very brief periods. That is, because of the presence of a central food supply each rat ate whenever another rat was observed to be eating. This interfered with the completion of other ongoing behaviors such as nesting, mating, and care of the young. Calhoun called this abnormal social situation a "behavioral sink." These data suggest some of the complexities of behavior of animals in groups in terms of the variables affecting it and its changing form.

Parent–Young Relations and Male–Female Relations. For many animals cooperation or close interaction between members of the same species reaches a high point in parent–young relations and in male–female relations. Details of the responses of the individuals in these interactions have been discussed in earlier chapters, Chapters 4 and 5. However, the cooperative aspects of the interactions were not considered.

It will be remembered that parent–young relations and male–female relations involve elaborate chains of mutual stimulations and responses. In the case of birds for example, the young call, the parent bird brings food to the nest, the young open their mouths, the parent bird stuffs food into the mouths, and the young become quiet, the parent flies away, and so forth. Some of these vocalizations of chicks of domestic fowl are described by Collias (1952*). Tinbergen's caution about the interpretation of such interactions as more than mechanical cooperation is appropriate. He notes that: "Although the chick's father and mother will furiously defend it as long as it is alive, they will devour it as soon as it is dead. They no longer hear the chick's calls, they do not see its movements, and that is sufficient to make it lose all significance as a chick and to become food" (Tinbergen, 1953, p. 74).

Collias, N. The development of social behavior in birds. *Auk,* 1952, 127–59.
    A general review of other research dealing with the development of social behavior of birds was first presented. Then the development of vocalization of chicks of domestic fowl was described. Two types of vocalizations were identified. They are "distress calls" and "pleasure calls." Being isolated, environmental temperature and contact with an object were found to affect the frequency of distress calls. In addition, responses to these factors were found to change as the chicks matured. For example, response to isolation had almost disappeared by the time the chick was five weeks of age.

The cooperative behavior of parent and young primates has recently received attention in terms of the concept of *affectional* behavior (Harlow, 1958). In these studies the responses of young monkeys have been investigated to determine the specific aspects of the parent that are related to the development of affectional behavior in the young and to determine the conditions under which the young show such behavior. Some of the characteristics of the parent or parent surrogate that are associated with the development of affectional behavior are as follows: texture of the body, size of the body, and the time in the life of the infant when the parent object is presented. Thus, as suggested in Chapter 7, affectional behavior of primates can be interpreted, at least in part, as an instance of imprinting. Several predictions about other behaviors follow from considering the development of affectional behavior of monkeys as an instance of imprinting. For example, it would be expected that the young monkey would approach the imprinted object when frightened and would direct sexual behavior toward the object. Harlow (1962) has reported some evidence that these consequences occur for his monkeys.

Social Groups and Learning. The effect of the presence of other members of the species on learning of an individual has also been

studied. Allee (1951, Chapter 7) summarizes a number of studies dealing with fish, birds, and cockroaches in which each species learned
mazes in groups and as individuals. When the learning scores of the
groups were compared with the scores of the individual animal,
neither facilitation nor inhibition of learning was consistently found.
Allee reports that individual cockroaches made fewer errors than
groups of cockroaches, individual parakeets learned as well as pairs
of parakeets, but individual goldfish learned more slowly than groups
of goldfish.

Crawford's review (1939) of the early experiments dealing with this
same problem also indicates an absence of consistent results. While
Crawford reports that the behavior of the individual in the learning
situation was affected by the presence of others, this did not lead to
consistent effects on the learning curves. One of the effects is on consummatory behavior. One animal will eat more readily if another is
eating. As will be discussed in Chapter 9, the presence of other members of the species facilitates consummatory behavior, particularly for
vertebrates. This fact is used in the early stages of some learning experiments to get animals to take reward. The procedure for training
one animal with another in the goal box is described by Denny
(1959**) in Chapter 11.

Theories of Social Behavior

The most detailed statement and classification of social behavior of
animals has been presented by Tinbergen (1953). He analyzes social
behavior, both fighting and cooperation, in terms of innate releaser
mechanisms, social signals, and innate response patterns. Although
Tinbergen acknowledges that some relationships between stimuli
and responses are learned, he does not develop the implications of this
idea. The outline of a theory of social behavior is suggested by Allee
who proposes that: "A general principle of automatic co-operation is
one of the fundamental biological principles" (Allee, 1951, p. 30).
Allee examines many instances of the operation of such a principle
and sketches the evolutionary development of the principle but does
not indicate the mechanisms by which the behavior of the individual
in a group is controlled.

A theory of social behavior is implicit in the work of psychologists
who suggest that social behavior, especially cooperative group behavior, is learned (Miller and Dollard, 1941). Such formulations suggest that organisms may learn care of the young, mating responses, and
fighting through imitation and reward. Since the execution of some

of these responses may have reward value, it is suggested that they are first performed by imitation and then learned through the occurrence of reward associated with making the response. However, the learning interpretation of social behavior does not seem adequate to handle many of the details of social behaviors, for example, the ritualized behavior of the young, the similarities in the behavior patterns across a species, and the occurrences of some of the elaborate social behaviors for individuals that have been raised in isolation. At the present time these behaviors seem best described in terms of innate behavior and its modification through learning.

EFFECT OF LEARNING TO BE SUBMISSIVE ON STATUS
IN THE PECK ORDER OF DOMESTIC FOWL

By STANLEY C. RATNER

*Department of Psychology, Michigan State University,
East Lansing*

A number of the variables which are related to dominance-submissive relationships among domestic fowl are summarized by Wood-Gush (1955) and Guhl (1953). As they have noted, the variable of past fighting experience has received some experimental attention. Collias (1943), studying predictors of success and failure in encounters between pairs of birds, found that a bird's prior success or failure was one predictor of its subsequent success or failure. More recently Douglis (1948) reported observations of hens which lived part-time in a number of different groups. From these studies she concluded, "The role of conditioning (in terms of learning to dominate or submit) in these experiments is difficult to ascertain" (p. 176). She based this conclusion on the finding that some birds consistently held similar ranks from group to group but others held widely different ranks. A study which was explicitly designed to investigate the role of prior conditioning experience on ranks of domestic fowl, was conducted by Smith and Hale (1959). They found that a bird's rank in a small group could be radically modified as a result of avoidance conditioning experiences in which one bird became the conditioned stimulus for avoidance reactions of others in the group.

While these studies suggest the importance of prior dominating or submitting experiences on peck order relationships, they do not provide a clear answer to the question of the effects of a bird's prior experiences with an opponent on its rank in a peck order which does not involve that opponent. The present study was designed to investigate this question. The study was designed with each experimental bird serving as its own control. That is, the rank of the bird in the peck order was determined and then redetermined after encounters with a despot. This design was adopted in view of the stability of peck orders which is found to occur with mature domestic fowl (Guhl, 1953).

MATERIALS AND METHODS

Four groups of mature White Leghorn chickens were used. Each group contained 14 birds which were maintained in indoor pens at the poultry laboratory of Michigan State University. The pens which housed each group were $8 \times 9 \times 14$ feet. Each had dirt and sawdust floors and an automatic feeder which extended the length of the pen. Pens were also provided with raised roosts, nesting boxes, water and grit. The pens were situated in a larger building which contained many other such pens.

The encounters between each experimental bird and the despot took place in a wire cage $24 \times 24 \times 27$ inches, which was located in a storage room across a hall from the living pens. A wire cage, similar to the one in which the encounters took place, served as a holding cage for the experimental birds during brief rest periods between encounters.

The study can be considered to have involved three phases: (*a*) determination of the original peck order, (*b*) encounters between experimental birds and the despot, (*c*) redetermination of the peck order. The three phases were then repeated with the same groups using different experimental birds.

The original peck order was determined in each of the four groups based on notations of fights, pecks, threats, and avoidance responses recorded during twenty 15-minute observations of each pen. A total of 1083 encounters were noted. The data were collected between March 1st and April 15th. Criteria used for defining the responses were the same as those used in a previous study (Ratner and Denburg, 1959). At the conclusion of the twenty observations, the peck order was determined for each pen. The rank of a bird in the peck order was evaluated according to criteria which are described in detail by Allee and Foreman (1955). Linear peck orders were assumed in assigning the ranks of the birds.

Following the determination of the original peck order, one experimental bird was selected from each pen for a series of ten encounters with a despotic hen which had been selected from another group. The experimental birds were selected from intermediate positions in the original peck orders so that either increases or decreases in ranks could occur. The original ranks of the first set of four experimental birds were: 8th, 7th, 5th and 3rd. Each of these birds was placed in the cage with the despot for two 5-minute sessions every other day for five days. The despot was in the cage prior to the entry of the experimental bird and food was scattered on the floor of the cage. After placing the experimental bird in the cage, the experimenter noted the behaviours of the two birds during the two 5-minute encounters and removed the experimental bird to the holding cage for a 2-minute rest between the two daily encounters. The order of placing the experimental birds with the despot was varied from day to day.

During the 10-day period when the encounters were taking place, the peck order was redetermined for each pen to evaluate the effects of the encounters on the status of the experimental birds. Ten 15-minute observations were made at each pen for the redetermination of the peck order. The smaller number of observations was used because the original observations provided sufficient data to know the general structure of the order in each pen.

The four groups were allowed to rest for a week to insure the stability of the peck orders and then one more experimental bird was selected from each of the four pens. The ranks of these birds were: 1st, 4th, 3rd and 4th. These birds were selected to provide evidence about the effects of the encounters on higher ranking members of the peck orders. Each of the experimental birds was treated as described for the first set. Each had ten 5-minute encounters with the despot which had previously been used and the peck orders of the four pens were redetermined during the 10-day period when the encounters took place.

Following the main investigation, the despot and several of the experimental birds were given Triflorperazine, a commercial tranquilizer, to determine if the intensity of the encounters would be affected by this activity-reducing drug (Ratner and Ringer, 1959). The drug was administered orally with a pipette. The mixture was prepared with 50 mg. of drug per 1 c.c. of water, and this was given at the dose level of 1 c.c. of mixture per 1,000 g. of body weight. Dose level was based on work by Ringer (in press). Encounters between the treated birds took place 2 to 2½ hours after the mixture was administered.

RESULTS

The main results of the effects of encounters with the despot are summarized in Table I, which shows the original ranks, new ranks, and changes in rank for each of the experimental birds. Data in the

TABLE I

ORIGINAL RANK, NEW RANK AND AMOUNT OF CHANGE
IN RANK IN THE PECK ORDER FOR EACH EXPERIMENTAL BIRD

Bird and Pen	Original Rank	New Rank	*Change in Rank
R2 (100)	6	8	−2
Y2 (99)	7	9	−2
B2 (98)	5	8	−3
O (96)	3	1	+2
B4 (100)	1	2	−1
R1 (99)	4	7	−3
B− (98)	3	10	−7
R1 (96)	4	6	−2

* Reductions in rank in the peck order are indicated by — and increases by +.

fourth column, which shows the change in rank of each experimental bird, indicates that the encounters with the despot led to a reduction in rank in the peck order for seven of the eight birds. The least reduction occurred for B4 (Pen 100) which moved from the top to the second place in the peck order. The greatest reduction occurred for B— (Pen 98) which moved from third to tenth place. The other experimental birds moved intermediate degrees. It will be noted that one bird, O, (Pen 96), rose in rank to the top position in the peck order from the third position. The changes principally involved a simple shifting in rank for the experimental birds in the pen. It was also observed that six of the seven birds, which were reduced in rank, pecked and threatened fewer birds than they had in the original determination of the peck order, and the seventh bird pecked and threatened the same number.

Analyses of the behaviours during the encounters with the despot showed that the despot strongly dominated each of the experimental birds. That is, with the exception of the relationship between O, (Pen 96) and the despot, all experimental birds received at least ten pecks from the despot per day. During the remaining minutes of the encounter, the experimental birds remained immobile in submissive posture while the despot scratched and ate the food on the floor of the cage.

The two experimental birds, O (Pen 96) and B— (Pen 98), which showed unusual changes in rank in the redeterminations of the peck orders, also had unusual relationships with the despot. Bird O (Pen 96), the bird which rose in the peck order, was the only experimental bird which was not completely submissive to the despot. Although it was pecked and threatened three or four times each session and it never pecked or threatened the despot, it did move about the cage and eat while the despot ate. Bird B— (Pen 98) showed the greatest reduction in rank. This bird received at least 20 pecks per 5-minute session and was judged to be the most severely treated. The treatment of the other experimental birds by the despot could not be quantitatively or qualitatively related to the changes in rank due to the limited variations in treatment and rank which were observed. The behaviour of the despot was quite stereotyped. The pattern of attacks, threats, and eating did not weaken during successive encounters with each bird.

Treatment with the tranquilizer Triflorperazine was undertaken to determine if the drug would alter the behaviour of the despot and/or submissive birds. The results of encounters between the despot and two experimental birds which were drugged, indicated that the aggressive and submissive behaviours were very similar to those observed during regular encounters. The despot pecked and threatened the drugged birds as frequently as it had previously. The visible effect of the drug was to give the birds a "sleepy appearance."

Results of encounters between previously used experimental birds and the drugged despot yielded findings similar to those above. The despot was sluggish in its responses but it pecked and threatened with great frequency and, in addition, quickly dominated two first-ranking birds with which it had had no prior experience.

DISCUSSION

The results of encounters between experimental birds and a despot in a situation different from the home pen indicated that the experiences affected status in the peck order. Specifically, the encounters were associated with a reduction in rank in the peck order for seven of the eight birds and an increase in rank for one of the birds.

These findings can be interpreted in terms of the concept of conditioning of submissive reactions to the despot which generalized to the birds in the home pens. That is, the encounters can be considered as conditioning trials in which the movements of the despot (conditioned stimuli) were repeatedly associated with vigorous pecks (unconditioned stimuli) which led to submissive and avoiding responses (unconditioned responses), on the part of experimental birds. The finding that the experimental birds spent much of the time during encounters in submissive postures and avoiding the despot even when not being pecked supports this interpretation. The study by Smith and Hale (1959) reports that as few as ten presentations of electric shock (unconditioned stimulus) were required to condition a chicken to avoid another for two to nine weeks. The present study, while not using shock, involved many presentations of the unconditioned stimulus of pecking for each experimental bird. Generalization of a conditioned response to stimuli similar to the original conditioned stimulus is commonly found. Thus, the reductions in rank in the peck orders involving the experimental birds are interpreted in terms of generalization of submissive reactions to those birds in the home pens which approached or threatened the experimental birds.

This interpretation suggests that the experimental birds should have dropped to the bottom of their respective peck orders, which did not occur. That is, they continued to peck and dominate some birds in their pens. However, these birds had had long histories in their pens and there is no reason to think that conditioning of submissive and avoidance responses should obliterate previously learned aggressive responses. Also the very low ranking birds which did not "know what the experimenters had done to the experimental birds" continued to make their previously conditioned avoidance responses to the experimental birds. The birds which were instrumental in reducing the status of the experimental birds were principally those close to them in rank.

The extreme change in rank shown by the bird B—, which dropped seven places in the peck order, can be interpreted as a result of the extreme degree of conditioning of submissive and avoidance responses which occurred for it. The increase in rank shown by one bird (O) cannot be readily interpreted with the present concepts. The bird was dominated by the despot but was not pecked and beaten as the others were. One interpretation of the added vigour of the bird's responses in the home pen is in terms of the occurrence of conflict between fighting and submitting during the encounters which was resolved in the home pen into increased fighting.

The results of moderate doses of tranquilizer on the behaviour of the despot and other birds indicated that the drug did not alter the direction nor the degree of encounters between the pairs of birds.

SUMMARY

The present study was designed to investigate the effects on rank in the peck order of encounters between experimental birds, which were taken from intact peck orders, and a despotic bird not involved in the peck orders. Four groups with 14 birds in a group were observed to determine the peck orders. A total of eight experimental birds was selected from these groups and each had a number of encounters with a despotic bird which was not a member of any of the groups. The peck orders were then redetermined to evaluate the effects of the encounters on the ranks of the experimental birds. Seven of the eight birds showed reductions in rank after the encounters, and the eighth showed an increase. The characteristics of the encounters were related to the changes in ranks of several of the experimental birds. Tranquilizers were found to have little effect on the behaviour of the despot or the experimental birds. The effects of the encounters are interpreted in terms of conditioning of submissive and avoidance responses which generalized to the home pens.

ACKNOWLEDGMENTS

The research was facilitated by a grant from Michigan State University, and tranquilizer, known commercially as Stelazine, was supplied by Smith, Kline and French Laboratories. Mr. K. R. Miller assisted in the collection of data and Dr. R. K. Ringer advised on the dose levels of tranquilizer.

REFERENCES

ALLEE, W. C. AND FOREMAN, D. (1955). Effect of an androgen on dominance and subordinance in six common breeds of *Gallus Gallus*. *Physiol. Zool.*, **28**, 89–115.

COLLIAS, N. E. (1943). Statistical analysis of factors which make for success in initial encounters between hens. *Amer. Nat.*, **77**, 519–38.

DOUGLIS, M. B. (1948). Social factors influencing the hierarchies of small flocks of the domestic hen: Interactors between resident and part-time members of organized flocks. *Physiol. Zool.*, **21**, 147–82.

GUHL, A. M. (1953). Social behaviour of the domestic fowl. *Tech. Bull. 73, Agric. exp. Sta., Kansas State College.*

RATNER, S. C. AND DENBURG, M. L. (1959). The effects of age on the social organizations of chickens. *Quart. Bull. Mich. Agric. exp. Sta., Michigan State University*, **41**, 544–49.

RATNER, S. C. AND RINGER, R. K. (1959). An activity cage and recorder for domestic fowl. *Anim. Behav.*, **7**, 245–47.

RINGER, R. K. (In press). Some physiological responses to tranquilizers. *Poult. Sci.*

SMITH, W. AND HALE, E. B. (1959). Modification of social rank in the domestic fowl. *J. comp. physiol. Psychol.*, **52**, 373–75.

WOOD-GUSH, D. G. M. (1955). The behaviour of the domestic chicken: A review of the literature. *Brit. J. anim. Behav.*, **3**, 81–110.

TERRITORIAL RANK IN STARLINGS

DAVID E. DAVIS

Johns Hopkins School of Hygiene and Public Health,
Baltimore, Maryland

Although the problems of territorialism and of social rank have been observed and discussed for many years, the relation of the two behaviour phenomena to each other is by no means clear. In some taxonomic groups territorial behaviour occurs while in other groups social rank behaviour occurs. The occurrence of both types of behaviour has been reported for captive doves (Bennett, 1942), some fish (Fabricius, 1954) and mice (Crowcroft, 1955; Davis, 1958). The research here reported describes the relation of territory to rank in wild and captive starlings (*Sturnus vulgaris*). In addition some other aspects of behaviour are mentioned.

The behavioural studies have been conducted for several years in Baltimore, Maryland, where large numbers of starlings breed. The local, nonmigratory birds are augmented in winter by migrants from the north. The birds nest in natural cavities and readily occupy nest boxes, which can be placed in locations suitable for research. The conventional procedures for observation with binoculars were used. The observations were described on a tape in the field and then transcribed and summarized. The observations of captive birds were made in a room about 12 ft. $\times$ 14 ft. that contained various numbers of males and females. Food (canned dog food mixed with chicken mash) and water were available at one place. The birds were watched through a one-way mirror and reported on a tape recorder.

These conventional methods have some deficiencies. The first is the chronic problem that many hours are required and therefore only a few individuals may be observed. Some 600 hours were spent in observation of three boxes from October to June, 1956–58 in addition to miscellaneous observations in other years. Unfortunately this paper, like most behaviour papers, has only limited generality because so few individuals can be observed.

The other deficiency is that few wild starlings were individually

445

marked. Unfortunately both male and female starlings destroy the eggs if captured on the nest either in day or night. The male may maintain possession of the box but the females desert. Marking is further prevented by our inability to catch local birds in traps or nets except occasionally when snow covers the ground (migrants are readily trapped). From October, 1957, to May, 1958, birds that entered nest boxes were caught even though it was expected that each would desert that box. During this time (Table I) 5 adult males, 5 subadult males, 6 adult females and 4 subadult females were banded with

TABLE I

SEX AND AGE COMPOSITION OF STARLINGS CAPTURED AT
BOXES OCTOBER, 1957, TO JUNE, 1958
(This sample is not random in respect to composition or to
time. Age characters described in Davis, 1959).

Month	Males		Females	
1957	Adult	Subadult	Adult	Subadult
October	1	1	0	0
November	1	1	1	1
December	0	1	0	0
March	3	0	3	1
April	0	2	2	2
	5	5	6	4

colours. Although all deserted the box many remained in the area and used another box or hole later. Some males were never trapped because in the fall they rarely enter the box after their first few days of exploration.

Most of the observations were obtained in a suburban area where large oaks, tulip trees, and maples provide a "forest" canopy 150 feet high. The understory consisted of the usual flowering trees and shrubs of residential districts. The starlings fed regularly on the lawns or flew to nearby open areas. Three boxes were used. The locations were changed partly for experimental reasons and partly because a tree blew down. The details of locations are unimportant.

For orientation of the reader a general description of the annual cycle is helpful. During July and August the birds moult and are reproductively inactive. By October most males have obtained nest holes which they defend. The females also defend holes but the fighting is not vigorous and hence is inconspicuous. Defence of the holes becomes less active in winter but by February becomes more active. Copulation occurs in early April and eggs are laid in late April. Additional broods may be had even in July. Details of the behaviour will be discussed below. The relation of behaviour to the male reproductive organs has been elaborated (Hilton, 1958).

VOCABULARY

A knowledge of the functions of the calls of a species is essential for understanding behaviour. Although the function of some notes has not been determined, some notes have clear functions and can be described. As is the custom, names for the notes are provided that are helpful, at least to the author, in discussion of function.

1. *Masculine aggressive:* (*a*) *Crowing.* The commonest note is a rasping chuckle, repeated monotonously from a perch. Usually the feathers of the lower throat are extended with each note so that a rhythmic sound and motion occurs. The volume varies according to circumstances. The bill is usually pointed upward at an angle during the crowing. The crowing is used by caged birds to establish dominance and to defend a nest box in the room. Crowing is clearly an aggressive note used to attack or repel. A common behaviour sequence is as follows: a new male arrives at a hole; the owner flies to the stranger, perches beside him and begins to crow and puff the throat feathers; the stranger may leave or may begin crowing and puffing; usually the owner, while crowing, will nudge the stranger and push him away along the branch or wire; the crowing by both birds may become very loud.

(*b*) *Scream.* A very loud, high-pitched note is given by a male when birds approach from a distance. It is usually accompanied by vigorous wing-waving. It appears to be aggressive.

2. *Attract female:* (*a*) *"Killdeer."* This call is named for its obvious resemblance to the call of *Charadrius vociferus.* Starlings give the "killdeer" call as early as November and continue all winter. Its function appears to be a long distance notification to a female that the male owns a nest hold. (*b*) *Crescendo.* Another note is a high-pitched ascending and descending phrase used in March and April. It appears to be an urgent notification of availability. (*c*) *"Whew."* An additional note is a soft call, given by the male when he is showing his hole to the female.

3. *Personal song.* A large number of songs or phrases of other species are imitated by starlings and here are called personal because each bird seems to have its own. Several birds, banded with colours, had personal songs. One bird that owned a box for spring of 1957 imitated the alarm of a redwing (*Agelaius phoenecius*). Another bird arrived on 26th March, 1958 and was banded the next day. It regu-

larly gave a call that resembled the call of the red-bellied woodpecker (*Centurus borealis*). Another bird owned a hole in a big oak for a week and regularly imitated the gurgle of a cowbird (*Molothrus ater*) Another bird imitated catbird (*Dumetella carolinensis*), robin (*Turdus migratorius*) and blue jay (*Cyanocitta cristata*) notes. One bird (whose history is described in detail below) had a characteristic "warble" that did not mimic any recognisable song. This warble was used in direct reference to a female several times. For example, once this male showed a female the box by the "whew" call and the female entered the box. The trap-door was pulled shut and he continued to warble even though the female was invisible.

4. *Feminine aggressive.* A "rattle" is given by a female when she attacks another female at a nest site. This note also occurs at the roost at night and may be the feminine version of crowing.

5. *Alarm notes.* Both sexes give a harsh "chuck" which clearly means that a crow, cat, man, or other danger is present. In addition a "rasp" is given when a person or crow is disturbing the nest. The "rasp" is used in the fall as well as the spring.

6. *Flocking call.* A raucous grating call is given by adults and juveniles when they form the post-breeding flock. The note may be given by a single bird as it flies to join the flock.

7. An assortment of whistles, chuckles, and other notes are produced but their functions, if different from those above, have not been determined. The female has a soft "chuck" call whose function is not clear. Its use may be to show the nest site to the male.

Parenthetically it should be noted that the male has "long-distance" and "short-distance" means of communication. The "scream" warns birds while still at a distance and the "crowing" serves for near birds. The "killdeer" call attracts the female from a distance and the "whew" call points out the nest hole to a nearby female.

TABLE II

EXAMPLE OF SOCIAL RANK OF STARLINGS. RESULTS OF FIGHTS
DURING FEBRUARY AND MARCH, 1957, IN CAPTIVITY

| | | | LOSER | | | |
| | | | Male | | Female | |
			G	R	W	Y
W	Male	G	—	12	17	8
I						
N	Male	R	1	—	8	1
N						
E	Female	W	0	1	—	5
R	Female	Y	0	0	2	—

AGGRESSIVE BEHAVIOUR

The captive birds in a room arrange themselves in a definite social rank (Davis, 1957) that is essentially the same as the type found in Domestic Fowl and many other species. Table II shows the results of encounters in a group of two males and two females. The rank is clear and was stable from 19th February to 22nd March, 1957. Note that the males dominated the females in this group. Many other groups, castrate males as well as in normals, showed rank clearly. Away from the feeding tray the birds crow and puff their throat feathers. The typical behaviour in captivity is as follows: a bird perches on a pipe, while others are feeding or drinking; another bird flies up to the pipe, perches, and begins to crow and to puff the throat feathers; if the first bird responds by puffing then the second increases its activity and both may crow and puff the throat feathers; eventually one quits and leaves and the other remains, often preening; if the bird does not respond, it usually promptly moves away at least a few inches. Females show essentially the same behaviour but at a much lower intensity. This behaviour occurs in a room in the absence of nest boxes.

Exactly the same behaviour occurs in the wild birds. Usually the conflicts occur between a stranger and the owner of a nest hole. The owner regularly perches between the stranger and the hole and by short hops along the perch forces the stranger away. In one case an owner gradually forced a stranger to move 50 feet along a wire. Generally the owner easily repels the stranger but sometimes actual bodily contact occurs. In prolonged and severe conflicts a curious flipping of the wings occurs. It is a very quick upward motion of both wings. The forearm comes forward and the bird bends the head downwards slightly. It has been performed by both the attacker and defender.

A behaviour called "wing-waving" consists of rapid upward flapping of the wings, while the bird crouches somewhat on its perch. The function of this behaviour is not completely clear. Certainly it is done most vigorously in the month before laying but it may be done weakly ("half wing-wave") in September or October. It is most characteristically given with the "scream" call and clearly serves as a visual warning to a bird that is flying over. However it may also be given with the "Killdeer" call at a female. Perhaps it serves the double advertising function to male and female alike that "here is a male that owns a hole." However females occasionally "wing wave" which suggests that the behaviour is defensive.

Apparently European birds perform the same way. Schüz (1943) describes wing waving, and throat puffing. He also observed males crowing inside a box and bringing in green leaves.

The defensive behaviour begins in August, at least for some birds, increases till November, decreases in December, and then increases greatly from January to April. This seasonal change has been reported for a number of places: Faroe Islands (Williamson, 1947), England (Bullough, 1942; Marples, 1936; 1936b; Morley, 1939; 1941), Germany (Wallraff, 1953), Holland (Kluijver, 1933; 1935), and for S. *cineraceus* in Japan (Kuroda, 1955). The defence revives before re-nesting; and the vocabulary changes somewhat. From August to December the aggressive behaviour consists of weak crowing and partial wing-waving. In late December the intensity begins to increase till early April when screaming and full wing-waving occur.

The male ceases puffing and crowing when a female comes near. On many occasions after January the male stopped crowing when the female perched nearby or started crowing when she left.

The female also defends a nest hole from October till nesting but the aggressive behaviour is mild. Puffing may occur in March and April and real fighting just before laying. In several cases a vicious fight inside the box has been observed (Allard, 1940).

Aggressive behaviour of wild birds when feeding on bread on the ground is the same as that seen in caged birds. Generally when several birds are together a warning thrust of the bill forces a bird away.

TERRITORIAL RANK

There is no territorial behaviour of the "typical" warbler or bunting type. Starlings do not select and defend an area of land in which the female will build. In contrast the males dominate a nest hole and drive other birds away. Birds of either sex may perch nearby in transit or feed on the ground but are not permitted near the hole while the owner is watching.

The females behave in essentially the same way, presumably all year but at least in spring when sex can be distinguished through binoculars. Commonly, females may fight within the nest hole. In one case (April 1957) two females fought for seven minutes inside a box. Although the birds were not visible they gave an assortment of screeches and squeals and pounded each other. Finally one bird burst out of the box and flew rapidly away. The other (who was the owner) followed a short distance and then perched.

The behaviour satisfies territorial criterion of exclusiveness but the patterns are the same as those shown in dominance in a cage. It is, of course, true that the same behaviour pattern may serve different functions, but the great similarity suggests that the starling dominates the birds that are close to it or to the nest hole. Since in nature a subordinate bird can leave the area, it does so and sets up a "rank" at another nest hole. Thus the whole breeding area is divided up into "groups" which have only one bird (the dominant one) because all the others have left. In this interpretation territorialism is a special case of social rank and is here called territorial rank.

Other authors have referred to territorial behaviour in starlings. Kluijver (1935) and Kessel (1957) were primarily interested in reproductive performance and referred simply to territorial behaviour. Schuz (1942) mapped territories and commented that the largest territories had a radius of five metres. His description agrees in almost every detail with the observations reported here, and he even reports that birds sleeping together in a box have a rank. Wallraff (1953) noted that "territorial" behaviour was inhibited by cloudy weather and described behaviour essentially identical to the type here reported.

Ownership of the hole is demonstrated by visits by the male and female. Table III shows days of regular observations (i.e. at least an hour starting at dawn) and the visits to box by the banded male and by R W female. In November and December the birds merely hung on the front or entered. In January the bird entered the box only once while being observed. In February the visits increased and once the male brought in twigs. In March the entrances were almost daily

TABLE III

Visits to Box by Banded Male and by RW Female (1956–57)

Month	Days Observed	Behaviour of the Male				Behaviour of Female	
		Hung	Enter	Twigs	Entice	Hung	Entered
Nov.	7	1	2	0	0	1	0
Dec.	9	2	0	0	0	0	0
Jan.	23	0	1	0	0	0	0
Feb.	11	4	5	1	0	5	0
March	15	13	3	3	3	3	5

Visits to Three Boxes by Several Males and Females (1957–58)

Sept.	11	0	5	1	0	0	0
Oct.	26	8	6	0	0	1	0
Nov.	30	7	9	0	0	0	4
Dec.	24	1	3	0	0	0	0
Jan.	31	0	1	0	0	0	0
Feb.	28	2	1	0	0	0	0
March	29	0	7	2	4	2	7

and some building and enticing (with "whew" call) occurred. In April the visits and building occurred daily and enticing was frequent.

The table also gives data for the subsequent year for several birds at three boxes. Since different numbers of birds are involved in different months no rates can be calculated. However seasonal changes in frequency for both male and female are apparent.

The behaviour for renests is essentially the same as above except condensed into a few days. The male resumes wing-waving and crowing vigorously and lines the nest with green leaves. He solicits any female and entices her to the box. After the laying period the male reduces his activities to mere passive presence.

A puzzling difference occurs in the roosting habits during the winter of birds observed in the Baltimore area and the reports of roosting in Europe and New York State. A number of authors (Kluijver, 1933; 1935; Kessel, 1957; Schuz, 1942; Fitter, 1949) found that birds (males and females) roost in boxes or holes. However, no bird roosted in three boxes during two winters in a residential area 8 miles from downtown. Furthermore, no bird was found in about 40 boxes on three visits in February. The boxes are located in a woods about 12 miles from city roosts and birds fly towards the roosts at night and from in the morning. An explanation for this difference is not apparent.

PAIRING

The analysis of pairing is seriously hindered by the impossibility of distinguishing sex till January unless the birds are captured. However, in January there is no evidence that birds are paired. A female, however, may own the same box as does a male. This curious distinction is based upon various observations. In one case a female (RW) defended two holes against all females from February to April before deciding on one hole. During all this time the males that owned each hole solicited all females that came along and attempted to entice each into the hole. Furthermore, after the first clutch was destroyed the banded male who was now the mate of RW solicited all females for several days but RW came back and drove a new female away. Many similar cases could be cited.

However, the pair from the first brood may remain together for a renest after destruction of the first nest. For example a pair nested in one hole and then took over another but when trapped deserted it.

The females may own a box as early as November and maintain it during the winter. The female tolerates the male at the box and may perch near the box as he goes inside. On several occasions in the fall one bird (presumably male) attempted to entice another to enter the box. However no clear pairing has been observed till April.

The defence by the female is so mild that very close attention is necessary to detect it. The best time to see the behaviour is about an hour after sunrise.

Apparently pairing does occur just before laying for suddenly two birds are regularly seen together. The birds feed on the lawn close together, fly off and perch near each other and fly off to the city together.

Some objective evidence is available from the numbers of doubles that are seen flying from the city where they roost at night. During most of the year the birds roost in the city (8 miles away) and return in scattered flocks the following morning. Table IV shows the results for April 1958. The number of "flocks" containing two birds suddenly increases and later many singles occur that are presumably the paired male whose female is incubating. The data from September 1957 through March 1958 are essentially the same as the data from 2–16th April. The increase in number of doubles on 17th April is clear. Presumably these are now paired rather than simply two birds flying along together. An egg was found on the ground on 19th April and the first egg laid in 60 boxes was deposited on 20th April. The drop in

TABLE IV
THE PROPORTION OF FLOCKS THAT WERE "DOUBLES"
DURING APRIL, 1958

April	Flocks	Proportion
2	17	·12
3	35	·26
4	23	·17
5	24	·17
7	21	·19
8	34	·15
9	24	·17
10	35	·08
14	22	·14
15	23	·17
16	32	·32
17	30	·33
18	51	·31
19	43	·42
20	38	·42
21	14	·39
22	17	·06
23	30	·23
24	15	·20
25	35	·11
26	30	·20

proportion of doubles on 22nd April is presumably due to the initiation of incubation by the females at night.

The same phenomenon occurred in the evening but for practical reasons it was difficult to get quantitative data. Regularly after 17th April a pair was observed sitting together on a branch near a box. After one-half to one hour the female would suddenly fly off toward the city and the male would follow. In all the cases that the sex could be identified the female led. In the morning the birds did not necessarily return together although many pairs did. After incubation began the male flew towards the city alone.

The conclusion that pairing occurs in the spring agrees with Kluijver (1935) who reported that pairing occurred late in spring even though in some cases a male and a female were found together in a box in February. Schuz (1942) reported that birds did not pair in the fall.

An unresolved problem is a behaviour pattern consisting of a rapid flight of one bird after another. The birds may turn and twist rapidly among the tree tops and back to the ground. The difficulty is that the sex can rarely be determined and sometimes three birds participate. Bayne (1933) called it a sexual chase but did not know the sex of the birds. In 1958 it was first observed on 24th March and became frequent around 15th April. Although many chases have been observed, sex could be determined in only a few cases. Twice the anterior bird was a banded female; once the posterior bird was a male; once the anterior bird was mounted by the posterior bird. Once a banded male chased a female. From these observations it seems that this behaviour really is a sexual chase; a possible function is to drive the female to the box since it occurred in birds not yet paired. (Copulation between paired birds was not preceded by this chasing).

THE HISTORY OF "WARBLER"

The observations described above have dealt with several birds and given as much quantitative data as possible. However, it seems likely that a more comprehensible and vivid understanding can be obtained by following the history of one male. A bird, called "Warbler" from his characteristic notes, provides a variety of illustrations of behaviour.

Warbler first appeared on 15th November, 1957, at 0644 hours and crowed vigorously at a hole in an oak tree. He was very obviously a stranger as demonstrated by hopping from perch to perch and frequent exploring. Later on (0730 hours) he entered a box (G). On 16 November at dawn he appeared in the oak and crowed but soon moved over to a maple near box G and began his unique warble (Since the bird was not banded there is no proof that this was the same bird. However, the behaviour was so distinctive that there is no doubt). For an hour Warbler fought with a bird and attempted to get a female to follow him into the G box. A banded bird (Black) who owned box B was an interested spectator.

From 17–20 November Warbler was present near the G box and entered several times, but on 21 November he began to fight with male B at Box B. Both birds crowed vigorously and eventually grappled and fell to the ground. B disappeared and was never seen after that fight.

For the next month Warbler regularly visited Box B. He sometimes went into the big oak or over near box G. On several occasions other males appeared but were driven away. Also females came and went. By the middle of December Warbler had a regular routine for arrival. Each morning when he came from the city, he landed in the top of a spruce. There he warbled for 5–10 minutes before going over to check his box. In December he drove away at least three males from his box. His bill was partially yellow but by February it was possible to see clearly the blue base to the bill.

In early March Warbler solicited females more actively. He "wing-waved" vigorously, gave the "whew" call when females came close and on several occasions warbled persistently at a female that was near the nest box. Also during early March he began to defend other holes occasionally when a female came near the holes. On 9 March he followed a female into G box and both birds were trapped (and banded). He did not go near G box after that experience but stayed at B. Another male took over G. On numerous occasions he drove away one or even two males from his box. In early April he regularly occupied the hole in the oak which formerly belonged to another male which had disappeared. However, by 10 April Warbler was again regularly defending box B. On 16 April at 0530 hours Warbler chased a bird around the area in rapid flight and eventually returned to B and warbled. At 0730 hours an unbanded female went into box B while Warbler watched (She was not trapped to avoid desertion). On 16 April a banded female entered B box while Warbler watched and then flew off followed by him. Later the two birds were seen on the ground together. Nothing noteworthy occurred on 17 and 18 April but on 19 April an unbanded female was trapped in B box and Warbler drove a male from the box. On 21 April he drove another male from the box. He was present on 22 and 23 April and on 24 April enticed into box B a female which was trapped. On 25, 26, and 27 April an unbanded male was present in B several times, but was driven out by Warbler. On 29 April a female entered B box and Warbler brought in some leaves. He then chased her in flight, copulated and chased again. In the late afternoon she entered the box several times and also copulated. On 30 April he was captured and autopsied. The testes were medium size and sperm were present in the seminal glomus.

To summarize this male's history very briefly, it seems clear that he defended a hole until a female chose it.

DISCUSSION

The observations here reported show that starlings behave aggressively in the wild the same as in captivity. The big difference seems to be that subordinate birds can flee in the wild but not in captivity. Indeed the behaviour of birds roosting in the city at night is apparently identical to that of birds in captivity. Thus, it appears that the starling has a social rank in the wild but the subordinate individuals are present only temporarily, and thus we have a superficial resemblance to territorial behaviour. Indeed, one may postulate that territorial behaviour is simply social rank without subordinates. A somewhat similar situation occurs in mice (Crowcroft, 1955; Davis, 1958) that may be territorial at low density of population but arranged in a rank at high density. The observations here presented on starlings agree with the hypothesis that a continuum exists from situations that are exclusively territorial at one extreme to those that are exclusively rank. For example, Mockingbirds are territorial for practically the entire year and apparently never form a social rank, whereas sage grouse are always ranked and never defend a territory. At various places on this continuum are other species such as cardinals, manikins, gulls and starlings.

SUMMARY

The starling (*Sturnus vulgaris*) presents some unusual aggressive behaviour patterns that may clarify the relation of territorial behaviour to rank behaviour. Birds were observed (600 hours) under natural conditions throughout the year at nest boxes. In addition birds in large cages were examined. The vocabulary is varied. The male has two aggressive calls and three calls to attract the female. In addition each male has an individual song and of course alarm and flock calls. The female has several calls as well as the alarm and flock calls.

The aggressive behaviour in captivity consists of "crowing" and puffing the throat while the birds are perched side by side. This occurs in the absence of a nest box and occasionally may culminate in a fight. In wild birds the same behaviour occurs at various places but usually near a box.

"Wing-waving" is a means of advertisement to a male or to a female that the nest hole belongs to a bird. Defensive behaviour begins in September and is maintained at low intensity till March. It increases before pairing in April and then declines. Pairing occurs about five days before laying.

No territorial behaviour of the conventional kind has been observed. The males and females drive other males away from nest holes in the same manner that is used to establish rank in cages. From this evidence it is suggested that territory is really a special case of social rank.

REFERENCES

ALLARD, H. A. (1940). The starling's family life and behaviours. *J. Wash. Acad. Sci.*, 30, 34–46.

BAYNE, C. S. (1933). The sexual chase among starlings. *Brit. Birds*, 27, 104–6.

BENNETT, MARY G. (1942). Effect of testosterone propionate on territoriality in flocks of ring doves. *Trans. Ill. Acad. Sci.*, 193–94.

BULLOUGH, W. S. (1942). The reproductive cycles of the British and continental races of the starling. *Phil. Trans. B.,* **231,** 165–246.

CROWCROFT, P. (1955). Territoriality in wild house mice, *Mus musculus.* L. *J. Mamm.,* **36,** 299–301.

DAVIS, D. E. (1957). Aggressive behaviour in castrated starlings. *Science,* **126,** (3267), 253.

DAVIS, D. E. (1958). The role of density in aggressive behaviour of house mice. *Anim. Behav.,* **6** (3 & 4), 207–10.

DUNNET, GEORGE M. (1955). The breeding of the starling *Sturnus vulgaris* L. in relation to its food supply. *Ibis,* **97** (4), 619–61.

FABRICIUS, E. and KARL-JOKOB GUSTAFSON (1954). Further aquarium observations on the spawning behaviour of the Char, *Salmo alpinus* L. *Inst. Fresh-Water Res. Rept.,* **34,** 58–104.

HILTON, F. K. (1958). Behavioural and biochemical aspects of the yearly gonadal cycle in male starlings. *Sc. D. Dissertation, Johns Hopkins University.*

FITTER, R. S. E. (1949). *London's birds.* London: Collins, p. 1–256.

KESSEL, BRINA (1957). A study of the breeding biology of the European starling *Strurnus vulgaris* L. in North America. *Amer. Mid. Nat.,* **58** (2), 257–331.

KLUIJVER, H. N. (1933). Bijdrage tot de biologie en de ecologie van den spreeuw *Sturnus v. vulgaris* gedurende zjin voortplantingstijd Versl. en Meded. *Plantenziektenk, Dienst, Wageningen,* **69,** 1–146.

KLUIJVER, H. N. (1935). Waarnemingen over de Levenswilze van den Spreeuw *Sturnus v. vulgaris* met Behulp van geringde Individen. *Ardea,* **24,** 133–66.

KURODA, NAGAHISA (1955). Field studies on the gray starling *Sturnus cineraceus* Temminck. I. From winter to breeding season. *Misc. Rep. Yamashima's Inst. Ornith. Zool.,* **7,** 277–89.

MARPLES, G. (1936). Starlings fighting for nesting sites. *Brit. Birds,* **29,** 321–23.

MARLES, G. (1936 b). Behaviour of starlings at the nesting site. *Brit. Birds,* **30** (12), 14–21.

MORLEY, AVERIL (1939). Rising and roosting of a pair of resident starlings in winter and early spring. *Brit. Birds,* **33,** 39–43.

MORLEY, AVERIL (1941). The behaviour of a group of resident British starlings *Sturnus v. vulgaris* L. from October to March. *Naturalist,* **788,** 55–61.

SCHUZ, E. (1942). Biologische beobachtungen an Staren in Rossitten. *Der Vogelzug,* **13** (3–4), 99–132.

SCHUZ, E. (1943). Brutbiologische Beobachtungen an Staren 1943 in der Vogelwarte Rossitten. *J. Ornith,* **91** (4), 388–405.

WALLRAFF, H. G. (1953). Beobachtungen zur Brutbiologie des Stares *Sturnus v. vulgaris* L. in Nurnberg. *J. Ornith.,* **94** (1–2), 36–67; B.A. **27,** 26649.

WILLIAMSON, K. (1947). Field Notes on the Faeroe Starling. *Ibis,* **89,** 435–39.

THE DEVELOPMENT OF SCHOOLING BEHAVIOR IN FISHES

EVELYN SHAW [1]

American Museum of Natural History

INTRODUCTION

Knowledge of the development of behavior is essential to the eventual understanding of the organism in its adaptation to the total environment (Schneirla, 1957). Knowing when and how patterns of behavior emerge, from their very beginnings, helps to define those features of the external and internal "milieu" which are critical to the manifestation of behavior. In undertaking a study of schooling, its development was followed. Observations were made on the first approaches and responses of fry to one another and on the subsequent events which led to schooling orientation. As these patterns were revealed and as they were incorporated in the animal's behavioral repertoire, it was possible to evaluate the extent of their flexibility and rigidity, particularly when the fish were reared under varied environmental conditions or when early experience with different situations was restricted or enriched. By observing all these aspects of development, a clearer understanding of the specific factors of attraction and orientation which result in continuous schooling was obtained.

MATERIALS AND METHODS

The development of schooling in the common silversides, *Menidia menidia* (Linnaeus) and *Menidia beryllina* (Cope) was observed during the summers of 1957 and 1958 at Woods Hole, Mass. These species live sympatrically in shoal water. During May, June, and July the adults are in spawning condition, and spawning takes place over wide areas (Bumpus, 1898). The extruded eggs sink to the bottom, adhering to the substratum by adhesive threads. *M. menidia* is reported to spawn in water more saline than water found at the spawning sites of *M. beryllina*.

[1] This research was supported by grants from the National Science Foundation (G–4986) and the National Institutes of Health (M–2322). The laboratory facilities at the Marine Biological Laboratory were provided by the Marine Biological Laboratory through their contract with the Office of Naval Research.

During the spawning season the adults were stripped of their gametes by applying gentle abdominal pressure. The eggs were fertilized readily and developed normally under laboratory conditions. No differences were detected in the embryonic development of both species; therefore, subsequent discussions do not distinguish between the two.

Rearing Technique

Approximately 40 eggs were placed into each finger bowl containing sea water, which was changed daily. Hatching at laboratory temperatures, 23–27° C., occurred 8–10 days after fertilization. Newly hatched fry were transferred to either shallow troughs with continuously running fresh sea water or to large finger bowls containing sea water, which was changed every third day. The fry were fed live nauplii of the brine shrimp *Artemia,* two days after hatching (Rubinoff, 1958). Approximately 1,000 fry were reared and observed in the laboratory and approximately 10,000 fry were observed in the field.

Fig. 1. Fry 5–7 mm. in length. Parallel orientation is not seen.

Fig. 2. Fry 8–9 mm. in length. The first indications of parallel orientation and incipient schooling are seen.

Observations

In the laboratory, observations of one half-hour each were made in the morning, afternoon, and evening from the time of hatching until the fry were four weeks old, posthatching. During this period the fry grew from 4.5 mm. to 14–16 mm.; they attained a length of 12 mm. by the third week after hatching. The fry were measured with calipers from the tip of the snout to the posterior edge of the caudal fin. The lengths of the fry from the same broods did not vary more than 0.25 mm.; the fry were kept at the same population density in the rearing tanks and fed standard quantities of food.

THE DEVELOPMENT OF SCHOOLING IN THE LABORATORY

During all the observations from hatching onward the fry were found in aggregations of 15–30 individuals, concentrated in only one or two areas of their holding vessels. The aggregates were found near the walls of the vessels, were a single "fish layer" in depth, and a few millimeters below the surface. No differences were noted in the behavior of fry reared in troughs as compared with those reared in finger bowls, nor were any differences detected in the schooling of *M. menidia* and *M. beryllina*.

Development of Approach and Orientation

Fry, 5–7 mm. in length.—A fry frequently approached the tail, the head, or the lateral mid-body region of another fry to within 5 mm.; both usually darted away rapidly (Fig. 1).

Fry, 8–9 mm. in length.—A fry frequently approached the tail of another fry and subsequently the two fry, when 1–3 cm. apart, generally took a parallel course for 1–2 seconds (Fig. 2). If either fry approached the other, head-first, or approached perpendicular to the mid-body region, no orientation occurred, and the fry darted off rapidly in opposite directions, very much like the behavior seen in fry, 5–7 mm. in length.

Fry, 9–9.5 mm. in length.—Often four or five fry, 1–3 cm. apart, lined up parallel and swam together for 5–10 seconds.

Fry, 10–10.5 mm. in length.—When a fry swam toward the tail of another fry, two responses often occurred; both fry vibrated when they were near each other, and one fry invariably followed the other with the result that, in a crowded area, 4–6 fry oriented and swam parallel for as long as 30–60 seconds. When these schools dispersed, the fry tended to remain aggregated.

Fry, 11–12 mm. in length.—As many as 10 fry swam together, in

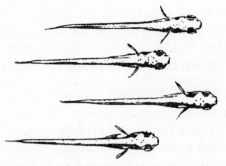

FIG. 3. Fry 11–12 mm. in length. Fry are oriented parallel and schooling is established.

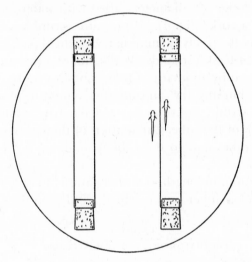

FIG. 4. Technique for experiments on visual attraction.

parallel orientation (Fig. 3). Occasionally the school disrupted but reformed within several seconds. The fish-to-fish distances ranged from 1.0 cm. to 3.5 cm., and considerable maneuvering of position occurred within the school.

Fry, 12–13 mm. in length.—Separate schools, containing 10–20 fry were formed. The fry were a single "fish layer" in depth, and they ranged freely over the tanks, no longer hovering near the walls.

Fry, over 14 mm. in length.—Often all the fry in the tank formed into a single school. The orientation of the fry was more precisely parallel and the fish-to-fish distance was less variable, ranging from 1.0 to 1.5 cm. On rare occasions the fry were as close as 0.5 cm. or as far apart as 2.5 cm.

In summary, schooling is seen to develop as a response, initially, between two fry, with the numbers of participating fry increasing as they grow. Approach and orientation follow characteristic patterns. The first approaches, head on, do not result in orientation; later approaches toward the tail do result in parallel orientation.

The Development of Visual Attraction

Vision is evidently the primary sensory stimulus in fish-to-fish attraction, as reported by a number of investigators and summarized by Atz (1953) and Breder (1959). To determine whether or not visual attraction develops parallel to the emergence of schooling, the following experiment was inaugurated (Shaw, 1958). A freely swimming fish was placed in a shallow bowl (9″ diameter) containing two narrow glass tubes (6″ long, ⅜″ diameter) filled with water and plugged at each end with a cork (Fig. 4). A 5-minute record was taken of the number of times the freely swimming fry oriented parallel and closely to the tube for at least 5 seconds. At the end of 5 minutes, one of the tubes was replaced by an identical tube containing a fry the same size as the freely swimming fry, and another 5-minute observation was taken. The fry within the tube was restricted to swimming up and down the length of the tube. Orientation of the freely swimming fry to the control tubes and to the tube, containing a fry, is given in Table 1.

No fry, 8–14 mm. in length, oriented parallel to either tube before 3½ min. Of these, 70 per cent oriented parallel to the tube contain-

TABLE 1

The Development of Visual Attraction

Size of Fish (mm.)	No. Tested	No. Orienting Parallel to Control Tube for 5 Seconds or More	No. Orienting Parallel to Tube Containing Fish for 5 Seconds or More
5.........	20	0*	0
6.........	20	0*	0
7.........	16	0*	0
8.........	18	1	9
9.........	20	3	13
11.........	20	2	10
12.........	20	2	12
13.........	18	1	3
14.........	18	0	8
15.........	22	0	15
16.........	12	0	10

* Did not orient, or approach.

ing a fry between $3\frac{1}{2}$ to $4\frac{1}{2}$ min.; 30 per cent between $4\frac{1}{2}$ to 5 min. Among the fry 15–16 mm. in length, one fry 15 mm. in length and two fry 16 mm. in length oriented parallel to the tube containing a fish within 50 sec.; the remaining fry responded within 3 min.

Fifty per cent of the fry 8–12 mm. in length oriented parallel to the inclosed fish for 10 sec.; 50 per cent oriented for 5 sec. Thirty-six per cent of the fry 13–14 mm. in length oriented for 20 sec.; 45 per cent for 10 sec.; and 19 per cent for 5 sec. Forty per cent of the fry 15–16 mm. in length oriented parallel for 60 sec.; 28 per cent for 30 sec.; and 2 per cent for 20 sec. One fry, which oriented for 60 sec., changed direction seven times.

A conspicuous pattern of behavior was seen among the fry as they approached and began to orient along the tube. The entire body of the fish vibrated for 1–2 seconds. This is quite different from that seen in typical swimming motion. It was not determined whether the fry in the inclosed tube also vibrated. The significance of this vibration is not yet understood, but it may possibly be important to the processes of orientation within the school.

Current Orientation as a Stimulus to Schooling Behavior in Menidia

Most fish including *Menidia* show a positive rheotaxis when placed in a moderate current flow. Newly hatched *Menidia* immediately orient upstream and maintain a constant swimming speed within the current. It seemed possible that orientation into a current could, for instance, accustom preschooling fish to seeing their species mates in certain visual patterns which would influence the fish in their mutual response in such a way that this familiar visual pattern would be maintained. To evaluate the influence of current flow on the development of schooling, fish were reared to a length of 15 mm. in bowls of still water. Under these conditions schooling developed at the same age and with the same characteristic patterns found among fishes reared in a moderate current flow.

Menidia Reared in Restricted Environments ("Isolation")

Embryos, in very early phases of development (the optic buds were just appearing), were placed in individual bowls containing sea water. The interiors of the bowls were lined with a thin coat of paraffin which prevented the embryos from seeing out of their respective bowls and from seeing their own reflection along the sides of the bowl. The major features of the environment consisted of the embryo, the bowl, and the water contained therein.

Of 400 fish reared in isolation only 4 grew to 15 mm. in length. When each of these 4 fish was presented to a school of fish of the same size, they joined the group immediately. Initially, however, they seemed unable to maintain their position in the school; they often bumped into species mates, and they occasionally swam away from the school. At the end of four hours, however, fish reared in isolation could not be distinguished from those reared in groups.

The high rate of mortality was not clearly understood, as the socially reared controls yielded high survival rates. It was noted that the "isolates" did not begin to feed and apparently died of starvation, implying that the presence of brood mates is a requisite to the initiation of feeding. Breder (1946) found great difficulty in rearing *Brachydanio* in "isolation." He suggested the possibility that the interaction of groups was such, metabolically, that it may have had a rather immediate survival value; for example, aquarium keepers know that a non-feeding fish will be stimulated to feed in the presence of an actively feeding fish. Welty (1934) also found that fishes in groups stimulated each other to greater activity and that they ate more food per fish when they were in groups than when they were isolated.

FIELD OBSERVATIONS OF SCHOOLING BEHAVIOR

During late June, July, and August thousands of small fry school in shoal waters in and around the Woods Hole area. Each school generally contains between 30–50 fry, either made up of the earliest schooling fry, 12–16 mm. in length, or of slightly larger fry, 16–20 mm. in length. Schools of fry 16–20 mm. in length swam at uniform speeds, exhibited consistent parallel orientation, and displayed an impressive synchronization. The fish-to-fish distance of 0.8–1.0 cm. varied little. Generally, 4 to 5 fry swam abreast in the school and 6 to 7 fry swam along its length, thereby creating a rectangularly shaped school.

In comparison with the above groups, schools of fry 12–16 mm. in length did not always swim at uniform speeds, nor did they consistently exhibit parallel orientation. The fish-to-fish distance varied between 0.5–2.5 cm., and stragglers were often seen. The school was generally rectangular in shape, but because of the variable fish-to-fish distances, it appeared more loosely structured than the above group.

Separate schools in the above size groups were sighted in relatively small areas; for example, an area 20′ × 10′ harbored 6 discrete schools. If these schools were disturbed, and forced to swim away from the locality, they would return soon after the disturbance subsided. Apparently schools tend to remain in the same areas, for as the summer progressed and return visits were made to the same spot, larger and larger fry were found. The gradual size increase can be attributed to the normal growth rate of the fry.

Preschooling fry were located only on two occasions. Once, 8 fry, 7–10 mm. in length, were observed drifting on the surface of the water, 6 feet in depth. The fry were randomly oriented, swimming activity was minimal, and the fish-to-fish distance varied from 6″ to 2′. On another occasion over 100 fry were found in shallow water along the bank, scattered among Sedge grass, *Spartina alterniflora,* roots. The fry were closely packed and randomly oriented. However, when these preschooling fry were disturbed, they formed into a temporary school for several seconds. Breder (1946) found that startling adult *Brachydanio* caused them to draw together temporarily into a school. In contrast, among the schooling fry a disturbance often caused a brief disruption of the school.

DISCUSSION

The most conspicuous features of schooling fish are their constancy in orientation and their synchronization of speed and direction of movement. Parr (1927) observed that schools are characterized by great stability through the most varied environmental conditions and that this stability and their schooling early in life indicate that schools must be dominated by internal factors. Keenleyside (1955) maintains that schooling is a separate and specific instinct as it has some of the characteristics of an instinctive activity. However, by assuming an "original nature" of primarily internal factors, one may overlook many stimulative influences upon the organism during its lifetime (Schneirla, 1957); and this assumption may ultimately preclude the study of changing influences, during the animal's life, upon any given behavioral phenomenon. A knowledge of the animal's life history is important, particularly since we know from numerous ontogenetic studies that past experiences and early experiences frequently affect subsequent behavioral responses (Beach, 1954). Although fishes have a relatively stereotyped behavioral repertoire, there is no reason to assume that their responses to social situations cannot be altered by past experiences, just as their responses to physical situations are altered by past experiences (Breder, 1959).

One way in which the effect of early schooling experience on later schooling can be determined is by rearing individuals in situations where they do not have the opportunity to gain any schooling experience. By rearing a fish in physical and visual isolation from species mates, we are able to learn which behavioral patterns will emerge. This type of experiment, however, will not tell us what is "native" to the animal (Schneirla, 1956); it will tell us only of the type of response that will appear from a fish reared in conditions of reduced environmental stimuli, since the organism is still capable of gaining many other types of experience during its so-called "isolation." Of the 400 fish reared in separate chambers, only 4 survived to the age of schooling. When each of the 4 was presented to a group of schooling fish, they joined the school. Recent evidence (Shaw, unpublished manuscript) has shown that acara (*Aequidens latifrons*) fry reared under similar conditions of "isolation" also joined a school, as Breder (1946) found to be the case in *Brachydanio*. However, in sharp contrast to these results, acara fry reared in "isolation" and subsequently placed together did not form a school, although they did aggregate into groups of two's and three's. It seems fairly obvious that the responses of the fry are influenced by the stimulating conditions of the situations into which they are placed.

Initially, when the four isolates mentioned above joined the school, they were unable to orient parallel to other fish or to maintain consistency in their fish-to-fish distances, frequently dropping out of the school or bumping into their species mates. Although these fish had no previous experiences with any species mates, they were able within four hours to adjust to the situation in which they were placed. However, the fact that they showed initial and early disorientation is significant, for it suggests that even though these fish are attracted to the schooling group, they need a certain amount of experience in orientation before they are able to orient. Tending to reinforce this view are the observations of schooling development. For contrary to Morrow's expectations (1948), schooling does not appear immediately after hatching but develops gradually over a period of several weeks. During development the direction of approach changes from primarily a head-on approach to an approach toward the tail. Fry 5–7 mm. in length show the head-on approach; fry over 10 mm. approach toward the tail; the transitional period is seen among fish 8–10 mm. in length. In the head-on approach each fry sees a changing visual pattern, an oval mass, bright black spots (the eyes) coming steadily closer until the intensity is great enough to force a withdrawal of the fry—in this case, a veering off. In contrast, a fish approaching toward the tail of another fish also sees a changing visual pattern of small silvery and black spots and a ribbon-like transparent tail; but this pattern is moving steadily away from him, presenting a stimulus of lesser intensity, which the fish continues to approach. In the earliest stages parallel orientation may simply reflect the forward momentum of the fish swimming in that direction. Later, as the visuo-motor co-ordination becomes more highly developed, the fish is able to select this more moderate stimuli and avoid "the more intense stimuli." Schneirla (1959) has postulated that in many organisms mild stimuli attract, strong stimuli repel.

Unfortunately, because of the high mortality rate of the isolates, it was impossible to determine whether there are critical periods of experience in the formation of a school. Judging by the rapidity which with "isolated" fry, 15 mm. in length, joined the school, we anticipate that later experiences, that is, those of fry 10, 11, or 12 mm. in length, may be more influential in schooling formation. Approaches during that time are toward the tail and result in brief parallel orientation, whereas the earlier responses, mainly head-on approaches, result in disorientation.

Paralleling to a large extent the development of schooling is the development of visual attraction. Freely swimming fry, 8 mm. or more in length, responded to fish inclosed in a glass tube, approaching the tube and orienting parallel to the tube. However, although two freely swimming fry, 5–7 mm. in length, approached each other, a freely swimming fry did not approach the fry in the glass tube. The discrepancy in this behavior has several possible explanations. First, fish of this age may have had an insufficient accumulation of experiences with species mates to be attracted to the modified image of a species mate in the tube. Second, at this time of early development they may require certain kinds of responses from species mates which cannot be given by a fish restricted in a glass tube. Third, the approach may be random and not necessarily related to schooling, and fourth, the fish may not be able to swim sufficiently well to orient. At later stages of development these fish are attracted to the visual image of a species mate and will orient parallel for a brief period, the time of orientation gradually increasing in length as the fry grow older. An important aspect of schooling is that it is an interaction between fishes, and inter-responses from each fish are required to maintain a school; and, although the visual image gradually becomes a stronger attracting stimulus for the freely swimming fry, it is insufficient for maintaining orientation.

A number of questions are raised regarding the development of schooling under field conditions. At first it appears that the vastness of the sea would enormously reduce the chances of these fish finding one another, forming into aggregates, and, finally, schooling. Yet when we examine plankton tows, we find that the tows frequently contain large numbers of preschooling *Menidia* (Williams, personal communication). These fry, therefore, do have the opportunity to gain orientative experiences with one another as they are carried by the currents. As they grow and develop both physically and in experience, the fry no longer drift with the plankton but form into the many schools of young found along the shores.

SUMMARY

1. The development of schooling behavior in *Menidia* is described. Schooling was observed in the laboratory and found to develop gradually, following characteristic patterns of approach and orientation.

2. Schooling development was also observed under natural conditions. Fry 7–10 mm. in length were not found in schools, whereas many schools of fry over 12 mm. in length were found.

3. Visual attraction develops gradually, paralleling the appearance of schooling.

4. Current is not a necessary stimulus to orientation within a school.

5. Four fry reared in "isolation" joined a school. The significance is discussed.

6. The significance of experience in the approach of fry to each other and in orientation within the school is discussed.

LITERATURE CITED

ATZ, J. W.   1953. Orientation in schooling fishes. Proc. Conf. Orientation in Animals. O.N.R., pp. 103–30.

BEACH, F. A., and JAYNES, J.   1954. Effects of early experience upon the behavior of animals. Psych. Bull., 51:239–63.

BREDER, C. M.   1959. Studies on social groupings in fishes. Bull. Amer. Mus. Nat. Hist., 117:397–481.

BREDER, C. M., and HALPERN, F.   1946. Innate and acquired behavior affecting the aggregation of fishes. Physiol. Zoöl., 19:154–90.

BUMPUS, H. C.   1898. The breeding of animals at Woods Hole during the months of June, July and August. Science (N.S.), 8:850–58.

KEENLEYSIDE, M. H. A.   1955. Some aspects of the schooling behavior of fish. Behaviour., 8:183–248.

MORROW, J. E.   1948. Schooling behavior in fishes. Quart. Rev. Biol., 23:27–38.

PARR, A. E.   1927. A contribution to the theoretical analysis of the schooling behavior of fishes. Occasional Papers Bingham Oceanog. Coll., No. 1.

RUBINOFF, IRA.   1958. Raising the atherinid fish *Menidia menidia* in the laboratory. Copeia, No. 2, pp. 146–47.

SCHNEIRLA, T. C.   1956. Interrelationships of the "innate" and the "acquired" in instinctive behavior. *In:* L'Instinct dans le comportement des animaux et de l'homme, ed. Masson & Cie, pp. 387–452.

————. 1957. The concept of development in comparative psychology, pp. 78–108. *In:* The concept of development, ed. DALE B. HARRIS, Minneapolis: University of Minnesota Press.

————. 1959. An evolutionary and developmental theory of biphasic processes underlying approach and withdrawal. *In:* Nebraska Symposium on Motivation, Lincoln: University of Nebraska Press.

SHAW, E. 1958. The development of visual attraction among schooling fishes. Biol. Bull., 115:365 (abstr.).

WELTY, J. C. 1934. Experiments in group behavior in fishes. Physiol. Zoöl., 7:85–128.

THE OCCURRENCE OF FIGHTING BEHAVIOR

IN THE GRAIN BEETLE TENEBRIO MOLITOR WITH THE

POSSIBLE FORMATION OF A DOMINANCE HIERARCHY[1]

ROBERT STEARNS HOWARD

*Department of Biological Sciences, University of Delaware,
Newark, Delaware*

INTRODUCTION

When two animals meet, there are two general types of behavior that might be exhibited. One of these is equivalent behavior of tolerance or indifference, in which neither challenge nor submission is displayed. The other is nonequivalent behavior of active dominance and subordination. The manifestation of any of these phenomena varies from group to group.

Observations of the behavior of the grain beetle *Tenebrio molitor* suggest that there is a strong degree of domination exerted by some of the individuals over others. Evidences of this are found in laboratory cultures of the grain beetle in the frequent appearances of injuries to the living animals (larvae, pupae, and adults).

MATERIALS AND METHODS

The animals used for these experiments were kept in separate petri dishes (9 cm. in diameter) with filter paper in the bottom of each dish. Water was added to the paper daily in sufficient quantity to moisten, but not to soak the filter paper. When the animals were not being tested, they were kept in the dark.

During the experiments, the animals being tested were introduced into a clean petri dish with dry filter paper, rather than the moist paper like that in their own dishes. This was found necessary because the beetles spent most of their time chewing on the paper when moist paper was available, showing little or no reaction to each other. Each

---

[1] This paper is part of a dissertation submitted to the Graduate School of Northwestern University in partial fulfillment of the requirements for the degree of Doctor of Philosophy.

animal was given a catalog number, and this was written on the top of the dish. It proved unnecessary to mark the animals because they were tested only two at a time, and there is sufficient individual variation in this species for the observer to distinguish them. The variations include slight color differences (from reddish fuscous to black), differences in the length of the elytra of a given beetle, differences in the over-all lengths of the animals, differences in lengths of the elytra with respect to the abdomen, and various imperfections in the anatomy of the beetles, either from imperfect eclosion, or from the effects of cannibalism on the parts of other beetles.

The two animals to be tested at a given time were removed from their respective dishes in as close succession as possible to eliminate the possibility of any behavior due to territorialism, etc. If the beetle being transferred accidentally fell over onto its back, it was removed and not tested until an hour later. This eliminated any possible effects of the strong righting behavior (characteristic of beetles when they lose their balance) upon the other beetle with which the subject beetle was being tested. After the two beetles had been introduced into the test dish, it was covered, and the activities of the beetles were recorded. The animals were observed for as long a period as it took for them to exhibit a definite interrelationship of dominance or subordination. If no such demonstration was given after 90 minutes, the beetles were returned to their respective dishes and tested at a later time. This was seldom necessary.

RESULTS AND OBSERVATIONS

In *Tenebrio,* equivalent behavior is demonstrated in the following ways: a. mutual antennation; b. mutual palpation (each stroking the palpi of the other with his own); c. mutual investigation with antennae and palpi of each other's anatomy; d. lack of akinesis (akinesis is lowering of head, remaining motionless, allowing encountering animal to walk over, to bite it, etc.); and e. resisting attacks with counter-attacks.

Non-equivalent behavior is much more common with *Tenebrio* and has numerous forms of exhibition. This category is divided into dominant and subordinate sorts of behavior. The dominant may exhibit the following types of behavior: a. walk over subordinate, as if it were an inanimate object; b. mount (regardless of sex of subordinate), with or without exserting the aedeagus, in copulating orientation or the reverse; c. palpate or antennate (or both) the subordinate roughly; d. nudge the subordinate, pushing it either to the side or into the air; e. "butt" the subordinate, frequently knocking it some distance (this may be accomplished either by rushing the subordinate from a distance and striking with head directed forward, or by coming into contact with the subordinate beetle first, then lowering the head, digging under the subordinate beetle slightly with it, then suddenly elevating the head, thus throwing the subordinate into the air); f. knock the subordinate over, either by catching it off balance or by overturning it from a stable position; g. bite or nibble at the antennae, palpi, legs, or elytra of the subordinate; h. kick the subordinate; or, i. threaten the subordinate (this may be accomplished by rushing at the subordinate, then stopping suddenly, which usually causes the subordinate to avoid, or by standing face to face with the subordinate, conspicuously moving the mouth parts which also may evoke an avoiding reaction on the part of the subordinate).

Manifestations of subordination are fewer in number, but just as diagnostic in character as are the signs of dominance. The following reactions characterize the subordinates: a. general avoidance of the dominant, either by turning aside or reversing orientation and running away; b. akinesis (see above); c. gentle antennation or palpation (or both) of the dominant.

The explanation of dominance or subordination is not always apparent, but there are some signs that are obvious. Size is often a determining factor. Almost without exception, within unisexual groups, when neither of the two animals being tested had any injury, the larger was the dominant. In mixed groups, the male was almost invariably dominant over the female, except when the female outsized the male by a wide margin. If a given beetle has recently emerged as an adult, it is extremely vulnerable, being soft and easy prey. These animals were always quiet and subordinate in their relationships with the older, more sclerotized (though not always larger) beetles. If a beetle had been injured, it would ordinarily assume a subordinate attitude in its contacts with other beetles. Lastly, as a beetle ages, it usually loses its dominant status gradually, just as the young beetles gain dominance as they grow older. In Table I, the constancy of the relatively subordinate positions of the beetles number DS2 and DS3 is noteworthy. The positions here may be attributed both to injury and to size. DS2 had an injured left antenna, and DS3 had one antenna completely missing. Both were smaller than DS1 and DS4. Since DS2 and DS3 were approximately the same size, the differences in their antennae may have been the cause of their positions with respect to each other.

TABLE I

DOMINANCE-SUBORDINATION RELATIONSHIPS AMONG FOUR MALES ON SUCCESSIVE DAYS

Date (1951)	Beetle Number	Rank	Beetles Subordinated			
June 21	DS1	1	3	2	4	..
	DS4	2	3	2	..	..
	DS2	3	3	..	..	..
	DS3	4	..	..	..	..
June 22	DS1	1	3	2	4	..
	DS4	2	3	2	..	..
	DS2	3	3	..	..	..
	DS3	4	..	..	..	..
June 23	DS1	1	3	2	4	..
	DS4	2	3	2	..	..
	DS2	3	3	..	..	..
	DS3	4	..	..	..	..
June 24	DS1	2	3	2	..	..
	DS4	1	3	2	..	1
	DS2	3	3	..	..	..
	DS3	4	..	..	..	..
June 25	DS1	2	3	2	..	..
	DS4	1	3	2	..	1
	DS2	3	3	..	..	..
	DS3	4	..	..	..	..
June 26*	DS1	2	..	2	..	..
	DS4	1	..	2	..	1
	DS2	3	..	..	..	..
June 27†	DS1	1	..	..	4	..
	DS4	2	..	..	..	..

* DS3 died
† DS2 died.

The original plan was to have three types of experiments: a. all males; b. all females; and c. males and females mixed. But it was found that in contacts in the mixed groups, the female almost invariably adopted a subordinate attitude, which is part of the normal mating behavior. For this reason, it was found more feasible to study the reactions of each sex separately. In the first set of experiments, only males were used. In contrast to the constancy of the positions of DS2 and DS3, a marked shift in the relative positions of DS1 and DS4 was found. These beetles were of the same size, but DS4 was missing its right mesotarsus. This injury was of apparently little consequence, for DS4 attained dominance over another of its own size (DS1) which had no apparent injury.

In the second group of tests, ten males were used, each beetle meeting each of the others three times. (DS7 and DS10 died after the first series of this group.) The results of this series are shown in Table II.

It is apparent from a comparison of the three series in this table that there is a tendency toward gradual stabilization of dominance-subordination relationships among animals which encounter each other more than once. It may also be noted in Table II that there is a tendency toward "ties" in respective dominance ratings. In the first series, there was only one animal (DS13) which did not tie with another. In the second series, there were three animals with no ties, and in the third series, there were five without ties. In an analysis of dominance-subordination relationships among animals, the existence of such ties as are found here is often characteristic of groups with a less rigid type of social organization (Allee 1938). The interactions among the beetles in group DS5–14 are shown diagrammatically in Figure 1.

TABLE II

THREE SERIES OF DOMINANCE-SUBORDINATION RELATIONSHIPS AMONG
TEN MALES (DS SERIES)

Beetle Number	Rank	Beetles Subordinated									
Series 1											
13........	1	5	6	8	9	10	7	14	11	..	..
12........	2.5	5	6	8	9	10	7	..	..	..	13
11........	2.5	5	6	..	9	10	7	14	..	12	..
14........	7	..	6	..	..	10	..	..	..	12	..
7........	7	..	6	..	..	10	..	14	..	..	..
10........	7	5	6	..	9	..	..	..	..	..	..
9........	4.5	5	6	8	..	10	7	..	..	..	..
8........	4.5	5	..	..	..	10	7	14	11	..	..
6........	9.5	5	..	8	..	..	..	..	..	..	..
5........	9.5	..	..	..	..	..	7	14	..	..	..
Series 2*											
13........	1	5	..	8	9	..	..	14	11	12	..
12........	3	5	6	8	9	..	..	14	..	..	..
11........	3	5	6	8	9	..	..	..	..	12	..
14........	3	5	6	8	9	..	..	..	11	..	..
9........	5	5	6	8	..	..	..	..	..	..	..
8........	6.5	5	6	..	..	..	..	..	..	..	..
6........	6.5	5	..	..	..	..	..	..	..	..	13
5........	8	..	..	..	..	..	..	..	..	..	..
Series 3*											
13........	2	5	6	8	9	..	..	..	11	12	..
12........	2	5	6	8	9	..	..	14	11	..	..
11........	4	5	6	8	9	..	..	..	..	..	..
14........	2	5	6	8	9	..	..	..	11	..	13
9........	5	5	6	8	..	..	..	..	..	..	..
8........	6	5	6	..	..	..	..	..	..	..	..
6........	7	5	..	..	..	..	..	..	..	..	..
5........	8	..	..	..	..	..	..	..	..	..	..

* DS7 and DS10 dead.

The third group of experiments involved a group of six females. The results of these experiments and observations are shown in Table III. In general, the sorts of dominance-subordination relationships are the same as with the groups of males. There is a conspicuous number of ties within each series. There are also several notable "triangles," as in the case of DS16, DS17 and DS18. The existence of such triangles is another characteristic of a less rigid type of social organization. In the triangle mentioned above, the organization in Series Two of this group was as follows: DS16 → DS17 → DS18 → DS16. Retesting of these three gave the following results: DS16 → DS17 → DS18, and DS16 → DS18. (The arrow is directed away from the dominant toward the subordinate.) The lack of significance of this retest is shown by the fact that DS16 ended up with the second lowest dominance frequency, despite the temporary successes en-

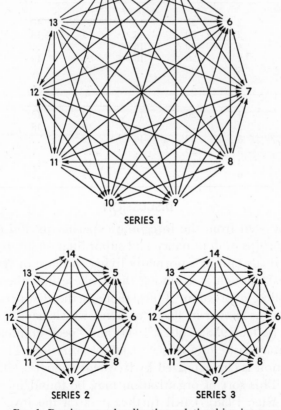

SERIES 1

SERIES 2   SERIES 3

Fig. 1. Dominance-subordination relationships in group *DS 5–14.*

countered in this retest series. Retesting other triangles gave comparable results. This seems to emphasize the fact that among these animals, with their almost total lack of social behavior, there is not a strict linear dominance, but rather a relative separation of individuals into categories that may be characterized as "usually dominant," "usually subordinate," and "sometimes dominant." Another complication arises in the attempt to solve these triangles, in that there is a constant shifting in the dominance status of each animal, which may be attributed to injury, old age, maturing, threatening, etc. That any of these factors may also be operating during the solution of any of these triangles is obvious.

TABLE III

TWO SERIES OF DOMINANCE-SUBORDINATION RELATIONSHIPS AMONG
SIX FEMALES (DS SERIES)

Beetle Number	Rank		Beetles Subordinated				
			Series 1				
15..........	2	20	16	..	18	17	..
17..........	2	20	16	19	18	..	..
18..........	4	20	16	..	..	..	..
19..........	2	20	16	..	18	..	15
16..........	5	20	..	..	..	..	..
20..........	6	..	..	..	..	..	..
			Series 2				
15..........	1	20	16	19	18	17	..
17..........	3	20	..	19	18	..	..
18..........	3	20	16	19	..	..	..
19..........	5	20	..	..	..	..	..
16..........	3	20	..	19	..	17	..
20..........	6	..	..	..	..	..	..

DISCUSSION

It may be seen from the foregoing experiments and observations that relationships of dominance and subordination are not restricted to social animals (animals normally living in more or less organized aggregations), though it is among these where this phenomenon attains its fullest expression. Thus, there is the distinction between "peck right," as shown in flocks of hens, which have a strict linear dominance (Allee 1938; Collias 1944) and "peck dominance" which is more characteristic of a looser social organization. The latter type of organization is characterized by frequent triangles, shifts in social status, etc. This sort of organization may be found in canaries and parakeets (Allee 1938). Until further data on the invertebrates are available, it is perhaps unwise to propose an analogy between the behavior of any invertebrate and any vertebrate group. Regardless of its degree of development, the attribute of dominance may be employed in various ways by different animals. One of the most common of these is the establishment and maintenance of territories, as shown in birds (Howard 1920; Nice 1933), in lizards (Evans 1936), etc., among the vertebrates, and among the invertebrates, territorialism has been demonstrated in fiddler crabs (Crane 1941) and wasps (Pardi 1948). From the observations made on *Tenebrio,* however, no display of territorialism was given. It has been shown that there is not a strict dominance-subordination arrangement. The effect that the dominant and subordinate actions of the individuals has upon the population is that the dominants eventually prove to be the survivors. They are the individuals that are left after successive injuring encounters have finally killed the subordinates. And they are the ones which will be the reproducing individuals, thus showing a tendency to prevent reproduction by the weaker individuals.

There are several conflicting views concerning the significance of the phenomenon of dominance and subordination. It is the view of Schjelderup-Ebbe, based on observations on many species of birds, that "despotism is the basic idea of the world, indissolubly bound up with all life and existence. On it rests the meaning of the struggle for existence" (quoted in Allee 1938, p. 161). On the other hand, Allee adopts the view that "competition, by establishing degrees of dominance and subordination, whether in the ecological or human sense, may furnish a basis for more effective community cooperation. Such organized communities may then compete with each other and the less fit cooperating systems may be weeded out to the general advantage of the survivors at least" (Allee 1940, p. 160).

The two views are not mutually exclusive, though they might appear to be so at first glance. On the one hand, the activities of *Tenebrio* seem to fit into the "despotism" scheme of Schjelderup-Ebbe in that there never is built up a rigid scheme by which the animals can cooperate against other groups as a unit. But on the other hand, there is an advantage not only to the survivors (which is in accord with Allee's view), but also to the species population, in that only the strongest survive to reproduce.

SUMMARY

1. A group of four males was tested on seven consecutive days for dominance and subordination. The dominant status of each individual was found to be commensurate with his size and degree of

injury. The two larger beetles were consistently dominant over the two smaller beetles. Loss of a mesothoracic leg by one of the larger beetles seemed to have little effect on its dominant status, whereas loss of an antenna by one of the smaller individuals was the only apparent morphological difference which might have contributed to its consistently subordinate status, relative to the other beetle.

2. In a group of ten males, each met each of the other three times in trials for dominance and subordination. A tendency toward stabilization of relative dominance standings was found on subsequent encounters. Ties and triangles (A dominant over B, B over C, and C over A) were frequent. Retests of the triangles were inconclusive.

3. In a group of six females, each meeting each of the others twice, the results were similar to those found in the male group. Again, ties and triangles were characteristic.

4. Preliminary tests showed that in mixed groups, the female assumed the subordinate role except when considerably larger than the male.

5. No linear order of dominance was established (as is characteristic of non-social animals). The individuals may best be characterized as "usually dominant," "usually subordinate," or "sometimes dominant."

6. Factors contributing to dominance are sex, size, degree of injury, and age as an adult (time from emergence from the pupal case).

7. A possible adaptive significance of such relationships of dominance and subordination is discussed briefly.

REFERENCES

ALLEE, W. C.   1938. The social life of animals. New York: Norton.
———.   1940. Concerning the origin of sociality in animals. Scientia, **67**:154–60.
COLLIAS, N. E.   1944. Aggressive behavior among vertebrate animals. Physiol. Zool., **17**:83–123.
CRANE, J.   1941. Crabs of the genus *Uca* from the west coast of Central America. Zoologica, **26**:145–208.
EVANS, L. T.   1936. A study of the social hierarchy in the lizard *Anolis carolinensis*. Jour. Genet. Psych., **48**:88–111.
HOWARD, H. E.   1920. Territory in bird life. London: Murray.
NICE, M. M.   1933. The theory of territorialism and its development. *In* Fifty Years' Progress of American Ornithology. Lancaster: American Ornithologists' Union.
PARDI, L.   1948. Dominance order in *Polistes* wasps. Physiol. Zool., **21**:1–13.

CHAPTER 9

CONSUMMATORY ACTIVITY:
MOTIVATION VIEWED AS BEHAVIOR

Motivation is an overburdened concept that we have used sparingly. Much of what is generally included under the concept of motivation is treated in this book under the headings of instinct and learning. For example, mating behavior, often treated as sex drive, is subsumed here under the concept of instinct; and the concepts of anticipation and incentive are treated in the chapters on learning. The present chapter is concerned with enlarging upon this indirect coverage in a way that is consistent with the behavioral approach which is followed in the rest of the book.

An objective and restricted way to view motivation is to view it as motivated behavior. Specifically, we mean by this the behavior which regularly consummates or terminates a recurring behavior sequence (see instinct, page 218). Such behavior is typically called consummatory behavior and refers to eating, drinking, copulation, brooding, grooming, manipulating objects (when an organism is exploring), etc. Some of the characteristics of the stimuli which elicit consummatory behavior have been the subject of considerable attention in the instinct chapters.

THORSON, G. Reproduction and larval ecology of marine bottom invertebrates. *Biol. Rev.*, 1950, **25**, 1–45.
Many invertebrates shed sexual products only if two sexes are in close proximity, and in some species females will *not* shed eggs unless active sperm are in the water.

Most consummatory behaviors are characterized by being dependent upon an extended chain of antecedent conditions. For example, eating follows a period of food deprivation and copulation follows courting. Even among naïve organisms consummatory behaviors, as specific occurrences, are highly predictable. This means that such behavior is the most strongly and directly elicited portion of a behavior sequence, or the portion least dependent on learning. For instance, in the case of a male rat in a box with a receptive female intromission is considered the consummatory response, and both the form of the response and the eliciting stimuli can be readily predicted or specified.

On the other hand, the behaviors leading up to the consummatory response, at least at the higher phylogenetic levels, are much less predictable. These behaviors, when they are involved in instinctive sequences, are called appetitive behaviors and are found both among invertebrates and vertebrates. The behaviors leading up to consummatory response are also called instrumental acts or operant behavior and will be studied in detail in the subsequent chapters on learning. Initially, instrumental behavior is under less control of unlearned stimulus-response relationships than consummatory behavior, being quite variable and relatively unpredictable for a given stimulus situation. But once a learned behavior sequence has been established the instrumental components become quite predictable, though hardly ever to the degree of consummatory behavior. Hopefully the present discussion has served to highlight this chapter as being transitional between the instinct section and the learning section.

LEES, A. D.   The sensory physiology of the sheep tick, *Ixodesricinus. J. Exp. Biol.*, 1948, 25, 145–207.
    The hungry sheep tick crawls to the tip of a blade of grass, ready to encounter a host; when satiated with blood it drops to the base of the grass stalk. The single appetitive or instrumental act of climbing the blade of grass for food is, in this case, quite like the consummatory act.

Measurement of Consummatory Behavior

Consummatory behavior is regularly measured or quantified. The amount of dry or wet food eaten in a given unit of time and the time it takes to begin eating once food is presented (latency of eating behavior) are examples of measures which are frequently used. To sound a note of caution, it turns out that these two measures, latency of eating and amount eaten, are less well correlated than one might expect, as shown by Chance and Mead (1955**) and by Moll (1959). Other common measures include the number of cc's of liquid drunk in unit time, the rate of licking for a liquid incentive, the number of intromissions per session by a male animal, and the number of contacts with a novel stimulus during exploration. These measures are generously illustrated in the selected studies; and the relative strengths of some consummatory behaviors in terms of these measures are assessed in the study by Zimbardo and Montgomery (1957*).

Brain Stimulation and the Absence of True Consummatory Be-

havior. A laboratory preparation has been developed, using implanted electrodes, that permits an experimenter to deliver small, momentary electrical pulses to a subcortical region of an animal's brain, say the hypothalamus. This procedure is called brain stimulation. The apparatus can be arranged so that an instrumental response by the animal produces the brain stimulation (see Olds, 1958**). In this behavioral sequence there is no true consummatory behavior to be measured. The animal's response, such as treadle-pressing, terminates a behavior sequence so far as overt responding is concerned, but the response is also obviously instrumental: it is learned, it may take many forms, and it can be quickly extinguished when brain stimulation is omitted.

However, the behavior associated with brain stimulation is also clearly in the motivational fold. This is true for the following reasons: (*a*) effective brain stimulation has either strong approach (positive) or strong avoidance (negative) properties; (*b*) the response mediating the common positive variety is quickly learned and often occurs in preference to eating or drinking in nonsatiated animals; (*c*) as the article by Olds indicates, behavior associated with brain stimulation reflects the same relationships as are observed in actual consummatory behavior for food and sex. In summary, brain stimulation behavior can be viewed as a special case of motivated behavior which is measured by rate of treadle-pressing or bar-pressing (number of presses per unit of time). The rate of responding varies with a number of factors, including such variables as placement of electrode and amount of electric current. The unusual circumstance about brain stimulation behavior is that it occurs without overt consummatory behavior as the final response in the sequence. This can be related to speculation that overt consummatory behavior may always involve some sort of electrical discharge in the subcortex.

The Variables That Affect Consummatory Behavior

Deprivation and Satiation. Many conditions influence consummatory behavior, but it appears safe to say that consummatory activity is always influenced to some extent by conditions of deprivation or satiation. One characteristic of these conditions is that they do not have an immediate effect upon the organism's behavior. In fact, food deprivation early in life may increase the degree of consummatory behavior many weeks later in life (Elliot and King 1960; Marx, 1952).

Under deprivation conditions the object toward which the consummatory act is directed (*the incentive*) is the object which is typically manipulated: deprivation of food, deprivation of water, deprivation of sex object, deprivation of young, etc. The procedure for establishing a deprivation condition, at least for most animals, can be rather complex. In the case of the sluggish turtle it is possible to speed up the process of food deprivation by forcing the turtle to exercise. One way to do this is to set the turtle on the ring of a ringstand with its legs hanging in air, thereby eliciting walking without locomotion. The Japanese quail, *Coturnix coturnix Japonica,* on the other hand, can be deprived just once for food or water for a period of several hours and then show considerable consummatory behavior.

However, for animals like the rat, effective food deprivation typically includes placing the animal on a reduced eating schedule (regimen) for 10 to 20 days. While on the regimen the animal eats a limited amount of food or eats for a limited amount of time each day at the same hour. This procedure has a cumulative effect on the organism, bringing about extensive weight loss. When the animal is tested for consummatory behavior, it has also been deprived of all food for a specified number of hours, e.g., 12, 24, or 48 hours. A further refinement of this series of manipulations is to specify the level of deprivation by specifying that the animal attain and maintain a certain percent of its original body weight when feeding was *ad libitum* or unrestricted, e.g., 80 percent of the original body weight.

Deprivation conditions can also include depriving the animal of more than one incentive at a time. As the result of multiple deprivation some rather complex interactions emerge, as can be seen below.

GREGERSON, M. I.   Studies on the regulation of water intake. II. Conditions affecting the daily water intake of dogs as registered continuously by a potometer. *Amer. J. Physiol.,* 1932, 102, 344–49.

Dogs on a reduced feeding schedule drink only one fourth their normal intake in a 24-hour period, doing all their drinking 2–5 hours after eating.

VERPLANCK, W. S. and HAYES, J. R.   Eating and drinking as a function of maintenance schedule. *J. Comp. Physiol. Psychol.,* 1953, 46, 327–33.

Animals under water deficit eat considerably less food (relatively dry) than when ample water is available and vice versa (see Gregerson).

ZIMBARDO, P. G. and MONTGOMERY, K. C.   The relative strengths of consummatory responses in hunger, thirst, and exploratory drive. *J. Comp. Physiol. Psychol.,* 1957, 50, 504–8.

Food and water deprivation, as such, result in a decrement in exploratory behavior. In the presence of the incentive, hungry rats in a normal situation explore first and then eat, while very thirsty rats drink first and then explore. The conflict between consummatory activity and exploring results in alternating these behaviors.

A manipulation which is the reverse of deprivation is satiation. Here the animal is permitted to have extended commerce with the incentive with the result that its consummatory behavior is altered markedly. Typically, satiation reduces or temporarily eliminates the consummatory behavior. In the cumalative response curve in Figure 9–1 the flattening out of the curve represents a failure to eat after extended feeding.

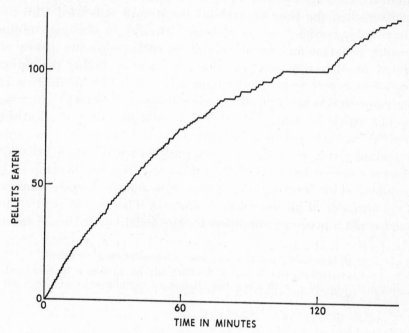

Fig. 9–1. Change in the rate of ingestion during a daily eating period. At each elevation of the writing point the rat obtained and ate a pellet of food. Note the delay and subsequent recovery toward the end of the period.

It would seem that increasing the deprivation level would produce a corresponding increase in consummatory behavior, and this is generally true fairly soon after the inception of deprivation conditions. But Moll (1959) has found that rats kept at 90 percent of their original body weight initially ate more in a 5-minute period than rats kept at 80 percent of original body weight (higher deprivation level), though as might be expected the eating latencies of the 90 percent group were initially longer. With continued test trials all differences between the two groups disappeared, indicating that the relation between deprivation level and consummatory behavior, at least among rats, is not very simple.

Prior Learning. The effect of a regimen of water deprivation is usually different from a regimen of food deprivation. With water deprivation there is little, if any, cumulative effect from repeated cycles of deprivation. Yet placing an animal on a reduced drinking schedule for several days (4–5) yields a definite gain in consummatory behavior. Here the variable is presumably one of learning. This same variable also enhances consummatory behavior following a regimen of food deprivation. What is meant here is that if an animal drinks all of its water for one day at the same hour of the day over a series of days, then the time of day and the stimuli associated with this time of day become cues (conditioned stimuli) for eliciting consummatory behavior and hence specify or enhance consummatory activity. Another way of saying this, if you wish, is that the animal learns to *expect* water at the hour when it is presented. This induced cyclical behavior is like getting hungry at 12 noon by humans.

The article by James (1960**) illustrates the effect of a learning variable on consummatory behavior. The social facilitation of eating in puppies (the presence of other pups increases eating behavior) does not appear immediately but takes some time to develop or be acquired. This learning takes place even though there is plenty of food available at all times for all animals. That is, competition for food is not a necessary condition for the social facilitation of eating.

CAPRETTA, P. J. An experimental modification of food preference in chickens. *J. Comp. Physiol. Psychol.*, 1961, 54, 238–42. (role of learning)

Food preferences can be reduced materially by pairing a specific food, designated by color, with a noxious alimentary stimulus such as a 'high salt loading.

KAHN, M. W. The effect of socially learned aggression or submission on the mating behavior of C57 mice. *J. Genet. Psychol.*, 1961, 98, 211–17.

Male mice trained to be aggressive showed significantly more sexual approach and contact behaviors with a female in heat than did male mice trained to be submissive. The submissive males were pursued by the females, and the females were in turn pursued by the aggressive males.

RABEDEAU, R. G. and WHALEN, R. E. Effects of copulatory experience on mating behavior in the male rat. *J. Comp. Physiol. Psychol.* 1959, 52, 482–84.

Highly arousable male rats that had initiated coitus within 15 minutes with a receptive female were little affected by prior sexual experience, but males of low responsiveness that had failed to initiate coitus within 15 minutes on three separate tests showed increased sexual behavior after copulatory experience.

Another factor which can enter the picture when the animal has learned to make a consummatory response in a specific stimulus context is frustration. Frustration exists when the expected incentive has been removed or made inaccessible; when this is true consummatory behavior in the complete sense is no longer possible. Consummatory behavior may proceed, however, in a partial or displaced way. In young animals when the unavailable incentive is food this may result in nonnutritive sucking (e.g. thumbsucking), as seen in the article by Benjamin (1961**) using infant monkeys. A similar finding is illustrated in a study by Gerall (1958). In this case interruption of normal copulation in male guinea pigs results in a marked increase in their making advances toward males as opposed to females.

SANFORD, R. N. The effects of abstinence from food upon imaginal processes: a preliminary experiment. *J. Psychol.,* 1936, **2,** 129–36.

College students deprived of food over a considerable period of time show a marked incidence of imagined consummatory behavior with respect to all kinds of food images.

Nature of the Incentive. Considerable research has been directed at the effect of the incentive variable on instrumental behavior; considerably less research has been done on the effect of the incentive variable on consummatory behavior. Nevertheless, the available data permit certain broad, though tentative, generalizations.

1) What will serve as an incentive or consistent elicitor of consummatory behavior is usually quite specific and limited, especially for lower animal forms. (see Chapters 4 and 5). The range of incentives increases in the higher vertebrates with certain exceptions, as with the Koala bear which eats only eucalyptus leaves.

2) Over a fairly wide range of the phylogenetic scale the preference for one incentive over another can be altered by habituation or stimulus satiation effects. By habituation or stimulus satiation is meant the reduction in the eliciting value of a stimulus with its repeated or prolonged presentation. This is a fundamental principle of behavior that will be referred to repeatedly. This phenomenon, as reflected in consummatory behavior, is pointedly illustrated in human eating behavior where we typically want a change in menu across the week rather than broiled chicken and peas day in and day out. The habituation effect is illustrated in the behavior of honeybees in that bees are more sensitive to sugars before leaving the hive than when returning with nectar (Kunze, 1933). Similarly, bees will refuse diluted syrup solutions during the season of the year when nectar with a high sugar concentration is easily available, whereas such syrup is readily acceptable at other periods of the year (Von Frisch, 1936). In the sexual behavior of rats, guinea pigs, cattle, and man the replacement of the "old" sex partner by a novel partner clearly increases the sexual response, especially in males (Welker's chapter in Fiske and Maddi, 1961).

3) When concentration of a liquid incentive is the independent variable in the study of consummatory behavior there is usually an optimal concentration that is preferred over those below and above this value. Evidence for this generalization has been found in rats by Young and Asdourian, 1957 *) and Myers (1962) and in other investigations as, for example, in mice with sucaryl solutions (Smith and Ross, 1960).

YOUNG, P. T. and ASDOURIAN, D. Relative acceptability of sodium chloride and sucrose solutions. *J. Comp. Physiol. Psychol.,* 1957, **50,** 499–503.

No matter what concentrations were used, rats preferred sucrose solutions to salt solutions, though a .01 sodium chloride solution was preferred over distilled water.

The Stimulus Situation as a Variable. The general stimulus situation can affect consummatory behavior either by facilitating or hindering it. For worker ants, digging dirt is a consummatory activity and the presence of other workers influences this behavior. In general, the presence of other ants has a facilitating effect, but if an ant is put in the company of slow diggers its digging is slowed down, while just the opposite is true if placed among fast diggers (Chen, 1938).

Altering just one aspect of a familiar stimulus environment introduces competing stimuli which can retard consummatory behavior such as eating (Chance and Mead, 1955**). Such a dissruption of consummatory behavior could probably be used in a systematic way to identify the relevant stimulus elements in a given situation, for a particular class of organisms. When the addition or removal of an object or of some characteristic of an object shows a reliable effect upon consummatory behavior, then the object or characteristic can be classified as a stimulus element for this class of organisms. As might seem quite obvious, pure bulk (e.g., water) in the stomach also competes with the stimulus for eating and reduces this consummatory activity, though the effect is somewhat complex (Smith, Pool and Weinberg, 1962*).

SMITH, M., POOL, R., and WEINBERG, H. The role of bulk in the control of eating. *J. Comp. Physiol. Psychol.*, 1962, 55, 115–20.
    When the rat is eating less than its normal daily caloric requirement bulk stops the rat from consuming more. A rat may learn to increase somewhat its intake when 40 percent of the chow is cellulose, but it loses considerable weight and can only maintain its normal weight when the food being eaten is of high caloric density.

Other Variables. Among the additional factors which affect consummatory behavior is room temperature which influences alcohol consumption; rats drink more at 27° C. than at 18° C. (Myers, 1962). In rats the dark-light cycle is also important. The rat is a nocturnal beast and most active during the middle of the night. In this connection it has been found that the rat eats more in the evening, on the upswing of the cycle than in the morning on the downswing (Siegel, 1961*). The state of the organism, as produced by hormone manipulations is, of course, critical to consummatory behavior, particularly to sex and maternal care. Such variables are treated in detail in Chapter 6. Early experience, another variable, is covered in Chapter 7. Finally, direct manipulation of neural structure can affect consummatory behavior. Lesions in the hypothalamus produce two to three times the amount of normal eating behavior until the animal is strikingly obese (Miller and Bailey, 1960).

AMSEL, A. and MALTZMAN, I.   The effect upon generalized drive strength of emotionality as inferred from the level of the consummatory response. *J. Exp. Psychol.*, 1950, **40**, 563–69.

Rats given an electric shock, just before a drinking test in a situation which is *different* from that in which they are tested, drink more than they do without prior shock. Whereas, as shown in other studies, they drink less if shocked in the same situation in which they are later tested (see Sterritt).

MASON, W. A.   The effect of social restriction on the behavior of rhesus monkeys. I. Free Social Behavior. *J. Comp. Physiol. Psychol.*, 1960, **53**, 582–89.

Socially restricted for two years, male monkeys in particular show markedly deficient sexual behavior. They are responsive to receptive females but their performance is poorly integrated and unsuccessful. They also show less grooming behavior and more fighting than monkeys captured in the field. Note: This sexually deficient behavior is in contrast to what is observed in birds and in lower mammals, such as the rat, which is unaffected by isolation (Beach, 1958).

SIEGEL, P. S.   Food intake in the rat in relation to the dark-light cycle, *J. Comp. Physiol. Psychol.*, 1961, **54**, 294–301.

Food intake is maximal in rats from 7 to 10 P.M. under natural dark-light conditions. When the rats are maintained under constant light illumination the pattern soon disappears but returns when the dark-light cycle is restored.

STERRITT, G. M.   Inhibition and facilitation of eating by electric shock. *J. Comp. Physiol. Psychol.*, 1962, **55**, 226–29.

Hungry rats when shocked for 5 seconds ate more pellets during the period of shock than during any other 5-second period without shock. They also ate more pellets than an unshocked control group for the same 5-second period. But during the "shock-off" period, the shocked animals ate less than the controls. In general, these findings confirm Ullman's 1951–52 results on "compulsive eating in rats." Shock was administered in the same box in which feeding occurred.

Phylogenetic Considerations in Consummatory Behavior

When we assume the posture of the comparative psychologist, we see at least one phylogenetic trend emerging from the data on consummatory behavior. That is, the number and variety of stimuli to which consummatory behavior is directed seems to increase with phyletic level. Low in the phylogenetic scale, the organisms have only fixed action patterns to specific stimulus elements, as discussed in Chapters 4 and 5. At this level the stimuli which elicit consummatory behavior and the responses which are made are often so reliably identified that they are used as taxonomic characters. Since these fixed behavior patterns are not subject to rapid evolutionary change they are *especially* useful in making taxonomic classifications (Tinbergen, 1951). In general, the higher one goes in the phylogenetic scale the greater the diversity of stimuli for consummatory behavior within a species. For example, so-called aberrations in sex behavior (homosexuality, masturbation, mounting unreceptive females, attempts to direct consummatory behavior toward inanimate objects or other animals, etc.) are almost completely lacking in lower forms but clearly appear in mammals, such as commonly observed in male dogs and as previously mentioned in guinea pigs (Gerall, 1958). Among chimpanzees and other infrahuman primates the sexual deviations come close to reaching the level of human sexual behavior as regards the various directions the behavior may take (Nissen's chapter in Stone, *Comparative Psychology*, 1951). In mammals, in general, when the normal incentive is absent or unattainable other stimuli are frequently responded to. Other higher vertebrate forms, such as birds, also display these substitute behaviors as when a greylag goose will accept a round rock for an egg when brooding (Tinbergen, *The Study of Instinct*, 1951). But here *roundness* is *the* stimulus (sign stimulus) and, as such, is probably being responded to in a particulate fashion.

What we have just been stressing is the phenomenon of behavioral plasticity. This phenomenon can be described in terms of S–R relationships. On one hand plasticity means that many different stimuli can elicit the same consummatory response. This could be called a stimulus generalization principle for unlearned responses and can be schematized as follows:

$$\left.\begin{array}{l} S_1 \\ S_2 \\ S_3 \\ S_4 \end{array}\right\} R \quad \begin{array}{l} \text{The greater the number of stimuli associated} \\ \text{with a consummatory response the greater the} \\ \text{plasticity.} \end{array}$$

Another way in which consummatory behavior may be involved in behavioral plasticity is that novel stimuli are incentives for the consummatory responses of investigation and manipulation, at the higher phylogenetic levels. When this happens the opportunity for many kinds of approach behavior is greatly increased. This in turn means that the opportunity for learning a multitude of associated response patterns is greatly increased. In other words, the availability of an incentive, such as food or water (reinforcer), or the opportunity to make many kinds of consummatory response is often contingent upon first exploring or manipulating the novel stimuli in the environment. These instrumental responses are thus learned, and this learning contributes immeasurably to the plasticity of behavior (novelty as an incentive is also referred to in Chapter 11).

A third and related way in which plasticity of behavior is effected, though not expressly through consummatory behavior, is that the same stimulus can innately elicit many different responses. This phenomenon is frequently labeled an unlearned response hierarchy (repertoire, array) and is typical of higher vertebrates. It can be schematized as follows:

$$S \begin{cases} R_1 \\ R_2 \\ R_3 \\ R_4 \end{cases}$$ The greater the number of responses elicited by the stimulus the greater the plasticity.

Some Summarizing Thoughts

A restricted way to view motivation is in terms of consummatory behavior. Such a view, though not the one of the typical textbook, is consistent with the current research emphasis as reflected in the journals.

Consummatory behavior is especially involved in the plasticity of behavior. In general, the higher the species the more plastic the behavior. Plasticity implies the following: (*a*) many different stimuli can elicit the same consummatory response; (*b*) novelty can function as an incentive eliciting behavior from which plastic instrumental behavior develops; (*c*) more than one type of response can be elicited by the same stimulus (incentive).

ADDITIONAL SUMMARIZED STUDIES

HINDE, R. A. The conflict between drives in the courtship and copulation of the chaffinch (*Fringella coelebs*). *Behav.*, 1953, 5, 1–31.

During normal courtship of chaffinches the male and female are primarily in a conflict between sex (approach) and fear (fleeing). The stronger the soliciting pattern of the female and the stronger the sex drive in the male the more likely copulation will be successful. Yet the closer the birds get to each other the stronger the tendency to flee or to act aggressively. Thus, the resultant behavior sequences for male and female are quite diverse.

JAMES, W. T. Social facilitation of eating behavior in puppies after satiation. *J. Comp. Physiol. Psychol.*, 1953, 46, 427–28.

Here, social facilitation referred to eating more in group than in individual feeding situations. Dominant beagle-terrier puppies were less affected by the variable of social facilitation than submissive animals. It was suggested that dominant animals enter into *any* activity in a vigorous fashion, even when satiated for the relevant incentive.

THE EFFECT OF RESTRAINT UPON COPULATORY

BEHAVIOUR IN THE RAT

By KNUT LARSSON

Department of Psychology, University of Göteborg

Ejaculation in the rat is preceded by a series of intromissions each separated from its predecessor by a short intercopulatory interval (ICI). When these intervals are artificially prolonged the number of intromissions required before ejaculation is effectively decreased (Gerall, 1958; Larsson, 1956; Rasmussen—unpublished), an extension to 1 minute duration reducing the frequency of intromission by half its normal value. Enforced intervals of up to 5 minutes give similar results, but short restraints lasting 15 seconds are ineffective. These findings show that the time factor plays an important part in regulating the processes of excitation which underly this aspect of mating behaviour, but so far the precise relationship between the duration of the ICI and number of intromissions necessary to achieve ejaculation has not been determined. The present experiment describes the effect of varying this interval from 0.1 minute to 2 minutes.

MATERIALS AND METHODS

Animals

Observations were made on the mating behaviour of eleven male rats approximately 12 months old whose mean weight was 372g. (range 346–404g.). All had previously taken part in similar experiments. The females used for mating were treated with 10μg. oestradiol benzoate 36 hours before being presented to the male.

Conduct of Tests

The animals were observed in open cages placed on the laboratory floor. After the male had been given time to adapt to the mating cage a female was introduced and was gently withdrawn as soon as intromission had occurred. The female was then reintroduced after a specified interval of time and again withdrawn immediately after the second intromission. This procedure was repeated until ejaculation had taken place, after which the male was rested for 4–5 days before further testing.

Measurement of Intercopulatory Intervals

A stopwatch graduated in 1/100 sec. was used to time (1) the interval between the presentation of the female to the male and the entry of the penis into the vagina (copulatory latency), and (2) the enforced intercopulatory interval, measured from the moment of intromission to the next presentation of the female. Intercopulatory intervals of 0.0 (*ad lib.*), 0.1, 0.2, 0.4, 0.6, 0.8, 1.0 and 2.0 minutes were enforced in this way, the performance of each rat being observed in relation to each ICI in accordance with a prearranged schedule.

RESULTS

Normal Duration of the Intercopulatory Interval

The duration of the ICI in the unrestrained rat is illustrated in Figure 1, which shows that 19 per cent. of all intervals were shorter than 0.1 minutes, 61 per cent. shorter than 0.2 minutes, and 85 per cent. shorter than 0.4 minutes. Only one interval was longer than 0.6 minutes.

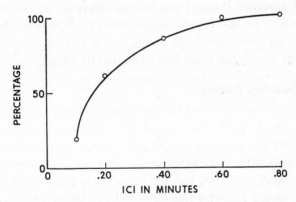

FIG. 1. The cumulative distribution curve showing length of the ICI in animals copulating *ad lib.* The abscissa gives the length of the ICI in hundredths of a minute, the ordinate the percentage of intervals not exceeding each duration.

Effect of Enforced ICI on Frequency of Intromission

The relationship between the number of intromissions preceding ejaculation and the duration of an enforced ICI is given in Figure 2. When the animals were allowed to copulate *ad lib.*, the mean number of intromissions was 7.8. Prolongation of the ICI from 0.2 to 0.4

minutes resulted in a decrease in the number of intromissions from
8.9 to 5.2, a still greater reduction being recorded when the intervals

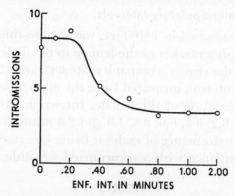

FIG. 2. The effect of restraint on the number of intromissions preceding ejaculation.
The abscissa gives the length of the enforced
ICI, and the ordinate the mean number of
intromissions preceding ejaculation.

were extended to 0.6 and 0.8 minutes. Thereafter, no further decrease took place even when the interval was prolonged to 2 minutes.
Analysis of variance showed the overall decrease in the number of
intromissions to be statistically significant $(P > 0.001)$ while the individual decrease resulting from an enforced ICI of 0.4 minutes was
significant at the 5 per cent level (single-tail t-test).

Effect of Copulatory Latency

The length of the interval between intromissions is slightly longer
than that recorded as ICI owing to the latency between the presentation of the female to the male and the occurrence of intromission.
The mean copulatory latency for the first intromission of animals
allowed to copulate *ad lib.* was 0.1 minute, and for rats in which an
ICI of 0.1 and 0.2 minutes was enforced the latencies were 0.07 and
0.06 minutes respectively. When the ICI exceeded 0.2 minutes the
male became highly excited, hurrying to the female and copulating
with the shortest possible latency. Premature ejaculation was sometimes seen. On two occasions when the female was dropped into the
mating cage the male took a few steps forward, stopped suddenly and
ejaculated in the air 20-30 cm. away from the female.

DISCUSSION

These results emphasise the importance of the variable of time for
the elicitation of mating behaviour. Successive intromissions may be

considered as building up an excitatory state which culminates in the ejaculatory reflex. Each intromission makes its individual contribution to this rising excitation, the extent of which, however, depends on the time relationships of the sequential sensory inputs. When a very short interval separates two copulations the excitatory effect of the first intromission has not reached its maximal height before that of the second supervenes. The full effect of each intromission does not appear to be realised for about 0.5 minutes and since, in the unrestrained rat, the intromissions succeed each other at very short intervals, the maximal effects of each are never attained. When, however, intercopulatory intervals are artificially prolonged and the full effect of each intromission can be utilised and the number of copulations necessary to cause ejaculation radically lowered, even to the extent that the reflex can appear in the absence of sensory stimulation from the glans penis. The optimum duration of the enforced ICI would seem to lie between 0.6 and 0.8 minutes, and the failure of longer intervals to cause any further decrease in the number of intromissions suggests that after 1.0 second the excitatory effect of each intromission begins to wane.

SUMMARY

Intervals, ranging from 0.1 to 2.0 minutes, have been enforced between the several intromissions of penis into vagina which comprise the copulatory behaviour of the rat.

The number of intromissions required for ejaculation is reduced as a result of increasing this intercopulatory interval. This reduction becomes significant when an interval of 0.4 minutes is enforced and is even more marked after an interval of 0.6 minutes.

In such circumstances the animals become excited, show a reduced copulatory latency, and may exhibit premature ejaculation.

ACKNOWLEDGMENTS

This study has been supported by the Magnus Bergwall Foundation. The hormone products used in this experiment were generously supplied by Pharmacia Corporation, Uppsala, Sweden.

REFERENCES

GERALL, A. A. (1958). Effect of interruption of copulation on male guinea pig sexual behaviour. *Psychol. Rep.,* 4, 215–21.

LARSSON, K. (1956). *Conditioning and sexual behaviour in the male albino rat.* Stockholm: Almqvist and Wiksell. p. 269.

RASMUSSEN, E. W. The effect of an enforced pause between each coitus on the number of copulations necessary to achieve ejaculation in the albino rat. *Unpublished manuscript.*

THE DEVELOPMENT OF SOCIAL FACILITATION

OF EATING IN PUPPIES*

W. T. JAMES [1]

Department of Psychology, University of Georgia

A. INTRODUCTION

A number of experiments have shown that animals eat more in group than in individual feeding. This has been demonstrated in fish (13), birds (2, 3, 12), rats (5), monkeys (6), and dogs (7, 8, 9, 10, 11). Reviews of the literature pertinent to this problem have been made by Crawford (4) and by Smith and Ross (12).

The question of whether social facilitation of eating is a natural response or is dependent on learning has been neglected. Harlow suggests that this form of social facilitation is independent of experience in rats.

A study at the University of Georgia indicated that learning was important for social facilitation in dogs. In this experiment three puppies were reared in isolation after weaning and were fed separately for 90 days, while a second group of three puppies was reared and fed together for the first 90 days of life. After this interval, both groups were tested in group and individual eating for 40 days to determine the effect of social facilitation on food intake. Those animals which were reared and fed separately did not show social facilitation at once, but did show it after two weeks experience. Those which were reared and fed together exhibited social facilitation at the beginning of the tests. It was concluded that secondary reinforcement of eating develops in the social feeding situation in dogs, and that it is specific to eating and not generalized from other forms of social activity.

In the above study social facilitation was not measured until after four months of age. It is of interest to determine how early this form of facilitation may develop in young animals.

* Received in the Editorial Office on September 9, 1958.
[1] This research was supported by the Graduate School of the University of Georgia.

B. PROBLEM

The problem in the present experiment was to observe the development of social facilitation in two groups of puppies as soon as they were shifted from sucking to eating.

C. METHOD AND PROCEDURE

A litter of 10 predominately hound puppies were used in the experiment. They were born in the psychology laboratory of the University of Georgia and remained together for the 21-days nursing period. At this time, they were separated into two groups of five animals each and placed on schedules of one feeding per day for 40 days. The food consisted of wet mash of Purina Dog Chow. On some days the animals of each group were fed separately (*S* single) and on other days were fed as a group (*T* together). The feeding schedule of Group 1 was as follows: TSSTTSSSTTSSSSSTTTSTTTTTTTTSSTTTT-SSTTSSTT. The schedule of Group 2 was just the opposite program, that is, while the members of Group 1 were fed together, those of Group 2 were fed separately and visa versa. The amount of food consumed under each condition was determined by weighing each puppy before and after eating. The animals were given plenty of time to finish in every case, and were not removed from the feeding situation until they had had an opportunity to return to the pan if they desired. Every attempt was made to rule out competition for food. A large pan was used in which each dog could eat without difficulty, and each time more food was placed in the pan than the animals could eat.

D. RESULTS

Curves have been constructed of the food intake of each animal under individual and social feeding. On examination of the curves it was quite evident that the puppies were eating more in social feeding after a number of tests. After these curves separated, the animals never did eat as much in individual as in social feeding. The curves did not separate at exactly the same time in each case, as one would expect, and in only one dog did they separate immediately. The number of days feeding under each condition before the animals began definitely to eat more in the social situation is shown in Table 1. The table also shows the number of times each animal had eaten together and separately before the appearance of social facilitation.

The average number of days before there was a definite difference in favor of social eating was 16 for Group 1, and 9.2 for Group 2. The number of days these animals were fed in social or individual feeding before this occurred can be obtained from Table 1.

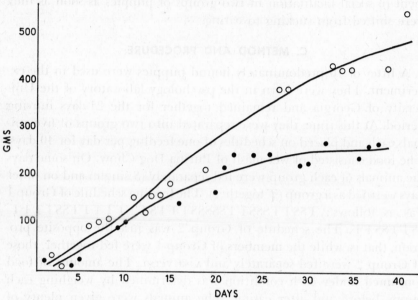

FIG. 1. This figure shows the average food intake of single feeding ●, and social feeding ○ of Group 1 for the 40-day tests.

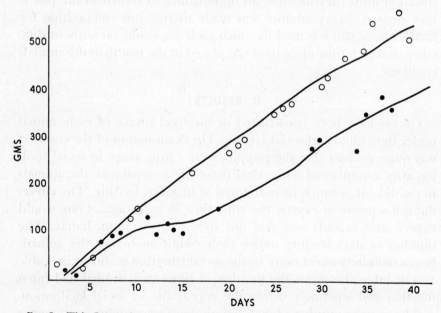

FIG. 2. This figure shows the average food intake of single feeding ●, and social feeding ○ of Group 2 for the 40-day tests.

Figures 1 and 2 show the curves of the average food intake for each day of both groups under S and T which have been smoothed out by inspection. This gives an over-all picture of the behavior.

The results of this study seem to substantiate the previous one that a period of eating together is required for the development of social facilitation in puppies. Apparently some of the factors involved in group eating act as reinforcing stimuli and increase eating behavior together. It is quite evident that social facilitation develops early in young puppies.

TABLE 1

NUMBER OF DAYS INDIVIDUAL AND SOCIAL FEEDING
BEFORE EACH DOG ATE MORE TOGETHER

Dog	Days for curves to separate	S. feeding	T. feeding
	Group 1		
173	19	8	11
174	12	5	7
175	26	15	11
176	3	1	2
177	22	11	11
	Group 2		
168	9	5	4
169	7	4	3
170	11	6	5
171	8	5	3
172	12	7	5

E. SUMMARY

Two groups of five puppies each were studied for the effect of social facilitation in eating as soon as they were weaned. On some days the members of each group were fed together, while on other days they were fed singly for a total of 40 days. The results indicated that social facilitation appeared after a number of social feedings in each animal except one. In one puppy it appeared on the first social feeding. Once social facilitation appeared the animals always ate more in the social situation. This study would seem to corroborate the previous one that secondary reinforcement of eating develops as the animals eat in groups and is not generalized from other forms of social activity.

REFERENCES

1. BAYER, E. Bietrage zur Zweikomponenten Theorie des Hungers. *Zsch. f. Psych.,* 1929, **112,** 1–54.
2. BREED, F. S. The development of certain instincts and habits in chicks. *Behav. Monog.,* 1911, **1,** No. 1.
3. CRAIG, W. Observations on doves learning to drink. *J. Anim. Behav.,* 1912, **2,** 273–79.

4. CRAWFORD, M. P. The social psychology of the vertebrates. *Psychol. Bull.*, 1939, 36, 407–46.
5. HARLOW, H. F. Social facilitation of feeding in the albino rat. *J. Genet. Psychol.*, 1932, 41, 211–21.
6. HARLOW, H. F., and YUDKIN, H. C. Social behavior of primates: I. Social facilitation of feeding in the monkey and its relation to attitudes of ascendence and submission. *J. Comp. Psychol.*, 1933, 16, 171–85.
7. JAMES, W. T. Social facilitation of eating behavior in puppies after satiation. *J. Comp. & Physiol. Psychol.*, 1953, 46, 427–28.
8. JAMES, W. T., and CANNON, D. J. Variation in social facilitation of eating behavior in puppies. *J. Genet. Psychol.*, 1956, 87, 225–28.
9. JAMES, W. T., and GILBERT, T. F. The effect of social facilitation on food intake of puppies fed separately and together for the first 90 days of life. *Brit. J. Anim. Behav.*, 1955, 111, 131–33.
10. ROSS, S., and ROSS, J. G. Social facilitation of feeding behavior in dogs: I. Group and solitary feeding. *J. Genet. Psychol.*, 1949, 74, 97–108.
11. ──────. Social facilitation of feeding behavior in dogs: II. Feeding after satiation. *J. Genet. Psychol.*, 1949, 74, 293–304.
12. SMITH, W. I., and ROSS, S. The social behavior of vertebrates: A review of the literature (1930–1950). *Psychol. Bull.*, 1952, 49, 598–627.
13. WELTY, J. C. Experiments in group behavior of fishes. *Physiol. Zool.*, 1934, 7, 85–128.

THE EFFECT OF FRUSTRATION ON THE NONNUTRITIVE

SUCKING OF THE INFANT RHESUS MONKEY[1]

LORNA SMITH BENJAMIN[2]

University of Wisconsin

Children, monkeys, baboons, chimpanzees, calves, puppies, and goats have been observed to engage in one form or another of non-nutritive sucking (McKee and Honzik, 1961). Explanations for this behavior have been plentiful, and controversies, vigorous. Much of the literature has been concerned with determining the origin of this behavior (Benjamin, 1961; Ross, Fisher, and King, 1957). In addition to exploring the reasons for the existence of nonnutritive sucking, it would seem useful to determine variables temporarily affecting the level of nonnutritive sucking once it has appeared in a given organism. One such variable is frustration, and it has been reported to increase thumbsucking in children (Honzik, 1948; Langford, 1939) and chimpanzees (Jacobsen, Jacobsen, and Yoshioka, 1932). The purpose of the present experiment was to investigate the effect of this variable on the nonnutritive sucking of the infant rhesus monkey.

In the present experiment frustration was defined as delay and interference with the attainment of a preferred food object. Infant rhesus monkeys were frustrated by being required to wait for 250 sec. before a Plexiglas partition in an observation cage was lifted, allowing the Ss to attain a preferred fruit.

METHOD

Subjects

Ten infant rhesus monkeys were assigned by a random procedure into a group of five experimental Ss and a group of five control Ss. These monkeys had been separated from their mothers within 10 hr. after birth and housed individually

[1] Appreciation is expressed to H. F. Harlow under whose supervision this work was done, and to A. H. Erlebacher for her helpful assistance. This investigation was supported in part by the writer's predoctoral fellowship, MF-8915, from the Division of Research Grants, United States Public Health Service, and by grants to H. F. Harlow from the Ford Foundation and from the National Institutes of Health (Grant M-722).

[2] Now a United States Public Health Service Postdoctoral Fellow in Psychology, Department of Psychiatry, University Hospitals, Madison, Wisconsin.

in wire cages 15 in. by 18 in. by 24 in. All Ss. had displayed nonnutritive sucking during a preliminary observation period beginning at the age of 62 days. The Ss were 90 days of age when the experiment began.

Apparatus

A cylindrical Plexiglas observation cage, 31 in. in diameter and 23 in. high, was divided into halves by a Plexiglas partition (see Fig. 1). One half contained a large food dish with or without fruit, and the monkeys were restrained in the other half. This apparatus was enclosed within a Masonite cubicle equipped with one-way-vision windows placed so that all parts of the cage could be seen by the observer. A recycling cam timer indicated 10-sec. observation periods by an audio-visual signal.

Procedure

Test days were grouped in five-day weeks. The Ss started at 90 days of age with the sequence of treatments: 30 days of adaptation to the test situation, 15 normative days, 15 frustration days, and, finally, 15 extinction days. During the adaptation and normative periods the food dish behind the Plexiglas partition was empty for both groups. During the frustration period, the dish was empty for the control group but contained each individual's preferred fruit for the experimental group. During the extinction period, the food dish was again empty for both groups.

Adaptation of the monkey to E was facilitated by handling the infant beside its home cage and offering it bits of food—banana, grapes, or apple—before the evening formula every test day. The fruit accepted most readily by each infant of the experimental group (in most instances, banana) was the one placed in the dish of the observation cage during the 15 days of frustration. Following the handling period, the infant was given its evening formula in an order which was counterbalanced over days.

Exactly 2.5 hr. after the evening feeding, each monkey was taken to the observation cubicle by the tester. After gently placing the monkey into one half of the Plexiglas cage, the tester stood for 2 min. with one arm in the cage, allowing the monkey to hold his hand or petting the animal. After this adaptation period, the cage was rolled into the Masonite cubicle, the door closed, and, following a second 2-min. period, testing was initiated.

Observations were made during a 250-sec. session divided into 25 intervals 10 sec. long. "Nonnutritive sucking" was defined as closure of the lips around any part of the body for 1 sec. or more, and "nonsucking oral activity" as biting or licking any part of the body or environment. A check was made on a time-ruled observation sheet for all types of nonnutritive sucking and nonsucking oral activity that occurred during each 10-sec. period. The cumulative nonnutritive-sucking score and the cumulative nonsucking oral-activity score for any test session was the number of checked 10-sec. periods.

After the observation session, E opened the cubicle door, removed the Plexiglas partition, and closed the cubicle door again. For approximately 5 min. the animal had access to the dish, and if food was present, usually finished eating it. If the monkey had not finished eating by the end of this time, E carried both the S and the remaining food back to the home cage.

At the close of the test situation, E rated the over-all motor activity of the animal on a five-point scale ranging from *very active* to *asleep*. Recording was also made at this time of any unusual responses.

RESULTS

Nonnutritive Sucking

Figure 2 shows that nonnutritive sucking was increased during the frustration period. The scores of the experimental animals were clearly higher than those of the control animals during the frustration period and the first five extinction days. The mean sucking scores for experimental monkeys were 13.9, 19.3, and 14.9 during the normative, frustration, and extinction periods, respectively. The mean sucking scores for the controls were 14.9, 14.4, and 13.2 in the successive periods.

Fig. 1. Observation cage divided into halves by a Plexiglas partition.

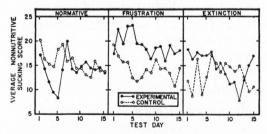

Fig. 2. Average daily nonnutritive sucking scores for experimental and control groups.

Comparisons of the experimental and control groups' daily scores by the Wilcoxon matched-pairs signed-ranks test showed a significant difference during the frustration period $(p < .01)$ and at no other time. The change in individual experimental animals' scores from the normative to the frustration period was greater than that of the individual control animals at a significance level of .05 by the Wilcoxon unpaired-replicates test. Nonnutritive sucking for one of the five experimental Ss took the form of sucking the scrotum, and for another, the penis. Both individuals showed increased nonnutritive sucking during frustration in accord with group trends.

Nonsucking Oral Activity

Analysis of the nonsucking oral-activity scores showed no significant differences by any test. The amount of nonsucking oral activity was small. The mean nonsucking oral-activity scores for the experimental group was 2.2, 1.5, and 2.2 for the normative, frustration, and extinction periods, respectively. The mean nonsucking oral-activity scores for the controls were 3.1, 3.1, and 3.9 in the successive periods.

Relationship between Nonnutritive Sucking and Nonsucking Oral Activity

Those individuals whose mean nonnutritive sucking scores ranked highest, tended to have the lowest-ranking mean nonsucking oral-activity scores. A Kendall's tau (Siegel, 1956, pp. 213–222) of —.42 described this reciprocal relationship, and it was significant at the .05 level.

Motor Activity

Ratings of activity on a five-point scale showed a slight and nonsignificant tendency for the experimental animals to be more active during frustration and for the control animals to show a progressive decline in activity with age and/or adaptation. Mean activity scores for the experimental animals during normative, frustration, and extinction periods were 2.5, 2.6, and 2.5, respectively, and the mean activity scores for the control animals were 2.8, 2.4, and 2.2 for the successive periods.

Behavior during Frustration

There was only one occurrence of a behavior indicating disturbance such as crouching or rocking (see Smith, 1960, Experiment III). Typical behavior of the experimental animals during the frustration period included sitting in front of the partition looking at the dish of food, jumping up and down vigorously, and moving back and forth in front of the cup while watching it continuously.

DISCUSSION

The data showed that nonnutritive sucking was increased by frustration, defined as delay and interference with the attainment of a preferred food object. The experimental animals clearly sucked more than controls during the frustration period, but not during the normative or extinction periods. Scores of the experimental animals remained above those of the control animals for the first five days of the extinction period probably because the experimental Ss did not extinguish immediately and were frustrated by no longer finding food in the dish (Tinklepaugh, 1932). Support for this suggestion is found in the observation that during early extinction, the experimental animals rushed to the dish when the partition was lifted and vocalized while inspecting it.

The present experimental definition of frustration as delay and interference with the attainment of a preferred food object is specific and limited, and the obtained data confirm for monkeys in a specific instance the more general clinical finding that frustration increases thumbsucking in children. They do not show that frustration in general leads to an increase in nonnutritive sucking in monkeys.

Since there was food behind the partition during frustration in the present experiment, a learning theorist might regard the nonnutritive sucking responses during frustration to be fractional anticipatory goal responses. Thumbsucking is not, however, an obviously relevant fractional part of the goal response of eating fruit. Biting, licking, and mouthing are more appropriate to eating fruit, but these nonsucking oral activities did not increase during frustration. Hence, it does not seem that the increase in thumb sucking was a simple anticipation of eating fruit.

A learning theorist might also suggest that the observed increase in nonnutritive sucking during frustration was due to the primary reinforcement of the nonnutritive sucking responses which preceded the ultimate attainment of food. If this is so, then one would expect that all other responses preceding the attainment of food would have also increased from the reinforcing effects of the fruit. Since neither nonsucking oral activity, nor motor activity, showed the significant increase that thumbsucking did, the primary reinforcement explanation does not seem adequate. There must be an accounting for the selective action of reinforcement on nonnutritive sucking. Possibly the primary reinforcement acted on secondary cues provided by thumbsucking, which derived their strength from the original mode of attaining nourishment, nursing. The question remains as to why frustration had a greater effect on sucking than it did on the more recently acquired consummatory responses of biting and licking. This could be answered in terms of appropriateness of available stimuli, stimulus generalization, response hierarchies, and perhaps still other complicated mechanisms. Without elaborating on such possibilities, let it be said that although the use of a nonfood object in the present experiment might have provided better generality, the present results may not be simply interpreted as being due to primary reinforcement provided by the food object. Further complications for interpretation are posed by the two individuals that showed increased sucking of the genitalia during frustration.

The results are also compatible with a psychoanalytic interpretation that the regression to nonnutritive sucking occurred as substitute behavior in face of interference with satisfaction (Fenichel, 1945).

This demonstration that frustration can increase thumbsucking should not be taken to mean that frustration is the only variable which can increase it, nor that all degrees of frustration will increase it. Elsewhere, thumbsucking behavior has been found to increase with hunger (Smith, 1958) and in the presence of mildly disturbing stimuli but to decrease with greater disturbance (Smith, 1960, Experiment III).

SUMMARY

Five experimental and five control infant rhesus monkeys were observed from 90 to 165 days of age in a cylindrical Plexiglas observation cage divided in half by a sliding Plexiglas partition. The cage was enclosed within a Masonite cubicle equipped with one-way-vision glass.

Frustration was defined as delay and interference with the attainment of a preferred food object. Five experimental monkeys were frustrated for 15 test days by placing preferred fruit in a dish on the other side of the Plexiglas partition in the observation cage and restraining them for a 250-sec. period before they were allowed to eat. Preceding and following the 15 frustration days were 15 normative and 15 extinction days, respectively. Control animals never received food in the experimental situation.

Higher nonnutritive sucking scores were made by the five experimental *S*s than by the five control *S*s during the frustration test period, and these differences were statistically significant. Differences between these two groups of Ss during normative and extinction periods were not significant.

REFERENCES

BENJAMIN, L. S. The effect of bottle and cup feeding on the nonnutritive sucking of the infant rhesus monkey. *J. comp. physiol. Psychol.*, 1961, 54, 230–37.

FENICHEL, O. *The Psychoanalytic theory of neurosis.* New York: Norton, 1945.

HONZIK, M. P. Biosocial aspects of thumbsucking. *Amer. Psychologist*, 1948, 3, 351–52. (Abstract)

JACOBSEN, C. F., JACOBSEN, M. M., and YOSHIOKA, J. G. Development of an infant chimpanzee during her first year. *Comp. psychol. Monogr.*, 1932, 12, 361–474.

LANGFORD, W. S. Thumb and finger sucking in childhood. *Amer. J. Dis. Child.*, 1939, 58, 1290–1300.

McKEE, J. P., and HONZIK, M. P. The sucking behavior of mammals: An examination of the nature-nurture question. In L. Postman (Ed.), *Psychological research: Illustrative histories.* New York: Knopf, 1961.

ROSS, S., FISHER, A., and KING, D. Sucking behavior: A review of the literature. *J. genet. Psychol.*, 1957, 91, 63–81.

SIEGEL, S. *Nonparametric statistics for the behavioral sciences.* New York: McGraw-Hill, 1956.

SMITH, L. J. Nonnutritive sucking in the infant rhesus monkey and its relation to feeding. Unpublished master's thesis, University of Wisconsin, 1958.

SMITH, L. J. The nonnutritive sucking behavior of the infant rhesus monkey. Unpublished doctoral dissertation, University of Wisconsin, 1960.

TINKLEPAUGH, O. L. Multiple delayed reaction with chimpanzees and monkeys. *J. comp. physiol. Psychol.*, 1932, 8, 207–43.

EFFECTS OF HUNGER AND MALE SEX HORMONE

ON SELF-STIMULATION OF THE BRAIN[1]

JAMES OLDS[2]
University of California at Los Angeles

Previous work (2, 3) shows a broad system of structures in the midline and rhinencephalic systems of the brain where electric stimulation has effects tantamount to primary reward. Three important questions arise concerning the relation of these apparent rewarding effects to primary drives. The first is whether or not the neural groups excited by the electric stimulus are the ones actually excited by gratifiers of primary drives such as hunger and sex. The second is whether or not there are hunger-reward systems differentiated from sexual ones and from others for other drives. The third is whether or not the electric reward reduces or arouses any drive as measured by consummatory behavior.

The present paper relates to the first two questions. If the electric-reward stimulus excites elements which are involved in the mediation of hunger reward, we might expect the animal's "appetite" for self-stimulation to increase with hunger and decrease with satiety as its appetite for food does. Similarly, if there are neural groups mediating sexual reward, the appetite for self-stimulation might go up and down with androgen level. In the present experiments hunger and androgen level are varied to see how these factors affect self-stimulation rates with electrodes in different parts of the hypothalamus and telencephalon.

METHOD

Subjects were 16 male rats weighing about 250 gm. at the start of the experiment. One pair of 0.01-in. silver wire electrodes was implanted in each rat. Elec-

---
[1] The author expresses his appreciation especially to C. V. Critchlaw, who castrated all the rats and helped to determine the course of the androgen experiments by suggesting doses and time courses. The author is also grateful to C. H. Sawyer and C. Barraclough, who gave much advice on the use of androgens. This study was supported by a grant from the Foundations Fund for Research in Psychiatry to H. W. Magoun and J. Olds, and by grants of the Carnegie Foundation and the Office of Naval Research to D. B. Lindsley and R. B. Livingston.

[2] Present address: University of Michigan.

trodes were insulated all the way down and stimulated only at the cross section of the tips. Tips were side by side about 0.004 in. apart. Electrode pairs were placed in the medial or lateral hypothalamus, or in the medial or lateral parts of some telencephalic structures. The assumption is that all rats are the same except for differences in electrode placement.

A circuit was arranged so the rat could stimulate its own brain with an electric shock by depressing a Skinner bar. The shock was turned off automatically after $\frac{1}{2}$ sec. if the animal held that long, and S had to release and press again for more. The stimulus was a 60-cycle sine wave, 1 v. R.M.S., through a total resistance of about 12,000 ohms; this is about 84 μa.

On the same day Ss were operated on to implant electrodes, a feeding schedule was begun of 24 hr. of feeding alternated with 24 hr. of deprivation. Four days later Skinner-box testing began. Animals were run for 80 min. each day. This continued for about 20 days before castration. All during this period (and the remainder of the experiment) animals were run one day fed and then one day hungry. Self-stimulation improved for the first two or three weeks and then became relatively stable. It is by comparison of the scores for days on which the animals were hungry with the scores for days on which they were fed that the effects of hunger on self-stimulation are gauged. Data prior to stabilization were not used in the analysis to be presented later; and data obtained at low androgen levels (to be defined) were not used in analysis of hunger effects.

After about 20 days of testing all animals were castrated and run for 9 or 17 days during the declining androgen levels which followed. Nine Ss in a first group were run 9 days; and seven in a later group were run 17 days. Then 2 mg. of testosterone propionate in oil was injected intramuscularly in each animal. This, according to available data (1), causes a rise in sexual activity (measured by seminal vesicle size) for about 7 days followed by a 7-day decline.[3] Twenty days after the first testosterone injection, some animals were given second injections. To gauge the effect of androgen level on self-stimulation, scores for 6 days of high androgen level (3 days prior to castration and 3 days at the height of replacement therapy) were compared with scores for 6 days of low androgen level (3 days after castration prior to replacement therapy and 3 days after the effects of replacement therapy had run their course). The animals were satiated on all days used to gauge androgen effects. Thus, Days 5, 7, 9 or 6, 8, 10 after androgen injection were always used as the high androgen days, depending on which triad found the animal in sated condition. Similar precautions were taken to assure uniform analysis in the case of low androgen levels. Hunger effects were measured in the normal animal, prior to castration, and from Days 5 to 10 after androgen injection. Thus, androgen effects were observed only in the sated animal, and hunger effects only in the animal with relatively normal androgen levels.

Hunger variation continued during periods of castration and replacement therapy. Because the two kinds of drive cycle ran very different time courses, their effects could easily be differentiated. After hunger and androgen tests, animals were sacrificed and brain slices were examined microscopically to determine the exact position of the electrode track.

RESULTS

[AUTHORS' NOTE: In the original article six figures were presented which daily described the data with reference to anatomical place-

---

[3] The physiological data cited here are not definite, androgen levels may rise for longer periods.

ment of the electrodes. Since a faithful reproduction of the photographs of the anatomical structures was extremely difficult and the related discussion assumed considerable sophistication on the part of the reader, these figures were omitted. The student is therefore directed only to Figure 7 which summarizes the basic findings.]

Figures 1 to 6 show the data for representative Ss. The brain slice on the left shows the approximate location of the electrode tip. The graph on the right shows self-stimulation rate variation as a function of hunger and androgens. The dotted line at the top gives a schematic representation of androgen levels. The first downward inflection point indicates the time of castration; the upward inflection point indicates the commencement of replacement therapy, i.e., the injection of testosterone. This is presumed to cause a slow rise, followed by a slow decline in androgen level (1). The line of dashes shows self-stimulation rates achieved on alternate days when the animal was hungry. The solid black line shows the rates achieved every other day when the animal was satiated. The graphs start on about the fifth day after the beginning of preliminary training and continue to the day before sacrificing.

Figure 1 shows self-stimulation rates with a medial telencephalic electrode. Hunger augments response rate; androgens diminish it. In Figure 2, the electrode is slightly more lateral, and both hunger and androgens have a positive effect on self-stimulation. Figure 3 shows a still more lateral electrode in the base of the telencephalon; here, hunger has no effect, but there is a strong positive effect of androgens. Figure 4 shows a medial electrode in the posterior hypothalamus; as with the medial telencephalic electrode, hunger augments self-stimulation, and androgens diminish it. Figure 5 shows a more lateral electrode in the posterior hypothalamus; here (as in the lateral telencephalon) hunger has no effect, while androgens have a strong positive effect on self-stimulation. Figure 6 shows results obtained with an electrode in the basolateral part of the middle hypothalamus; in this case androgens do not affect the self-stimulation rate, but hunger causes a slowdown.

In general, more laterally placed electrodes ($1\frac{1}{4}$ mm. from the midline) showed covariation with androgens, and medially placed ones ($\frac{3}{4}$ mm. from the midline) showed covariation with hunger. Furthermore, there was a pronounced inverse correlation between hunger and androgen effects, such that electrodes positively sensitive to androgens were insensitive (or inversely sensitive) to hunger, and vice versa.

The data on all rats are shown in Figure 7. Here percentage

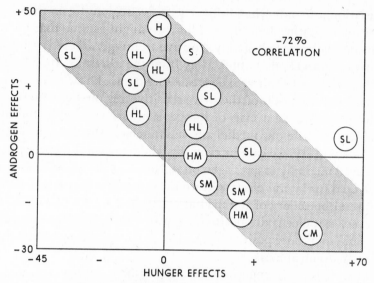

Fig. 7. Comparison of hunger changes with those produced by androgens. Scores indicate changes produced by high hunger drive or high androgen level (as percentages of self-stimulation rates during low-drive conditions). The negative correlation indicates that for electrodes where androgens increase self-stimulation rates, hunger inhibits, and vice versa. By a simple correlation of ranks (4), the negative correlation amounts to .72, which is significant at the .01 level. Abbreviations inside the circles indicate electrode placement (S = septal or telencephalic regions, H = hypothalamic region, C = caudate nucleus; L = lateral, M = medial).

changes caused by hunger in the rat at normal androgen levels are plotted on the horizontal axis and those caused by androgens in the full animal are plotted on the vertical axis. Each point stands for one rat; the letters contained in the points denote the electrode placement as medial or lateral in the hypothalamus, septal area, or caudate nucleus. The negative correlation indicates that in places where hunger causes the greatest rise in self-stimulation rates, androgens cause a depression; and in places where androgens cause the greatest rise in self-stimulation rates, hunger causes a depression.

DISCUSSION

Later work suggests that the 1-v. electric stimulus used in these experiments creates a suprathreshold electric field of about 1½-mm. diameter. Furthermore, it appears that hunger causes a change in self-stimulation rate only when hunger-sensitive regions lie on the boundary of the suprathreshold field. Thus, we might assume that for each electrode placement positively sensitive to hunger, there is a hunger-sensitive region about ¾ mm. away from the electrode tip. The same may be true of the androgen effects. As we do not know from the present data the direction of the drive-sensitive region from the tip, we cannot as yet define a map of hunger-sensitive regions in the hypothalamus. Because our medial and lateral electrodes differ by only ½ mm. in laterality, we cannot even say whether or not hunger systems are placed medially to androgen ones. Note that the medial boundary of the field for lateral electrodes would be more medially placed than the lateral boundary of the medial electrodes. We can say definitely, however, that electrodes positively sensitive to androgens are usually different from those positively sensitive to hunger; and this difference has an anatomical basis.

Thus, there are hunger-reward systems anatomically distinct from androgen-sensitive ones. This finding is not easily fitted into the classical theory that there is basically only one drive mechanism in the organism.

SUMMARY

Self-stimulation rates, with electrodes in medial or lateral parts of the hypothalamus or septal forebrain regions, were measured under conditions of high and low hunger drive and high and low androgen levels. Electrodes positively sensitive to androgens tended to be insensitive or inversely sensitive to hunger, and vice versa. This difference appeared to have an anatomical basis, suggesting a localized hunger-reward system within the regions studied differentiated from a localized sexual-reward system.

REFERENCES

1. EVERSOLE, W. J., LEATHAM, J. H., and SCHRAER, H. Testosterone preparations with prolonged activity. *Endocrinology*, 1950, 47, 448–53.
2. OLDS, J. A preliminary mapping of electrical reinforcing effects in the rat brain. *J. comp. physiol. Psychol.*, 1956, 49, 281–85.
3. OLDS, J., and MILNER, P. Positive reinforcement produced by electrical stimulation of septal area and other regions of rat brain. *J. comp. physiol. Psychol.*, 1954, 47, 419–27.
4. SNEDECOR, G. W. *Statistical methods.* Ames: Iowa State Coll. Press, 1946.

COMPETITION BETWEEN FEEDING AND INVESTIGATION

IN THE RAT

by

M. R. A. CHANCE and A. P. MEAD[1]

(Department of Pharmacology, University of Birmingham)

(Rec. 18-I-1955)

INTRODUCTION

Investigation is part of exploratory behaviour. Our observation of rats living in cages or enclosed runs revealed that the rat rapidly established a home base from which it explored the remainder of the available space. We wish to restrict the use of the term exploration to investigatory behaviour in partially familiar circumstances. The investigation of the surroundings was, however, repeated at intervals throughout the whole period that the rat lived in the cage; even after, as will be apparent below, this aspect of its behaviour ceased to conflict with other activities, such as feeding. Investigation *per se,* therefore, can be investigation either in a totally unfamiliar environment, when it dominated the behaviour (Chance and Mead, unpublished), or in conditions of established familiarity, when it appeared from time to time, but did not conflict with other activities.

Rats (Steiniger, 1950) like other mammals (Hediger 1950) establish territories. Chitty and Shorten (1946) have shown that in circumstances where rats feed at a distance from their burrows "new objects" or changes introduced into the environment close to the runs leading from the burrows to the food site are avoided and produce a temporary reduction in the rate of feeding as measured by the distribution in time of visits to the food site.

In the following study an explanation of the "new object" reaction was sought in the possibility that the rate of feeding would be reduced whenever the circumstances provided a stimulus for exploration by the presence of some unfamiliar aspect.

In order to study the resulting conflict feeding and investigation,

[1] We wish to thank Professor A. C. Frazer for his interest and comments and Dr. W. M. S. Russell for most valuable criticisms.

511

we measured feeding activity in different conditions. Russell *et al.* (1954) have objected to the practise of lumping together different types of measure of the same basic behaviour activity, and have predicted that instances would be found where 'threshold' and 'intensity' measures of the same activity might be affected by different sets of variables. We therefore studied both the latency and the rate of feeding separately.

METHODS

Males of an inbred strain of Albino rats, body weight 250 to 350 gms (100 to 160 days old) were kept in cages for five days prior to the test, and starved for 24 hours. Five rats per group were used except where stated otherwise in Table I. The cages, size 9½ in. × 9½ in. × 7 in., were made of wire, half the top at one end lifting as a lid. The top and sides were supported on a tray containing sawdust. Changes were introduced into this environment by:

(1) The addition of new features. One or two new wire food containers (size 7½ in. × 2 in. × 4 in.) were hung touching the back of the cage underneath the fixed roof and with 3 in. clearance from the floor.

(2) Deletion of parts of the environment by removal of the food grids.

(3) Changing the environment, but keeping the visual and tactile characteristics the same by (*a*) replacing the surround by a clean one of the same type and (b) changing the sawdust.

(4) Changing the visual and tactile nature of the surround (*a*) by removal of the sawdust and replacing by a rough metal surface (*b*) by inverting the tray and thus providing a smooth metal surface.

(5) Changing the lapse of time away from the familiar cage.

Food was supplied as rat cakes. In order to effect the necessary changes in the environment the rat was removed by hand to a neutral cage for ten minutes before replacing in the test situation. The effect of these changes was measured on the latency, *i.e.* the period elapsing before the rat started to eat (bites off and chews a piece of food). With a stop watch the total time spent in eating was measured and the amount of food eaten was measured by weighing the pellet before and after the experiment.

Preliminary observations had shown that rats began feeding in this situation within a few minutes and, except in a few instances, continued to eat for at least thirty seconds once they had begun. This period of continuous feeding was taken as an arbitrary sign that the rat had started feeding. The occasional rat bit at the pellet several times with an interval of a few seconds between each bite before settling down to the initial feeding period. The time to the start of this period was measured as the period of latency.

Once the rat had settled down to feed at a point in the cage it occasionally showed investigatory movements of the head while continuing to chew, and this time was counted in the time spent feeding. If, however, the rat began to clean itself, or moved away from the food and began investigating the cage, the watch was stopped, even if the animal was chewing while doing so. The watch was restarted when the rat took up the pellet and resumed feeding. A resumption of feeding began only when the rat bit off a new piece.

DETERMINATION OF SATISFACTORY METHODS FOR THE EXPERIMENTAL PROCEDURE

Since it was necessary to observe each rat separately, the amount of time taken up on any one day for the observation of rats in different situations, was considerable.

It was, therefore, decided to find out whether the same observations made at different times during the day showed any appreciable variation. A comparison of the latency and rate of feeding of five rats was therefore made at 10 a.m., 1 p.m. and 4 p.m. on different days. No difference was found when these rats were reintroduced and allowed to feed in their familiar cage after removal for ten minutes to an intermediate cage.

Before deciding on the best metameter for the rate of feeding it was decided to investigate the effect of handling and some degree of unfamiliarity on both the latency and the amount eaten during the first ten minutes in the experimental situation. The results of this are shown in Table I, from which it is clear that handling the rats has a significant effect on the latency but the effect on the amount eaten is less marked falling below statistical significance at a P value of 0.05. A P value for any difference of less than 0.05 is indicated by a square link in the tables.

The effect of unfamiliarity on the amount of food eaten may be due to the animal spending less time feeding rather than to an altered rate of feeding when it was eating. Therefore the variance of the time (min.) spend feeding during the first ten minutes was compared with the rate of feeding (g/min.) as two possible measures of the feeding response. The mean duration of feeding per ten rats was 6.78 min. with a S.D. 1.76 and the mean rate of feeding was o.27 g/min. S.D.

TABLE I

EFFECT OF HANDLING AND UNFAMILIARITY ON LATENCY AND
AMOUNT OF FOOD EATEN

Experimental Procedure	No. of Animals	Latency (Sec.)	Amount Eaten (g) in 10 Min. after Food Introduced
Rats undisturbed	10	47.5	1.63
Rats handled into neutral cage and returned to familiar cage	5	75.0	1.25
Rats handled into neutral cage and returned to unfamiliar (cleaned) cage	5	125.0	0.67

0.002. Thus the 95 per cent confidence limits for the mean rate of feeding varied by only 0.7 per cent, whereas the same confidence limits for the duration of feeding varied by 26 per cent. This indicated clearly that although the animals were feeding for various periods of time, they were all feeding at more or less the same rate, and that thus the rate of feeding is largely independent of the feeding duration.

RESULTS

Removal of Familiar and Addition of Unfamiliar Elements

Each of the steps in Table II except the last represent a progressive decrease in the familiar elements of the original isolation cage and bring about statistically significant progressive falls in the rate of feeding. On the other hand the effect on the latency has a greater individual variation and thus, while the mean figures show a steady increase, the differences are not statistically significant at every stage; the change in the texture of the floor having the least effect.

The addition of a new surround (new type cage) has a more marked effect on the rate of feeding than the deletion of any part of the environment, though its effect on the latency is not exceptional (See Table II).

As expected, the addition of unfamiliar elements to a familiar cage induced a marked increase in the latency and decrease in the rate of feeding as with the deletion of parts of the familiar situation (Table III). Moreover, the deletion of the same elements as parts of the familiar environment and their addition as unfamiliar elements to a familiar environment, decreased the rate of feeding to the same extent; but the removal of these elements as part of the familiar environment produced no statistically detectable effect on the latency, but did so when they were introduced as new objects (see Table IV).

TABLE II

Effects of Progressive Deletion or Replacement of Parts of Familiar Situation on Isolated Rats Previously Handled into Neutral Cage, before Placing in Experimental Situation

Experimental Procedure	Latency (Min.)	Rate (g/min.)
Returned to familiar cage.	103.0 (122.2)	0.324 (0.210)
Returned into familiar cage with new sawdust:— equivalent to deletion of faeces and some change of smell.	146.4 (179.0)	0.254 (0.179)
Returned on to tray with new sawdust; equivalent to deletion of surround, faeces and partial change of smell.	272.0 (237.0)	0.237 (0.151)
Handled on to inverted tray; equivalent to deletion of surround, faeces and change of texture and almost complete change of smell.	291.8	0.204
Returned into new type cage with new sawdust; equivalent to change of surround, deletion of faeces and partial change of smell.	242.0	0.177

Note. Figures in round brackets represent a separate experiment.

TABLE III

The Effect of the Addition of New Features to a Familiar Situation on Isolated Rats Previously Handled into a Neutral Cage

Experimental Procedure	Latency (Sec.)	Rate (g/min.)
Returned to familiar cage.	141.4	0.223
Returned to familiar cage + two food grids.	215.6	0.176

TABLE IV

COMPARISON OF EFFECT OF DELETION AND ADDITION OF NEW OBJECTS TO FAMILIAR SITUATION ON ISOLATED RATS PREVIOUSLY HANDLED INTO NEUTRAL CAGE

Experimental Procedure	Latency (Sec.)	Rate (g/min.)
Returned to familiar cage.	114.8	0.280
Returned to familiar cage, less one food cage.	125.2	0.229
Returned to familiar cage, plus one food cage.	145.6	0.234

EFFECT OF SEPARATION IN TIME

Whether the various changes in the earlier experiments produced their effect on the feeding behaviour by the introduction of an unfamiliar element into the environment was subjected to test by separating the animal from its home cage for varying lengths of time, thereby altering the amount of unfamiliarity in the original cage without alteration of the structure of the cage.

Table V shows that the longer the period of removal the greater the effect, both on the latency and on the rate of feeding. The effect of this separation in time becomes most marked after five days, but the difference between three and five days is not significant, though the earlier effects show a marked statistical differentiation.

TABLE V

THE EFFECT OF LAPSE OF TIME AS A MEASURE OF INCREASING UNFAMILIARITY ON LATENCY AND RATE OF FEEDING

Experimental Procedure	Latency (Min.)	Rate (g/min.)
Returned to cage after 10 minutes.	121.8	0.245
Returned to cage after 24 hrs (1 day).	186.2	0.228
Returned to cage after 73 hrs (3 days).	210.2	0.195
Returned to cage after 120 hrs (5 days).	218.2	0.189

EFFECT OF LENGTH OF STARVATION

The introduction of unfamiliarity to part of the environment postponed feeding and depressed the rate. When the animal had begun to feed the rat was in conflict between hunger and investigation, and from observation of the animals it is clear that the rat paid repeated attention to the food whilst it was investigating the cage, during the period of latency. If therefore it is found that when the period of starvation is increased there is a proportionate reduction in the latency and increase in the rate of feeding then further evidence is forthcoming in favour of this hypothesis. Table VI shows this to be the case, but again in this instance the effect on the two variables is different dependent upon the period of food deprivation.

TABLE VI

EFFECT OF PERIOD OF DEPRIVATION ON LATENCY AND RATE OF FEEDING

Experimental Procedure	Latency (Min.)	Rate (g/min.)
After 24 hrs food deprivation.	147.8	0.222
After 48 hrs food deprivation.	123.8	0.238
After 72 hrs food deprivation.	119.2	0.274

DISCUSSION

The results suggest that within the conditions of these experiments the latency reached a maximum at about 4½ minutes.

Comparisons between the effects of deletion and replacement by different type of object, as well as deletion and addition of the same type of object, have been made in Tables II and IV. In Table II the replacement of the surround by a different type had the same effect on latency as the removal of the original surround, but decreased the rate of feeding still further. On the other hand (Table IV) the addition of a new object rather than its removal from the cage produced a greater effect on latency and the same effect on the rate of feeding.

This evidence shows that change in the same element of the environment may be reflected either in latency or in the rate of feeding.

Several interpretations are possible. Either the latency is increased without an effect on feeding when complete investigation is possible before feeding starts, *i.e.* before the period of maximum latency has been reached, or the investigation confirms a difference of type and the recognition of these differences is reflected in a decrease of the feeding rate.

Our finding that the two feeding measures could vary independently and were affected by different sets of variables confirms the general prediction made by Russell *et al.* (1954). They postulated that measurements of a given type of activity might not all relate to the same central nervous variable, and that the underlying mechanism might have at least two parameters, separately measurable, namely 'Tendency' (*e.g.* latency of feeding) and 'Intensity' (*e.g.* rate of feeding). It would appear that their concepts have analytical value, since they permit the discrimination of two processes associated with a particular overt activity, as well as the measurement of each.

SUMMARY

1. Rats delay feeding (latency) and eat at a slower rate when some part of the environment is unfamiliar. These responses are more marked with an increase in the unfamiliar elements of the environment.

2. The addition of a new object to a familiar environment has a greater effect on one or other of these responses than the deletion of the same object.

3. Unfamiliarity with a situation previously occupied is complete within three to five days on return to it.

4. Latency decreased, and the rate of feeding increased, when the period of starvation was prolonged from 24 to 72 hours.

5. It is concluded that the effect of unfamiliar situations on the latency and the rate of feeding represents a competition between hunger and investigation, but that latency and rate of feeding are influenced by different sets of variables.

REFERENCES

CHITTY, D. and SHORTEN, M. (1946). Technique for the study of the Norway Rat (*Rattus norvegicus*). — J. Mammal. **27**, (1), p. 63.

HEDIGER, H. (1950). Wild Animals in Captivity. — London. Butterworth.

STEINIGER, F. (1950) Beiträge zur Soziologie und sonstigen Biologie der Wanderrate. — Z. Tierpsychol. **7**, No. 3.

RUSSELL, W. M. S., MEAD, A. P. and HAYES, J. S. (1954). A basis for the quantitive study of the structure of behaviour. — Behaviour **6**, (3), p. 153.

EFFECT OF POST PARTUM SEPARATION OF MOTHER AND KID ON MATERNAL CARE IN THE DOMESTIC GOAT

by

LEONARD HERSER, State University of New York
A. ULRIC MOORE, Cornell University
JULIUS B. RICHMOND, State University of New York

Abstract. Twenty-four goat mothers were separated from their newborn kids for 1 hour immediately following birth. Two months later these mothers were observed to nurse their own kids less and alien kids more than nonseparated mothers. Separation of mother and young in half the flock also resulted in abnormal "rejecting" behavior in some nonseparated mothers.

Recent studies (*1*) have demonstrated that the appearance of some types of normal, species-typical maternal behavior, often classed as "instinctive," is dependent upon the occurrence of specific experiences during critical periods in the life of the individual animal. Experimental or accidental changes in the "natural" environment at these times often result in the development of decidedly abnormal, species-atypical behavior.

Domestic sheep and goats normally rear their young within an individual-specific family structure. The suckling relationship between mother and young is typically limited to a particular parent and her offspring, and any attempt by a lamb or kid to nurse, or sometimes even to approach, a mother not its own results in that mother's withdrawal from and often violent repulsion of the alien offspring.

Descriptions of sheep and goat parturition indicate that the experience of the mother immediately following birth is critical to the development of this individual-specific infant-rearing pattern. Separation of mother and newborn for a short time at birth results in at least the temporary rejection of the young by the mother when mother and offspring are reunited (*2*).

Some observations of the behavior of separated mothers, however, suggest that maternal behavior often is unstable. Separated mothers who at first reject their own or foster young may occasionally later accept them, and mothers who at first accept young sometimes later reject them (2, 3). The study described in this report was undertaken to investigate the long-term, general effects of early mother-young separation on the individual mother and on the population as a whole.

Twenty-four domestic goat mothers were separated from their newborn kids for periods ranging from ½ hour to 1 hour, 5 to 10 minutes immediately following birth. The kids were permitted, or helped, to nurse their own mothers when mother and kid were reunited. A control group of 21 mothers, equated for age and parity, were allowed to follow the normal newborn care-taking pattern. The usual life of the flock was not specifically interfered with further until approximately 2 months (Table 1, observation 1) and, again, 3 months (Table 1, observation 2) after birth, when mother-kid interaction was studied in the following manner.

All the kids in the flock were housed in a room apart from all the adult goats for from 6 to 10 hours. The kids were deprived of both food and water during this time; the mothers received food and water as usual. Three of the kids, of approximately the same age, were then brought into the experimental room. One minute later the mother of one of the three kids joined them, and all four were observed for 15 minutes through a one-way-vision glass. An observer recorded the time in seconds of the mother's nursing and butting behaviors by activating separate electric clocks for the duration of each type of behavior as it occurred. This procedure was repeated until each mother had been observed with her kid and two others.

In each instance, the three kids appeared highly excited and fearful when they were first brought into the unfamiliar room. With the appearance of the mother, all three kids rushed toward her and attempted to nurse. The immediate reaction of all the mothers was to back away from this onslaught for the first 30 seconds. After this initial period, most nonseparated (control) mothers began the process of establishing a private territory for herself and her own offspring, by butting away the two other kids each time they approached her. After several minutes of being butted the other kids kept their distances, while the mother nursed her own kid in the usual manner.

In contrast, the separated (experimental) mothers behaved in a distinctly abnormal manner during both observation periods (Table 1), nursing their own kids less than the nonseparated mothers ($p = 0.01$) and nursing other kids more ($p = 0.01$). Separated mothers nursed other kids as long as they nursed their own, whereas nonseparated mothers nursed other kids relatively little, as compared with the time spent nursing their own ($p = 0.01$) (mean differences were

TABLE 1

MEAN DURATION, IN SECONDS, OF MATERNAL ACTIVITIES OCCURRING DURING THE 15-MINUTE
OBSERVATION PERIODS

Condition	Separated Mothers (N = 24)		Nonseparated Mothers (N = 21)	
	Observa-tion 1	Observa-tion 2	Observa-tion 1	Observa-tion 2
Nursing own kids				
Mean	36.2	23.2	50.4	61.8
Standard deviation	11.4	9.7	16.5	22.3
Nursing other kids				
Mean	37.2	27.6	7.1	10.5
Standard deviation	9.3	10.1	6.8	8.8
Butting own kids				
Mean	0.0	0.0	0.0	0.0
Standard deviation	0.0	0.0	0.0	0.0
Butting other kids				
Mean	16.1	14.8	19.3	13.9
Standard deviation	15.3	12.6	15.7	10.0

tested for significance by t tests, which were computed separately for each observation period).

All butting behavior for both groups was normal; none of the mothers butted their own kids, although they butted other kids frequently.

An unexpected result of the study was the appearance of "rejecting" behavior nursing neither their own nor other kids) among the mothers of the nonseparated group. Similar experimental analysis of the *post partum* behavior of another herd in which none of the kids had been separated at birth revealed no instances of "rejecting" behavior or of "indiscriminate" behavior (nursing other kids as long as, or longer than, their own), suggesting that the act of separating half the kids in the experimental herd had probably been the principal factor affecting maternal-young relationships of the nonseparated "rejecting" mothers. Although the specific cause of this effect on the nonseparated mothers is unknown, the "rejecting" behavior of the nonseparated mothers may have developed because their own kids wandered off shortly after birth and were accepted by the separated-"indiscriminate" mothers, since both separated and nonseparated mothers were kept together as one flock except for the short period during which the experimental mothers were separated from their young. Separation of some of these highly gregarious animals had thus influenced the social structure of the herd as a whole, changing the behavior of "control" animals whose early *post partum* experiences had not deliberately been disrupted, but whose environment had been affected in turn by abnormal maternal and filial behavior produced in the experimental members of their group (*4*).

REFERENCES AND NOTES

1. D. S. LEHRMAN, *J. Comp. and Physiol. Psychol.* 51, 32 (1958); H. G. Birch, *Am. J. Orthopsychiat.* 26, 279 (1956); B. F. RIESS, *Ann. N.Y. Acad. Sci.* 51, 1093 (1950); F. A. BEACH, in S. S. Stevens, *Handbook of Experimental Psychology* (Wiley, New York, 1951), p. 387.
2. N. E. COLLIAS, *Ecology* 37, 228 (1956).
3. H. BLAUVELT, in *Group Processes,* B. Schaffner, Ed. (1955), p. 221.
4. This study was conducted at the Behavior Farm Laboratory of Cornell University and was supported in part by grants from the Josiah Macy, Jr. Foundation and the Ford Foundation. We thank Dr. Howard Liddell, director of the laboratory, and Dr. Helen Blauvelt for advice and aid in planning and in carrying out this study.

CHAPTER 10

GENERALITY OF CONDITIONING

The previous chapters have concentrated on a discussion of innate behavior, namely, the behavior that must be present before learning can take place. This, in turn, is the very same behavior that undergoes modification when learning occurs, as described and emphasized in Chapter 5. So, now that the *raw material* for learned behavior has been dealt with it is appropriate to begin a discussion of conditioning. The phenomenon of conditioning was recognized in an anecdotal fashion for hundreds of years. But not until the studies of Pavlov, beginning near the turn of the century, was there a systematic experimental investigation of the phenomenon. Since the time of these early experiments research has proceeded almost unabated both in this country and in Russia.

Definition and Characteristics of Conditioning

Conditioning, frequently called classical conditioning, is the establishment of a new stimulus-response relationship (S–R): typically the response has previously been made by the organism and the stimulus may be quite familiar to it, but the *association* is new. Briefly described, conditioning occurs when a stimulus, which does not elicit the response in question, is paired a number of times with another stimulus which consistently or unconditionally elicits this response. The former stimulus is called the conditioned stimulus (CS), while the latter is called the unconditioned stimulus (US). The response originally elicited by the US is called the unconditioned response (UR). The response elicited by the CS after a number of CS–US pairings (conditioning trials), is labeled the conditioned response (CR). In the Pavlovian situation a ticking metronome was commonly the CS; the onset of this stimulus was followed after a few seconds by the US, meat powder blown into the dog's mouth. The UR was salivation; and the CR was defined when the dog began to salivate to the tick of the metronome prior to the presentation of the US.

523

A CR, since it precedes the UR, is an anticipatory response; accordingly, the CR can serve to prepare the organism for subsequent events and behaviors. The CR is never identical with the UR: it has a longer latency, occurs less consistently, has less amplitude, is less complete, and may otherwise differ in topography from the UR. Unlike the UR it also undergoes experimental extinction. Given trials with the continued omission of the US, the CR becomes weaker and weaker and eventually is said to be extinguished.

The point was just made that the CR is typically not the same as the UR. Some possible reasons for this will now be entertained. Theoretically, the components of a response pattern which are most readily conditionable are the ones which can easily become anticipatory, that is, can come forward in the behavior sequence without interfering with the remainder of the ongoing behavior. For example, conditioned salivation would not interfere with an alerting reaction that is commonly the UR given to a suddenly presented CS; but direct approach to the food *would* interfere with the UR aspects of the CS. Again in the case of fear conditioning, the components typically conditioned are the ones which are compatible with an alerting reaction to the conditioned stimulus, namely, freezing, flinching, or a galvanic skin reaction (GSR). A second factor, which complements the compatability notion, is the point that response components which can run off without additional stimulus support are going to be the most readily conditionable. For example, mouth opening can take place without there being anything to chew on and can be conditioned quickly (Mateer, 1918). Salivation as a response satisfies both sets of conditions. It can occur while an animal is running, climbing, pushing, pulling, etc. and requires no additional stimulus for its maintenance, as would chewing or swallowing. Thus, in salivary conditioning the readily identifiable CR would be salivation, whereas the UR would also include chewing, swallowing, and the like.

Methodology. The apparatus and procedures generally employed in conditioning experiments, especially with dogs or human subjects, have reached a high level of technical sophistication, primarily with respect to the objective recording of conditioned responses and the automatic programming of the conditioning trials. Thus, in this country there are probably less than a dozen fully equipped conditioning laboratories with a continual research operation. When smaller animals are being conditioned, the responses are often recorded as objectively as possible with the naked eye; hence, numerous laboratories are equipped for this sort of research. Studies in this category, as well as the more rigorously controlled experiments, are both represented in this chapter.

In the conditioning setup there are two main ways to present the CS in relation to the US: (1) the CS is a momentary stimulus like a click which terminates a fraction of a second or even a second or two before the onset of the US. Because there is no temporal overlap of the stimuli, as defined *external* to the organism, this type is called *trace* conditioning. The perseverative trace of the CS in the nervous system of the organism is presumably what overlaps the US; (2) the CS precedes the US but is of sufficient duration to overlap with the US for a fraction of a second or so. This type is called *simultaneous* conditioning because the CS and US are on together. Other types of conditioned responses are variations upon these two themes, including the special case of *backward* conditioning where the US precedes the CS. Although still a questionable phenomenon, backward conditioning appears to occur under certain special conditions. Its occurrence is evaluated solely by the use of test trials where the US has been omitted. Such test trials are also frequently incorporated in regular forward conditioning experiments, to test for the occurrence of conditioning.

SINGH, S. D. Conditioned emotional response in the rat: I. Constitutional and situational determinants. *J. Comp. Physiol. Psychol.*, 1959, 52, 574–78.

A conditioned emotional response (CER) was evaluated by a depression in rate of bar-pressing when the CS was introduced into the Skinner box. The CER was significantly increased by greater emotional reactivity of rat strain (strains selectively bred for defecation scores in an open-field test) and by stronger shock. Whether the CS, a 3-minute flashing light, just preceded or just followed the US (2 seconds of shock) made no significant difference. So-called backward fear conditioning in this instance was as good as forward.

In a classical conditioning experiment, considerable control is exercised over the important variables, per the procedures described in the selected articles:

1) A quiet, isolated or sound-conditioned room or chamber is typically used and kept free of extraneous stimuli.
2) The animal is first habituated (familiarized) to the laboratory surroundings, including harness and other equipment.
3) Any initial reactions to the CS resembling the UR are usually permitted to adapt prior to conditioning trials or are otherwise controlled for.
4) The onset, duration, and intensity of both the CS and US are rigidly and automatically controlled.
5) The responses are recorded by electrical or photographic techniques which permit an accurate determination of the occurrence of the CR as well as its latency and amplitude.

A common methodological problem in conditioning lower animals involves devising some sort of harness or stock which keeps the animal in one place. This is done so as to control the CS and US presentations and reliably record the response. However, this procedure is not always followed. The conditioning of free-moving dogs has been successfully conducted in Russia, and the dogs conditioned faster under such an arrangement (Razran, 1961). And in the study by Ratner and Miller (1959 **) the earthworm, though unrestricted in movement, was always where it should be.

Variables Affecting Conditioning

Stimulus Factors. As implied above, the US must be the dominant or prepotent stimulus in the conditioning situation. If the laboratory situation is new and strange, then strong investigatory or fear-type responses are elicited and no conditioning will occur (Pavlov, *Conditioned Reflexes,* 1927). A stimulus is only an effective US when it can consistently elicit the UR, that is, when strong competing stimuli are absent. In keeping with this is the fact that increasing the intensity of the US facilitates conditioning as exemplified in the study by Spence *et al.* (1958 **). Furthermore, when a series of adaptation trials to the US, which effectively serve to weaken the US, are presented prior to the conditioning trials then conditioning is impaired (Taylor, 1956, MacDonald, 1946).

Anything which can be reasonably categorized as making the CS more discriminable or distinctive also seems to facilitate conditioning: increasing the number of components of a compound CS (e.g., light plus metronome plus tactile stimulus); keeping the duration of the CS fairly short; reducing the amount of overlap between the CS and US to some minimal value (another type of temporal differentiation); and increasing the intensity of the CS up to some moderate value—a value too weak to bring it into conflict with the US—are all manipulations which facilitate conditioning (Barnes, 1956 *, Behrend and Bitterman, 1962; Razran, 1957).

BARNES, G. W. Conditioned stimulus intensity and temporal factors in spaced-trial classical conditioning. *J. Exp. Psychol.,* 1956, 51, 192–98.
Classical conditioning in the dog using strong shock and a leg-flexion response was facilitated by increasing CS (tone) intensity and hindered by increasing the degree to which the CS overlapped shock termination.

An interesting manipulation of the CS is to omit it altogether, presenting only the US periodically. When a CS is then introduced a response like a true CR may occur. Such a phenomenon is called *pseudo-conditioning.* To the extent such conditioning takes place it probably represents conditioning to the general stimulus situation plus the fact that the sudden onset of the CS is similar, neurologically speaking, to the sudden onset of the US (a special application of the principle of stimulus generalization).

Temporal Conditions. There are two main kinds of time variables affecting the development of the CR. One factor is called the CS–US interval or the interstimulus interval. For both trace and simultaneous conditioning this interval refers to the time elapsing between the *onset* of the CS and the *onset* of the US. At least for unconditioned stimuli of moderate intensity the optimal CS–US interval approximates .5 seconds. The main comparative point to be made here, however, is that too few species have been examined to permit a decision as to whether or not the .5-second value holds broadly across phyla and species. When there is widespread UR involvement, as with electric shock or big pieces of food, then it does appear that the optimal interstimulus interval can be in the neighborhood of 5 seconds (Razran, 1957). Under special procedural conditions, to be ignored in the present discussion, the length of an effective CS–US interval can be appreciably lengthened.

NOBLE, M. and ADAMS, C. K. Conditioning in pigs as a function of the interval between CS and US. *J. Comp. Physiol. Psych.*, 1963, 56, 215–19.
Early in conditioning a CS–US interval of 2 seconds yielded better classical conditioning than either shorter or longer intervals. Late in conditioning an 8-second interval was best of all. The US was an electric shock of 1-second duration applied to the leg. The ITI varied from 30 to 90 seconds. *Note:* These results are in agreement with those of Behrend and Bitterman (1962) on instrumental-avoidance-conditioning in fish, though not with the bulk of the data on human subjects. The increase in performance with increase in the CS–US interval, because of the latency data, cannot be solely attributed to the greater opportunity to respond.

The other temporal factor is the time between trials (time between successive CS presentations) and is commonly called the intertrial interval (ITI). It is typical in conditioning to give a fairly long block or series of trials in any one session. Therefore, the ITI variable, which is measured in seconds, is typically operative. The optimal interval for straightforward classical conditioning, in the few species studied, is approximately 90 seconds. Longer intervals neither hinder nor facilitate, but shorter intervals clearly impede the conditioning process. Again the comparative data are too sparse to specify the generality of the 90-second value, but even in earthworms 90 seconds yields better conditioning than 10 seconds (Ratner and Miller, 1959b). The emphasis, when attempts are made to interpret the ITI data, has usually been directed at the CS but it could just as well be directed at the US. For instance, it may be that the longer intervals reduce the amount of adaptation to the US (greater time for recovery) and thus yield better conditioning (Ratner, 1962).

The ITI in conditioning may be constant, the same between all trials, or may vary symmetrically around a central value as would be possible with the five following values: 10, 20, 30, 40, 50 seconds. The constant ITI introduces another consistent cue (CS) into the conditioning situation, namely, what goes on interoceptively in the organism over this time interval. A constant ITI gives better conditioning than a variable ITI and a CR may occur with the omission of the regular CS. To the extent conditioning to this interoceptive CS takes place it is called *temporal* conditioning.

Relation to Learning in General. A sizable number of other variables have been studied in relation to conditioning but in this book we are concerned more with comparative issues. One comparative issue of sorts is how does conditioning compare with learning in general. It has often been said that conditioning is a simple form of learning. Fundamental or basic it might be, but it is far from simple. One recent conception likens conditioning to a kind of discrimination learning where the animal must learn to respond only to the conditioned stimulus, that is, must not respond when the conditioned stimulus is absent, as during the ITI. Presumably, this is one reason why conditioning may proceed quite slowly and hardly ever reaches a level of consistent occurrence. Pavlov noted 50 years ago that the CR may develop quite rapidly to the total situation—that the dog may salivate indiscriminately while in the harness but not necessarily when the discrete conditioned stimulus is presented. In fact, when the CS is specified as the act of placing the animal into a total unique situation where discrimination is minimized, then conditioning has occurred in one or two trials, at least for the conditioning of escape—avoidance behavior (Maatsch, 1959, Denny, Koons and Mason, 1959).

The facts of higher-order conditioning also point to the complexity of conditioning and may also suggest an intimate relationship between classical conditioning and instrumental learning (trial and error learning). Higher-order conditioning is possible only after a CR has been well established to the CS (first-order conditioning). Second-order conditioning involves conditioning the same CR to a new CS, using the original CS as the US. Evidence for second-order effects is present as far down the phylogenetic scale as the fish (Sanders, 1960 *), though one is hard pressed because of the dearth of data to make any broad comparative statements. One might expect that the

higher-order procedures could be similarly extended almost indefi-
nitely, that is, to third-, fourth-, fifth-order CR's or higher. But in
actuality only under very special conditions indeed can a CR be established above the second order. The point here is that the first-order
CR to the original CS undergoes extinction in the absence of the
original US; when this happens the CS can no longer function as a
US (consistent elicitor), and the whole house of cards collapses.

SANDERS, F. K.   Second-order olfactory and visual learning in the optic tectum
of goldfish. *J. Exp. Biol.,* 1940, 17, 416–34.

Five goldfish trained to respond to a visual stimulus (disk) for food reward
were then able to learn to approach the disk (the only reward) when an
olfactory CS or cue was presented (amyl acetate).

Higher-order conditioning, however, is not unlike the establishment of behavior chains or sequences in instrumental learning situations. For example, a rat can be trained to climb a ladder, squeeze
through a tunnel, pull a chain, and finally press a bar in order to get
a pellet of food. For each member of the S–R chain there is a distinctive cue (CS) which elicits the next response in the chain and so on
until the food is presented. For the sake of the present argument the
food is considered the US. Though there is this similarity between
higher-order conditioning and instrumental chaining in the building
on of S–R units, there is also a big difference: the US is not actually
omitted in the instrumental sequence and the animal eventually
receives the US (food). Thus extinction is prevented, and consequently long chains are fairly easy to establish and maintain. Another possible difference here is that the components of an instrumental response chain are more tactic or tropistic in origin than
reflexive, involving movement of the whole organism toward or away
from a stimulus (see p. 167). For a further comparison of conditioning and instrumental learning, see Denny and Adelman (1955).

The upshot of this discussion is to suggest that classical conditioning is probably not a special kind of learning divorced from other
learning; yet neither is the conditioning model basic to or representative of all learning, particularly at the human level.

Generality of Conditioning

One undeniable generalization about conditioning is that just
about any stimulus can be used as a CS so long as it is above threshold
and not too intense. Thus, tactual, olfactory, gustatory, and proprioceptive stimuli can perform this role as well as auditory and visual,
though for particular organisms certain kinds of stimuli are probably
more effective than others (Spence *et al.,* 1958 **).

The stimuli which can serve as good unconditioned stimuli are much more limited. A US must *consistently* elicit a response. For one, this means it must be prepotent, that is, stronger than the other stimulus elements in the situation. Secondly, it means that the US must not undergo adaptation too quickly or to any great extent. Very likely there is a third restriction upon the US; namely, whether or not the stimulus elicits a relatively broad response pattern involving a sizeable number of response components. When the response elicited is a single, simple reflex conditioning is quite difficult or impossible. The knee jerk, an isolated, segmental type of reflex, has always given notoriously poor conditioning (Schlosberg, 1928). The latest research on the pupillary CR indicates rather conclusively that if the pupillary response is a simple contraction elicited by a bright light (US), then no conditioning occurs (Young, 1958). If, however, the pupillary response is just one component of a general autonomic reaction as when the US is electric shock, then conditioning of the pupillary response readily occurs (Gerall, Sampson, and Boslov, 1957).

What we are saying is in no way inconsistent with ordinary conditioning data. The salivary response is just one component among many in a hungry dog stimulated by food. In eyelid conditioning the blink is part of a mild startle pattern including flinching and visceral reactions. In the study by Gormezano *et al.* (1962 **) on conditioning the nictitating membrane in rabbits, the eyelid, also a responding member, had to be taped shut so as not to obscure the nictitating response. Response involvement increases with a strong unconditioned stimulus and, as shown by Spence *et al.* (1958 **), the greater the intensity of the US the better the eyelid conditioning.

Part of the story for the response side of the generality question has already been indicated. As long as there is sufficient involvement just about any response is conditionable, smooth muscle or striated. Much of the evidence for this conclusion comes from Russian research (Bykov, 1957). According to this work the activity of the kidney, spleen, and bladder, among others, can be conditioned. For additional coverage, see the summarized studies below.

HILGARD, E. R. and MARQUIS, D. C. Acquisition, extinction and retention of conditioned lid responses to light in dogs. *J. Comp. Psychol.*, 1935, **19**, 29–58.

All four dogs used showed good eyelid conditioning. The latency of the conditioned eyeblink averaged 165 milliseconds (ms), while latency of closure to the air puff (US) was 22 ms. Frequency and amplitude of the CR increased during conditioning, while latency decreased. With 5 daily sessions of 60 trials each the dogs later in training showed a loss from the beginning of the session to the end (decremental effects). Experimental extinction reversed the conditioning process: frequency and amplitude decreased and latency increased. Massed extinction trials yielded faster extinction than spaced. The CR was retained for as long as three months.

CHAMBERS, R. M. and FULLER, J. L. Conditioning of skin temperature changes in dogs. *J. comp. physiol. Psychol.*, 1958, **51**, 223–26.

A drop in muzzle temperature in the dog was reliably conditioned to a metronome CS, using shock as the US. Many other stimuli such as noises, sight of mouse, and odors were found to serve as unconditioned stimuli of temperature drop. The temperature of the pinna of the dog's ear showed effects similar to the nose but to a lesser degree.

KELLOGG, W. N. and SPANOVICK, P. Respiratory changes during the conditioning of fish. *J. Comp. Physiol. Psychol.*, 1953, **46**, 124–28.

Twenty-four mullet, *Mugil cephaleus*, kept in an aquarium, were classically conditioned either to a light or to an auditory CS with electric shock as the US; the CS–US interval was 2 seconds and the CS and US overlapped for 1 second. The UR was a frenetic dash *toward* the positive electrode. The CR, on the other hand, was a slow *withdrawal* from the positive electrode. Conditioning rose to a 98 percent level within 70 trials and proceeded faster for the visual stimulus than the auditory CS. Concomitantly there was a progressive increase in respiration rate (gill opening count) in a 15-second period which followed the US. *Note:* Could the change in respiration rate possibly be an example of backward conditioning?

SCHLOSBERG, H. Conditioned responses in the white rat. *J. Genet. Psychol.*, 1934, **45**, 303–35.

When a CS was paired with shock to the rat's tail, conditioned breathing, tail movements, and squeals were established in that order. Two hundred trials per session prevented conditioning while 15 to 20 appeared optimal. The CR was quite resistant to extinction but was hardly retained at all over a two-month interval. *Note:* This last result contrasts with good retention in the dog (Hilgard and Marquis*).

Limits to Conditioning

Phylogenetic Limits. Here again the generality of the conditioning process is striking. Good evidence for conditioning exists as far down the scale on the invertebrate stem as the molluscs (snails) and annelids (earthworms) (Thompson, 1917 *; Ratner and Miller, 1959a **) and as far down as the fish on the vertebrate trunk (Harlow, 1939 **; O'Connell, 1960 *; Sanders, 1940 *; Kellogg and Spanovick, 1953 *). Suggestive evidence of conditionability exists on the vertebrate branch (see the diagram on page 32) at the level of the echinoderms (starfish) (Thorpe, 1956) and at the level of the platyhelminthes (planaria) on the invertebrate branch (Hovey, 1929 *; Thompson and McConnell, 1955 *; Halas, James, and Stone, 1961 *). More research and careful exercise of controls are needed to decide the exact limits of conditionability; but it is clear that conditioning, if it does occur in the lower ends of the phylogenetic scale, is poorly developed and relatively unimportant in the adaptation of the organism to its environment.

THOMPSON, E. L.   An analysis of the learning process in the snail, *Physa gyrina* say. *Behav. Monogr.*, 1917, **3**, 97.

By means of a fork-like instrument habituated snails were prodded on tne foot (CS) and touched on the mouth with lettuce (US). By 250 trials a mouth movement CR to foot prodding was well established and lasted for four days without reinforcement.

O'CONNELL, C. P.   Use of the school for conditioned response experiments. *Anim. Behav.*, 1960, **8**, 225–27.

Twenty-one adult sardines were conditioned to respond in unison to a "light on" CS (5 sec.) which signaled the dropping of food pellets into the water at the feeding port of the aquarium. The intertrial interval approximated 2 minutes. Within 150 trials the sardines were well conditioned to react to the light by swimming toward the food place and catching the food before it hit bottom. When a member of the school died it was replaced by a new fish which responded like the school on its first trial! (See Shaw, E. on schooling, Chapter 8.)

HOVEY, H. B.   Associative hysteresis in flatworms. *Physiol. Zool.*, 1929, **2**, 323–33.

Flatworms, *Leptoplana,* are positively photokinetic but this can be inhibited by blocking them repeatedly with a smooth match stick right after presenting the light. Thus, light becomes a CS to inhibit movement. Good controls were employed.

THOMPSON, R. and McCONNELL, J.   Classical conditioning in the Planarian, *Dugesia Dorotocephala. J. Comp. Physiol. Psychol.*, 1955, **48**, 65–68.

Planaria in a classical light-shock conditioning situation showed a significant increase in contraction and turning responses over trials. The three control groups used for shock, light, and spontaneous responding did not exhibit the progressive behavior change.

HALAS, E. S., JAMES, R. L. and STONE, L. A.   Types of responses elicited in planaria by light. *J. Comp. Physiol. Psychol.*, 1961, **54**, 303–5.

Light is an unconditioned stimulus for a turning response in planaria. This fact is to be appreciated in interpreting the Thompson and McConnell study.

Ontogenetic Limits.   Once more the data indicate broad conditionability, this time as a function of the age of the organism. In primates at least, conditioning can occur either prior to birth or just after it (Spelt, 1948 *; Mason and Harlow, 1958 **). In fact, leg-twitch conditioning appears to take place within the embryo chick after 14 days of incubation, about 7 days before hatching. This conditioned response may even persist beyond the point of hatching so long as the chick remains in the dark and is not tested in a drastically changed stimulus environment (Hunt, 1949). It is very likely that the main ontogenetic restriction on conditioning is whether or not the response being conditioned is sufficiently strong in the repertoire of the organism at the age tested. Avoidance–fear-type responses in chicks, for example, do not appear to any great extent until about 10 days after hatching. Instead, the first few days after hatching the chick is ripe for imprinting on a new stimulus or approaching it (see Chapter 7). Just prior to the fear stage the chick is more or less indifferent to new stimuli, (summarized study, Chapter 7, Ratner and Thompson, 1960). In this connection, an as yet unpublished study by Peters (1964) has shown that avoidance conditioning in chicks is impossible until 10 days after hatching.

SPELT, D. K.   The conditioning of the human fetus *in utero. J. Exp. Psychol.,* 1948, **38,** 338–46.
 Human fetuses 6½ to 8½ months of age were conditioned to give a startle-like response (kick) using a loud noise as the US and tactile stimulation of the mother's abdomen as the CS.

When comparisons are made at the human level between normal and mentally retarded children two informative generalizations appear possible. Retardates above an IQ of 30 condition just about as rapidly as normals, even when the groups are matched on chronological age (the retarded children have a lower mental age). This is true either when the US is a positive stimulus, such as candy, or an aversive stimulus, such as electric shock (Mateer, 1918; Razran, 1933). Variations in mental age or chronological age, over an extended range of values, do not appreciably affect the course of conditioning.

The other generalization takes quite a different form. When the CR undergoes experimental extinction the retarded show a deficit, extinguishing more slowly than the normal (Mateer, 1918; Razran, 1933). The fact that mental age in human beings is a relevant variable when it comes to inhibiting a response is in good agreement with the fact that chronological age shows a similar relationship in lower animals. Among normal, youthful organisms, such as birds and rats, the very youngest extinguish the slowest (Vince, 1958; Panchenkova, 1956).

When only the normal adult end of the age scale is examined the evidence is scanty but what there is indicates that conditionability is somewhat impaired as age increases. Possibly this may be due to habituation to unconditioned stimuli over the years (Brown and Geiselhart, 1959).

In summary it can be said that conditioning, establishing new associations between stimuli and responses, is neither a simple learning process nor a special kind of learning which is divorced from other learnings. The generality of conditioning is seen in terms of the variety of stimuli that can be used in establishing the associations, the variety of responses conditioned, and the range of species and ages over which conditioning occurs.

FORWARD CONDITIONING, BACKWARD CONDITIONING, AND PSEUDO-CONDITIONING IN THE GOLDFISH*

H. F. HARLOW[1]

Department of Psychology, University of Wisconsin

A. PURPOSE

The purpose of the following experiment was to study the formation of new stimulus-response capacities in the goldfish (*Carrassius auratus*). Although tests were made for delayed and trace forward conditioned reflexes and for backward conditioned reflexes, the primary emphasis was placed upon the phenomenon of "pseudo-conditioning," described by Grether (4) in a previous article, in which the substitute stimuli are never paired with the original stimuli but attain the capacity to elicit a response spontaneously after the original stimulus (a strong, shock stimulus) has been presented a number of times.

B. PERTINENT LITERATURE

The literature of conditioning in fish not only proves that conditioning can take place, but also shows clearly that true conditioned inhibition [Froloff (3)] and conditioned discrimination [Froloff (2), Bull (1)] can be established. There is also substantial evidence that such conditioned responses are retained for a considerable period of time, a week to a month or longer.

The observations of Sears (5) made on two goldfish are of particular importance to the problems of this paper since Sears not only described "pseudo-conditioning" but also discussed its characteristics of fairly rapid acquisition (less than 70 trials), resistance to "experimental extinction," and good retention. Furthermore, Sears inter-

---

* Received in the Editorial Office on August 13, 1938.

[1] The author wishes to express thanks to Mrs. Norma Metzner, Miss Rachel Stare, and Miss Audrey Beatty who assisted in conducting the reported experiments.

This research was supported in part by a grant from WPA.

preted this phenomenon correctly as being a cortical dominant, "produced . . . by either *strong external stimulation*[2] or by secretion of certain hormones. . . ." Sears, however, chose deliberately not to investigate the phenomenon further in his study of the effect of optic lobe ablation.

Sears did not point out that his observations differed in one characteristic (probably more apparent than real) from those of the other workers who had investigated the dominant in frogs, toads, cats, and dogs. The dominant of earlier workers was obtained as a result of hormic or of visceral afferent stimulation of centers in the nervous system. Sears' dominant was induced as a result of *external afferent stimulation*. The dominant of the earlier workers explained how the organization of primarily *unlearned, inherent* responses took place. The dominant described by Sears was a new, *individual* acquisition, a special (learned?) capacity of the particular animal, not of the species. Furthermore, in spite of the fact that earlier workers [Ufland (7), Uchtomsky (6)] had claimed "persistence" to be one of the characteristics of the dominant, the new stimulus-response capacities in their studies persisted little if any longer than the primary stimulating agency, e.g., the hormones of visceral tensions. The dominant obtained by Sears obviously persisted long after the stimulation source, external afferent stimulation had ceased, since great difficulty was encountered in "experimentally extinguishing" these connections. Sears' work suggests and Grether's work proves that dominants established by strong exteroceptive stimulation may persist for at least as long as most response patterns acquired by paired stimulation.

C. SUBJECTS, APPARATUS, GENERAL METHOD

Forty-nine goldfish (*Carrassius auratus*) were used as subjects. Between test periods these animals were kept, singly or in pairs, in a separate "home" room in small glass containers $2.5 \times 3.5 \times 7.5$ inches in size. The test chamber was a glass bowl 3 inches deep and 12 inches square. Each of two opposite sides of the test chamber was lined with a copper electrode, covered on the exterior with a piece of perforated cardboard which prevented the fish from making direct contact with the copper.

Regular 110 volt alternating current served as a current source and was led through two circuits, one containing a resistance of 925 ohms, the other a variable resistance of 1–65,000,000 ohms. The

---

[2] Italics ours.

constant resistance provided the unlearned stimulus and the variable resistance provided one of the acquired stimuli. An audio-vibratory stimulus used as a second substitute stimulus was produced by an oscillator and amplifier which fed a loud speaker placed on the table back of the bowl.[3]

The fish were tested once a day save during the retention periods and each fish was allowed sufficient time after being brought from the living bowl to the test bowl to become adjusted to the new situation. Usually 5–10 minutes sufficed to produce a quiescent state. Since the specific procedure varied in the different part of the experiment this is briefly mentioned for each part.

D. METHOD, RESULTS

1. Formation of Forward Conditioned Reflexes

Forward conditioning was established by presenting the conditioned stimulus (weak shock or vibration) for three seconds and immediately following with a strong shock. Variable intervals, fluctuating up to 30 seconds around a 2-minute average, were allowed between successive trials. This procedure was repeated 10 times per day. From Day 2 on, the training period was preceded by five retention trials in which the conditioned stimulus alone was presented.

Where shock was used as a conditioned stimulus in this test and in all subsequent tests a shock just strong enough to elicit pectoral fin movements was employed. This was determined by starting with approximately 1,000,000 ohms resistance and then gradually decreasing the ohmage until pectoral fin movements appeared. The ohmage was then increased and the point at which no movements appeared recorded. The procedure was repeated 3–4 times; the fish were then isolated for 24 hours and the threshold previously found, checked. This was repeated for 5–10 days until a true threshold had been obtained.

The response to the strong shock was a violent struggling or flight response, and the conditioned responses to the conditioned stimuli *after* training were similar in form though usually of less intensity. Every response was rated for intensity on a 5-point scale.

Conditioned responses were obtained in 11 fish. In Tables 1 and 2 the following four measures are given: (*a*) The number of trials before the appearance of the first conditioned response, (*b*) the

---

[3] No attempt was made to determine whether or not the stimulus was a true auditory or vibratory stimulus, since this was not essential to the general plan of the experiment.

TABLE 1

FORWARD CONDITIONING IN 11 GOLDFISH

(CS*—"liminal" shock; US—"strong" shock.)

Fish No.	Trials Required		Trials before 100% Retention	Maximum Retention in Days
	1st CR	Criterion		
1	2	46	60	7
2	16	88	110	7
3	8	20	50	7
4	21	49	50	7
5	15	36	70	7
6	13	27	40	7
7	15	38	90	7
30	7	26	100	16
31	8	29	70	16
32	4	16	40	16
33	9	27	60	16
	10.7	36.5	67.2	10.2

* Where abbreviations are used throughout this paper CS = conditioned stimulus, US = unconditioned stimulus, CR = conditioned response, PCS = pseudo-conditioned stimulus, and PCR = pseudo-conditioned response.

TABLE 2

FORWARD CONDITIONING IN 6 GOLDFISH

(CS—vibration; US—strong shock.)

Fish No.	Trials Required		Trials before 100% Retention	Maximum Retention in Days
	1st CR	Criterion		
11	9	27	70	14
12	14	68	120	14
13	5	19	60	7
14	28	57	80	7
15	17	79	90	3
16	41	88	100	7
	17.3	56.3	86.6	8.6

number of trials before the appearance of five conditioned responses in the 10 trials of a single test period, (c) the number of training trials before obtaining 100 per cent retention for 24 hours (five conditioned responses in five trials) and (d) the maximum period of retention which was tested. An arbitrary criterion of three conditioned responses in five trials was followed here.

Forward conditioning was established in all fish tested and the speed of learning is in keeping with that found by other investigators (Sears, Froloff) both in the number of trials before a single conditioned response appeared and the number of trials before the response became stable and reliable. One characteristic deserves mention and this is the apparent non-specificity of the conditioned responses. After training, any slight noise or jar served frequently to produce flight responses even though the true conditioned reflex was not presented. Furthermore, after training had been established the threshold for the *CS* of liminal shock became markedly lowered, as indicated by the fact that though many times the original amount of resistance might be used, a strong flight response would still be obtained.

2. Formation of Backward Conditioned Reflexes

In the formation of backward conditioned reflexes the unconditioned stimulus of liminal shock was presented as soon as the fish had become quiet, usually in 20 to 30 seconds. The results of this test are presented in Table 3. Since the time interval varied from

TABLE 3

BACKWARD CONDITIONING IN GOLDFISH

(*CS*—"liminal" shock; *US*—strong shock.)

Fish No.	Trials Required		Trials before 100% Retention
	1st C-R	*Criterion*	
20	5	115	140
21	6	134	140
22	12	128	130
23	9	91	140
	8.0	117.0	137.5

trial to trial and since it was always longer than for the forward conditioning, a control forward conditioning series was tested in which for every fish the time interval between presentation of the conditioned and unconditioned stimulus was matched for every trial. These results are presented in Table 4.

TABLE 4

CONTROLLED FORWARD CONDITIONING IN GOLDFISH

(*CS*—"liminal" shock; *US*—strong shock.)

Fish No.	Trial Required		Trials before 100% Retention
	1st C-R	*Criterion*	
24	11	16	40
25	6	34	60
26	14	17	50
27	8	19	30
	9.7	24.0	45.0

These results indicated that backward conditioned reflexes could *apparently* be formed but that they became stable only after a relatively long period of time. Since, however, Grether (4) had previously shown that backward conditioned reflexes in monkeys were in reality "pseudo-conditioned" reflexes the same control was run for the goldfish that had previously been run for the monkeys, the control being described below.

3. Formation of "Pseudo-Conditioned" Reflexes

Pseudo-conditioned reflexes were obtained by presenting the strong shock stimulus independently of any other stimulus 10 times a day at irregular intervals varying up to 30 seconds around a 2-minute standard. The previously indifferent stimulus was then presented five times and the responses were noted. From the second day on, the previously indifferent stimulus was presented for five trials (and, of course, never reenforced), 10 training trials were next given (the strong shock presented, but never paired with an indifferent stimulus), and then the originally indifferent stimulus was presented five times. All other criteria were the same as those used in the previously described forward conditioning experiments. Two groups of four fish each were tested; the first group were "trained" individually; the second group were placed together in the bowl when the strong shocks were presented but were separated for the tests of responsiveness to the "liminal" shock. The results for these subjects are given in Tables 5 and 6.

The results for pseudo-conditioning indicated that *the new stimulus-response connections were formed as rapidly without pairing of stimuli as they were with pairing of conditioned and unconditioned* stimuli. Furthermore, retention was at least as good for the pseudo-conditioned responses as for the conditioned responses.

TABLE 5

PSEUDO-CONDITIONING IN GOLDFISH, SUBJECTS TRAINED SEPARATELY
(Pseudo—*CS*—"liminal" shock; *US*—strong shock.)

Fish No.	Trials Required 1st CR	Criterion	Trials before 100% Retention	Maximum Retention in Days
100	10	20	20	21
101	10	20	30	21
102	10	10	20	21
103	10	10	20	21
	10.0	15.0	27.5	21.0

TABLE 6

PSEUDO-CONDITIONING IN GOLDFISH, SUBJECTS TRAINED IN A GROUP

(Pseudo—*CS*—"liminal" shock; *US*—strong shock.)

Fish No.	Trials Required 1st CR	Criterion	Trials before 100% Retention	Maximum Retention in Days
110	10	10	20	21
111	10	20	30	21
112	10	10	20	21
113	10	10	20	21
	10.0	12.5	20.0	21.0

Though not indicated in the two tables above a total of 40 strong shock trials were given. From the 20th trial on the fish became extremely excitable and it was actually difficult to test for pseudo-conditioning. In all cases where tests could be carried out it was found that the limen to shock was greatly depressed and that the very weakest shocks almost invariably elicited a response. Actually there was indication that the pseudo-conditioned responses were formed more rapidly than the conditioned responses and that the former were more reliable and were better retained.

4. Non-Specificity of Forward Conditioned Responses to Modality of the CS

Non-specificity of forward conditioned responses was measured by first testing for limens to both shock and vibratory stimuli. (No limen for the latter was found even when the amplifier produced a vibration of 128 dv/sec. at an amplitude of approximately 50 decibels.) Training for forward conditioning was then carried out, the *CS* being a "liminal shock" and the *US* a strong shock. Non-specificity was tested by presenting a tone of 128 dv/sec. with an intensity of about 30 decibels. Spread of conditioning from "liminal" shock to vibration (a different sense modality) is indicated in Table 7.

TABLE 7

SPREAD OF CONDITIONING FROM "LIMINAL" SHOCK TO AUDIO-VIBRATORY STIMULI

Fish No.	Trials for Forward Conditioning "Liminal" Shock—Strong Shock 1st CR	Criterion	Trials before Responses to Audio-Vibratory Stimuli Appeared 1st CR	Criterion
301	14	46	20	49
302	22	38	40	76
303	9	40	10	48
304	13	39	20	55
	14.5	40.8	22.5	57

5. Non-Specificity of Pseudo-Conditioning to Other Modalities than That of the US or Related "Liminal" Shock PCS

To show non-specificity of pseudo-conditioning, limens to both shock and vibratory stimuli were first obtained, the results being the same as in Section 4 above. Ten strong shocks a day were then given to four fish for five days. At the end of each day's trials five "liminal" shocks and five auditory stimuli were presented. As is indicated in Table 8 non-specificity of pseudo-conditioning was clearly demon-

TABLE 8

Non-Specificity of Pseudo-Conditioning

| | Trials before "Pseudo-Conditioned" Responses Appeared | | | |
| Fish No. | To "Liminal" Shock | | To Audio-Vibratory Stimulus | |
	1st PCR	Criterion	1st PCR	Criterion
310	10	10	10	20
311	20	20	10	10
312	20	30	20	20
313	10	20	10	20
	15.0	20.0	12.5	17.5

strated; the new stimulus response capacities appeared early, were very consistent, and the responses were strong. Indeed, better pseudo-conditioned responses were obtained to the vibratory stimulus than to the "liminal" shock stimulus.

6. Non-Specificity of Environment in Which Forward Conditioned Responses Could Be Elicited

To determine whether or not the role of the training environment is a factor, determining or partially determining the elicitation of formed conditioned reflexes, audio-vibratory conditioned reflexes were set up in four goldfish in the training situation previously described. After conditioned reflexes had been firmly established the conditioned stimulus was presented to the animals when they were in the "home" bowl both in the experimental and "home" room. These "home" bowls had been made as dissimilar to the experimental bowl as possible, being not only smaller in size but also ornamented with rocks and weeds. In all cases conditioned responses were obtained, no apparent difference being found between strength and frequency in any of the situations.

7. Non-Specificity of the Environment as a Factor in the Elicitation of Pseudo-Conditioned Responses

The effect of varying environments on pseudo-conditioned reflexes was also tested, the conditions being similar to those of Section 6 above, save for the fact that the unconditioned stimulus (shock) and the (audio-vibratory) pseudo-conditioned stimulus were never paired. After pseudo-conditioned responses to audio-vibratory stimuli had been formed in four goldfish they could be elicited in either the experimental bowl or the "home" bowl and in either the experimental room or the "home" room with equal ease. No distinguishing characteristics were observed. In Grether's experiment on monkeys it should be noted the pseudo-conditioned responses were specific to the total training situation.

E. SUMMARY AND CONCLUSION

1. Both delayed and trace conditioned reflexes were established in the goldfish. After being firmly established these responses were quite stable and could be retained for two weeks or longer.

2. Backward conditioned responses were apparently firmly established in two or three times the number of trials necessary for the formation of the forward conditioned reflexes.

3. Pseudo-conditioned reflexes, in which the unconditioned and "conditioned" stimuli were never paired were also formed in goldfish. These reflexes were established as rapidly, if not more rapidly than the true, forward conditioned responses. Pseudo-conditioned responses once firmly established were quite stable and were retained for at least three weeks, as long as or longer than the forward conditioned responses.

4. Forward conditioned responses are not specific to the sensory modality of the conditioned stimulus. Thus after the formation of a conditioned response in which a "liminal" shock was associated with a strong shock, a previously inadequate audio-vibratory stimulus also elicited a response.

5. Pseudo-conditioning is not specific to the sensory modality of the unconditioned stimulus. Thus after repeated strong shocks both previously inadequate "liminal" shocks and also audio-vibratory stimuli elicited pseudo-conditioned responses.

6. After both conditioned and pseudo-conditioned responses have been formed they may be elicited in other environments than that of the environment in which the "learning" took place.

REFERENCES

1. BULL, H. O.   Studies on conditioned responses in fishes: I. *J. Mar. Biol. Assoc.*, 1928, 15, 485–533.
2. FROLOFF, J. P.   Bedingte Reflexe bei Fischen: I. *Pflüger's Arch.*, 1925, 209, 261–71.

3. _____. Bedingte Refiexe bei Fischen: II. *Pflüger's Arch.*, 1928, **220**, 339–49.
4. GRETHER, W. F.   Pseudo-conditioning without paired stimulation encountered in attempted backward conditioning. *J. Comp. Psychol.*, 1937, **25**, 91–96.
5. SEARS, R. R.   Effect of optic lobe ablation on the visuo-motor behavior of gold-fish. *J. Comp. Psychol.*, 1934, **17**, 233–65.
6. UCHTOMSKY, A. A.   Neues aus der Reflexologie und Physiologie des Nerven-systems (Leningrad, 1926), (Russian with German summary), Quoted by Ufland (7).
7. UFLAND, I. M.   Die Reflexerregbarkeit des Frosches Während des Umklam-merungsreflexes. *Pflüger's Arch.*, 1928, **221**, 605–22.

CLASSICAL CONDITIONING IN EARTHWORMS,

LUMBRICUS TERRESTRIS

STANLEY C. RATNER and KLIEM R. MILLER

Michigan State University

The investigation of classical conditioning in annelids, segmented worms, has been largely neglected. The marine annelid, *Hydroides dianthus,* received some attention from Yerkes (1906), who conditioned two specimens to react negatively to bright light when paired with a weak tactual stimulus. Copland (1930) demonstrated an apparent conditioned response to a change in illumination level with the clam worm, *Nereis virens.* He found that a sudden decrease or increase in light level regularly followed by the presentation of food led the animal to leave the tube in which it lived. Examination of Copland's study shows that he used only one worm, and the details of the procedure suggest instrumental learning as well as classical conditioning. Thus, 15 to 20 sec. after illumination level was changed, clam juice was put into the water and movement toward the end of the tube was elicited. When the worm got to the end of the tube, it obtained a piece of clam meat, and the illumination level was changed to the pretrial level. Copland observed that the worm eventually began moving toward the end of the tube shortly after the illumination level was changed and before the juice and clam meat were presented.

Several studies specifically using an instrumental paradigm have also been reported. Yerkes (1912) used several earthworms to show modifiability of behavior in a T maze. Heck (1920) and Swartz (1929), using larger samples, verified Yerkes' observations of modifiability in a maze situation. However, the studies of classical conditioning using segmented worms have involved very small samples, and proper control groups and procedures were lacking.

The purpose of the present experiment is to demonstrate the facility with which earthworms (*Lumbricus terrestris*) develop conditioned responses (CRs) with massed training. The unconditioned stimulus (US) consisted of presenting a bright light, which evoked rearing and withdrawal of the anterior segments of the animal's body. A vibration served as the conditioned stimulus (CS).

METHOD

Subjects

Thirty-two earthworms (*L. terrestris*) varying in length from 10 to 17 cm. were used. The Ss were obtained from an area of about 25 sq. yd. on the Michigan State University campus and were placed in the apparatus within 1 hr. after removal from the natural habitat. During this transfer period Ss were kept in sphagnum moss.

Apparatus

A sketch of the apparatus is shown in Figure 1. Two identical units were constructed so that two Ss could be run at the same time. One S was run during the intertrial interval of the other S. The main part of the apparatus consisted of a clear, round, Koroseal tube vented on the top and sides with 1-mm. holes at 3-cm. intervals. The tube was 62½ cm. long, with an inside diameter of 0.8 cm. The tube was mounted on a ⅜-in. thick plywood base in such a way that both ends met, thereby producing a circular runway for the animal. A 6-v. d.c. doorbell buzzer, with the bell removed, was attached securely on the base at the center of the plastic tube to maintain an equal amount of vibration to all parts of the runway. One #2 (G.E.) photo flood bulb in a 12-in. spun aluminum reflector was mounted 18 in. from the animal and constituted the source of the US. An 8-c.p., dark-red bulb placed immediately below and inside the US light-source reflector provided general illumination.

The CS and US were timed and automatically presented by two Time-O-Lite master timers. Intertrial intervals were timed with a stop watch.

Procedure

The tube which was to contain S was moistened with 0.3 cc. of water immediately prior to S's entry. The S was then transferred from the moss to the apparatus by allowing S to crawl into one end of the tube, which had been removed from the base. After S entered, the end was replaced, and S was given a 20-min. dark-adaptation period before the trials began.

LIGHT SOURCE
AT 18"

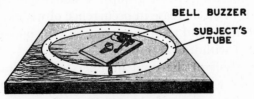

BELL BUZZER

SUBJECT'S
TUBE

FIG. 1. Conditioning apparatus.

Four groups with eight Ss per group were used: Experimental group (E), vibration control group (V), random-response control group (R), and light control group (L). A method of random selection was used to establish the order in which the different groups and Ss were run.

Group E was given a total of 130 trials with a 50-sec. intertrial interval. The first 100 trials were conditioning trials, and the last 30 were extinction trials. For conditioning trials the vibratory stimulus (CS) was presented for 6 sec.; after the first 4 sec. of vibration, the light (US) was presented for 2 sec. Thus, the CS and US overlapped for 2 sec. and were terminated together. A response occurring during the first 4 sec. of the CS, prior to the presentation of the US, was recorded as a conditioned withdrawal response.

The unconditioned response to light (US) was determined in a preliminary study. It was found to consist of a rearing of $1/8$ to $1/4$ in. and withdrawal of $1/4$ to 1 in. of the anterior segments of the S's body. If S were moving at the time of stimulation, the response consisted of an abrupt stop followed by the above response. Thus, responses of these kinds which occurred prior to the US were counted as CRs.

The response, which was relatively unequivocal, was identified visually by E during each trial. Observation was facilitated by some magnification of the S which came about from the curvature of the clear plastic tube and from continuous illumination from a dark-red bulb.

The 30 extinction trials consisted of a 6-sec. vibration in which all responses that occurred in the first 4 sec. were recorded.

Group V was given a total of 100 trials which were administered and recorded in the same manner as with Group E except that the US was not presented at any time.

Group R was used to determine the number of spontaneous responses. This group was observed for 100 tirals of 4-sec. duration during which neither vibration nor light was presented.

Group L was employed primarily to determine if the light, US, would sensitize the animals to the vibratory stimulus. The Ss in this group were given a total of 105 trials, consisting of 70 light and 35 vibration trials. The 2-sec. light stimulus was given in blocks of 10 trials followed by a block of five 6-sec. vibratory trials. All responses which occurred within the first 4 sec. of vibration were recorded.

A 50-sec. intertrial interval was used for all groups.

RESULTS

The percentages of withdrawal responses for successive blocks of trials for each group, including L, are shown graphically in Figure 2. The curve for Group E, the conditioned group, shows a clear, sharp increase in percentage of CRs throughout the conditioning series and a typical decrease in percentage of CRs during the 30 extinction trials.

The curves for the control groups, V and R, which did not receive the US, show an increase in occurrence of withdrawal responses for the first ten trials and then show an irregular but steady decrease in percentages of withdrawal responses.

Statistical analysis of the total numbers of withdrawal responses made by Groups E, V, and R supports the interpretations of the graphic data. The means of the total numbers of withdrawal responses for the first 100 trials made by Groups E, V, and R are 29.6, 14.1, and 4.7, respectively. Differences in total numbers of withdrawal responses between the groups were tested by Mann-Whitney U tests (Siegel, 1956, p. 119). Group E, the conditioned group, differed significantly from both Group V ($U = 6$, $p < .01$, $n_1 = n_2 = 8$) and Group R ($U = 0$, $p < .01$, $n_1 = n_2 = 8$). Group V, vibratory control group, also differed significantly from Group R, random-response control group ($U = 10$, $p < .05$, $n_1 = n_2 = 8$).

To test the reliability of the decrease in withdrawal responses during extinction as compared with conditioning, the total number of responses made by each S during the last block of conditioning trials (Trials 91 to 100) was compared with the total number made during the last block of extinction trials (Trials 21 to 30). The mean percentage of CRs during the last block of conditioning trials is 42.50, and the mean percentage of CRs during the last block of extinction trials is 15.00. The decrease in the percentage of responses from conditioning to extinction was tested by a Walsh test for related samples (Siegel, 1956, p. 85) and was found to be significant at the .03 level.

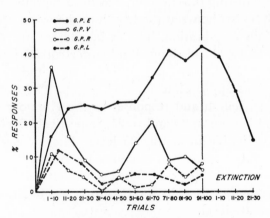

FIG. 2. Percentages of withdrawal responses for experimental and control groups.

The results from Group L, the light-sensitization control group, were first analyzed to determine if increased numbers of presentations of the light led to increased responding to the vibratory stimulus. During the first 15 test trials, the total number of responses to vibratory stimuli was 8 ($M = 1.0$). During the last 15 test trials, Ss made a total of 5 responses to the 15 vibratory stimuli ($M = 0.6$). The difference between responses on the first and last 15 test trials was tested by the binominal test of the chance hypothesis. That is, the number of Ss that made fewer responses during the last 15 trials as compared with the first 15 trials was compared with the number that made an equal number or more during the last 15 trials as compared with the first 15 trials. Four Ss made fewer responses during the last 15 test trials, and four made an equal number or more responses during this time. Thus, the chance hypothesis cannot be rejected.

As an additional check on any sensitizing effect of the light on reaction to vibration, the percentage of withdrawal responses to vibration during the 35 test trials for Group L, was compared with the percentage of withdrawal responses to vibration during all the trials for Group V. Group V had not received any light stimulations. Group L had a mean of 5.6% withdrawal responses, and Group V had a mean of 14.1%. A Mann-Whitney U test of the difference between these groups yielded a significant U ($U = 10$, $p < .05$, $n_1 = n_2 = 8$). In view of the finding that Group V made a reliably higher percentage of responses to vibration than Group L, it is concluded that the light did not sensitize Ss to respond to vibration, and, if anything, it inhibited responses.

Observation during the running of Ss in each group suggested that a relationship exists between the length of the worm and its responsiveness to light or vibration. The Ss in each group were from approximately 10 to 11 cm. long. Rank-order correlations were computed between Ss' lengths and numbers of withdrawal responses under conditions appropriate for each group. The correlations obtained between length and responses to the vibratory stimulus for Groups E and V were —.24 and —.21, respectively. Neither of these correlations is significant at the .05 level. The correlation between length and number of random responses for Group R was —.54 and is not significant at the .05 level. The correlation between length and number of responses to light for Group L was —.81, which is significant at the .01 level.

DISCUSSION

The results clearly indicate the acquisition and extinction of a conditioned withdrawal response in earthworms, *L. terrestris.* The fact that the mean percentage of CRs during the last block of conditioning trials only reached 42.50 is probably due to the extreme massing of the conditioning trials. It is expected that higher percentages of CRs would be obtained with more widely spaced trials.

The data from the three control groups support the interpretation that the behavior change in the conditioned group, Group E, was true conditioning. That is, results from the control groups show decreasing numbers of responses on successive blocks of trials and fewer total numbers of responses as compared with Group E. Thus, the behavior change shown by Group E, the conditioned group, is not due to the vibratory stimulus alone, random responses, or sensitization by the light, the US.

Light-sensitive cells have been noted on earthworms, and avoidance reactions to light are commonly reported (Storer, 1943, p. 419). Bright light was also used by Yerkes (1912) in his study of maze learning with worms. While auditory receptors have not been found in earthworms, their sensitivity to tactual and vibratory stimuli is reported (Storer, 1943, p. 421) and was found in this study.

The significant negative relationship found between length of Ss and their responsiveness to the US does not have a clear interpretation. The nearly normal distribution of lengths of Ss from approximately 10 to 17 cm. is well within the expected range for specimens of approximately the same age. The differences in length are attributable to such factors as contribute to individual differences in any species, for example, heredity, food supply, and general health. One possible interpretation of this negative correlation is that a long worm, like a long train, accelerates slowly. This hypothesis is testable since the worms can be made shorter by surgical means and their responsiveness then checked.

The phylum Annelida, of which the earthworm is a member, and Platahelminthes, of which the planaria, a flatworm, is a member, are of more than casual interest in studies of comparative behavior. This is due to the biological characteristics which begin to clearly emerge within these phyla. As Thompson and McConnell (1955) point out in their study of conditioning of planaria, "Such evolutionary advancements as true synaptic nervous transmission, definite encephalization, and bilateral symmetry, to mention only a few, appear for the first time . . ." (p. 65).

SUMMARY

The purpose of the present study was to investigate the facility with which earthworms (*Lumbricus terrestris*) develop conditioned withdrawal responses under conditions of massed training. Thirty-two Ss were divided randomly into four equal groups: experimental group, vibration control group, random-response control group, and light control group. For the experimental group, vibration (CS) and light (US) were paired for 100 conditioning trials. The percentages of avoidance responses occurring prior to the onset of the light increased during successive blocks of trials and then decreased during extinction trials. That this systematic change in behavior was not due to either sensitization by the vibration or light or to random responses was indicated by the behavior of the control groups. A significant negative correlation was found between lengths of worms and responsiveness to light.

REFERENCES

COPLAND, M. An apparent conditioned response in *Nereis virens. J. comp. Psychol.,* 1930, **10**, 339–54.

HECK, L. Über die Bildung einer Assoziation beim Regenwurm ouf Grund von Dressurversuchen. *Lotos Naturwiss Zeit,* 1920, **68**, 168–89.

SIEGEL, S. *Nonparametric statistics for the behavioral sciences.* New York: McGraw-Hill, 1956.

STORER, T. I. *General zoology.* New York: McGraw-Hill, 1943.

SWARTZ, R. D. Modification of behavior of earthworms. *J. comp. Psychol.,* 1929, **9**, 17–33.

THOMPSON, R., and McCONNELL, J. Classical conditioning in the planaria, *Dugesia dorotocephala. J. comp. physiol. Psychol.,* 1955, 48, 65–69.

YERKES, R. M. Modifiability of *Hydroides dianthus* V. *J. comp. Neurol.,* 1906, **16**, 441–50.

YERKES, R. M. The intelligence of earthworms. *J. anim. Behav.,* 1912, **2**, 332–52.

NICTITATING MEMBRANE: CLASSICAL CONDITIONING AND EXTINCTION IN THE ALBINO RABBIT

by

I. GORMEZANO
NEIL SCHNEIDERMAN
EDWARD DEAUX
ISREAL FUENTES
Department of Psychology
Indiana University, Bloomington

Abstract. The distribution of response latencies and the percentage performance curve of a classical conditioning group, by comparison with a control group, indicated that the extension of the nictitating membrane elicited by a puff of air to the cornea was successfully conditioned to a previously neutral stimulus.

The nictitating membrane (plica semilunaris) in the albino rabbit consists of a curved plate of cartilage covered with glandular epithelium. It is drawn from the inner canthus of the eye laterally across the cornea by a sheet of smooth muscle, but the mechanism of its action is not clearly understood (1).

Though there have been no reported attempts to condition this membrane in the rabbit, incidental observations in our laboratory have indicated that an extension of the membrane is reliably elicited by a puff of air to the cornea. We have observed that when the membrane is activated it rarely extends past the midline of the pupil and always leaves a portion of the cornea exposed, and that even highly conditioned rabbits do not appear to be capable of a sustained extension of the membrane. These two properties would appear to provide the experimenter with an even greater degree of control over the sensory consequences of the unconditioned stimulus than that existing in our previously reported study of conditioning of the rabbits outer lid (2).

The conditioning apparatus and manner in which the rabbit was restrained within a Plexiglas box has been described (2, 3). To permit the recording of movement of the membrane and to insure continual exposure of the cornea, the upper and lower eyelids of the rabbit's right eye were taped open. When the restraining box was positioned in a nonactivated refrigeration unit, a 6-inch speaker and a rod supporting an air jet and gravity-return potentiometer were positioned about 5 inches in front of the rabbit. A silk thread was attached to a rod which was mechanically coupled to the shaft of the potentiometer. A small metal hook connected to the other end of the silk thread was attached to a nylon loop which was sutured in the nictitating membrane of the rabbit's right eye. The signal from the potentiometer was amplified and graphically recorded. The orifice of the air jet was adjusted to deliver an 80-mm puff of compressed nitrogen of 100 msec duration from a position about $\frac{1}{2}$ inch from the dorsal region of the right cornea. The conditioned stimulus (CS) consisted of an 800-cy/sec tone of 72 db SPL, presented for 600 msec.

Eighteen albino rabbits, 85 to 100 days of age, were assigned to one of two groups for 2 days of adaptation, 8 days of acquisition training, and 8 days of extinction. In each day of acquisition a control group of six rabbits (group C) received a random presentation of 70 CS alone and 70 unconditioned stimuli (UCS) alone trials restricted within two trials blocks at randomized intertrial intervals of 5, 10, and 15 seconds (mean of 10 seconds). A classical conditioning group of 12 rabbits (group E) received 70 paired presentations of the CS and UCS a day at a CS–UCS interval of 500 msec and randomized intervals between trials of 15, 20, and 25 seconds (mean of 20 seconds). For each of the 2 days of adaptation a measure of spontaneous membrane movement was obtained in both groups by recording the frequency of responses in intervals corresponding to the 70 CS–UCS trials that were employed in acquisition for group E.

In adaptation and acquisition all membrane extensions of at least 1 mm deflection from the baseline were recorded from 0 to 525 msec after initiation of the trial. In extinction the interval was extended to 600 msec. The distribution of response latencies for group E in acquisition and extinction is shown in Figure 1. The left-hand side of the figure shows that the distributions are unimodal and the modal latency systematically decreases from 525 msec on the second day of acquisition to 150 msec on the eighth day. The finding is consistent with the progressive decrease in response latency reported by Pavlov (4) for simultaneous conditioning of the salivary response. An analysis of variance of the mean latency of conditioned responses over days revealed that the decrease in response latency was significant $P < .01$).

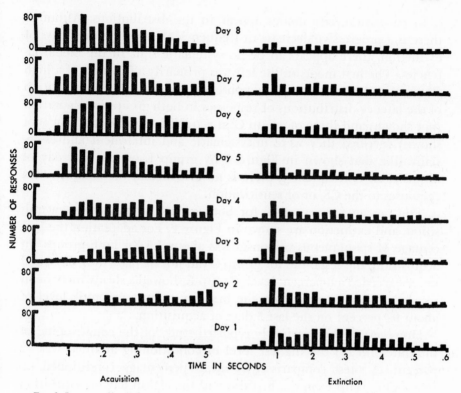

FIG. 1. Latency distributions of all membrane responses of group E in acquisition and extinction.

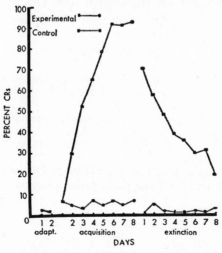

FIG. 2. Mean percentage of responses plotted in 70 trial blocks in acquisition and extinction.

In extinction, two modes appear in the distributions. Although there is a progressive decrease in frequency of responses over days of extinction, there appears to be no systematic shift in the modal latencies. The first mode on the left was primarily a function of a high frequency of short latency responses in two rabbits. Examination of the latency distributions of responses in both groups in adaptation (not shown) and those of group C in acquisition and extinction (not shown) revealed they were unsystematic and infrequent and essentially like that shown in Figure 1 by group E on the first day of acquisition. Consequently, there is no evidence in the data of reflex responses to the CS, or of sensitization.

The percentage responses for both groups in adaptation, acquisition, and extinction are shown in Figure 2. For adaptation the percentage of spontaneous responses was about 1.5 for both groups. In acquisition, the responses for group C did not increase over days, and never exceeded a 6-percent level. Group E showed a steady increase in responses from 6 percent on the first day to an asymptotic level of about 92 percent on the last 3 days of acquisition.

However, in the previously reported study of the conditioning of the outer lid (2) the highest level of conditioning attained was 72 percent. A *t*-test comparison of mean percentage conditioned responses of group E on the first day and the eighth day of acquisition was highly significant ($P < .001$). Group E showed considerable resistance to extinction. The mean response was from 71 percent on the first day to 20 percent on the eighth day. On the other hand, in group C extinction and adaptation were closely parallel (5).

REFERENCES AND NOTES

1. S. Duke-Elder, *System of Ophthalmology* (Kempton, London, 1958), vol. 1; R. J. Last, *Wolff's Anatomy of the Eye and Orbit* (Saunders, Philadelphia, 1961).
2. N. Schneiderman, I. Fuentes, I. Gormezano, *Science* 136, 650 (1962).
3. J. W. Moore, and I. Gormezano, *J. Exptl. Psychol.* 62, 552 (1961).
4. I. P. Pavlov, *Conditioned Reflexes,* translated by G. V. Anrep (Oxford Univ. Press, London, 1927).
5. This study was supported by NSF grant G-16030. One of us (I.F.) participated under the NSF undergraduate participation program (grant G-16282).

FORMATION OF CONDITIONED RESPONSES IN

INFANT MONKEYS[1]

W. A. MASON and H. F. HARLOW
University of Wisconsin

The conditioned-response technique is in theory one of the most useful and efficient methods available for the study of neonatal learning. The conditioned and unconditioned stimuli can be so arranged that the absence of well-developed orienting responses will not be a serious handicap, and a response measure can be selected which will minimize the effect of neonatal locomotor deficiencies.

Although there have been no previous investigations of the conditionability of neonatal monkeys or apes, there have been several studies of conditioning in the newborn human being. Some authors have reported evidence of learning (5, 7), but questions concerning these claims have been raised by the carefully controlled experiment by Wickens and Wickens (8). These investigators found that the incidence of so-called conditioned responses among their pseudo-conditioning control group, which had never experienced the CS and US as contiguous events, was practically identical with that of the group undergoing conventional conditioning procedures. Such findings reopen the question of the existence of neonatal conditioning and emphasize the importance of adequate experimental controls.

METHOD

Subjects

The Ss were 13 infant macaques, 10 of which (no. 8 through 17) had been born in the laboratory and separated from their mothers within a few hours of birth. Their training in this experiment began on the third day of life. The other 3 Ss were born outside the laboratory. One (no. 103) was separated from its mother on the thirteenth day of life and tested initially on the fifteenth day. The remaining 2 Ss (no. 101 and 102) were separated from their mothers at an estimated age of four days and started in the experiment on the seventh day of life.

Upon removal from the mother all animals were housed individually in wire-

[1] Support for this research was provided through funds received from the Graduate School of the University of Wisconsin, Grant M-772, National Institutes of Health, and Grant AT 11-1-64 (Project No. 11) Atomic Energy Commission.

mesh cages 15 in. by 18 in. by 24 in. Throughout the period of the experiment the monkeys were bottle-fed on a formula described by van Wagenen (6).

Apparatus

The basic components of the conditioning apparatus include a plastic stabilimeter cage[2] 9 in. by 9 in. by 9 in. with a grid floor, a Jackson Audiofrequency Oscillator for producing a 1000-cps tone, a shock generator (9), and an Esterline-Angus Recorder, which graphically recorded the onset and duration of shock and tone as well as movements of the conditioning cage. Tone and shock intervals were mechanically fixed at 3 and 1 sec., respectively, and could be administered separately or paired. The cage and a loud-speaker for tone delivery were contained in an insulated booth equipped with a one-way-vision screen, as shown in Figure 1. Shock was delivered through the grid floor of the stabilimeter cage and was inescapable. The cage and operator's controls were isolated from other parts of the apparatus within a sound-shielded room.

Procedure

On the day of separation from the mother and on the following day the Ss were placed in the conditioning apparatus for a 10-min. adaptation period, and training sessions began the following day.

The ten Ss born in the laboratory were randomly assigned to three groups and the three Ss born outside the laboratory were randomly, but independently, distributed among the three groups. The experimental group had five Ss, and the two control groups had four Ss each. The specific testing procedures for the groups were as follows:

Group TS. This group, the tone-shock experimental Ss, received eight training trials daily in which the CS (tone) preceded the US (shock) by 2 sec. and was then paired with it for 1 sec., and two test trials in which the CS was presented alone.

Group PC. The pseudoconditioning Ss were given eight trials daily with the US alone and two test trials in which the CS was presented alone. The duration of shock and tone was the same as for group TS, but the US and the CS were never paired. The PC group, as the name implies, served as a control for sensitization or pseudoconditioning.

Group TO. The tone-only Ss were presented with the CS ten trials daily, but they never received the US. In treating the data, two of their daily trials were arbitrarily designated as test trials in accordance with the TS and PC group schedules. Group TO served to check the possibility that positive reactions to the tone might appear as a result of maturational changes in sensitivity or responsiveness independent of the conditioning procedures.

For all groups the serial order of test trials changed from day to day according to a predetermined schedule so arranged that a test trial occurred in each block of five trials with at least one training trial separating the test trials. Between-trial intervals varied in a predetermined order from 1 to 3 min. All Ss were tested daily for 30 days.

Generalization and retention. Beginning 24 hr. after the conditioning sessions, steps were taken to measure the generality and retention of the conditioned response (CR). First, all the Ss were trained to leave the home cage and traverse a 6-ft. enclosed runway for food. Preliminary training continued for six days and testing for the following six days. Throughout this period the Ss were fed at 4-hr. intervals, and all feedings occurred in the runway situation. One feeding each day was designated a test period, and tests were never given at the same hour on

---

[2] The authors are indebted to Dr. G. E. McClearn and Mr. A. R. Schmidt for the design and construction of the stabilimeter cage.

Fig. 1

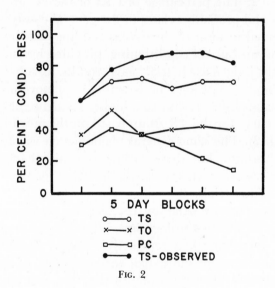

Fig. 2

two consecutive days. On the tests the tone used as the CS was sounded for 3 sec. before the entrance door of the runway opened.

On the day following the final test in the runway situation, the Ss were returned to the stabilimeter cage for ten retention trials with the tone only. The tone used as the CS was sounded for 3 sec. before the entrance door of the runway opened.

Measures

Two Os were present during the conditioning sessions and they independently judged and recorded the presence or absence of CRs and the general form of the observed responses.

Frequency of CRs was also measured on test trials by comparing the number of cage movements recorded on the Esterline-Angus tape during the 3-sec. interval immediately preceding. Any increase in cage movements during the CS interval over the preceding interval was scored as a CR or pseudo-CR.

Measures taken on both test and nontest trials in the runway situation included latency of exit, running speed, and amount of formula consumed during the 10-min. feeding period.

RESULTS

The percentage of CRs for successive blocks of ten test trials for all groups are presented in Figure 2. Group TS attains a level of 58 per cent during the first five days of training, rises to 70 per cent within the next five days, and shows little change thereafter. The mean TS group score of 68 per cent is significantly greater than the mean PC group score of 31 per cent or the mean TO group score of 41 per cent, as measured by t tests ($p < .05$). The means of the control groups do not differ significantly. Pseudoconditioning was observed in one animal, and its data are included in the tests of significance and in Figure 2. The percentage of CRs of the PC group decreases progressively and probably relates to the general constriction of cage activity observed in most of these Ss as training continued.

The second measure of conditioning, provided by the two Os who independently judged each trial, gave results in substantial agreement with the conditioning data based on cage movements. The observational data, however, showed a higher incidence of CRs, as indicated by the curve for the TS group based on the mean judgments of both Os (Fig. 2). The same general phenomenon was found for the PC and TO groups, but these curves are omitted for purposes of clarity. Inter-rater agreement was high, being 90 per cent for the entire series of test trials.

Tests in the runway situation revealed no consistent differences between the TS and control groups. The TS group showed some evidence of retention when returned to the conditioning cage, although a high degree of individual variability makes interpretation difficult. The mean retention score for the TS group was 26 per cent as measured by cage movements and 40 per cent according to Os' judgments. There were no perfect scores, and only one S gave CRs on more than five of the ten retention trials. The percentage of CRs for the TO and PC groups as measured by cage movements was 20 and 17.5, respectively, and no intergroup difference was significant.

DISCUSSION

The present experiment gives unequivocal evidence of learning in the neonatal monkey. Conditioned responses to shock developed rapidly, frequently in the first two training sessions, when most of the Ss were only 2 or 3 days old. Although the present research represents the first controlled experimental demonstration of learning in the neonatal monkey, the results are in keeping with existing data. Foley (1) reported that his 3-day-old rhesus monkey learned to avoid a noxious stimulus in a single trial, and object recognition was observed by Hines (2) in rhesus monkeys 11 days old.

The observational data show that the form of the CR changes progressively during learning from a poorly organized and diffuse response to one that is specific and precise. As training progressed most Ss responded to the CS by standing erect, sometimes on one foot. This phenomenon of progressively developing precision of the CR has also been observed during conditioning in puppies (3) and in human infants (4).

Assuming that the CS in the present experiment acquired the capacity of arousing fear or anxiety, one might expect broad situational generalization. This, however, did not obtain, the conditioning being limited to the testing situation. The limited retention was surprising and must be attributed either to the extreme immaturity of the animals or some artifact imposed by the training situation.

SUMMARY

Three groups of rhesus monkeys ranging from 2 to 14 days of age were Ss in a conditioning experiment.

The five Ss in the conditioning group received eight training trials daily pairing the CS (tone) and the US (shock) and two test trials in which the CS was presented alone. As a control for pseudoconditioning, a group of four Ss was given eight trials daily with the shock alone and two test trials with the CS alone. A second control group of four Ss was presented with the CS ten trials daily but never received shock. It served to check the possibility that positive reactions to the tone might appear as a result of maturational changes in sensitivity or responsiveness independent of conditioning procedures.

The conditioning group showed early, rapid learning and made significantly more CRs on the test trials than either control group. Subsequent tests for generalization and retention of the CR yielded essentially negative results.

REFERENCES

1. FOLEY, J. P., JR. First year development of a rhesus monkey (*Macaca mulatta*) reared in isolation. *J. genet. Psychol.*, 1934, 45, 39–105.
2. HINES, M. The development and regression of reflexes, postures, and progres-

sion in the young macaque. *Contr. Embryol. Carnegie Inst., Wash.,* 1942, **30,** 153–209.

3. JAMES, W. T., and CANNON, D. J. Conditioned avoiding response in puppies. *Amer. J. Physiol.,* 1952, **168,** 251–53.
4. KASATKIN, N. I. Early ontogenesis of human conditioned reflexes. *Comm. 19th int. Physiol. Congr.,* 1953.
5. MARQUIS, D. P. Can conditioned response be established in the newborn infant? *J. genet. Psychol.,* 1931, **39,** 479–92.
6. VAN WAGENEN, G. The monkey. In E. J. Farris (Ed.), *The care and breeding of laboratory animals.* New York: Wiley, 1950, pp. 1–42.
7. WENGER, M. A. Conditioned responses in human infants. In R. G. Barker, J. S. Sounin, and H. F. Wright (Eds.), *Child behavior and development.* New York: McGraw-Hill, 1943, pp. 67–86.
8. WICKENS, D. D., and WICKENS, C. A study of conditioning in the neonate. *J. exp. Psychol.,* 1940, **26,** 94–102.
9. WYCKOFF, L. B., and PAGE, H. A. A grid for administering shock. *Amer. J. Psychol.,* 1954, **67,** 154.

INTRASUBJECT CONDITIONING AS A FUNCTION OF THE

INTENSITY OF THE UNCONDITIONED STIMULUS

by

K. W. SPENCE
D. F. HAGGARD *
L. E. ROSS

Department of Psychology, State University of Iowa, Iowa City

Abstract. Subjects conditioned concurrently to two different conditioned stimuli, light and tone, exhibited a significantly higher level of conditioning to the stimulus paired with a strong unconditioned stimulus than to the stimulus paired with a weak one. The findings suggest that habit strength in aversive conditioning varies with the intensity of the unconditioned stimulus.

In a number of experiments (*1*) concerned with the problem of whether habit strength (H) is a function of the intensity of the unconditioned stimulus (UCS), the conditioning performances of two different groups of subjects (*S*'s), equated for level of drive (*D*) but differing with respect to reinforcement conditions, were compared. The finding of a higher level of performance on the part of *S*'s that received a strong UCS on trials producing conditioning (that is, habit growth) as compared with *S*'s who were given a weak UCS on such trials was interpreted to mean that habit strength (H) varies with the level of intensity (noxiousness) of the UCS.

In the present experiment (*2*) we attempted to obtain further evidence on this problem by comparing the conditioning performances of a single group of *S*'s under two different reinforcement intensities. All *S*'s were conditioned concurrently to two different conditioned stimuli (CS's) (light and tone). Half of the *S*'s had the light paired with a strong UCS and the tone paired with a weak UCS. In the case of the other half of the *S*'s these relations were reversed, the tone being paired with the strong UCS and the light with the weak UCS. Our primary interest lay in a comparison of the level of conditioning performance to the CS paired with the strong UCS with that to the CS

---

* Present address: Human Resources Research Office, Unit No. 1, Fort Knox, Ky.

paired with the weak UCS. On the basis of the findings of the previous experiments and the interpretation offered by them, namely, that a greater amount of H is established to a CS paired with a strong UCS than to one paired with a weak UCS, it may be predicted that a higher level of conditioning performance will be made to the CS paired with the stronger UCS.

Twenty-four men and 24 women from an introductory course in psychology served as S's in this experiment. Nine other S's were eliminated, including three who met the criterion defining a voluntary responder (*3*), two who gave conditioned responses (CR's) to initial test trial presentations of the CS, and four who adapted to the air puff. An S was considered to have adapted to the puff if the mean amplitude of the unconditioned responses (UCR's) made on the last 10 trials involving the weak puff was less than 50 percent of that on the first 10 weak puff trials.

The apparatus was the same as that used in earlier studies (*1*) except for the addition of a 1000-cycle tone CS produced by a loudspeaker driven by a Hewlett-Packard oscillator.

Instructions and preliminary trials were similar to those of the previous studies. A variable (15, 20, 25 sec) intertrial interval was used, as well as a ready signal which preceded the onset of the CS by 2, 3, or 4 seconds.

Each S received 100 conditioning trials, 50 of which involved a tone CS and 50 a light CS. The two CS's were given in a prearranged sequence within which neither of the CS's occurred more than twice in succession. For half of the S's the tone was always paired with a strong (2 lb/in.²) puff and the light with a weak (0.33 lb/in.²) puff, while the other half received the reverse pairing, a 0.33 lb/in.² puff with the light and a 2 lb/in.² puff with the tone. The CS–UCS interval was 500 msec, with the duration of the CS 550 msec and the duration of the UCS 50 msec. At the end of the experiment all S's were questioned regarding their understanding of the purpose of the experiment and cautioned not to discuss the experiment with other members of the class.

Acquisition curves in terms of the number of anticipatory CR's given to the CS paired with the strong UCS and to the CS paired with the weak UCS are shown in Figure 1. As may be observed, the curve for the strong puff is consistently above the curve for the weak puff, with the difference gradually increasing during the course of conditioning. A summary of an analysis of variance, involving three within-subjects factors and one between-subjects interaction (*4*, p. 279, Type VII), based upon the first and last blocks of ten conditioning trials is presented in Table 1. As may be seen from the lower portion of this table, the differential effect of the UCS variable was highly significant, the obtained F proving a P value of .001. Also of interest is the fact that the interaction between the UCS variable and blocks of conditioning trials was significant $(P = .025)$, thus indicating that the divergence of the conditioning curves was not a chance one.

TABLE 1

SUMMARY OF ANALYSIS OF VARIANCE OF FREQUENCY OF
CR's FOR TRIALS 1 TO 20 AND 61 TO 80.

Source	df	MS	F	P
Between S's	47			
A B (b)	1			
Error (b)	46	14.94		
Within S's	144			
CS (A)	1	40.33	11.86	.005
Puff (B)	1	44.08	12.96	.001
Trials (C)	1	752.08	191.37	.001
A C	1	3.01	1.11	$> .200$
B C	1	18.76	6.90	.025
A B (b) C	1	1.34	< 1.00	
Error W	138	3.35		
Error$_1$ W	46	3.40		
Error$_2$ W	46	3.93		
Error$_3$ W	46	2.72		
Total	191			

Further examination of Table 1 reveals that the CS variable—that is, whether tone or light—also significantly affected the level of conditioning performance. Indeed, this variable gave a slightly larger value of F than did the UCS variable. It will be observed, however, that the interaction term between CS and trial blocks was not significant. This implies that the acquisition curves for the tone and light did not diverge. Presumably the different performance in the case of the two CS's reflects Hull's stimulus dynamism variable, V.

The results of this experiment add still further evidence supporting the interpretation that habit strength (H) is a function of the intensity of the UCS. In the previous experiments (1) the performance of two independent groups of S's whose drive level (D) was equated by employing two different puff intensities equally often was compared. It was found in every instance that the group which had the CS paired with the strong UCS exhibited a higher level of conditioning performance than did the group which had the CS paired with the weak UCS. The present experiment involves a comparison of the levels of conditioning to two different CS's, light and tone, established concurrently in the same group of *S*'s. Controlling for any possible effects of the two CS's per se, the analysis of the data of this experiment clearly shows

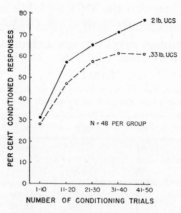

FIG. 1. Percentage of CR's in blocks of ten trials made to CS paired with 2-lb. UCS and 0.33-lb. UCS.

that a higher level of response was given when the CS was paired with the strong UCS than in the case in which the CS was paired with the weak UCS. Since the two conditionings were within the same *S*, the level of *D* must have been the same and thus equal for the two CR's. This performance difference reflects, then, a greater development of *H* in the case of the conditioned reflex established with the stronger UCS.

As the number of conditioning trials in our several experiments concerned with this problem was not sufficient to reach the performance asymptote, one cannot infer for certain whether it is the maximum to which *H* grows that is related to intensity of the UCS, or whether it is the parameter determining the rate of approach of *H* to its asymptote. Examination of the curves from the several experiments, including Fig. 1 of the present study, suggests that it is the asymptote of *H* which is affected and not the rate-of-approach parameter.

In concluding, we should like to call attention once again to the fact that, while the findings of these studies may be interpreted as supporting the drive-reduction versions of reinforcement theory (5), we prefer to continue our interpretation to the more general conception that habit formation in such aversive types of conditioning is some function of the intensity of the UCS. Evidence with regard to the precise nature of the reinforcing mechanism in such learning requires other, presumably physiological, types of experimentation.

1. K. W. SPENCE, *Behavior Theory and Conditioning* (Yale Univ. Press, New Haven, Conn., 1956); K. W. SPENCE, D. F. HAGGARD, L. E. Ross, *J. Exptl. Psychol.* **55**, 404 (1958).
2. This study was carried out as part of a project concerned with the role of motivation in learning under contract N9 ONR–93802, project NR 154–107 between the State University of Iowa and the Office of Naval Research.
3. K. W. SPENCE and J. A. TAYLOR, *J. Exptl. Psychol.* **42**, 183 (1951).
4. E. F. LINDQUIST, *Design and Analysis of Experiments in Psychology and Education* (Houghton-Mifflin, New York, 1953).
5. C. L. HULL, *Principles of Behavior* (Appleton-Century, New York, 1943); N. E. MILLER and J. DOLLARD, *Social Learning and Imitation* (Yale Univ. Press, New Haven, Conn., 1941).

CHAPTER 11

GENERALITY OF INSTRUMENTAL LEARNING

Instrumental learning, already alluded to, refers to learning in which the response is instrumental in bringing about reinforcement (producing an incentive or removing an aversive stimulus). Operant conditioning which means essentially the same thing is a term initiated by B. F. Skinner. Skinner's term refers to the fact that the response being learned is one where the organism operates on the environment; and reinforcement, as described above, is contingent upon the operant response. Operant behavior is called emitted rather than elicited behavior by Skinner (1938) because of the difficulty involved in isolating the original eliciting stimulus, but in this book operant behavior is looked upon as investigatory or manipulatory and is considered to be elicited by novel stimuli.

A common distinction between instrumental and operant learning, at least in the laboratory, is that the animal is free to respond at any time in the operant situation but is usually given discrete trials when the learning is labeled instrumental. This distinction generates different measures of performance. Rate of responding is almost the exclusive measure in operant situations, whereas speed or latency of response, probability of occurrence, and amplitude (force) are the main measures in the instrumental situation.

The earliest studies in this general area were considerably more complex than is the case today. These are exemplified by the cat-in-the-puzzle box experiments by E. L. Thorndike (1896) and the complex maze studies by Small (1901) and Watson (1907) using rats. Such studies are often categorized as selective learning and are more appropriately considered in the next chapter on learning with complex cues.

Methodology

Today, studies on instrumental learning are fairly well limited to a few simple, almost standard, experimental situations: the most common involve locomotor behavior in a straight runway and two-choice behavior in a simple T-maze or discrimination apparatus. The responses most typical of free operant situations are bar-pressing, panel-pushing, wheel-turning, or treadle-pressing in mammals, and key-pecking in birds. This listing of the common response modes in learning experiments serves to highlight two different emphases in the area of animal behavior. On one hand, the ethologist and ecologist have focused on identifying the behaviors of various species in more or less natural settings. Their emphasis is on species-specific behavior, genetic-evolutionary variables, adaptive considerations, and to a certain extent on general principles which apply across species. The psychologist, on the other hand, has been chiefly concerned with the general laws of learning. This has led him to select convenient, readily measurable modes of response which are common to most organisms. The two approaches are in no way incompatible and given free interchange each can profit from the other.

Escape and Avoidance Learning. The learning of *instrumental-escape* (responding so as to *remove* the aversive or noxious stimulus) and the learning of *instrumental-avoidance* (responding so as to prevent the occurrence of the aversive stimulus) are also studied with the response modes listed above; but certain differences should be noted. Locomotor behavior, for example, is often studied in a two-chambered box (shuttlebox) in which the animal learns to shuttle from one side to the other each time a warning signal (CS) is given (avoidance learning). Avoidance occurs when the animal responds to the CS by crossing the mid-line of the box *before* the onset of the shock. Sometimes shuttling involves jumping over a central barrier and sometimes the animal only runs in *one* direction, from one distinctive side to the other (e.g., from black to white). Operant responses, such as bar-pressing, provide on the whole a poorer learning situation for instrumental-avoidance than for instrumental-approach (reward learning). This is discussed in greater detail on page 578.

Discrimination Learning. To some degree discrimination learning is involved in any learning situation, but it seems appropriate to discuss it in the context of instrumental learning where discrimination learning is most often studied as a separate phenomenon. Learning to respond to a *particular* stimulus and not to others more or less like it is a simple definition of discrimination learning. That such differentiations need to be learned clearly implies the phenomenon of stimulus generalization (see summarized studies). Stimulus generalization is the converse of discrimination, referring to the fact that stimuli which are similar to the original cue or CS tend to elicit the same response (learned) even though these stimuli have never before been associated with the response. Without stimulus generalization, learning and performance would be virtually impossible. The total stimulus complex impinging upon an organism is continuously undergoing change. Therefore, if what was learned on one occasion did not generalize to another there would be no profiting from experience.

Discriminations are usually established in the laboratory by a procedure of differential reinforcement, using either classical conditioning (differential conditioning) or instrumental learning techniques. When either operant or differential conditioning procedures are used, the stimuli which are to be discriminated (the discriminative stimuli) are presented successively rather than simultaneously. In several respects, the operant and differential conditioning techniques are similar, though the terminology may seem different. The discriminative stimulus (cue) which is present when the response is reinforced is called an S^D (operant) or $+$ CS (differential conditioning) and the discriminative stimulus present when a response is nonreinforced is called an S^Δ (operant) or—CS (differential conditioning). When establishing a discriminated operant each and every response to S^D does not have to be reinforced (intermittent reinforcement schedules are actually quite effective). The net effect, in any case, is to develop and maintain the response to S^D and extinguish the response to S^Δ; thus a discrimination is established.

Simultaneous discrimination learning, where the cues to be discriminated are presented together, is usually studied in the familiar two-choice discrimination apparatus. Here the reinforced stimulus, called the S^D in the operant situation, is usually called a positive stimulus (cue); and the nonreinforced stimulus, called the S^Δ in the operant situation, is called a negative stimulus. These stimuli are each presented half the time on the left and half the time on the right in a random order, for control of position cues.

The two-choice situation can also be used for *successive discrimination learning*. With the successive method the animal is typically trained to turn left when one cue is presented and to turn right when the other is presented. When the stimuli used can be discriminated either simultaneously or successively, as with visual cues, then the learning of a *single, uncomplicated* simultaneous discrimination seems to take place in fewer trials than learning by the successive method. The findings in studies by Davis (1957) and MacCaslin (1954) with rats, by Shepp (1962) with mentally retarded children and

Sutherland *et al.* (1963) with the octopus suggest that the simultaneous method is superior. Opposite results which have been found by some investigators specifically occur when the organism is confronted with more than one simultaneous discrimination to make on any single trial. When there are several two-choice decision points or units in the maze this introduces additional complicating discriminations as, for example, between units rather than within units (Bitterman and Wodinsky, 1953; Weise and Bitterman, 1951). The superiority of the simultaneous method for the single situation presumably hinges on the fact that the approach habit to the positive cue and the avoidance habit to the negative cue can effectively summate, increasing the tendency to approach the + cue. Whereas in the successive condition the two habits (a right turn and a left turn) are essentially independent and cannot summate.

Discrimination Learning and Operant Conditioning. Even the simplest operant conditioning situation involves learning discriminations. The first response learned in a bar-pressing device (Skinner box) is to approach the food tray (water dipper). This response is the one most quickly followed by reinforcement and may also have been intentionally strengthened by the experimenter before the animal had begun to press the bar. However, going directly to the food tray *without* first pressing the bar does not pay off or does not continue to pay off. The S^D for a successful trip to the food tray consists of all the stimuli attendant upon just having pressed the bar (tactual, kinesthetic, auditory, visual). Typically this included the loud click of the food magazine. Thus, the click is usually an important S^D for visiting the food tray; and the absence of the click constitutes an $S^\triangle$ for this response (this discrimination sometimes is never perfected). In turn the click is said to reinforce the response just preceding it (the bar-press); as such the click is *also* called a conditioned reinforcer or secondary reinforcer (S^r).

When operant conditioning is further complicated by modifying the schedule of reinforcement then additional discriminations are introduced. The following intermittent reinforcement schedules are the ones chiefly used. When reinforcement does not follow every bar-press but comes after a fixed number of bar-presses it is called *fixed-ratio reinforcement*. For example, if reinforcement occurs on the fifth bar-press since the last reinforcement, this schedule is called 4:1 fixed-ratio reinforcement (FR 4), 4 nonreinforced presses to 1 reinforced bar-press. When an animal is randomly reinforced, sometimes after two bar-presses, sometimes after 10, etc., the schedule is called a *variable-ratio schedule.* If the number of nonreinforced responses averages out to be five the schedule is symbolized VR 5. Intermittent reinforcement can also be scheduled for passage of time, commonly 1 to 3 minutes, rather than for number of responses. During *fixed-interval reinforcement* the animal is reinforced on the first bar-press which occurs after a fixed interval of time has elapsed since the prior reinforcement. If the interval is one minute, it is symbolized FI 1. When the interval varies around and averages 1 minute this is a *variable interval schedule* (VI 1). Because the VI schedules yield the most steady rate of responding and the greatest resistance to extinction, they are a frequently used schedule, particularly when studying stimulus generalization effects.

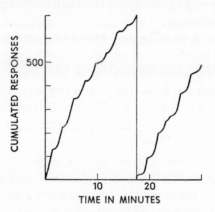

Fig. 11–1. Representative cumulative-response curve for fixed interval responding (FI 2). The curve is displaced to the base line after approximately 600 responses have accumulated. Reinforcements are indicated by short diagonal lines.

Guttman, Norman and Kalish, H. I.   Discriminability and stimulus generalization. *J. exp. Psychol.,* 1956, 51, 79–88.

Four groups of pigeons were trained to peck at an illuminated disk of 530, 550, 580, and 600 mu respectively, under a VI schedule. Bidirectional generalization gradients were obtained from measures of response rate during extinction. These gradients were comparable in slope for the various spectral regions tested (these regions typically yield differential difference limens, per Hamilton and Coleman, Chapter 3). Therefore, it appears that the slope of the stimulus generalization gradient is independent of the discriminability of stimuli.

Hanson, H. M.   Discrimination training effect on stimulus generalization gradient for spectrum stimuli. *Science,* 1957, 125, 888–89.

Pigeons were trained to peck a key in the presence of a light (550 mu) for a food reward under VI 1 minute and then were divided into five groups.

One group received no further training, but the other four groups were given discrimination training to a positive stimulus of 550 mu and to a negative stimulus of 555, 560, 570, or 590 mu, respectively. The birds were then given generalization tests with stimuli ranging from 480 to 520 mu. The post-discrimination gradients were higher than that for the control and the area of highest responding was displaced away from 550 mu toward the shorter wave lengths. The discrimination training altered the symmetrical bidirectional aspect of the stimulus generalization gradient, making shorter wave lengths more positive than the original stimulus (550 mu).

Under all of the intermittent reinforcement schedules the customary click of the feeding device becomes a more critical S^D than is true under continuous reinforcement (100 percent reinforcement). For under intermittent reinforcement bar-pressing is cued to more bar-pressing rather than to a trip to the food tray. In fact, under *both* variable schedules the *only* S^D for visiting the reward tray is the *click*. Under the fixed-ratio schedule the number of bar-presses (attendant tactual-kinesthetic-visual stimuli) becomes an S^D for rapid bar-pressing (the more bar-pressing the sooner the reinforcement). Under a fixed-interval schedule a certain passage of time (interoceptive stimulus) is an S^D for bar-pressing, while just having been reinforced is an $S^\triangle$ for bar-pressing. This discrimination is revealed in the traditional scalloping of the cumulative response record for fixed-interval reinforcement (waiting to bar-press until some time has elapsed since the previous reinforcement).

Similarly, discriminated operants can be learned when reinforcement is made contingent upon any one of a number of response-produced cues: cues associated with the duration of a response, low rates of responding, high rates of responding, pausing, etc. The differential reinforcement of low rates and high rates is called drl and drh, respectively, but an adequate description of these reinforcement procedures is beyond the province of this book.

The determination or control of behavior by discriminative stimuli S^D's and $S^\triangle$'s) is often called stimulus control (Ferster and Skinner, 1957). In greater detail, stimulus control means 1) that an S^D will elicit a particular response because previously when the stimulus (S^D) was present the response had been reinforced and/or 2) that an $S^\triangle$ will inhibit or tend to inhibit a particular response because previously when the stimulus ($S^\triangle$) was present the response had been *nonreinforced*. Many psychologists believe that the concept of stimulus control, when it is extended to language behavior, social behavior and even disturbed behavior, plays the major role in understanding behavior. This proposition, at least when applied to birds and mammals, cannot be lightly dismissed. Stated more generally so that all eliciting and inhibiting properties of stimuli are included, a principle of stimulus control applies equally well to behaviors labeled as innate and therefore applies across the phylogenetic scale.

Variables Affecting Instrumental Learning

The Reinforcement Variable. In the past ten years the thinking of psychologists has undergone considerable expansion with regard to what constitutes a reinforcement in a learning situation. One way to view this enlarged array of reinforcers is to see it as functionally equivalent to the scope of consummatory behavior. That is, what can serve as a reinforcer includes more than food and water: A reinforcement can be observing or manipulating new stimulus objects, the turning on or off of a light, disassembling a puzzle, turning an activity wheel, subcortical brain stimulation, availability of sand for digging (mice), an imprinted stimulus, the spending of an extended amount of time in the "safe" region (avoidance of learning), etc. (Butler, 1953; Kling, *et al.*, 1956 *; Premack, 1962; Lilly and Miller, 1962; Petersen, 1960; Denny and Weisman, 1964; King and Weisman, 1964). One of these reinforcements is discussed below. More discussion of the nature of reinforcement will be presented later; our main mission at this time is to examine some of the traditional reinforcement variables.

KLING, J. W., HOROWITZ, L. and DELHAGEN, J. E. Light as a positive reinforcer for rat responding. *Psychol. Rep.,* 1956, **2**, 337–40.
The bar-presses of the experimental group were immediately followed by the onset of a momentary light, whereas no light followed the bar-presses of the control group. Presentation of the light following a bar-press resulted in an immediate and significant increase in the rate of responding, but this rate decreased progressively as the experiment continued. It was suggested that the light acts as a novel stimulus and loses its reinforcing properties as the exploratory tendency adapts. When a food reward was introduced, the reinforcing properties of the light became contingent upon the amount or type of food presented.

Magnitude of Reward. To the extent that the magnitude of the incentive *specifies* the response to be learned it is a relevant learning variable. For example, in a two-choice situation in which a large reward is associated with one choice and a small reward with the other (a within subjects design) then the size of the reward object is crucial. The animal learns to go to the side (cue) where the large incentive is located. Presumably it approaches the cue associated with the large incentive with greater vigor than the cue associated with the small incentive (Festinger, 1943; Denny and King, 1953). However, when one group of animals receives a *large* incentive for making the correct response and nothing for making the incorrect response and another group receives a *small* incentive only for the correct response (between groups design), then there is very little difference in the learning between the two groups: both the large and the small incentive specify the *correct* response. What difference there is, in favor of the large reward group, seems attributable to the fact that the large incentive reduces the amount of competing response more than a small incentive (Pereboom and Crawford, 1958). In this sense the large incentive is a better specifier than the small incentive. Consequently, the large incentive does produce markedly better performance: the animal starts sooner, runs faster, pushes harder, etc. (Pavlik & Reynolds, 1963 *; Armus, 1959 **; Guttman, 1953; Pubols, 1960; Furchtgott and Salzberg, 1959).

An interesting finding in recent years (Armus, 1959 **) is that the magnitude of reinforcement during the acquisition of a runway response, when all acquisition trials are reinforced, may be inversely related to resistance to extinction. An earlier study by Zeaman (1949) and a recent one by Hill and Spear (1962) show no such relationship, but acquisition consisted of 18 and 25 reinforcements, respectively, while Armus gave 75 acquisition trials. In other words, it looks as if the inverse relationship between magnitude of reward and resistance to extinction occurs only if a large number of reinforcements have been given during original learning. Such an interpretation is in accord with the results of recent studies which have investigated the effect of number of original reinforcements on subsequent resistance to extinction. Beyond an intermediate number of reinforcements (approximately 20–40) any increase in the number of reinforcements results in faster extinction. This is particularly true in the later stages of the extinction session. The evidence on this point, so long as the incentive is fairly sizable and/or the extinction trials are *not* highly spaced, seems quite convincing (Ison, 1962, Clifford, 1962; North and Stimmel, 1960).

That both magnitude of reward and number of reinforcements can have this seemingly unexpected effect makes good sense when extinction is conceived of as the learning of a competing response and when the competing response is assumed to be elicited by frustration or removal of the incentive (Adelman and Maatsch, 1955; Birch, 1961). The bigger the reward the greater the "expectancy." The greater the "expectancy" for the incentive the greater is the subsequent frustration effect upon the removal of the incentive during extinction (Denny and Adelman, 1955).

On the other hand, in operant conditioning or a free-responding

situation resistance to extinction tends to increase as the number of
original reinforcements is increased. That this is so can be accounted
for in a number of ways, but probably the most convincing is the fact
that the Skinner box animal has frequently encountered an empty
food tray and is therefore quite used to nonreinforcement prior to the
introduction of an extinction session. But the amount of data available on the issue is too meager to warrant further analysis. In any
event, the direct positive relationship between number of reinforcements and strength of habit is *not* necessarily being challenged by the
runway data. In the runway situation the number of reinforcements
is not only strengthening the running habit but also is increasing the
subsequent reaction to frustration. If late in learning the buildup of
the "expectancy" for the incentive is greater than the increase in the
strength of the running response, then the curvilinear effect is derived.
Presumably, a strong frustration effect in the runway is due to a lack
of contact with nonreinforcement prior to extinction (unhabituated).

   *Intermittent or Partial Reinforcement and Resistance to Extinc-
tion.* The main effect of partial reinforcement is to increase resistance to extinction. This is true both for the free operant and the
discrete-trial data, but more so for the former. In the operant situation
with intermittent reinforcement as described earlier on p. 571, there
is the opportunity for a sequence of bar-presses (key-pecks) to become
chained together as a response unit so that most of the bar-presses are
simply instrumental for making the terminal or the reinforced bar-
press of the sequence. Without the early bar-presses there can be no
terminal bar-press. To the extent that an animal learns the discrimination of *not* visiting the reward tray after every bar-press, yet visits it
after the click has occurred, we have *objective* evidence that the
animal has learned to anticipate food only after the terminal bar-press
(or only after the click). Experimental evidence for the development
of such a discrimination, though never completely attained, can be
found in a study by Denny, Wells, and Maatsch (1957). Given the
establishment of such a discrimination, the following explanation of
the effects of partial reinforcement is possible. Extinction comes about
through nonreinforcement, and nonreinforcement occurs only if the
animal *visits* the area that was formerly reinforced. Thus, everytime
the animal makes a bar-press and fails to visit the "reward" area during extinction it is *not* being nonreinforced and extinction is delayed.
In other words, an animal which has been intermittently reinforced
for bar-pressing is *actually* nonreinforced intermittently during ex-

tinction. This interpretation has much in common with the response-unit explanation by Mowrer and Jones (1945) and Humphrey's original expectancy model (1939).

It also follows from this interpretation that the greater the intermittancy of reinforcement the greater the resistance to extinction. This is a well-documented relationship. By greater intermittency is meant increasing the ratio of a ratio schedule, for example, from 4:1 to 10:1, or lengthening the interval of an interval schedule, as from 1 minute to 3 minutes.

The above interpretation does not apply to discrete-trial data where chaining as just described is impossible. Instead, two other interpretations are necessary to account for most of the data. One of these explanations is called the habituation hypothesis (Weinstock, 1958) which can also be applied to the free operant situation as an additional explanation. The hypothesis is best understood in the context of a counter-conditioning or interference theory of extinction as already exposued. It is assumed that the presence of frequent frustration (nonrewarded trials) during partial reinforcement results in the habituation or lessening of the frustration effect. Thus the extinction trials which follow intermittent reinforcement elicit fewer competing responses and produce less of an extinction effect than would extinction trials which follow continuous reinforcement (no habituation to frustration). The habituation principle is especially important because it accounts for the partial reinforcement effect which is found when the acquisition trials are as highly spaced as one per day (Weinstock).

A third interpretation of the partial reinforcement effect, often called the discrimination hypothesis, only holds when the trials are relatively massed, when the stimulus aftereffects of a trial can serve as part of the cue for the response on the subsequent trial. The distinctive aftereffects of a nonrewarded trial in a partial reinforcement learning situation are frustration effects; these aftereffects are present on all trials which follow a nonreinforced trial and are conditioned to the learned response. When a partially reinforced animal is shifted to extinction there is less of a cue change than if the animal had been continuously reinforced. Thus there is less reduction in the strength of the original response tendency due to changing cues (generalization-decrement) and thus greater resistance to extinction in the partially reinforced animal. This third explanation is the most commonly given interpretation of the partial reinforcement effect and was first formulated by Clark L. Hull.

GROSSLIGHT, J. H. and RADLOW, R.   Patterning effect of the nonreinforcement-reinforcement sequence in a discrimination situation. *J. comp. physiol.
Psychol.*, 1956, 49, 542–46.

   Rats were required to learn a discrimination problem terminating in food
reinforcement in the positive (white) arm of a Y-alley or in the negative
(black) arm where they were retained for 30 seconds. Training occurred under
three schedules of reinforcement: UR in which nonreinforcement was directly
followed by reinforcement; RU in which nonreinforcement was never followed on the same day by reinforcement; and RR which denoted continuous
reinforcement. The goals were then reversed (black was positive and white
was negative). The UR group, which permitted a nonreinforcement to serve
as a cue for subsequent reinforcement, demonstrated a significantly slower
habit reversal than either RU or RR. To obtain slower rates of extinction or
habit reversal, a UR sequence of partial reinforcement is recommended.

   S–R Contiguity.   As with classical conditioning, the cue and the
response must occur closely together in time if a differential instrumental response is going to be learned. Learning a differential instrumental response is learning to make one particular response in a situation in which two or more responses are possible. If the response at
the choice point of a two-choice apparatus is not permitted to occur
within 2 to 4 seconds after a momentarily presented cue has been presented (Wilson, 1934; Smith, 1951) then there is virtually no learning.
The method used here is similar to successive discrimination learning
in a two-choice situation. The cue designates which choice is correct
on any particular trial, for example, turn right after the buzzer is
sounded, turn left when the buzzer is omitted. The difference is that
the animal is prevented from making an immediate response once the
momentary cue is presented.

   A comparable time limit holds for the data on *delay of reinforcement,* and learning is best when reinforcement follows the instrumental act immediately. If instrumental learning is viewed as a chain
of higher-order CR's then the delay of reinforcement variable, it can
be argued, is actually an S–R or CS–US interval. For example, the
time between the *arrival at the food tray* (cue) and the *procuring of
the food pellet* (response) is an S–R interval, though it is traditionally
called delay of reinforcement. The view that delay of reinforcement is
just a special case of an S–R interval is supported by the fact that the
upper limit for learning for both intervals is 4 or 5 seconds (Grice,
1948).

   More on the Nature of Reinforcement.   Much of the foregoing
discussion bears upon the role of reinforcement in learning and suggests that Thorndike's law of effect and Hull's drive reduction principle are incomplete statements. Most of the relevant research in this
regard has been conducted with rats. However, an interesting experiment with bees by Opfinger (1931) can also be viewed as illuminating

the reinforcement issue. Bees were trained to approach dishes of sugar water set on clear glass plates underneath of which were sheets of colored paper. The paper (blue, red, and white) was stacked in a pile, and the uppermost piece (blue) was left in place until the bee alighted. Then the top piece was pulled away so that the bee ate on a red background. When it stopped feeding, but before it flew off, the red sheet was removed revealing the next sheet (white). On its return the bee was confronted with all three colors from which to choose. The color displayed while the bee *approached* the food was the one learned. The interpretation we should like to offer here is that the incentive, in this instance the sugar water, functions as the specifier of the to-be-learned response, in this case approach; thus only the cue which is present while approach is being made acquires approach value.

Deprivation Conditions. The best generalization that appears to apply to learning and the variable of deprivation is as follows. If the deprivation is sufficient to bring about the response(s) to be learned then learning occurs regardless of level of deprivation. However, as was true with magnitude of reward, *performance* is clearly enhanced when the deprivation level is increased (Clark, 1958 *; Haralson, 1958). In two-choice learning the deprivation level, except when very low (Eisman, 1956), has not been found to have any appreciable effect. On the other hand, in multiple-choice or complex maze situations where it is *more difficult to maintain the animal's orientation toward the goal (incentive)* then level of deprivation does appear to be quite relevant. The higher levels yield better learning and better retention (O'Kelley and Heyer, 1951; MacDuff, 1946). Again, as was true with magnitude of reward, the main effect of increasing the deprivation level when a relevant incentive is present is to reduce the number of competing responses (Cotton, 1953; Campbell and Kraeling, 1954), providing for better specification of the response(s) to be learned and thus for better learning in any situation in which there are several alternative responses available.

CLARK, F. C. The effect of deprivation and frequency of reinforcement on variable interval responding. *J. exp. Anal. Behav.*, 1958, 1, 221–27.

Three groups of rats were given 20 reinforced bar-presses followed by 1 hour of extinction. Then each group was given additional reinforcements (60 per day for 6 days) under their respective variable interval schedules (1, 2, and 3 minutes). Both deprivation and frequency of reinforcement were found to affect the rate of responding and their interaction was significant: Equal increases in deprivation resulted in greater increments in rate of responding when the frequency of reinforcement was higher.

PAVLIK, W. B. and REYNOLDS, W. F. Effects of deprivation schedule and reward magnitude on acquisition and extinction performance. *J. comp. physiol. Psychol.*, 1963, 56, 452–55.

Eighty rats (4 groups) were given 80 runway trials under 2 conditions of food deprivation and 2 conditions of reward magnitude, followed by 50 extinction trials during which half the rats were extinguished under each deprivation level. The large reward and the higher level of deprivation *independently* increased running speed during acquisition. During extinction the large reward produced significantly faster extinction after the first five extinction trials than the small reward, confirming Armus' ** results. The same relationship held for level of deprivation during extinction: the high deprivation group extinguished more rapidly. *Note:* The last finding is rather unusual but consistent with the frustration analysis made of extinction runway data in the text.

Variables Affecting Instrumental-Avoidance Learning. Many of the variables in avoidance learning are common to approach-reward learning, but some are not. If we examine a few typical avoidance learning situations some of these new variables will come to light. A uniformly colored, say all black, shuttlebox yields slow avoidance learning. A box with distinctive compartments, with a distinct shock side and a distinct escape side ("safe" region), yields fast learning—within 2 to 3 trials on the average. In both types of apparatus the animal is shocked on the early trials. For the animal in the regular, undifferentiated shuttlebox this means that when the warning signal is presented it must run right back to the side where it was just previously shocked. Such a conflictual state of affairs persists in the shuttlebox until the animal is no longer being shocked—until the warning signal, independent of the animal's location in the box, has acquired sufficient strength to elicit consistent running to the opposite side. This takes 50 to 100 trials for the average laboratory rat. In contrast, when there is a clear-cut "safe" region present from the beginning of training, no such conflict exists and many rats learn in one trial. This is particularly true if the animal has been permitted to remain in the distinctive "safe" region for about 3 minutes where it presumably can relax (Knapp, 1960; Denny, Koons and Mason, 1959; Weisman, 1961). In other words, at least two new important variables are operating in avoidance learning: 1) the presence of a distinctive "safe" region and 2) the amount of time spent in this region after escaping or avoiding (as found by Weisman, the greater the amount of time spent in the "safe" region up to 4 minutes, the faster the avoidance learning). As mentioned earlier, the avoidance learning of a free operant is usually very poor. This is quite possibly due, at least in part, to the absence of a clear-cut "safe" region with the operant procedure.

BEHREND, E. R. and BITTERMAN, M. E. Sidman avoidance in the fish. *J. exp. Anal. Behav.*, 1963, **6**, 47–52.

Goldfish were trained in a shuttlebox under conditions in which each shuttle response postponed electric shock for 20 seconds (Sidman procedure). The fish learned to avoid, in terms of a significant increase in rate of crossing (shuttling). A control for sensitization showed that true learning took place, that is, yoked-control animals which were shocked whenever an experimental animal was shocked did not show an increase in shuttling. In the experimental group, in the second half of the experiment, a warning stimulus (light) was introduced 5 seconds before shock might occur; the rate of crossing decreased during the first 15 seconds and increased during the last 5 seconds. These results are remarkably similar to those obtained with rats, birds, and other higher animals in this type of avoidance learning situation.

The Generality of Instrumental Learning

Here we are concerned with describing the scope of the process of instrumental learning across responses, species, and age levels.

Response Class as a Variable. In avoidance learning the response being learned can be compatible with the response that is elicited by the aversive stimulus or it can be incompatible. In the first case learning is facilitated: It is easy to train animals to run or jump in order to escape or avoid because these responses are themselves elicited by an aversive stimulus such as shock. On the other hand, when the response to be learned is one like bar-pressing, then the vigorous escape responses compete with the manipulatory behavior and impede learning. When the aversive stimulus is a bright light the same sort of relationship holds. It is easier to make the termination of the light contingent upon hiding in a corner than pressing a bar.

The variable of response class is especially prominent in the learning of lower animals where instinctive behavior constitutes a large proportion of their behavioral repertoire (see p. 230, Chapter 5). Herring gulls, for example, can readily learn to distinguish their own young during the first 5 days after hatching, refusing other young forced upon them *after* this period. But the gull does *not* learn to distinguish its own eggs which vary much more than the chicks do (Tinbergen, 1953). The digger wasp learns the location of each new nest it builds in the ground with amazing rapidity but shows no such learning of the location of nectar-yielding plants, while the honey bee can readily learn where such plants are. Yet both species feed on nectar (Tinbergen, 1953).

An experiment by Hess (1956) illustrates the necessity of being able to make the response in order to learn. If chickens wear goggles which displace the apparent location of a kernel of grain by several millimeters they never learn to peck in such a way as to compensate for the spatial discrepency. This is because instinctively they never peck far enough off the target, as they see it, to hit the grain. If the instrumental response which procures the grain is not made it cannot be learned.

Species. The claim exists that instrumental-type learning occurs as far down the phylogenetic scale as to include unicellular animals such as the paramecium. Whether this is the case or not is explored in the selected study by Katz and Deterline (1958 **) and the studies by Jensen (1957), and Gelber (1952 *). At the present writing the experimental evidence in support of such learning is not particularly convincing, yet neither can we flatly reject the possibility. Such a stand seems even more reasonable when it is understood that the existence of instrumental learning in organisms, which are considerably higher in the phyletic scale, has not been unequivocally demonstrated, even in animals which show conditionability of the classical sort. The earthworm and starfish are cases in point. Many of the methods used for evaluating learning in these lower species introduce extraneous variables such as changing the media in which these organisms live, as emphasized by Jensen and Katz and Deterline in the paramecium studies. Such procedural factors may involve sensitization (summation of stimulus effects leading to heightened responsiveness) rather than learning or may bring about behavioral effects which are tactic or kinetic in origin rather than learned (Best, 1954; Best and Rubinstein, 1962).

FRENCH, J. W. Trial and error learning in paramecium. *J. exp. Psychol.,* 1940, **26**, 609–13.

A single paramecium was put into a glass tube permitting freedom ot movement but allowing escape only through the lower end of the tube. The time required by each subject to swim downward through the tube and escape was recorded. The median time required for escape decreased as the number of trials increased (with a decrease in what appeared to be trial and error escape patterns), but there was considerable variability. French suggests these results indicate that the decrease in escape time was due to learning.

GARDNER, L. P. and NISSEN, H. N. Simple discrimination behavior of young chimpanzees and comparisons with human aments and domestic animals. *J. genet. Psychol.,* 1948, **72**, 145–64.

Domestic animals (i.e., horses, cows, and sheep), chimpanzees, and human aments (feebleminded) were presented with a discrimination situation which involved: (*a*) preliminary adaptation and orientation; (*b*) formation of a discriminative response; (*c*) transfer tests and training to new positions of the cue; (*d*) retest of original learning; (*e*) extinction of original habit and establishment of opposite discrimination. The results indicated no regular increase in rate of simple habit formation at progressively higher levels in the mammalian series.

GELBER, BEATRICE. Investigations of the behavior of *Paramecium Aurelia I.* Modifications of behavior after training with reinforcement. *J. comp. physiol. Psychol.,* 1952, **45**, 58–65.

A platinum wire was repeatedly lowered into cultures of homozygous paramecium providing the experimental group with food reinforcement. After 40 "training" trials and a count of the number of paramecia adhering to the wire, a final test trial was made. From the increase in the number of paramecia adhering to the wire in the experimental group it was concluded that learning in this unicellular organism had been demonstrated. (See Katz and Deterline, 1958 **).

Ontogenetic Limitations. For man as well as the infrahuman species, maturation plays a critical role in specifying what responses are going to be learned and when. Apparently the issue is not so much with the learning process, as such, but with whether or not the response to be learned is ontogenetically available to the animal. Several investigators (Shepard and Breed, 1913; Cruze, 1935) have found that maturation can have a facilitating effect on a chick's learning to peck accurately at kernels of grain. Delaying the opportunity to peck 4 to 5 days results in a steeper learning curve than is found in newly hatched chicks. But, as described in the study by Padilla (Chapter 7), if the pecking experience is withheld from chicks for two weeks or more by keeping them in the dark all during this period the chicks can no longer peck and cannot learn to peck. The chicks in the Padilla study were fed a liquid gruel from an eyedropper, while living at all times in the dark. If the gruel is fed to them beyond the end of the two-week delay period, being made less moist each day it is presented, until it finally becomes grain, then these chicks can learn a response which is in their repertoire. They can eventually learn, say in 7 weeks, to scoop up the grain, for scooping is part of the drinking pattern, as already practiced. Here, then, we have an example of the critical period as it delimits when learning can take place, which in turn clarifies the role of maturation in learning and underlines the importance of response availability in the learning process.

Another example of the ontogenetic factor may be found in the behavior of the immature Eskimo dog. It is characteristic of these dogs to live in groups of 5–10 and to defend the territory of the group to which they belong. The pup, however, shows no tendency to learn its territory and continually trespasses other territories despite being chased and attacked. But, as soon as the pup reaches sexual maturity, it learns within a week the territorial rights of its group and others' (Tinbergen, 1953).

Finally, we can point to data which show the generality of instrumental learning when learning per se is the point at issue. As was true of classical conditioning, the infant monkey can readily learn an instrumental response. The summarized study by Mason and Harlow (1958) shows that 15-day-old rhesus monkeys can learn a spatial response in a Y-maze as well as 45-day-old monkeys. And many years ago an unpublished study from the psychological laboratory of the University of Michigan showed that if a complex maze were reduced in dimensions to fit the size of recently weaned 30-day-old rats they could learn as well as the 90-day-old animals (Hawke, 1942). When transfer from past learning situations becomes relevant then, of course, older animals have an advantage, as frequently demonstrated in human beings. Since it is difficult to identify the transfer variable, it may well be that ability to learn, independent of transfer considerations, increases with age. But what evidence there is, as just cited, would argue against such an interpretation. On the other hand, when the relationship between *retention* and age is examined the picture may be different. In a study by Kirby (1963) 25-day-old rats learned an avoidance response as quickly as 50- and 100-day-old rats but retained significantly less than these animals for retention intervals of 25 and 50 days. If forgetting is due in part to changes in structure and changes in internal stimulation this finding is not surprising.

ADDITIONAL SUMMARIZED STUDIES

Klopfer, P. H.   Influences of social interactions on learning rates in birds. *Science,* 1958, **128**, 903.

Single and paired greenfinches were placed in an experimental situation requiring discrimination between a palatable and unpalatable food source (presented ad libitum). Single birds learned faster than paired birds which in several instances failed to learn the discrimination. When in pairs both birds participated in feeding simultaneously. Thus it was concluded that observing a partner's feeding response effectively competed with an avoidance response to nonpreferred food (specific to greenfinches which have a limited diet).

Wodinsky, J. and Bitterman, M. E.   Partial reinforcement in the fish. *Amer. J. Psychol.,* 1959, **72**, 184–99.

Two groups of African mouthbreeders (*Tilapia macrocepha*) were given a series of training and extinction trials on a task which involved displacing or butting a target. One group was given continuous reinforcement and the other partial reinforcement. It was found that resistance to extinction was initially greater in the group given continuous reinforcement. This finding contrasts, in particular, with the data obtained from rats. *Note:* This discrepancy might be due to differential reactions to nonreinforcement (frustration) for fish and rats.

EFFECT OF MAGNITUDE OF REINFORCEMENT ON

ACQUISITION AND EXTINCTION OF A

RUNNING RESPONSE[1]

HARVARD L. ARMUS
Institute of Psychiatric Research, Indiana University Medical Center, Indianapolis

Zeaman (1949) found starting time in a runway to be inversely related to magnitude of food reinforcement during both acquisition and extinction. Metzger, Cotton, and Lewis (1957) and Crespi (1942) found similar relationships for acquisition using total response time. The present study was designed to provide further data on these relationships, with total response time broken into starting time and running time.

METHOD

Subjects and apparatus.—The Ss were 28 male Sprague-Dawley rats, aged 128–136 days, divided into two groups of 13 and 15. The apparatus was an enclosed, 3-ft. runway with a 9-in. starting box and an 18-in. right-angled goal box. The entire apparatus, with the exception of the unpainted hardware cloth lids, was painted dark grey. Time measurements were taken photoelectrically. The light beams were located immediately beyond the starting box door and immediately before the goal box door. Doors were of the guillotine type.

Procedure.—After approximately 2½ weeks on a feeding schedule of 1½ hr. on dry Purina Laboratory Chow checkers every 24 hr., each S was given two daily 10-min. exploration sessions, food and food cup being absent from the apparatus. During training and extinction each S was given five daily trials, spaced approximately 15 min. apart, while under 20–21-hr. food deprivation. Group 1 was reinforced with one 45-mg. food pellet; Group 10, with 10. On each trial, S

---

[1] The author wishes to thank Elizabeth Ives for collection and computation of the data and James Norton for the design of the statistical analysis.

[2] Frequently during extinction a rat would dart partly out of the starting box, breaking the first beam, and then return to the starting box for a period of time. Even on such trials, the breaking of the first beam defined the end of starting time and the beginning of running time.

[3] The interactions were computed as follows: Each rat was assigned a difference score consisting of its mean time (starting or running) for the first third of extinction minus its mean time for the last third of acquisition. These difference scores were then ranked and the *U* test applied.

was placed into the starting box facing the door. After 5 sec., the starting box door was opened regardless of the position of S. There were 15 days of acquisition and 30 of extinction.

RESULTS

As the greatest differences would be expected during the later stages of acquisition and the early stages of extinction, the statistical analysis deals only with the last one-third of the acquisition period and the first one-third of the extinction period, except as otherwise noted. The complete data are presented in Figures 1 and 2. Because of the presence of extreme scores, resulting in marked skewness and heterogeneity of variance, all probability values were determined by means of the Mann-Whitney U test.

Group 10 was superior to Group 1 during the relevant acquisition period in terms of both starting time ($P < .001$) and running time ($P < .001$). For extinction running time the reverse relationship held, Group 10 showing poorer resistance to extinction than Group 1 ($P = .03$). Extinction starting time yielded no significant differences ($P > .10$.[2] The interaction between amount of reinforcement and condition (acquisition-extinction) was significant for both starting time ($P < .02$) and running time ($P < .02$).[3] For neither response measure were the group differences for the first acquisition trial or first acquisition day significant. The running time data for the first extinction day (Trials 2–5) revealed nonsignificantly greater extinction for Group 10 than for Group 1, while a nonsignificant difference in the opposite direction was found for the second extinction trial of this day.

DISCUSSION

The data reveal that, at least for the somewhat less variable running time measure, the relation between amount of reinforcement and performance is reversed from acquisition to extinction. Although Zeaman (1949) reported starting times only, he stated that his unreported running time findings were similar to, but not as significant as, the starting time data. The results of the present study agree with previously reported acquisition data (Crespi, 1942; Metzger, Cotton and Lewis, 1957; Zeaman, 1949), but do not support Zeaman's extinction findings.

There is at least one difference in procedure between the present study and that of Zeaman which might be of some importance in accounting for the discrepancies in the results. Zeaman's animals received 18 trials with the appropriate amount of reinforcement, as contrasted to 75 in the present study. It is likely that the effects of magnitude of reinforcement on extinction are partly determined by the number of exposures to the reinforcement magnitude before the start of extinction. However, it is problematic whether manipulation of this variable would alter the relationships during extinction between groups having had different magnitudes of reward during acquisition.

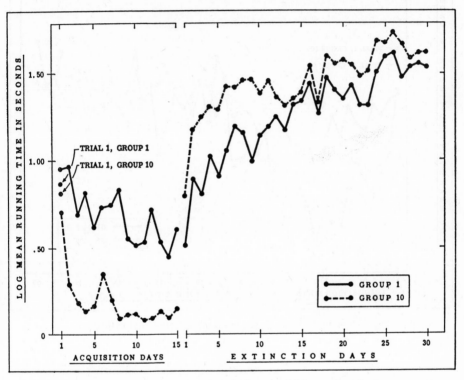

Fig. 1. Log mean running time during acquisition and extinction.

SUMMARY

In rats given runway training under 20–21-hr. food deprivation, it was found that the group reinforced with ten 45-mg. food pellets showed faster acquisition in terms of both starting and running times than the group reinforced with only one such pellet. During extinction, the reverse relationship held for running times; starting time differences were not significant. While the acquisition results supported previous findings, the extinction data did not.

REFERENCES

CRESPI, L. P. Quantitative variation of incentive and performance in the white rat. *Amer. J. Psychol.*, 1942, **55**, 467–517.

METZGER, R., COTTON, J. W., and LEWIS, D. J.   Effect of reinforcement magnitude and order of presentation of different magnitudes on runway behavior. *J. comp. physiol. Psychol.*, 1957, **50**, 184–88.

ZEAMAN, D.   Response latency as a function of the amount of reinforcement. *J. exp. Psychol.*, 1949, **39**, 466–83.

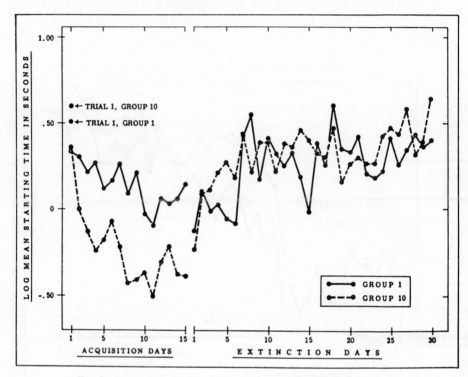

FIG. 2.   Log mean starting time during acquisition and extinction.

ONE BAR-PRESS PER DAY:

ACQUISITION AND EXTINCTION

M. RAY DENNY
Michigan State University

Ordinarily, when a learned response is no longer followed by reward, the probability of the occurrence of this response is diminished and ultimately the response is extinguished. The present study explores the possibility of preventing the extinction of a bar-pressing response under one-trial-a-day acquisition and one-trial-a-day extinction when the bar is always removed immediately after it has been pressed.

EXPERIMENT I

Subjects

The Ss were 16 naive female hooded rats, 80–90 days old at the beginning of the experiment, from the colony of the Psychology Department of Michigan State University. The animals served as Ss for extended periods, in one case as long as 6 months.

Apparatus

A very simple bar-pressing apparatus was used. The box was a plywood 10-inch cube with a 5-by-7-inch glass window on the side opposite the bar. The top was covered with hardware cloth through which the rat was observed. The cylindrically shaped bar was 6 millimeters in diameter, located midway in one wall 2 inches above the floor. The bar extended $2\frac{1}{2}$ inches into the box and a 10-gram pressure was required to depress it. A metal food tray was located on the floor 1 inch to the right of the bar. Following an excursion of $\frac{1}{4}$ inch or more of the bar, as determined by the release of a pendulum on the outside of the box, a pellet of food (approximately 0.05 gram) was dropped manually through a short metal tube into the food tray. The bar could be immediately retracted by a simple manual movement.

Preliminary Training

Five days of handling and being on a reduced diet were followed by six days of preliminary training. Once a day during this period each

S was placed, two at a time, in a box with the bar removed. The food tray contained 20 pellets and each pair of rats remained in the box until all the pellets were consumed. The pairings differed randomly from day to day .Throughout this period and the remainder of the experiment the *S*s were fed 9 grams of food 5–10 minutes after being removed from the box. A variety of experimentation in our laboratory indicates that this interval is sufficiently long to prevent incidental reinforcement of a prior response.

Training

There were two main groups of subjects, the control (N = 6) and the experimental (N = 10). Two additional animals were discarded, one from each main group, because they failed to press the bar within 5 minutes on five successive days. The experimental *S*s were divided into two sub-groups, E — 10 (N = 5) and E — 50 (N = 5). E — 10 made one reinforced bar-press per day for 10 days and was then immediately shifted to the extinction schedule. E — 50 made one reinforced bar-press per day for 50 days and then was placed on the extinction schedule.[1]

The control group (N = 6) received no reinforced bar-pressing trials. Immediately following preliminary training they were given one extinction trial per day for 25 days. All control *S*s were given 25 trials, irrespective of reaching the 5-minute extinction criterion. It was found to be neither necessary nor feasible to give more than 25 such trials. In every other way the control and experimental groups were treated alike.

At the start of each trial (training or extinction) *S* was introduced to the box through the top and placed directly in the middle of the floor at a right angle to the bar. The bar was always in the box prior to introducing the *S*. It was thus possible to measure the latency of each bar-pressing response by means of a stop watch, without introducing an opportunity for *S* to make *alternative responses* in the box *before* presenting the bar. As soon as *S* pressed the bar, the bar was withdrawn. On training trials each experimental *S* received a pellet of food immediately after pressing the bar. Following the withdrawal

---

[1] Ordinarily, each *S* was run every day of the week at about the same time of day. However, during the extinction series there was a period of 20 days for six *S*s of the experimental group during which time *E* was hospitalized. During this period, all *S*s were fed, watered, and cared for but not run in the apparatus. In every case, however, the latency on the first day after this 20-day intermission was the same as or slightly less than the latency of the day prior to the intermission. In no way was the intermission detectable in the performance of the *S*s.

of the bar, S remained in the box anywhere from 75–150 seconds before being placed in an individual cage. If S failed to press the bar within 5 minutes, the bar was withdrawn and S removed as above.

Extinction

The extinction trials were in every respect like the training trials except that no food pellet ever followed bar-pressing. All animals of the experimental group were given one non-rewarded trial per day for 75 days or until the extinction criterion of no bar-pressing response within 5 minutes was attained. (All Ss, but *one* in the E — 10 group, received the 75 trials.) At the end of this period the nine remaining Ss were given a set of massed extinction trials, that is, both the S and the bar remained in the box until the 5-minute extinction criterion was attained. The S could press the bar ad libitum, as in the customary bar-pressing procedure; and the number of responses to extinction was recorded. The day following the massed extinction session each S was given a single extinction trial to test for spontaneous recovery from the massed regimen. One S from E — 10 was also given 50 additional extinction trials, one per day, followed by another set of massed extinction trials and another test for spontaneous recovery.

RESULTS AND DISCUSSION

The performance measure was a latency score based on the median latency for each S for each block of five trials. The mean of this median latency for each group of Ss constituted the latency score as plotted in Figure 1. A median was employed because of the several 5-minute scores in the control group; the mean and median were in close correspondence in the experimental group.

Five of the six control Ss reached the extinction criterion on at least one trial by the 25th day. The other S showed no improvement in mean latency from the first block of five trials to the last block of five trials. The data for the control group as a whole are plotted in Figure 1.

The data for the first block of five acquisition trials and the last block of five acquisition trials for the two experimental groups are plotted in the far-left portion of Figure 1. The remainder of Figure 1 presents the course of performance for E — 10 and E — 50 during the so-called extinction trials. E — 50 appears to have reached an asymptotic level of performance by the beginning of the extinction period and continued to perform at this level throughout the extinction trials. The curve for E — 10 is based on the data

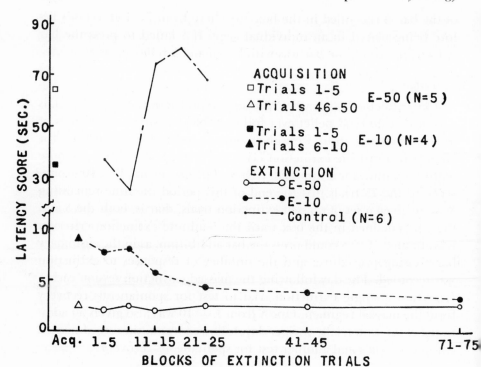

FIG. 1. The first and last blocks of five acquisition trials of the E groups and the extinction curves for all groups.

for four Ss rather than five because one animal extinguished on the 13th extinction day. In no other experimental animal was any tendency to extinction ever noted. At the end of acquisition the strength of the bar-pressing response in this anomalous animal, as measured by latency, was very weak. The median latency for the first and second block of five acquisition trials was in both cases 1 minute, which is considerably out of line with the latency of the four other Ss of E — 10 on the second block of acquisition trials as can be seen in Figure 1.[2]

It is apparent in Figure 1 that E — 10 had progressively decreasing latencies until it met the level of the E — 50 group. The control group, on the other hand, had very high and increasing latencies. Thus, it does *not* seem reasonable to assert that the bar-pressing response in the experimental groups failed to extinguish because a rat in the restricted area of the box would depress the lever anyway, or that bar-pressing was reinforced by removal and placement in a familiar cage.

[2] In this connection it is relevant to point out that two animals in a preliminary study which were given only 5 reinforcements performed erratically with high latencies and met the extinction criterion.

The behavior of each S of the E group was remarkably similar and there was little day-to-day variation in the E — 50 group, as was also true of the E — 10 group after approaching asymptotic performance. The one S of the E — 10 group which was given 50 more extinction trials showed no tendency to extinguish during this period, having a mean latency of 4.3 seconds on trials 121–125 as compared with a mean of 2.3 seconds on trials 71–75. The slight increase in latency, in view of the general behavior of the animal, might very possibly be attributed to an increase in age.

An analysis of the massed extinction trials shows that the E — 10 group gave a mean of 46 responses to extinction and E — 50 a mean of 77 responses to extinction. If anything, more responses to extinction were obtained here than in a conventional bar-pressing experiment employing a large number of continuous reinforcements. On the day following the massed extinction trials there was complete spontaneous recovery. The mean latency on this day was 0.4 second less than on the 75th day. Complete spontaneous recovery was also present on the second test for the E — 10 subject given 50 additional extinction trials.

Although the present results demonstrate a failure of extinction, they would probably be more meaningful if it were known whether the one-trial-a-day schedule was essential. Perhaps the immediate removal of the bar alone is crucial. To this end Experiment II was performed, using a spaced five-trial-a-day schedule.

EXPERIMENT II

Method

The Ss, after discarding nonresponders, consisted of 7 naive hooded female rats approximately 110 days old and 3 male albino rats approximately 200 days old.

The procedure, except as described below, was exactly like the procedure for the E — 10 group in Experiment I. Five trials a day were given both during acquisition and extinction, and at least 5 minutes elapsed between trials. S was kept in an individual running cage rather than the home cage between trials. In order to be sure that five trials per day during acquisition were as effective as one trial per day, each S was reinforced until the median latency of the last five trials was 9 seconds or less (9 seconds was the mean Mdn latency on the last five acquisition trials of the four E — 10 Ss which failed to extinguish). The Ss received a mean of 13.5 rewarded trials (Range = 11–23) as compared to the 10 trials received by each S of E — 10. Extinction began the same day if the acquisition criterion was achieved before five trials were given on any one day. Because of the absence of extinction effects in the four E — 10 Ss with which these Ss were being compared, the extinction criterion was made somewhat less stringent (3 minutes of no response). A record was kept of each S's behavior during extinction.

Results

The mean Mdn latency on the five trials prior to extinction was 7 seconds. It therefore seems reasonable to assume that the response tendency in this group was of the same order as in E — 10 of Experiment I. The extinction results are quite different, however. All 10 Ss extinguished. The median number of trials to extinction was 35.5 (Range = 26–59). The two groups began to diverge on the latency measure by the second block of five extinction trials.

DISCUSSION

The results of the two experiments taken together seem to indicate that 1) bar-retraction immediately after discrete bar-pressing does not itself prevent extinction; and 2) one trial a day, or at least highly spaced trials, is essential to the virtual prevention of extinction. Whether bar-retraction would yield different results than other methods or insuring a single response has yet to be determined. The importance of bar-retraction was definitely suggested, however, since E observed that approach to the ever present food tray extinguished during the non-rewarded trials even though bar responding did not.

What aspect of the relative massing of trials is important in effecting extinction is also in doubt. One compelling observation by E in Experiment II was that on the trial or two just before S extinguished, all Ss began to make vigorous attempts to escape from the box. An implication here is that frustration effects may accumulate with a 5-minute intertrial interval and become sufficiently strong to instigate competing responses.

Actually, given the conditions of Experiment I, neither the occurrence of learning in E — 10 during early extinction trials nor the failure to extinguish is incompatible with theories of Guthrie (1953) or Denny and Adelman (1955).

SUMMARY

In Experiment I two groups of rats, E — 10 and E — 50, were trained to press a bar one trial a day for 10 and 50 trials, respectively, and were then given 75 extinction trials, one per day. A control group which received no training was given 25 unrewarded trials, one per day. The bar was always removed from the box as soon as *S* had depressed it.

The latency of the bar-pressing response increased markedly for the control animals, but reached a low, stable level in the E groups. One *S* in the E — 10 group, which was performing with a high latency at the end of training, extinguished. There was no evidence of extinction behavior in the remaining nine *S*s.

In Experiment II, 10 rats were trained to press a bar five trials a day until each *S*'s performance was at least equal to that of the E — 10 group in Experiment I (a mean of 13.5 trials) and were then given extinction trials until a 3-minute no-response criterion was attained. All daily intertrial intervals were at least 5 minutes. All *S*s extinguished in less than 60 trials under this condition, indicating that something close to one trial a day is crucial in preventing the extinction of a bar-pressing response.

REFERENCES

DENNY, M. R., and ADELMAN, H. M. Elicitation theory: I. An analysis of two typical learning situations. *Psychol. Rev.*, 1955, 62, 290–96.

GUTHRIE, E. R. Psychology of Learning. New York: Harper, 1953.

SOME OBSERVATIONS ON AN OPERANT

IN THE OCTOPUS

P. B. DEWS

Department of Pharmacology, Harvard Medical School

Operant behavior has been successfully demonstrated in all species of mammals and birds for which a serious attempt has been made. Comparatively little attention has been paid to invertebrate species. This paper reports preliminary exploration of the behavior of the octopus (*O. vulgaris.* Lamark) to see whether components of its behavior could be found which fulfill the definitive requirements necessary to identify them as operants. The octopus has the advantage over most invertebrate species in that it has well-developed motor behavior of a nature which makes the selection of an arbitrary, objectively recorded response quite easy. In addition, Young and Boycott (1955) describe behavior in the octopus which is almost certainly operant in nature, i.e., not elicited, but maintained by its consequences. One reason for interest in this problem is that the octopus belongs to a phylum (Molusca) which has evolved independently of the pathway which leads to the vertebrates since Cambrian times (some 500 million years ago). If the phenomena of operant behavior are to be found in the octopus as well as in the vertebrate species studied, then these phenomena probably are of very general biological significance.

Three octopuses have been studied. All three were trained to pull a lever which led to the delivery of food. In two, reasonably consistent lever-pulling behavior was maintained until extinction; only partial success was obtained with the third octopus.

METHOD

Subjects were three octopuses (*O. vulgaris*), each weighing 500 grams, designated for identification purposes Albert, Bertram, and Charles. Each lived in its own tank of circulating sea water from which it was never removed during the experiments. The tanks of Albert and Charles were 4 feet 6 inches long by 2 feet 6 inches wide, and contained a depth of about 2 feet 6 inches of sea water. The tank of Bertram was 6 feet long and 2 feet 3 inches wide, and contained a depth of 2 feet 6 inches of sea water. At one end of each tank at the bottom were two or three bricks, which the octopus arranged to make a house. The undisturbed octopus spent almost all its time sitting in its house, "looking" out with one eye.

The lever was $\frac{1}{4}$-inch brass rod which entered the water vertically and reached to within about 3 inches of the bottom. It was pivoted at a board which was rested across the top of the tank during an experiment. The pivot permitted the lever to be moved in only a single plane; but movement in either direction in that plane activated a light precision switch.[1] Operation of the switch led to illumination of a lamp which in definitive experiments was arranged to shine vertically into the water from above at the end of the tank opposite to that of the "house" of the octopus (the "far" end of the tank). The lever was arranged about the middle of the tank, somewhat nearer the far end. Only one lever and light assembly was used, the whole being moved from tank to tank for experiments on the various octopuses.

The response was movement of the lever so that the lamp lighted. Reinforcement was delivery of a small piece of fish about one-tenth of a filleted 3-inch sardine. The fish was on a nylon line with a small glass sinker.

PROCEDURE

The animals were deprived of food a day, and then responses were shaped as follows:

1) Taking the fish from the line when presented close by, moving up and down, in the beam of the light.

2) Swimming to the far end of the tank and taking the fish when presented in the beam of the light.

3) Approach to the lever.

4) Finally operation of the lever.

A similar shaping procedure was followed for all three octopuses. The following representative account gives in detail the sequence used with Bertram; the sequences used in the other two animals did not differ in any important particulars.

Day 1 No food. Previous to this the octopus had been fed with "several" small crabs per day.

Day 2 Took pieces of fish from line when presented 10–20 centimeters away in light beam.

---

[1] "Acro" switch.

Day 3 Octopus took total of nine pieces of fish over 5-hour period,
         starting each time from "house." First piece was presented
         20 centimeters away, but remaining eight presented about
         middle of tank (i.e., about 80 centimeters away).
         Initially, animal took fish only when it had been presented
         about 15 minutes, but last three were taken in 2–5 minutes.
Day 4 Eight pieces of fish taken over 6 hours. First three taken from
         positions intermediate between middle and far end of tank,
         remaining five from far end. Animal started from house each
         time. Last four were taken within 1 minute of presentation.
Day 5 Took five pieces of fish, each with 1 minute of presentation,
         from far end of tank on each of four occasions through day
         (total, 20 pieces of fish).
Day 6 Took 10 pieces of fish in single session; required to return
         to house between presentations.
Day 7 Lever introduced. Octopus ignored lever except to avoid
         touching it when swimming by.
Day 8 Like Day 7.
Day 9 Small piece of rubber tubing put around lower end of lever,
         to provide what was hoped would be more attractive surface
         for octopus tentacles. Also attached to lower end of lever,
         by short piece of thread, was a small maltese cross. The stream
         of water responsible for circulation and aeration of water in
         the tank was directed towards the lever, causing the cross to
         dance and twirl. These additions to the lever were adequate
         to cause the octopus to approach the lever, whereupon a
         piece of fish was presented. After a few such approaches, it
         was possible to require that the lever be encircled by two
         or more tentacles before the fish was presented. On two oc-
         casions, obtained fish while still having tentacle around lever;
         pulled lever at this time and was promptly given second piece
         of fish. Encircled lever with tentacles (and was given fish) 22
         times during period of 1 hour; on three of these occasions,
         actually operated the lever.
Day 10 et sec. Required to operate lever before fish was presented.
         When the lever was operated and the light came on, the
         light was then kept on by manual switch and the fish intro-
         duced at far end of tank. When the octopus came over and
         took the fish, the light was kept on a few more seconds. When
         the fish line was released—free of fish—by octopus, a stop
         watch was started and the time to the next lever operation

noted. This cycle was continued until the animal had had 20 pieces of fish, or until more than 10 minutes elapsed between release of line and operation of lever. The octopus was given the opportunity of obtaining these 20 pieces of fish (two fillet sardines total) at each of two sessions, one in the morning and the other some 3–4 hours later in the afternoon. This was the only food obtainable by the octopus during the experiments.

RESULTS

All three octopuses obtained 40 reinforcements on several consecutive days without the latency between release of the fish line and operation of the lever exceeding 10 minutes on any occasion.

An attempt was made to reinforce lever-pulling by Albert intermittently on a small fixed-ratio schedule—two, then three (Table 1, Day 5). The first 10 reinforcements on this day were given on the *crf* procedure above described. The next 10 were given at every other lever-pull; each time the lever was operated the lamp lighted in the usual way and was kept lit until the octopus released the lever and moved to the far end of the tank. At this time, either the light was extinguished and timing to the next lever-pull started (following odd-numbered responses), or food was presented in the usual way. The animal completed 20 more lever-pulls under this procedure without any latency rising to 10 minutes. In the afternoon session, after reinforcement of the initial response, the ratio was raised to 3:1. Under this procedure, the animal obtained five more reinforcements (i.e., 15 lever-pulls), but the latencies progressively rose and, after the 16th response, reached 10 minutes, the arbitrary cut-off point. On Day 6, only a few responses (4) were not reinforced, and 19 reinforcements were obtained before a latency of 10 minutes occurred. *Crf* was reintroduced, and over the next 6 days (Table 1, Days 7–12) the animal made 260 consecutive responses each within 10 minutes of release of the fish line. On the 13th day, extinction was instituted; the lamp lit on a response and remained on until the octopus came to the far end of the tank; but it was then turned off without presentation of fish. In the a.m. session of Day 13, 20 responses were made without occurrence of a latency of more than 10 minutes; but in the afternoon session, only 13 were made before a 10-minute pause. On the 14th day, 15 and 9 responses were made before a 10-minute pause in the morning or afternoon sessions, respectively. Since this animal had made 260 consecutive responses without a latency exceeding 10 minutes when on *crf,* the repeated occurrences of these long latencies when reinforcement of the response was discontinued are evidences of operant extinction.

TABLE 1: ALBERT

Day	Mean Latency.*	Range	Remarks
4 (am)	70	20–178	crf**
4 (pm)	48	6–220	crf
5 (am)	30	11–48	crf: 10 responses
5 (pm)	68	27–180	Alternate lever-pulls reinforced: 20 responses, 10 reinforced.
5 (pm)	98	18–	Every 3rd response reinforced: 16 responses, 6 reinforced. Latency > 10 min on 17th.
6 (am)	93	15–	21 responses. 6,8,9, & 12 not reinforced. Latency > 10 min on 22nd.
6 (pm)	86	23–	crf: 15 responses. Latency > 10 min on 16th.
7 (am)	49	5–132	crf
7 (pm)	58	28–128	crf
8 (am)	53	17–115	crf
8 (pm)	48	21–73	crf
9 (am)	41	12–165	crf
9 (pm)	109	20–327	Alternate lever-pulls reinforced: 40 responses, 20 reinforced.
10 (am)	68	18–497	crf
10 (pm)	74	11–180	crf
11 (am)	62	23–130	crf
11 (pm)	86	17–369	crf
12 (am)	46	19–160	crf
12 (pm)	40	20–133	crf
13 (am)	194	33–375	Ext†
13 (pm)	108	20–	Ext: 12 responses. Latency > 10 min on 13th.
14 (am)	113	2–	Ext: 15 responses. Latency > 10 min on 16th.
14 (pm)	150	50–	Ext: 9 responses. Latency > 10 min on 10th.

  * From release of fish line to operation of lever, in seconds. Mean of 20 except where otherwise indicated.
  ** Food presented each time lever operated.
  † Extinction: no fish given.

On Days 14 through 17, Bertram made 120 consecutive responses; the mean latency fell to less than 30 seconds on Days 16 and 17 (Table 2). Reinforcement was then discontinued; 79 responses were made on Days 17 (p.m.), 18, and 19, until a latency of 10 minutes occurred. On Day 20, no response occurred in 20 minutes, again giving clear evidence of operant extinction. There was some "spontaneous recovery" on Day 21, but a performance of 20 consecutive responses without more than a 10-minute latency was not achieved.

TABLE 2: BERTRAM

Day	Mean Latency*	Range	Remarks
10 (pm)	40	16–121	*crf***
11 (am)	18	5–45	*crf*†
12 (am)	38	4–170	*crf*
12 (pm)	41	6–125	*crf*
13 (am)	57	16–150	*crf*
13 (pm)	56	10–120	*crf*: 5 responses.
13 (pm)	69	37–380	Ext†: 15 responses.
13 (pm; later)	90	12–	Ext: 16 responses. Latency > 10 min on 17th.
13 (pm; still later)	98	20–	Ext: 11 responses. Latency > 10 min on 12th.
13 (pm; yet again later)	110	40–	*crf*: 5 responses. Latency > 10 min on 6th.
14 (am)	76	29–	Ext: 15 responses. Latency > 10 min on 16th.
14 (pm)	38	5–82	*crf*
15 (am)	54	20–129	*crf*
15 (pm)	56	30–161	*crf*
16 (am)	22	7–60	*crf*
16 (pm)	22	12–45	*crf*
17 (am)	20	8–43	*crf*
17 (pm)	46	25–75	Ext.
18 (am)	72	46–108	Ext.
18 (pm)	46	6–245	Ext.
19 (am)	165	30–	Ext: 19 responses. Latency > 10 min on 20th.
20 (am)	–	–	"Ext.": Latency to 1st response > 10 min.
20 (pm)	155	61–	Ext: 3 responses. Latency > 10 min on 4th.
21 (am)	171	26–	Ext: 7 responses. Latency > 10 min on 8th.
21 (pm)	61	10–	Ext: 6 responses. Latency > 10 min on 7th.

* From release of fish line to operation of lever, in seconds. Mean of 20 except where otherwise indicated.
** Food presented each time lever operated.
† Extinction: no fish given.

Charles was more capricious and effective, and sustained control was not achieved. The best series was achieved on Days 9 and 10, when 80 consecutive responses were made without a latency in excess of 10 minutes. The behavior of this animal, however, differed from that of the other two in a number of interesting respects.

1) Whereas Albert and Bertram gently operated the lever while free-floating, Charles anchored several tentacles on the side of the

TABLE 3: CHARLES

Day	Mean Latency*	Range	Remarks
7 (am)	94	10–490	*crf***
7 (pm)	129	25–	*crf:* 10 responses. Latency > 10 min on 11th.
8 (am)	81	15–287	*crf*
8 (pm)	25	25–	*crf:* 1 response. Latency > 10 min on 2nd.
9 (am)	49	7–218	*crf*
9 (pm)	82	17–383	*crf*
10 (am)	93	17–417	*crf*
10 (pm)	98	15–570	*crf*
11 (am)	Broke Lever		
11 (pm)	101	5–385	*crf*
12 (am)	57	10–	*crf:* 14 responses. Latency > 10 min on 15th.
12 (pm)	124	35–	*crf:* 14 responses. Latency > 10 min on 15th.

* From release of fish line to operation of lever, in seconds. Mean of 20 except where otherwise indicated.
** Food presented each time lever operated.

tank and others around the lever and applied great force. The lever was bent a number of times, and on the 11th day was broken, leading to a premature termination of the experiment.

2) The light, suspended a little above the level of the water, was not the subject of much "attention" by Albert or Bertram; but Charles repeatedly encircled the lamp with tentacles and applied considerable force, tending to carry the light into the tank. This behavior is obviously incompatible with lever-pulling behavior.

3) Charles had a high tendency to direct jets of water out of the tank; specifically, they were in the direction of the experimenter. The animal spent much time with eyes above the surface of the water, directing a jet of water at any individual who approached the tank. This behavior interfered materially with the smooth conduct of the experiments, and is, again, clearly incompatible with lever-pulling.

The activities described in 2 and 3 above became progressively more predominant as the experiments proceeded; and on Days 20 and 21 they had become so predominant as to lead to cessation of lever-pulling behavior before 20 reinforcements had been obtained. The variables responsible for the maintenance and strengthening of the lamp-pulling and squirting behavior in this animal were not apparent.

DISCUSSION

The behavior of lever-pulling in these experiments showed the following characteristics of an operant:

1) It was found possible to differentiate the response by deliberate shaping.

2) The occurrence of the response was maintained by its consequences (the presentation of fish).

3) The tendency of the response to occur fell when it was no longer reinforced.

The attempt to establish the response as a free operant, permitting continuous observation of its frequency of occurrence, was not successful. At least two factors contributed to this failure:

1) Once an octopus has taken firm grip of an object, it has a high tendency to retain a firm grip. In its natural environment, the train of events following seizure of an object has probably usually only one of two conclusions: either the eating of the object, or its release to pursue another object. In these experiments, once an octopus had operated the lever, it tended to maintain the lever in the operated state, and could only be dislodged by the provision of an alternative object (light beam and dangling fish). It was further necessary to make sure these objects were presented too far from the lever for the octopus to be able to reach them while still retaining possession of the lever. These measures were effective in obtaining a discontinuous response, but only at the expense of severely reducing the possibility (and significance) of obtaining a "rate-of-occurrence" measure of the operant.

2) Only relatively short sequences of *crf* were presented before the attempt was made to introduce a fixed-ratio schedule of reinforcement.

CONCLUSION

The "law of effect" appears to operate in the octopus as in vertebrates. In view of the wide phylogenetic separation of these types of animals, these findings add to the evidence of the very general biological applicability of this law.

ACKNOWLEDGEMENT

This work was carried out at the Stazione Zoologica, Naples, Italy. I wish to thank the director, Dr. P. Dohrn, and his staff for their hospitality and help, and in particular, Mr. M. J. Wells for lessons on the handling of octopuses. The cost of the apparatus used in this work was defrayed by a Grant from the National Institutes of Health (M-2094).

REFERENCE

B. B. BOYCOTT and J. Z. YOUNG: A memory system in *Octopus vulgaris* Lamark. *Proc. Roy. Soc. Lond. B.* 143: 449, 1955.

THE LEARNING CURVE OF A LAND SNAIL

THOMAS R. GARTH and
MARY PINKNEY MITCHELL[1]
University of Denver

NOTE TO READER: Notice the difference in the style of research and report writing for this early study.

In the fall of the year 1923 the writers undertook the training of a land snail to run a class "T" maze such as Yerkes used in educating an earthworm in 1912. (1) A fresh water snail, Physa gyrina Say, was the subject of an experiment in training by Elizabeth Lockwood Thompson (2) but there are not published accounts of the learning of a land snail[2] excepting a preliminary report of our study (3).

While the training of these snails was done under the directions of the senior member of this collaboration, the actual work of training the subjects of the experiment was performed by the junior member during the fall, winter, and spring running over five months, beginning October 15 and ending March 18.

The apparatus was a "T" maze made of plate glass 3.5 cm. wide, 2.75 cm. deep. The stem was 18 cm. long and the length of the arms, 15 cm., was divided equally by the stem. The "T" was covered by and cemented to a sheet of window glass. The "T" thus fastened to its cover rested on another and similar sheet of window glass, as a floor to which it was not cemented but left unattached so that the whole maze might be raised and this bottom sheet might be easily washed to avoid "tracking" on the part of the subjects.

---

[1] The writers beg to acknowledge the assistance of Dr. Wm. H. Dall, Hon. Curator, Div. Mollusks, United States National Museum, Dr. Junius Henderson, Curator of Museum, University of Colorado, and Dr. Henry A. Pilsbry, Curator, The Academy of Natural Sciences of Philadelphia, in identifying the subjects of this experiment as *Rumina decollata* Linne. The snails are natives of Europe. Dr. Dall says they "were introduced into the West Indies and known to flourish in South Carolina and Texas. In Bermuda they became such a pest as to be subject to legislation."

[2] An interesting account entitled "Intelligence of a Snail," probably one of the group H. albolabris, by W. H. Dall, is to be found in American Naturalist, xv, (1881), 976–77.

In that part of the glass floor covered by the left arm of the maze were bored small holes for entrance of small copper wires ending in loops. These wires were connected with a Columbia battery of 1.5 volts and served as electrodes for punishment in case the subjects proceded toward the left instead of the right. After a time, however, this means of punishment was abandoned for a continuous wire which would be heated by the passing of the current when shunted on at the proper moment. In the beginning of the experiment an effort was made to use sunlight for a drive but the lighting conditions from the windows made this impractical, so after a few trials a Mazda electric light globe of 75 watts was suspended before the foot of the maze to serve as a drive, when lighted, to the negatively phototropic subjects. To avoid the reflection of light rays the screen surrounding the maze was lined with black dull finish paper. In order to maintain some control of temperature an ordinary Fahrenheit thermometer was added to the apparatus.

This describes the apparatus. But it might be mentioned that for properly housing the snails an incubator was devised because the temperature of the room at night was rather low for snail activity. The snails were kept in tin cans filled with moldy leaves brought from their habitat and these were always quite moist.

As we have said, the subjects of the experiment were land snails, Rumina decollata Linne.[3] Because of fatality due to lack of knowledge as to how the creatures should be handled and kept there were many subjects. Just when a promising subject was beginning to show signs of learning its death ensued and a new subject was brought into the experiment.

On one memorable occasion the janitor left the nearby radiator on at full tilt and next morning all the snails were dead. This gives some idea of the difficulties encountered in learning how to control the conditions necessary to the training of Rumina decollata Linne. One very important item was keeping the snails supplied with fresh lettuce leaves and to prevent the decay of these and a rather baffling difficulty was presented by the presence of a (to the experimenters) nondescript parasite that interfered with the well-being of the subjects.

Finally, on December 5 a hardy subject, snail XX, presented itself for training and by that time a technique in snail training had been acquired by the trainer. The technique of the training was to

---

[3] They were provided from the campus of the University of Texas.

see that the temperature surrounding the maze was around 78° F. to take the snail from its home container and place it on the glass at the foot of the "T" maze and then to turn on the light. Practically always the snail was snugly withdrawn into its shell. It was now a matter of waiting until the effects of the heat from the lamp sufficiently aroused the subject to activity when the head was protruded from the shell and it began moving slowly away from the source of irritation. Simultaneously with the starting of the subject up the stem of the "T" a stop watch was started. The snail's movements were followed and if it turned definitely to the left instead of to the right at the parting of the ways an error was recorded. If the subject persisted in going to the left it was allowed to be punished slightly by the electric wires. If the snail went to the right it reached a dark box and was rewarded by being allowed to remain in the dark for a short time. The time beginning with starting up the stem of the "T" and ending with reaching the dark box was recorded. This was called a trial. If the subject was sufficiently active, four trials a day, or six at the most were given, but sometimes only one trial a day was made. However, snail XX averaged about two trials a day. There were occasions when snail XX refused to come out of its shell at all or merely started and then withdrew into its shell stubbornly remaining there at some point in the maze, refusing to perform. This was a failure and is indicated in the table as F.

In our presentation of the data on the learning of Rumina decollata Linne to run a "T" maze we have three lines of evidence. One is the time curve for the "prize" subject, snail XX, the second is the error curve for same, the third is given in plats of paths of this and other subjects. Table 1 gives the number of days, the number of trials, and the time in seconds for any trial for snail XX. The snail was not trained on Saturdays and Sundays. In Figure 1 we have a time curve of the learning of this snail obtained by averaging the number of seconds required for every successive five trials. Table 2 gives the total number of errors for each successive five trials and Figure 2 is an error curve derived from Table 2. These curves represent the performance of this snail whose training began December 5, 1923, and ran to March 3, the forty-third day. On this last day the subject had two trials, the first requiring 286 seconds to run the maze, and the second 205 seconds. In terms of time learning is certainly indicated. This is likewise indicated in the table showing reduction of errors and the curve of errors.

TABLE 1

TIME IN SECONDS FOR EACH TRIAL EACH DAY FOR SUBJECT, SNAIL XX

Training began December 5 and ended March 3.

Day	Trial	Seconds	Day	Trial	Seconds	Day	Trial	Seconds
1	1	625	18	1	422	29	1	411
	2	F.		2	388		2	251
2	1	1,090		3	240	30	1	505
	2	F.		4	345		2	632
3	1	F.		5	330	31	1	313
	2	615	19	1	523		2	284
4	1	2,434		2	319		3	200
5	1	485		3	425	32	1	500
	2	937		4	289		2	319
6	1	F.		5	208	33	1	271
	2	F.		6	268		2	275
7	1	1,556	20	1	495	34	1	271
	2	230		2	716		2	234
8	1	297	21	1	712	35	1	270
	2	2,376		2	505		2	306
9	1	629		3	311	36	1	391
	2	331		4	241		2	241
10	1	630	22	1	325	37	1	252
	2	260		2	312		2	320
11	1	1,440		3	336	38	1	276
	2	231	23	1	763	39	1	433
12	1	200		2	273		2	302
	2	630		3	251	40	1	441
	3	471		4	296		2	326
	4	505		5	302	41	1	292
	5	F.	24	1	481		2	209
13	1	689		2	413	42	1	257
	2	390		3	349		2	227
	3	271		4	455	43	1	286
14	1	344	25	1	523		2	205
15	1	390		2	310	(30 days of rest inter-		
	2	285	26	1	399	vened here)		
16	1	503		2	261	44	1	483
	2	433		3	613	45	Failure.	(Snail
	3	360	27	1	336		died next day)	
17	1	1,100		2	261			
	2	337		3	324			
	3	315	28	1	335			
	4	1,195		2	312			

F. indicates failure to perform.

Just after the second trial on the forty-third day an unfortunate accident occurred, the snail was accidentally dropped on a nearby table and its shell was cracked leaving an aperture through which the creature persistently tried to emerge. The subject was then allowed to rest from training for thirty days so that the hole in the shell might be closed by the process of nature. After thirty days had elapsed the aperture had partially closed and the subject was again placed in the

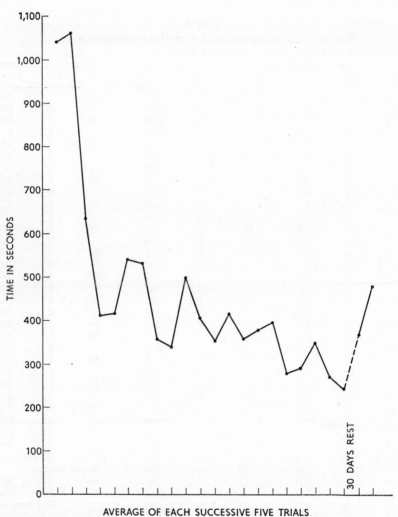

FIG. 1. Showing Learning Curve of Snail XX Derived by Averaging Each
Five Successive Trials.

maze for another trial. This made the subject's one hundred and third
trial. It was with some interest that the trainer noted that the time
of the trial was only 483 seconds—this after an interval of thirty days.
The subject had not "forgotten" completely the learning secured
during the previous training. The snail was not made to perform
again that day but on the next day when it was tried, it failed to come
out of its shell and the next day following the trainer discovered that
the creature was dead, presumably from the attacks of the parasites
that had killed many of the other snails.

TABLE 2
TOTAL NUMBER OF ERRORS FOR EACH FIVE SUCCESSIVE TRIALS

Trials	Total Errors	Trials	Total Errors
1–5	4	61–65	0
6–10	4	66–70	1
11–15	6	71–75	0
16–20	0	76–80	0
21–25	2	81–85	0
26–30	1	86–90	0
31–35	1	91–95	0
36–40	2	96–100	0
41–45	0	101–102	0
46–50	0	Rest of 30 days	
51–55	1	103	0
56–60	0		

The third line of evidence of the learning of the snails is supplied by the plats of paths. See Figure 3 which shows path no. 1 of ten snails. On the whole these are extremely tortuous. Figure 4 shows the tendency towards directness in path of another snail, XXX, for successive trials. Its learning was never consistently reduced as expressed in terms of time but the path was slowly becoming more direct when the training stopped. Figure 5 shows the paths of the snail that really ran the maze for one hundred and three times beginning with the ninety-fifth trial.

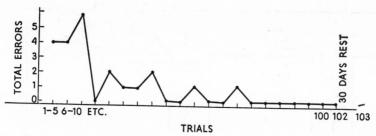

FIG. 2. Showing Error Curve of Snail XX Derived by Totaling Errors for Each Successive Five Trials.

We believe that our lines of evidence as offered herewith justify the conclusion that Rumina decollata Linne, a land snail, has capacity for learning.

It would be interesting to bring this study of snail learning into relation to the only other reported study of snail learning to see in what respects they agree or disagree. We refer to the study of Elizabeth Lockwood Thompson (2) made in 1917 at University of Michigan.

The subject of Miss Thompson's study was Physa gyrina Say, a fresh water snail. There are at least two phases to her experiment; one is adaptation—the other is learning. Of the latter there are two phases. Miss Thompson (2, p. 87) found much evidence of "capacity for adaptation—the getting-used-to the stimulus." She also found a modifiability by experience such as forming associations between two stimuli. This was brought out by using a method somewhat

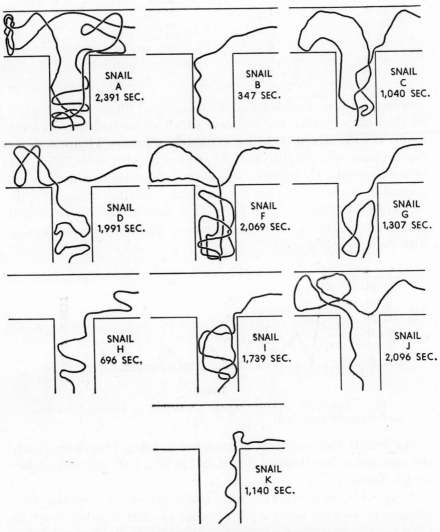

FIG. 3. Showing Path No. One of Each of Ten Snails.

similar to that of Pawlow—learning through conditioned stimuli, i.e., associating pressure on the snail's foot with simultaneous presen-

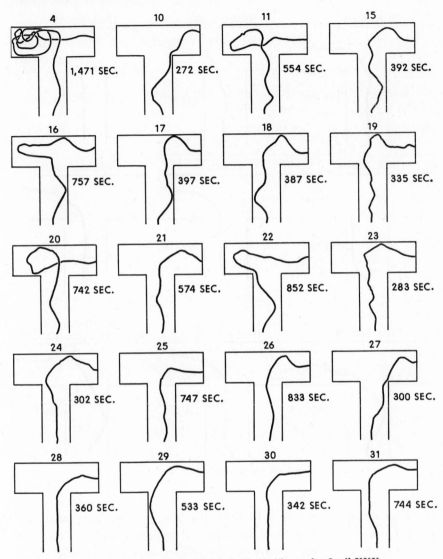

FIG. 4. Showing Paths for Trials 4, 10, 11, 15, etc. for Snail XXX.

tation of food and the consequent arousing of the salivary reflex. In the mind of the experimenter (2, p. 36) the evidence is sufficient for making the statement that the response is available for experimental purposes. The other phase of the study of snail learning in Miss Thompson's experiment was one in which she sought to teach Physa gyrina Say to run labyrinths, one a U-shaped labyrinth and the other a Y-shaped labyrinth in the water. According to the experimenter the results are negative—"it shows no capacity to solve the labyrinth" (2, p. 87).

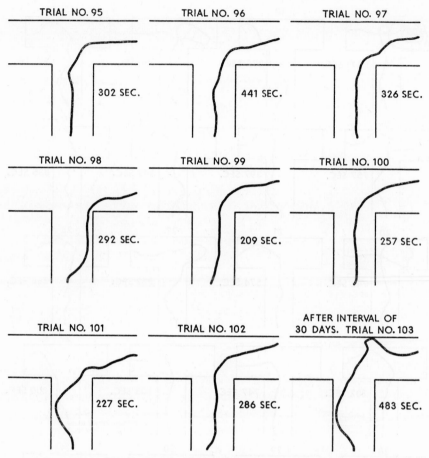

Fɪɢ. 5. Showing Paths of Snail XX Beginning with 95th Trial.

The two studies disagree in that our subject was a land snail, Rumina decollata Linne, which by the way is sometimes mistaken for a fresh water snail from its outward appearance (4). That this land snail learned is evident from the reduction with successive trials in time (as shown above), in errors and in directness of path in running a "T" maze.

REFERENCES

(1) Yᴇʀᴋᴇs, Rᴏʙᴇʀᴛ M.: The intelligence of the earthworm. Jour. Animal Behav., ii, 332.
(2) Tʜᴏᴍᴘsᴏɴ, Eʟɪᴢᴀʙᴇᴛʜ Lᴏᴄᴋᴡᴏᴏᴅ: An analysis of the learning process in a snail, Physa gyrina Say. Behav. Monographs, no. 14.
(3) Gᴀʀᴛʜ, Tʜᴏᴍᴀs R.: The learning curve for a snail. Science, lix, no. 1533, 440.
(4) Gᴀʀᴛʜ, Tʜᴏᴍᴀs R.: Correction of name of snail. Science, lx, no. 1543, 83.

APPARENT LEARNING IN THE PARAMECIUM

MILTON S. KATZ
University of Rochester
and WILLIAM A. DETERLINE
Alma College[1]

Early efforts to demonstrate learning in paramecium proved unavailing (9). Those which appeared to achieve some success (1, 3, 4, 10) aroused objections, and counter-experiments suggested that behavior modifications classed as learning were due either to adaptation or to uncontrolled stimulus conditions (2, 7).

More recently, Gelber (5) sought to reinforce a low-frequency reaction from the normal behavior repertoire of paramecium. The relatively infrequent reaction was adherence upon contact with a solid object instead of avoidance. *Aerobacter aerogenes* in exhausted culture fluid was used as the reinforcer. Gelber lowered the tip of a platinum wire 40 times into a culture of about 128 paramecia. A cotton swab, previously dipped into the bacterial mixture, was rubbed on the wire every three immersions. She found that the number of paramecia adhering to the wire and the number congregated in an area about the wire increased steadily during the "training" trials. No change in behavior occurred either in a group which received the "training" series without "reinforcement" or in control groups which were not given the "training" series. Gelber dismissed the nutrient value of the bacteria as negligible, and attributed the change in gathering and attachment behavior to the "acquisition of an approach tendency" to the wire. She noted, in another study (6), that groups subjected to the experimental "reinforcement" treatment failed to acquire the approach response if the criterional test trial was conducted in darkness, with illumination restricted to the brief period of time required to make a count.

Jensen (8) demonstrated that Gelber's procedure actually might have given rise to a significantly high bacterial concentration in the vicinity of the wire. The steps Jensen reported differed from the pro-

[1] The research was conducted by the authors at the University of Pittsburgh.

611

cedure employed by Gelber in that the bacteria were dipped into a well containing no paramecia and measured after a series comparable in other respects. He further showed that paramecia tend to gather in bacteria-rich areas, where their attachment tendency increases markedly.

The following study is, in part, a replication of Gelber's experiment (5) with more detailed and extended observations of behavior, an added control group to assess the relative merits of Gelber's and Jensen's conflicting views, and an attempt to measure the durability of the behavior modifications reported by Gelber.

METHOD

Subjects

Paramecium aurelia of unspecified stock were isolated from a parent culture and washed in successive baths of distilled water to remove food matter. They were separated, with the aid of 1.5-v. dry-cell-battery electrodes, into groups of 125 each, and placed in 20 individual well-slides containing a mixture of exhausted culture fluid and distilled water. Each sample was used several hours after isolation, and then only if it contained active, vital animals.

Apparatus

The animals were observed in slides with wells 17 mm. in diameter with walls 3 mm. deep, perpendicular to the level floor of the well. A platform similar to Gelber's was constructed of metal with a cutout section large enough to hold a single slide. Fastened to the platform was a knifeswitch with a 3-in. length of platinum wire, 0.5 mm. in diameter, bent to extend vertically when the switch was closed. The platform was mounted on the stage of an air-cooled slide projector so that approximately 2 in. intervened between the slide and the stage. Directly on the projector stage rested a dish full of water for the purpose of intercepting heat. An image of the entire well was projected with approximately 25× magnification at the wall screen, upon which was demarcated a circle corresponding to an area of 6-mm. diameter in the well, and concentric with the projected image of the wire tip.

Procedure

Experimental and control groups. The 20 samples were distributed into four groups of 5 each. Each slide was placed on the projector platform and transilluminated only while counts or observations were made.

Group I corresponds to Gelber's "reinforced" group. A cotton swab was dipped in a rich mixture of *Aerobacter aerogenes* and exhausted culture fluid, allowed to dry for 2 min., and wiped on the bent tip of the platinum wire. The wire was then lowered into the sample medium for a series of 40 "trials." Each "trial" consisted in immersing the tip of the wire for 15 sec., and then raising it for 25 sec. The wire was swabbed after every three "trials," and the swab was dipped into the bacterial mixture after every third trial on which "reinforcement" was applied to the wire.

Before the first "reinforcement" trial, the sterilized platinum wire was lowered into the culture medium for 3 min., and an "initial" count taken of the number of paramecia adhering to the wire, and of the number present within a radius of 3 mm. about the wire. In the course of the "reinforcement" procedure, counts were taken during the last of each five "trials." The projector light was turned on for 15 to 20 sec. during each "trial" in which a count was taken, permitting observations of response to the immersion of the wire tip. At the end of "Trial" 40 (during which a count was made), the wire was raised, flamed, and washed before being lowered into the well for 3 additional minutes and a "final" count. After the "final" count, the wire tip was removed from the well for flaming, while the well fluid was stirred by a stream of air blown onto the surface through a micropipette. The wire tip was then lowered, and after another 3 min. the "post-stir" count was taken.

Group II is comparable with Gelber's "nonreinforced, trained" cultures. The same procedure was followed as in Group I, except that no bacteria were introduced at any time. The number and spacing of wire immersions and of counts were the same.

Group III parallels Gelber's "control" cultures. The "initial," "final," and "post-stir" counts were collected as in Group I and II, and a count corresponding to the Trial 40 count was taken 26 min. after the "initial" count (a period of time equal to that required for the 40-trial series).

Group IV was treated like Group III except that a small drop of the bacterial mixture was lowered by means of the wire at the end of the Trial 40 count. Three minutes later the "final" count was taken, with stirring and a "post-stir" count following in sequence.

RESULTS

Approach Tendency Measured by Number of Paramecia in Vicinity of Platinum Wire Tip

The number of paramecia collected within a circle about the wire tip increased steadily on successive counts throughout the "training" series of Group I, substantiating Gelber's finding with "reinforced, trained" cultures (counts on Trials 15 through 35 were conservative estimates since the gathering was too thick to count during the 15 sec. allowed for observation). No change occurred in the counts of Group II, which sustained a relatively stable level during the "nonreinforced, training" series. Successive counts of animals within the 6-mm.-diameter circle for Groups I and II are shown in Figure 1 along with parallel counts within a 3-mm.-diameter circle reported by Gelber. The "final" count was reported only in the present experiment.

Approach Tendency Measured by Number of Paramecia Adhering to the Wire

The number of paramecia adhering to the wire during the "final" count in Groups I and IV could not be accurately determined (see Qualitative Observations). Gelber (5, p. 61) states that ". . . by the final, or fortieth, trial (the eighth count), the animals were thickly piled about the end of the wire and almost no animals were in the periphery. This very striking phenomenon (observed only in rein-

forced cultures) rendered impossible any accurate count during the
15 sec. while the wire was down." On the other hand, no animals were
judged to be adhering to the wire in Groups II and III of the present
experiment.

Comparison of Counts in Vicinity of Wire Tip under the Four Treatment Conditions

Figure 2 is a graphic arrangement of counts within the 6-mm.
circle for all four groups to show temporal changes and differences
between groups in centripetal gathering. An analysis of variance indicates no significant difference between groups on the "initial" and
"post-stir" trials (Table 1). However, "initial" differ significantly from
"post-stir" trials, with a decrease in Groups I, III, and IV and no
change in Group II. Counts on Trial 40 for Groups II, III, and IV
do not differ systematically from one another, but the count for Group
I is clearly higher (Fig. 2).

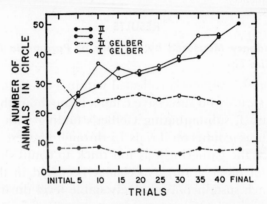

FIG. 1. Number of animals in circle on every
fifth trial during "training" period.

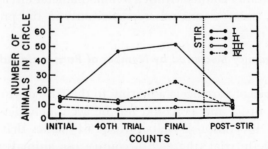

FIG. 2. Number of animals in circle on "initial,"
Trial 40, "final," and "post-stir" counts.

The variance analysis of "initial" and "final" counts (Table 1) yielded significant F ratios $(P < .05)$ for groups, for trials, and for the interaction, attributable mainly to the increase in "final" counts of Groups I and IV. The "final" mean of Group I (50.8) is higher than that of Group IV (25.4), which, in turn, exceeds the means of the control groups, II (7.0) and III (12.0).

TABLE 1

SUMMARY OF VARIANCE ANALYSES FOR GROUPS I, II, III, AND IV

Source of Variation		"Initial" and "Post-stir"			"Initial" and "Final"	
	df	Mean Square	F	df	Mean Square	F
Between groups	3	39.30	1.18	3	1090.09	6.70**
Between Ss (within)	16	33.32		16	162.81	
Total between Ss	19			19		
Between trials	1	78.40	4.95*	1	1265.63	11.31**
Interactions						
T × G	3	16.67	1.05	3	878.62	7.85**
Pooled T × S	15[a]	15.84		16	111.94	
Total within Ss	19[a]	19.26		20	284.62	
Total	38[a]			39		

* $P < .05$
** $P < .01$
[a] One "post-stir" count missing in Group II.

Qualitative Observations

Eccentric gatherings. In two samples of Group I the food material introduced during the first "trial" apparently spread from the wire toward the periphery of the well. On the following count ("Trial" 5) an elongated cluster of paramecia had formed, extending from the center of the well to beyond the limits of the 3-mm. radius. The appearance of such a culture is given in Figure 3.

Activity and thigmotropic responses. The animals near the wire in Groups I and IV, whether in eccentric or concentric clusters, remained motionless for the most part, many adhering to the bottom of the well. Such thigmotropic behavior contrasted sharply with the active, roving movement which characterized Groups II and III. An increase in the number of paramecia gathered in the vicinity of the wire, when food had been introduced, was accompanied by a reduction in activity at the center of the well. It is particularly noteworthy that the progressive increase in number of animals gathered about the wire tip in Group I was not due to an approach response to wire-dipping, but to the circumstance that animals which had gathered in the center of the well did not disperse, but remained there between trials.

On later trials, when the wire was lowered into the midst of the thickly gathered and almost motionless animals in the Group I cultures, whole clusters appeared to be swept passively toward the wire. Bits of dust which had settled onto the surface and into the water were also swept against the wire by the slight disturbance. Except for the intial brief disturbance, the introduction of the wire did not produce any noticeable change in activity in the animals. Re-examination of the well-slides on the day following experimental treatment revealed that the animals were once more active.

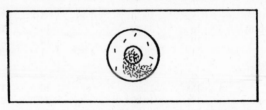

Fig. 3. A Group I culture in which an elongated cluster of paramecia formed. The inner circle represents the 6-mm. diameter test area about the wire.

DISCUSSION

At the outset, no response to the introduction or presence of the wire was observable in any of the four groups. The variance, for Groups I and II, in number of paramecia on successive counts in a circular area with the platinum wire as center (see Fig. 1), is comparable with the results obtained by Gelber (5). That is, when the wire was dipped at regular intervals without food ("training"), no change occurred. When food material was added, an increasing number of animals gathered in the center of the well on successive "trials" ("training with reinforcement") and remained there between "trials." Only isolated instances of adhering to the wire occurred, with the exception of Groups I and IV after food material had been introduced (in both groups, positive attachment responses were also made to objects other than the wire, e.g., the bottom and walls of the well, other animals, and debris).

The hypothesis, expressed in Gelber's studies, that the demonstrated behavior modifications were induced by operations apart from the addition of food material seems untenable when the behavior of Group IV in the present study is considered. This group manifested so marked and significant an alteration in response to the area centered on the wire within 3 min. after the addition of food material as to approach the change obtained in Group I after several "training" and "reinforcement" trials. The behavior of the two groups was strikingly similar in all respects, and it is reasonable to ascribe the difference in number congregated to the brief opportunity afforded Group IV for gathering and feeding. Thus, "training" and "reinforcement" may, in this instance, be a laborious technique for introducing food material into the center of the well.

In a more recent article by Gelber (6), it was concluded that paramecia subjected to the "training-reinforcement" procedure exhibited modification in attachment behavior only if exposed continuously to light during the 3-min. final test trial. In the present study, the wells were unlighted except during counts, yet results were similar to reports of data collected under fully lighted conditions by Gelber. The contradiction, however, may be ascribable to differences between unselected and genetically controlled strains of paramecia.

In order to assess the durability of the induced approach behavior, the contents of each well were stirred after the "final" count with the wire tip removed, and the "post-stir" count was made after 3 min., with the wire tip immersed. For evidence of retention it would only be necessary for Group I's "post-stir" count to exceed its "initial" count. Actually, all "post-stir" counts were equal to or smaller than the "initial" counts (as were the "final" counts of Groups II and III). In Groups I and IV, activity remained at a low level, and the animals displayed no tendency to return to the vicinity of the wire. Their behavior in the periphery of the well was similar to that at the center noted earlier, i.e., lethargic motion, with attachment to the walls and to the bottom of the well, probably because the food material had also been blown to the periphery. Animals in the remaining two groups responded no differently to the wire in passing than they had during the "initial" counts.

The authors conclude that the behavioral changes induced are attributable to the presence and effect of food material, as suggested by Jensen. Gelber's demonstration of "reinforcement-training" effect, therefore, was based on the typical response of paramecia to stimuli, in this case food, and possesses no relevance to conditioning or learning. It is not possible, from these data, to ascertain whether or not paramecia learn. The present results offer no evidence of learning since the observed changes are more parsimoniously accountable. If paramecia can learn (a possibility by no means excluded) this technique fails to isolate the phenomenon unequivocally.

SUMMARY

This study is an evaluation of two possible explanations for the modifications of approach response to a platinum wire by *Paramecium aurelia* following "training with reinforcement." One explanation invokes the concept of learning, the other accounts for the behavior as an unlearned reaction to the food material used as "reinforcement." Control groups of paramecia into which food was introduced without the "training" series showed behavior modifications essentially equivalent to those of the experimental groups, and the absence of continuous illumination appeared to have no effect on the criterional behavior in either series. The durability of the "approach tendency" was tested and found to depend on the presence of food material. The authors reject the interpretation of the experimental results as a demonstration of learning.

REFERENCES

1. BRAMSTEDT, F. Dressurversuche mit Paramecium caudatum und Stylonchia mytilus. *Z. vergl. Physiol.*, 1935, 22, 490–516.
2. BUYTENDIJK, F. J. Acquisition d'habitudes par des êtres unicellulaires. *Arch. néerl. Physiol.*, 1919, 3, 455–67.
3. DAY, L. M., and BENTLEY, M. A note on learning in Paramecium. *J. anim. Behav.*, 1911, 1, 67–73.
4. FRENCH, J. W. Trial and error learning in Paramecium. *J. exp. Psychol.*, 1940, 26, 609–13.
5. GELBER, B. Investigations of the behavior of *Paramecium aurelia*: I. Modification of behavior after training with reinforcement. *J. comp. physiol. Psychol.*, 1952, 45, 58–65.
6. GELBER, B. Investigations of the behavior of *Paramecium aurelia*: III. The effect of the presence and absence of light on the occurrence of a response. *J. genet. Psychol.*, 1956, 88, 31–36.
7. GRABOWSKI, U. Experimentelle Untersuchungen ueber das angebliche Lernvermoegen von Paramecium. *Z. Tierpsychol.*, 1939, 2, 265–82.
8. JENSEN, D. D. Experiments on "learning" in Paramecium. *Science*, 1957, 125, 191–92.
9. SMITH, S. The limits of educability in Paramecium. *J. comp. Neurol. Psychol.*, 1908, 18, 499–510.
10. SOEST, H. Dressurversuche mit Ciliaten und Rhabdocoelen turbellarien. *Z. vergl. Physiol.*, 1937, 24, 720–48.

CHAPTER 12

LEARNING WITH COMPLEX CUES

This chapter treats complex learning and performance situations. The position to be taken in this chapter is that complex behavior is called complex because it typically involves the operation of subtle or complex cues. By complex cues we mean the following: 1) an extended sequence of stimuli; 2) the perservative trace of a stimulus (stimulus aftereffects); 3) response-produced stimuli particularly when produced by minimal responding; 4) a situation in which the relevant stimuli vary with or are determined by the stimulus context, for example, when the background is light, the form of the object is relevant and when the background is dark, the color of that object is relevant; 5) a situation in which the relevant stimuli must be abstracted from a larger, often changing, context, as in concept formation. These categories of complex stimuli are frequently used to characterize the complex behaviors herein discussed. According to the present treatment, the relation of complex behavior to simple learning situations may be succinctly stated: What holds for the simpler situation holds as well for the complex; the differences are due chiefly to cue complexity as just defined. Among other things, this implies that the assumption of elaborate symbolic behavior in lower animals is unwarranted.

Types of Learning Situations

Complex Mazes and Cue Utilization. When a maze consists of a series of choice points it is considered complex. Such a maze typically involves all but the stimulus context aspect of stimulus complexity, as noted above ($\#4$). The learning of a complex maze is characterized by a number of interesting features. When the maze approximates uniform difficulty throughout it is usually learned by lower animals in roughly a backward order. The errors first eliminated are near the goal and those last eliminated are near the start. This is particularly true when errors consist of taking a longer path to the goal rather than entering dead-end blinds (unpublished research by J. F. Shepard). Another way of saying this is that learning proceeds in a backward order when approach to the goal is the main sequence of responses being learned. On the other hand, when the learning involves the avoidance of dead-end blinds it tends to be learned, as found by Shepard, in a more or less all-over-at-once fashion, complicating a smooth backward order of maze learning. The backward learning of a complex maze is presumably mediated by the backward chaining of approach responses to the goal object in much the same way as chaining was described in operant conditioning.

In human beings, complex mazes are typically learned in a sequential order that is characteristic of all serial learning in the human: Whenever events occur in a constant order the initial portion of the behavior sequence is learned first, then the final portion of the sequence, while the central portion is learned last (the serial position effect). The fact that the serial position effect describes human maze learning indicates that the way human beings learn mazes is probably different from the way lower animals learn them. For one, the human uses language (verbal mediators); secondly, the final goal region lacks real importance for the human subject. Therefore, from the beginning of learning the human being is verbally oriented to be correct at every choice point and hardly more so at the final choice point than the others. Thus he starts learning the beginning of the maze from the very beginning, and the bow-shaped serial position effect, just described, describes his progress over trials. The serial order effect also operates to a slight extent among lower animals, further complicating the backward order effect in their maze learning.

A complex maze is learned proportionately much faster than a single unit is learned, for example, 10 units are learned in many fewer than 100 trials if one unit is learned in 10. This is as true for the chicken as it is for the rat (Warden and Riess, 1941 *; Warden and Hamilton, 1929). This is probably true for at least two reasons: 1) after a few trials learning proceeds in all units on each trial; 2) the tendency to alternate or explore different directions is partially satisfied in the complex maze because the true path, as in a multiple T-maze, can point in any one of four different directions. In contrast, the alternation tendency is satisfied in a single unit T-maze only when the animal makes an error.

WARDEN C. J. and RIESS, B. F. The relative difficulty of mazes of different lengths for the chick. *J. Psychol.*, 1941, 11, 411–19.

Five groups of chicks were trained to run bilateral mazes with alternating left turns. The mazes were differentiated on complexity by the number of turns in each (2, 4, 6, 8, 10). The absolute number of trials required to learn all mazes was approximately the same (though least for the shortest), but the *relative* number of trials decreased progressively as the length of the maze increased.

An animal uses whatever cues are available to it in learning a complex maze. Eliminating the cues of an entire sense modality either by surgical means or by indirect experimental manipulations has practically no deleterious effect on maze learning; even eliminating two avenues of stimulation still permits learning to occur, though eliminating three avenues, for example, by making a rat deaf, blind, and anosmic, virtually prevents learning.

Vision, if available, is the cue most often used by rats and even by some species of ants (genus Formica). Such ants can learn mazes nearly as complex as those learned by rats (Schneirla, 1929). The saliency of visual cues is indicated in a number of ways. For instance, elevated (open-alley) mazes which provide a wealth of visual cues are learned faster than enclosed mazes and also mediate better positive transfer effects when the original route to the goal is no longer available (so-called insight or reasoning effects).

In the early stages of complex-maze learning kinesthesis plays much less of a role than other cues because it is not a constant stimulus. This is the case because early in learning the animal responds in a variable way, making a variety of errors and different kinds of errors each trial. The early ineffectiveness of the kinesthetic cue explains why the blind, deaf, and anosmic rat is unable to learn. Once the maze habit is well established, however, the kinesthetic stimuli just preceding each choice-point response become *constant* and can then serve as the sole cue for the maze habit. Evidence for the exclusive use of kinesthetic cues in complex mazes comes from studies by Hunter (1940), Shepard (1929, 1931, unpublished), and Spragg (1933).

In demonstrating learning on the basis of kinesthesis, Shepard used what he called a unit-alike maze (see Fig. 12–1). This maze was an extended chain of identical units all of which were accessible from the same long corridor like the compartments of a European train. He started the animal in different units on different trials but always kept the food reward a constant number of units from the start-unit, say three units away (the animals were always running in the same direction so that the kinesthetic rhythm was constant). Shepard's work on the kinesthetic cue in the unit-alike maze has been essentially replicated and confirmed in an unpublished study by Denny, Thomas, and Elliott. By using a "crutch-cue" they found that an 85–90 percent level of correct response could be achieved in most rats when

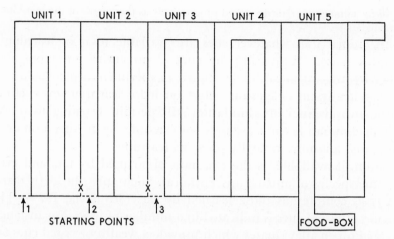

FIG. 12–1. The unit maze used by Curtis. The arrows indicate different starting points which may be used. The sections marked *X* are removable. They are inserted only when the latter part of the maze is used. (*Courtesy of Q. F. Curtis.*)

they were trained to enter the third unit of a maze regardless of starting position. By "crutch-cue" is meant that the entrance to the third unit away was specified by a ¾″ square of black tape stuck to the floor just at the threshold of the correct unit. When a 90 percent level of responding was achieved the piece of tape ("crutch-cue") was eliminated and after a slight drop in performance the rats quickly reattained the 85–90 percent performance level. When the order in which the units were run was reversed, creating quite a different pattern of kinesthesis, performance fell to a chance level and remained there. Thus the rats were not in any abstract or symbolic sense counting to three.

In the process of studying kinesthetic cues Shepard also discovered another subtle cue for the rat, which he called a "floor-cue." This he found by carrying out the following manipulations. Instead of varying the location of the food from trial to trial he always placed the food in the same unit and started the animal at varying number of units away from the goal-unit; such a procedure eliminated any possibility of kinesthesis serving as a cue. Under this condition many rats learned the food location even when the walls and immediate floor of all units were continuously interchanged. Not until the subfloor structures were also manipulated did these rats fail to learn. The available evidence seems to indicate that the "floor-cue" is mediated auditorially as the animal walks across the floor. Many rats' sensitivity to this cue is remarkable. The complex cue here would be classified as response-produced and is virtually undetected by humans. Such a cue may well be related to the echolocation cue used by rats, as described in the summarized experiment by Riley and Rosenzieg, 1957 * (see Chapter 3).

Delayed Reaction Studies. Delayed response refers to the ability to respond appropriately in the absence of the external cue. The animal is first trained to respond appropriately to a particular stimulus in order to obtain the incentive. For primates with well-developed perceptual orientation this training procedure is often unnecessary: the animal is shown where the incentive is by placing the lure under a particular container (position cue, color cue, form cue, etc.). After the cue-approach association has been established the cue is momentarily presented and the animal is permitted to respond only after a certain passage of time. In the case of primates, this simply means that the incentive is hidden and the animal is permitted to respond later. The occurrence of the appropriate response after the removal of the cue and after the delay interval has elapsed is the delayed response.

The ability of infrahuman animals to delay a response, that is, to bridge the time gap between the cue and the response, was once thought to be evidence of symbolic (representative) behavior. But there is a simpler explanation which fits the data better. In essence the explanation consists of viewing the maximum delay possible in delayed response as the time it takes to forget after one learning trial. The response to be delayed is minimally elicited, either by the lure or the appropriate cue, as in making an orienting response, and is thus conditioned to the stimuli that prevail on a particular trial. Subsequently, the main conditioned stimuli (cues) for eliciting the delayed response are the differential proprioceptive stimuli resulting from making an orienting response plus the particular external stimuli to which the animal last oriented. So long as the interval remains short the effects of one learning trial are sufficient to mediate a correct response. But as the delay interval increases, more and more response-produced stimuli undergo change and the stimuli of the last trial become indistinguishable from those of prior trials; thus the animal can no longer delay successfully. This interpretation receives support from the fact that the more nearly the animal is allowed to come close to completing the instrumental response prior to the introduction of the delay the longer it can delay successfully. A rat which is just permitted to orient to the cue can typically delay a response for 3–4 seconds (Hunter, 1912); but it can delay as much as

45 seconds if permitted to run up toward the cue before the delay is introduced (Honzik, 1931). In the latter experiment the differential stimulation is more profound, and the learning is better because learning comes through responding.

BAERENDS, G. P. Frontpflanzungsrerhalten und Grientierung der Grabrnespe *Ammophila compestos. Jur. Tijdchr. Entomol.,* 1941, **84,** 68–275.
Under special conditions even insects appear to show the kind of one-trial learning that we have suggested is involved in delayed response. In caring for the young, the female digger wasp tends two, and sometimes three, separate nests daily for several days. The nests contain larva which the mother wasp supplies with extra food in the form of dead caterpillars. Each day the wasp's behavior is determined by the amount of food she finds in a nest on the first visit of the day. If there is more food present in some nest (s) than in the other (s), then the return visit with food is directed at the appropriate nest, even when the return visit is delayed for a number of hours. However, when other cues are substituted for quantity of caterpillars in the nest, there is no evidence that one-trial learning is possible in the digger wasp.

Further support for the one-trial-learning interpretation comes from recent studies on the effects of deprivation level and incentive level on the success of delayed response. As pointed out in Chapter 11, the main role of both incentive and deprivation in learning is to help specify the appropriate response. Obviously, if learning is going to occur in one trial the response must be nicely specified. Therefore, one would predict that increasing the value of the incentive or increasing the deprivation level would facilitate delayed response. The data on this are strongly confirmatory. Gibbons delay significantly better when preferred food is the incentive than when nonpreferred food is the incentive. They also perform better for a nonpreferred incentive when food deprivation is increased (Berkson, 1962). The clincher, however, is a study by Gross (1963) using both normal and brain-operated monkeys which were compared on spatial-delayed response and spatial-delayed alternation as a function of deprivation level. In the delayed alternation situation, the monkey was presented with two stimulus plaques to choose from with a delay of 3 or 5 seconds between a choice-response and the next stimulus presentation. The animal received a raisin each time it alternated its response from trial to trial. Here the bait (raisin) is presented after the correct response has been made and therefore cannot serve as a cue and cannot directly specify the correct response, whereas in delayed response the bait is the *cue* for the correct response. The results clearly indicated that increased deprivation improved delayed-response performance in all animals, but had no effect on delayed-alternation performance.

Various species vary considerably in how long they can delay a response, given roughly comparable experimental situations. This fact may reflect several things: 1) differences in one-trial learning ability; 2) whether or not the incentive can be used as the cue (monkey v. rat); 3) general activity level of the animals (rat v. turtle); 4) how responsive the organism is to external stimulus changes, etc. The fact that mentally retarded children can delay for less time than normal children of the same MA could reflect the greater distractability of the retarded child to external stimuli (Pascal *et al.,* 1951). Among the higher primates (chimpanzee, gorilla, orangutan), the latest experimental data seem to indicate only minor differences in delayed-response performance as well as in performance on the patterned string problem, a complex perceptual-motor task (Fischer and Kitchener, in press). The similarity in performance is quite in keeping with our ignorance as to which species is more primitive.

The variable of language can be virtually excluded from man's performance in delayed response by using the multiple delayed-response technique. When this is done, an adult chimpanzee performs as well as adult human beings and better than 7- to 9-year-old children (Tinklepaugh, 1932). In the multiple delayed-response situation there are, say, 32 identical containers arranged in pairs and located at different places in a large room. One member of each pair is baited as the subject watches, and afterwards the subject is permitted to respond to each of the pairs in turn. Due to the large number of pairs in unspecified places, verbalizing that the lure is on the right or on the left is of no aid to a human subject. Since the human being cannot verbally rehearse during the delay period he has only one learning trial, as is always the case with infrahuman organisms. Thus the performances of the chimpanzee and human are roughly equivalent.

Practice with delayed-response problems has been shown to be an important variable in experiments conducted in the Wisconsin Primate laboratory (Weinstein, 1941; Finch, 1942). After many trials, rhesus monkeys and chimpanzees can successfully delay for 30 to 60 seconds in the difficult nonspatial delayed-response problems where an orienting response is of no help to the animal (objects, colors, forms are the cues rather than position). Adult human beings can delay responses to all sorts of cues for extended periods of time, days or even weeks. Presumably one reason for this, in conjunction with the language factor, is the wealth of experience which they have had in delaying responses.

Double Alternation.   Another behavioral phenomenon which has
been used to infer symbolic behavior in lower animals is the double-
alternation problem in a temporal maze. But as was true with delayed
response, the behavior can be analyzed in terms of learning to subtle
cues. The temporal maze is shown in Figure 12–2. In this piece of ap-

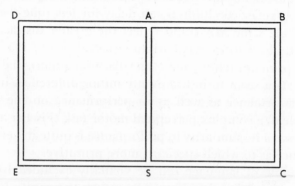

Fig. 12–2.   Diagram of the temporal maze. The pathways consist of elevated poles. The animal is required to
run two right circuits (*S–A–B–C–S*) and two left circuits
(*S–A–D–E–S*) in succession after which it is rewarded.
During the training the direction of the animal's progress
is controlled by blocking off the incorrect route. (*Modified from Hunter, 1929, p. 527.*)

paratus the animal is called upon to make successive responses at the
very same choice-point. The only cue for differential responding is
the preceding pattern of response-produced stimuli. If the animal is
posed with the problem of a simple alternation of left and right turns
(LRLR) then there is a distinctive proprioceptive stimulus for each
response. Having just turned left provides the cue for a right turn,
and having just turned right is the cue for a left turn. Most mammals,
including mice and rats, can readily learn the simple-alternation problem (they tend to alternate spontaneously anyway). But when the cue
is made more subtle by using a double-alternation pattern (LLRR),
then rats typically fail to learn, though other mammals such as cats,
dogs, and racoons are capable of learning a LLRR problem. Since
these animals fail to learn a longer sequence than LLRR it is gratui-
tous to assume that a symbolic process is operating here.

For the learner, two main difficulties arise with the double-alternation learning problem. 1) The cues for the correct response do not
come from the immediately prior response but from the previous *two*
responses. This means that there can be two distinct stimulus patterns
for the same correct response: The cue for turning right is having just

turned left twice in a row, *or* the cue for going right is having just turned right after having turned left [the cue varies with the context, (#4, page 619)]. 2) As if this were not complicated enough, solution of the double-alternation problem also requires the consistent production of each response so that consistent kinesthetic stimuli, no matter how complex, can prevail at the choice point each time the problem is presented. Experimenters often help the animal out here by inserting a barrier in the wrong alley to shorten any errors made. Thus the animal is kept on the track as much as possible.

Presumably simple alternation, double alternation, delayed response, and unit-alike mazes all require the specific use of perseverative kinesthetic cues. The rat, which cannot delay a response for as long as the dog or racoon, probably does not keep the kinesthetic cues for as long as other mammals. The maximum for the rat appears to be about 45 seconds (Perkins, 1947; Honzik, 1931). Since considerable time can elapse between making a response and arriving at the choice point one or two responses later, the rat would appear to be especially handicapped in learning the double-alternation problem. In other words, if the time between successive responses were kept short the rat might solve the double-alternation problem. Such an interpretation is nicely supported by the fact that a rat *can* learn to press two adjacent levers in a Skinner box in a double-alternation pattern (Schlosberg and Katz, 1943).

HEARST, E. Delayed alternation in the pigeon. *J. exp. anal. Behav.*, 1962, **5**, 225–28.

Pigeons were first trained to peck at two response keys alternately; then a delay was introduced (a blackout period) between reinforced key pecks. All birds learned to perform at better than 75 percent accuracy with delays of 5 seconds or less and performed better than chance on a 10-second delay.

Overt postural orientation appeared to facilitate appropriate delay of response.

"Insightful" Problem Solving. The main point to be made here is that the studies which allegedly support the notion of "insight" or "reasoning" in lower animals, in the sense of seeming to attribute a symbolic process to the infrahuman organism, all employ open-field situations where visual cues abound and where the animal's solution response can be elicited by distal (distant) stimuli. When studies of comparable problems have been conducted in enclosed mazes or in a homogeneous surround the animals uniformly fail to perform insightfully (Tolman and Honzik, 1930; Wolfe and Spragg, 1934; Graziano, 1956; McNamara *et al.*, 1956 *; Grice, 1948 *).

GRICE, G. R. An experimental test of the expectation theory of learning. *J. comp. physiol. Psychol.*, 1948, **41**, 137–43.

This experiment is a test of the Spence–Lippitt type of latent learning, a type which was *not* described in the text. The method is used in simple T- or Y-mazes and is a specific test of Tolman's hypothesis about cognitive maps in infrahuman organisms. The description of procedure and results below indicate the method. Grice found no evidence of this type of "latent" learning with his design. Twenty-three thirsty rats were given 48 water-rewarded trials in an enclosed T-maze, half to each side. Food, in obvious quantities, was also consistently present on *one* side. When the animals were made hungry and satiated for water and given further trials they showed no preference for the previous food side and learned to go the food side no sooner when the food was on the same side than when it was placed on the side opposite to the original location (2 subgroups).

McNamara, H. J., Long, J. B. and Wike, E. L. Learning without response under two conditions of external cues. *J. comp. physiol. Psychol.*, 1956, **49**, 477–80.

In this study rats did not run through the maze but were drawn through in a cart. On test trials when the animal did run, these rats showed learning if there were distictive extra-maze cues. But when extra-maze cues were eliminated there was no learning. Without extra-maze cues, learning requires complete overt responding at the choice point.

It is not an uncommon observation in maze experiments to see a fairly well-trained rat prematurely jump out of the experimenter's hand, and run across the top of a shallow maze directly to the goal box. Such behavior has been labeled insightful. But it is neither "insightful" nor contradictory to a careful stimulus-response analysis. The best learned response of the animal is to *approach* the stimuli associated with the goal region, including the extra-maze cues. In fact, the chain or sequence begins with the learning of this response. Thus it is no surprise that the rat shows appropriate responding (positive transfer) when so permitted. In addition, we are saying here that it is inappropriate in the initial stages of maze learning to classify the animal's learning as a series of right and left turns, for this implies that the responses are guided primarily by kinesthesis. Only in the later stages of learning is this the case.

Furthermore, even in open-field situations an animal as high in the phylogenetic scale as the chimpanzee fails to show "insight" in a situation which rigorously controls and defines "insightful" behavior (Razran, 1961 **). Many studies which purport to show "reasoning" in lower animals are in the final analysis only slightly complicated delayed-response problems with minimal delay. When this delay is increased to 45 seconds, as has been done with Maier's well-known three-table problem, the rats fail to "reason" (unpublished research by Goy and Denny, 1948). Finally, Schiller (1957), who was himself an early proponent of insight in animals, has impressively pointed out that the behavior which has been referred to as insightful in the chimpanzee is behavior which is dominant in their original behavioral repertoire. Without lures, chimpanzees stack boxes when boxes are available and poke sticks together when such sticks are about.

None of this is to imply that lower animals do not solve problems. They in fact do. When lower animals solve problems, it appears to be a trial-and-error procedure, which is usually the way that human beings solve problems. However, the presence of language and the diversity of prior experience in humans can make a mammoth difference. The double-alternation problem, for example, becomes trivially easy when one can verbalize "twice to the right, twice to the left." Any rudimentary representative behavior possessed by lower animals is quite ineffectual by comparison. This is not to say that language represents an entirely new process; the role language plays is quite understandable in stimulus-response terms. In fact, an excellent case can be made against the use of such concepts as "reasoning" and "insight" even at the human level. One definite value of studying the behavior of lower animals is to view ourselves more objectively.

Latent Learning and the Complex Maze

What follows in this section is a rather lengthy abstract of an, as yet, unpublished Ph.D. dissertation by P. K. Jensen (1957). This investigation, in our view, is an informative piece of research which deserves a broad audience. The point of departure for the study was the now rather defunct issue of "latent" learning. Its current significance is that it brings into focus a "new" variable in the learning of a complex maze. The study dealt specifically with the Buxton–Haney type of latent learning though its implications apply to the Blodgett type as well. In the Blodgett type of "latent learning" the animal is given several nonrewarded discrete trials in a complex maze containing dead-end blinds, as in a multiple T-maze (the animal is removed from the maze soon after it enters the goal box). A goal box incentive is then introduced on, say, the 10th trial (day); on the subsequent trial performance shows distinct improvement ("latent" learning). Tolman's interpretation of this finding was that the animal was learning a "cognitive map" of the maze during the early trials even though this was not manifest in performance prior to the introduction of reward (cognitive map can be thought of as learning "what leads to what"). The Buxton–Haney type of latent learning, which is similarly interpreted, refers to the situation in which prior exploration of a maze (not discrete trials in a maze) results in the facilitation of subsequent learning when regular, reinforced, learning trials are subsequently given. One point about the Buxton–Haney experiment is that letting an animal explore the maze ahead of time may bring about an adaptation effect, resulting in fewer emotional reactions to the maze during the subsequent learning trials. To control for this contingency it is necessary to use a control group which is permitted to explore a *simple* maze structure similar in appearance to the complex maze, for a comparable period of time.

Jensen's experiment was a test of the hypothesis that latent learning, as just defined, is due to the greater development of stimulus satiation or habituation effects in the blinds of the maze than in the true path. Presumably, an exploring animal spends more continuous time in a blind, including retraceal, than any single portion of the true path. When a rat is moving unidirectionally in the true path, the path is a continuously changing stimulus environment. Thus the animal will be less satiated for the true path stimuli than for the stimuli of the blinds. Such an analysis is supported by the data of Reynolds (1945) and MacCorquadale and Meehl (1951) for the Blodgett type of experiment. The rats in these studies penetrated the blinds less and less on successive nonrewarded trials during the period which preceded the introduction of the incentive. It follows from the analysis that an animal which is given an initial exploratory period is simultaneously learning to avoid the blinds and to approach successive sections of the true path during this period. Thus, when the regular rewarded learning trials are introduced, the animal will learn quickly: "latent" learning is derived. The issue at stake here is not reinforcement versus nonreinforcement in learning but Tolman's cognitive map versus a more parsimonious analysis, as represented by the stimulus satiation hypothesis.

To test the hypothesis, Jensen devised the seven-unit multiple hexagon-maze which is schematically shown in Figure 12–3. By inserting blocks at the points indicated in the figure the maze could readily be transformed into a multiple Y-maze with real blinds. Otherwise, without any blocks, it was a maze with only circle-blinds. As such, the circle blind alleys could not become any more satiated than the "correct" pathway. In the circle-blind or hexagon-maze the *shortest* path to the goal was considered the correct path during learning. According to the experimental hypothesis, "latent" learning should occur when the blocks are in place but should not occur when the hexagon-maze is used. It also follows that "latent" learning should not occur when *only* the true pathway is explored.

Three experimental groups and three control groups, a total of 77 rats, were used for evaluating the three-pronged hypothesis just re-

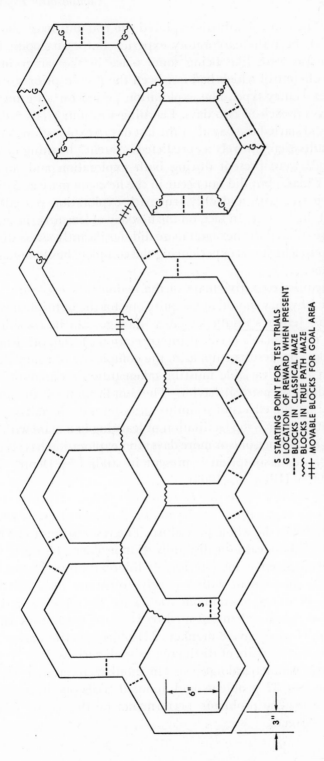

S STARTING POINT FOR TEST TRIALS
G LOCATION OF REWARD WHEN PRESENT
---- BLOCKS IN CLASSICAL MAZE
〜〜 BLOCKS IN TRUE PATH MAZE
+++ MOVABLE BLOCKS FOR GOAL AREA

FIG. 12–3. The seven- and two-unit mazes with positions for blocks.

ferred to. The control animals explored the two-unit maze shown in Figure 12–3; here the exploratory experiences for any point in the two-unit maze were like being some place in the larger maze, a specificity of control which had not been the case in prior studies of the Buxton–Haney type. The exploration period for all groups was three hours on each of two days. Learning was four trials a day for four days and started the day after the last day of exploration.

The results were entirely as predicted: "latent" learning occurred when blinds were present during both exploration and final test (multiple Y-maze) but did not occur in the hexagon-maze and did not occur when true-path and only true-path exploration preceded the learning of the Y-maze. In fact, on the first day of learning the animals which had explored the hexagon-maze did significantly *worse* than the control group which was experiencing the complete hexagon-maze for the first time.

If rats acquire cognitive maps of the region they explore it is difficult to see why they should not acquire one for the multiple hexagon-maze. Thus, Jensen's results, as far as they go, can be considered a refutation of Tolman's classical interpretation of "latent" learning. In particular, the results emphasize the complexity of complex-maze learning: a "new" variable must be taken fully into account in the understanding of maze behavior. The implication of the present analysis is that the effects of stimulus satiation must be fairly permanent or learned, since the facilitation of learning in a maze with dead-end blinds takes place one or more days after exploration has occurred. Support for this assumption is present in studies by Denny (1957), Leckart (1963), Hill *et al.* (1963).

Learning Set and Successive Reversal Learning. The first time an animal is presented with a discrimination problem in the laboratory, it is quite naïve to the whole procedure. The result seems to be that it takes many trials to learn the discrimination problem. However, when the animal is given a long series of different problems, it shows progressive improvement with successive problems until finally the animal may be able to learn in one trial. This "learning how to learn" phenomenon was first demonstrated by Harlow (1949), who called it learning set. Harlow gave 8 monkeys 344 object-discrimination problems (344 different pairs of distinctive stimuli such as dime-store objects and solid geometrical figures). The monkeys received 50 trials on each of the first 32 problems and about 9 trials on the remaining problems. After 256 problems, performance on the second trial was 97 percent correct.

In the past few years it has been demonstrated that rather marked differences in ability to form learning sets exist among species of primates, as well as across the mammalian class. Among the primates the chimpanzee, gorilla, and rhesus monkey are at the top and the marmoset at the bottom, with other species ranging in between, in much the order that phylogeny might predict. Simple discrimination learning does not ordinarily yield these ladder-like differences. Thus learning set has been entertained as a comparative psychology measuring stick of degree of intellectual development.

One possible interpretation of learning set, in keeping with the present approach, is in terms of cue utilization. The first assumption which needs to be made in this interpretation is that the *perceptual* discrimination between the to-be-discriminated stimuli requires little or no learning (a natural discrimination exists—the animal immediately sees the "ash tray and sponge" as different). This means that the large number of trials initially taken in learning a discrimination problem is due in large measure to the special methodology of the discrimination learning experiment, not to any inherent difficulty in perceiving stimulus differences. When an animal is given a long series of problems to learn it is then in a position to solve the method, so to speak. Reinforcements and nonreinforcements, as such, can become the most relevant cues in the learning situation. They are the only cues which remain constant across problems, and with a large number of problems there are sufficient trials to mediate learning. In other words, the animal gradually learns that when an *object* is reinforced, it continues to be reinforced (to select it consistently), and that when an object is nonreinforced the other object is to be selected. In the jargon of the experimental investigator, this is becoming known as "win, stay; lose, shift." An adult human being already knows this is typically the case, based on his wide experience with two-choice situations and the usual meaning of "right" and "wrong." Thus he typically "learns" a simple discrimination by the second trial on the very first problem. A young child, on the other hand, does not know this very well and shows the development of "learning set" at a rate which is comparable to the chimpanzee (Kaufman and Peterson, 1958). Likewise, a profoundly retarded child may develop a "learning set" no faster than a rat (House and Zeaman, 1958).

HAMILTON, G. V. A study of trial and error reactions in mammals. *J. Anim. Behav.*, 1911, 1, 33–66.

    A variety of mammals are capable of learning the following multiple-choice problem. In a five-choice situation the animal can learn to choose the alley or doorway which it has not yet visited, avoiding all repetitions until all choices have been made. The pattern of responding is haphazard rather than systematic. In a certain sense this learning seems akin to learning set except that the animal is required to learn *not* to repeat the response that was previously correct rather than to learn to repeat the response that was just correct.

The reference to the rat just above refers to a special case of "learning set" which has been labeled successive reversal learning. This concept usually applies to the learning of a spatial response, as in a T-maze, where the correct side, once learned, is successively reversed a number of times, say 10. The first reversal ordinarily results in an increased number of trials to learn, but with successive reversals performance improves until learning can occur in one trial. The successive reversal method, spatial or nonspatial, is one which is suitable for use with submammalian species and has been used with birds, fish, sowbug, turtle, newt, and crab. Progressive improvement in habit reversal below the mammal *using traditional methods,* has only been conclusively found in birds, namely, chickens and pigeons (Bullock and Bitterman, 1962; Bacon, Warren and Schein, 1962). See also below.

SEIDMAN, E.   Relative ability of newt and terrapin to reverse a direction habit. *J. comp. physiol. Psychol.,* 1949, 42, 320–37.

The amphibian newt and reptilian terrapin were trained in a simple T-maze to go to one side to darkness plus water and then successively trained on 9 reversals of the direction habit (learning set). The criterion of learning was three correct runs in succession. The terrapin showed clear superiority over the newt. The greater plasticity in the higher organism was reflected most in the ability of the turtle to learn the maze without error by the 9th reversal; the newt showed more errors throughout learning and made a mean of 2 errors on the 9th reversal. On the first problem the newt and terrapin made 8.7 and 3.7 errors, respectively. *Note:* The remarkable aspect of this study is the fact that the animals did so well; rats after 9 reversals make 1 to 2 errors. Several special features of the procedure probably account for the excellent performance by both newt and terrapin: (*a*) each animal was given all sets of trials (all reversals) in one evening; (*b*) between each reversal the animal was given a 15-minute rest interval in a shaded container of water; (*c*) during this interval the paper linings of the mazes were replaced by fresh bond paper. The typical successive reversal study is run over several days with the reversal coming one day after criterion has been reached. Nor is a distinctive cue, such as changing the lining of the maze, presented to signal the start of a reversal. Perhaps if the pill bug were run under such favorable conditions it would also show clear evidence of learning set (see Thompson, 1957 *, below).

STEVENSON, H. W. and SWARTZ, J. D.   Learning set in children as a function of intellectual level. *J. comp. physiol. Psychol.,* 1958, 51, 755–57.

A group of normal children (CA = 11.6) and two groups of mentally retarded children (a higher IQ group with CA = 11.5 and a lower IQ group with CA = 14.2) were presented with a maximum of 24 object-discrimination problems. N = 10 in each group. All 10 normals caught on very quickly and showed errorless performance on Trial 2 of a problem no later than the fifth problem. Only one subject in the lower IQ group showed clear-cut learning set, though there was a significant decrease in the mean number of trials to learn in this group with successive problems. Eight of the 10 subjects in the higher IQ group finally acquired a learning set but they were clearly inferior to the normal group. Acquisition of learning set is clearly a function of intellectual level; normal children appear to bring the appropriate "learning set" with them to the learning situation.

THOMPSON, R. Successive reversal of a position habit in an invertebrate. *Science,* 1957, **126,** 163–64.

Seven pill bugs, *Armadillium vulgare* (Crustacean), were tested in a successive reversal learning situation, using a simple T-maze. Copper grids were in each arm just beyond the choice-point and the attractive end boxes were dark and had a wet sponge floor. Eight trials were given a day and the positive (unshocked) side was reversed the beginning of a day after the criterion of seven correct responses in a day was reached. Eight reversals were given. In this period no significant drop in errors occurred though a slight trend for learning set was apparent. The pill bug does not appear to profit from successive reversals like the newt or turtle, though it was not run under as favorable conditions as was true of the experiment on the newt and terrapin.

Oddity Learning and "Concept" Formation. An interesting experimental technique which has been exploited in the Wisconsin Primate laboratory is the oddity problem. Two different pairs of identical stimuli are used, but only three stimuli are presented on any one trial. Let us say the two pairs of stimuli are two wooden blocks and two doorbells. On a particular trial two doorbells and one block are presented. Here, the block is singly represented or odd and its choice is reinforced. On another trial the doorbell may be odd and the one to select. Each stimulus is equally often odd over trials; thus the other cues, position and object, are irrelevant and must be disregarded. The relevant cue is determined by context. Adult primates have no particular difficulty with oddity problems, while most subprimates have considerable difficulty. Given a series of oddity problems, monkeys soon develop learning sets to the point where one-trial oddity learning occurs. Further complications of the context as a determiner of the relevant cue still yield learning in primates. For example, monkeys can be trained to respond to the odd *form* when the stimuli are presented on a dark background and to the odd *color* when presented on a light background.

PASTORE, N. Discrimination learning in the canary. *J. comp. physiol. Psychol.,* 1954, **47,** 389–90.

Canaries are capable of learning the oddity problem even when the absolute stimulus values are reversed from trial to trial. The objects used for discrimination were a black chess pawn and an aspirin tablet.

WODINSKY, J. and BITTERMAN, M. E. Solution of oddity problems by the rat. *Amer. J. Psychol.,* 1953, **66,** 137–40.

Rats are capable of learning the oddity problem if the stimuli used are vertical- and horizontal-striped panels or pairs of black and white figures. The animals perform better on later problems, manifesting the acquisition of a learning set.

Primates also excel in *concept formation* where the relevant stimulus is presented in a multitude of ways and contexts, though cats, dogs, and rats also appear to be capable of such learning. Upon appropriate signal rhesus monkeys have learned to select all red objects from a mixed group of red and blue objects, upon a different signal to select all blue objects, and upon neither signal to inhibit all responses (Weinstein, 1945). High proficiency was attained in this experiment even though size, number, form, brightness, and saturation of the stimuli varied from trial to trial.

BERNSTEIN, I. S.   The utilization of visual cues in dimension-abstracted oddity by primates. *J. comp. physiol. Psychol.*, 1961, 54, 243–47.

Rhesus monkeys, pigtailed monkeys, chimpanzees, an orangutan, and human beings were compared on the learning of complex-oddity problems where there were several irrelevant cue dimension and only *one* relevant cue dimension. The subject had to learn to select the object which was odd with respect to size, let us say, and ignore all the other stimulus dimensions along which the other four objects could be the same or different (the other four objects were of course the same size). Such problems are quite difficult as attested to by the fairly high error level of the adult human subjects, but all groups eventually solved the "dimension-abstracted oddity problems." After training, a mean of 1,440 trials, the monkeys performed at about the same level as the untrained humans who had all been given verbal instructions as to the principle involved (90 percent correct). The monkey groups did not differ significantly from each other and neither did the apes, but the apes learned significantly faster than the monkeys. Form as a cue dimension was at times preferred over color for both the rhesus monkeys and the humans. What was a good form cue for the monkey was not necessarily a good one for the human and vice versa. But, what is important is that color is not always dominant over form as a cue, as has been emphasized in the past.

NISSEN, H. W.   Analysis of a complex conditional reaction in chimpanzees. *J. comp. physiol. Psychol.*, 1951, 44, 9–16.

A young chimpanzee was found capable of learning, concurrently, 16 two-choice discrimination problems. Five distinct cues in various combinations or contexts provided the 16 problems. The simplest type of problem could be represented as follows: If the two plaques were white the larger was rewarded, but if they were black the smaller was correct. Now add three more dimensions, form (square or triangle), margin (absent or present), and presence or absence of a light-green peg stuck into the plaque. The complexity of the problem becomes immense. For example, when one stimulus was a large, *white,* square and without margin and peg, and the other stimulus was the same except for being small then the first one was correct. But when the stimulus was small, *black,* square, and without margin or peg and the other was large, *black,* square and without margin or peg, then the first one was again correct (this time small). The relevant contextual dimension varied from problem to problem with size as the only cue which differentiated the two plaques for all problems.

There is no necessary implication here that "concept" formation in lower animals involves symbolization. In fact, when adult human subjects sort stimuli in a concept-learning experiment, they typically sort correctly before they are able to identify (verbalize) the concept or principle upon which the sorting is based. In other words, the human and subhuman may learn the task in much the same way despite the amount of verbalizing, often irrelevant, that the human subject may engage in during the learning situation (the study by Kelleher, 1958 **, is relevant at this point).

Imitation. The concept of imitation includes several varieties of behavior which depend upon different factors. Thorndike, in his original study of imitation, used a problem-box method where the animal had to learn to pull a chain or turn a knob or make some such instrumental act in order to escape from the box and obtain an incentive. In the "imitation" phase of the experiment an animal which had learned the correct resonse was used as the demonstrator animal, while a naïve animal which was watching was the observer. Later the observer was tested to see what it had learned from the observation. Using cats, dogs, and monkeys, Thorndike concluded that there was *no* evidence for imitation behavior in any of his animals. More recently, other investigators claim that cats as well as monkeys show some evidence of imitation even in problem-box situations. This is particularly true when the imitation test *immediately* follows observation. A study by Darby and Riopelle (1959) nicely demonstrates the imitation effect in monkeys in the context of a learning set experiment. Here the observer monkey learned to make use of the information gained from the demonstrator's successes and failures by performing well above a chance level on the very first trial of each newly presented problem.

In the rat a rather different kind of imitation has been demonstrated by Miller and Dollard (1941). They trained rats to follow or not to follow the leader rat through a T-maze. The imitating rat thus learns to use either direction taken by the leader as the cue for its own turning response. Here the rat is not necessarily copying a response and is *not* gaining information about the consequences of the observed response. Such a cue is readily used by the rat, and the effect is much more pronounced than the inferential sort of imitation which was described in the Darby and Riopelle study.

A third type of imitation is simply imitative copying, as clearly exhibited in the song patterns or talking behavior of birds. The Hayeses report many examples of this kind of behavior in their home-reared chimpanzee, Viki, who was normally quite imitative and learned to imitate all kinds of behavior on the command, "Do this." Here the consequences of the behavior are of no particular moment, and we are not really talking about complex learned behavior but about the elicitation of responses as they are visually or auditorially represented.

Phylogenetic and Ontogenetic Considerations. A number of phylogenetic and ontogenetic comparisons have already been made but need to be reemphasized. Also, certain concluding remarks are in order.

Higher vertebrates are better able to use complex cues, as previously defined, than lower vertebrates. And, everything else being equal, more mature organisms perform complex learning tasks better than immature organisms of the same species. These trends are borne out in delayed-response learning, double alternation in a temporal maze, learning set, concept formation, and oddity learning. One interpretation of such consistent findings is that these learning situations favor the organism with well-developed perceptual equipment which is *like our own*. For other learning situations where this bias does not operate or where the subtle cues involve quite different perceptual equipment, such as olfactory mechanisms, the consistent superiority of the higher vertebrates is not found. Examples of the latter situations include complex-maze behavior, tracking, imitative copying, and homing.

ADDITIONAL SUMMARIZED STUDIES

Boycott, B. B. and Young, J. Z. Reversal of learned responses in *Octopus vulgaris. Anim. Behav.,* 1959, **6**, 45–52.

After an octopus has learned a black-white discrimination, measured in terms of attacking or not attacking a singly presented stimulus figure, it can learn a reversal. During reversal learning the positive stimulus becomes negative. Response to the positive stimulus is followed by food (crab) and response to the negative cue is followed by electric shock. Training in this new direction takes more trials than original training, and the longer the original training the greater the number of trials required to learn the reversal. There is some evidence that reversal learning takes place more slowly after removal of most of the vertical lobe of the brain.

In one instance after the reversal had been learned the experimenters rewarded responses to either stimulus with food. The initial effect here was to increase the number of attacks toward the negative stimulus, but the animal's attacks toward *both* stimuli soon declined and, with the continued rewarding of both stimuli, practically ceased altogether. (Perhaps this is akin to conflict-produced experimental neurosis in dogs, sheep, goats, and pigs).

Ettlinger, G. Cross-modal transfer of training in monkeys. *Behav.,* 1960, **16**, 56–65.

Four rhesus monkeys, two trained on a shape discrimination in the light using vision only and two trained in the dark using only tactual cues, were then required to make the same discrimination in the other modality. There was no evidence of transfer across modalities. The second discriminaton was learned no faster than when it came first. *Note:* Presumably a human being, were he able to use verbal labels for the shapes, would have little difficulty in making the transfer.

THOMPSON, R.   Transient memory in albino rats. *Science*, 1959, **129**, 845–43.

Rats were trained one way in a water T-maze and the next day in the reverse direction and so on for 12 days. An animal was allowed to correct an error; it climbed a ladder out of the water on each trial. The trials were massed and were discontinued when 3 trials out of 4 were errorless. The same day three retention tests were given, one 1 minute after reaching criterion, one 1 hour later, and one 5 hours later. Each animal's position preference was also evaluated. All animals which took significantly longer to learn to turn one direction than the other were said to have a strong position preference (about half the subjects). All animals remembered for 1 minute but those with the strong position preference forgot after 1 hour and 5 hours if they had last been trained against their preference. No other tendency to forget was in evidence. Subsequent tests given after the position preference had been greatly weakened showed improved memory. *Note:* Retention is good when the competing response is weak. When the competing response is strong and the transient cues have disappeared retention is poor. Note the parallel between these findings and the phenomenon of delayed response.

WARREN, J. M.   Effect of geometrical regularity on visual form discrimination by monkeys. *J. comp. physiol. Psychol.*, 1953, **46**, 237–40.

Seven rhesus monkeys were tested on a large variety of form-discrimination problems. The results showed that discriminability increased with increase in the area of the figure and that monkeys discriminate better between a regular form and an irregular form than between two regular or between two irregular forms. Discrimination of two irregular forms was as good as between two regular.

MAZE LEARNING OF A TURTLE

O. L. TINKLEPAUGH
Laboratories of Comparative Psychobiology, Yale University

This report on the maze running of a single turtle is made not because this lowly subject learned the maze, but rather because of the nature of its behavior during the process, the rapidity with which it learned, and the conditions under which the results were secured.

Yerkes [1] reported the learning behavior of a 4-inch speckled turtle. The maze was constructed from a box 3 feet long and 2 feet wide divided into four portions, by means of partitions through each of which was a hole just large enough for the turtle to pass. The turtle's nest, which constituted the lure in this case, was located beside one corner of the box. The turtle was placed in the corner of the maze box most remote from the nest, and then permitted to find his way to this latter point. In the first trial, "After wandering about almost constantly for thirty-five minutes, it chanced to find the nest, into which it immediately crawled, there remaining until taken out for another experiment two hours later." Succeeding trials took fifteen minutes, five minutes and three and a half minutes. Times for the twentieth, thirtieth, and fiftieth trials were forty-five, forty and thirty-five seconds, respectively, and in the two latter instances perfect scores were made. "During the first three trials the courses taken were so tortuous that it seemed foolish to try to record them. There was aimless wandering from point to point within each space, and from space to space" (p. 521). "There was remarkably little aimless wandering, crawling up the sides of the box and sulking in the corners after the third experiment. In fact, the animal soon began to behave as if it had the goal in mind and was intent on making directly for it" (p. 522). "*Very frequently halts* [2] just in front of the holes were noticed. It looked as if the animal were meditating upon the course to be taken" (p. 522).

After the introduction of three inclined plants in the maze, the

---

[1] Yerkes, R. M.: The formation of habits in the turtle. Pop. Sci. Mo., 1901, lviii, 519–25.
[2] Italics by the present writer.

experiment was repeated. Running times dropped from one hour and thirty-one minutes on the first trial to four minutes on the tenth trial and four minutes ten seconds on the fiftieth trial. During this second experiment the turtle shortened its path by crawling up one of the inclines to a platform and then instead of sliding all the way down the next incline it would turn toward the nest and permit itself to fall over the side.

The turtle subject whose behavior we wish to report here was the common wood turtle, Clemmys insculpta (LeConte), male, and measured about 6 inches in length. It was kept at the Yale Primate Laboratory during the late summer of 1929, where it was confined in a large outdoor cage with a young Macacus rhesus monkey. The turtle's food consisted of earthworms and ground beef and also ripe bananas, of which it was extremely fond. Other foods it refused to accept.

The meat and worms were administered by dropping them into a shallow pan of water. Banana was laid upon the ground. Within a few weeks' time the turtle learned to anticipate his daily feeding, and would come to the pan of water or to the writer when he entered the cage.

In the fall the turtle was taken to my home where it was released in the basement. The temperature there remained between 50° and 60° F. throughout the winter. The turtle spent most of the time behind boxes or other objects, but when the sun shone through the basement windows it would occasionally come out of its semihibernation, seek a spot of sunlight and bask there for an hour or two. On these occasions I offered it food. Within a short time it began to appear at intervals of from three to ten days, when I entered the basement in the morning.

It became evident that the turtle had become sufficiently domesticated so that food was anticipated in connection with my appearance. For that reason, it seemed desirable to attempt to utilize this drive in connection with a learning problem. A T-maze of the type developed by Stone (Fig. 1) was constructed. The width of the alleys was 8 inches and each alley whether true or false extended a distance of 20 inches to the right or left of each successive choice point.

If it was not hungry and was brought out into the room the turtle would draw within its shell and remain there for many minutes or even hours without moving. The same occurred when it was initially placed in the maze without having appeared of its own accord.

The first successful trial with the turtle was made on April 5 after

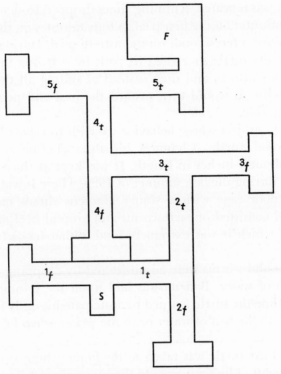

Fig. 1.   Floor Plan of Maze. *S,* starting box; *F,* food
box. Blind alleys are designated by *f;* true paths by *t.*

the animal had not taken food for a period of two weeks. The maze
was placed on the floor of the basement room in such a position that
the food box was in the location where the turtle had customarily
found food. The turtle was placed in the starting chamber and the
observer withdrew to a point several feet distant. The animal's behavior during the first trial was as follows: Placed in maze at 10:55
a.m. Head gradually protruded and he seemed to look around from
side to side as well as in front of him. The turtle then turned around
through an angle of 45° and remained stationary for a few seconds.
He turned completely around and stopped with his head protruding
into alley 1. After looking first right and then left several times, he
turned to the left and proceeded till he reached the end of 1_f. There
he paused and looked right and left and also extended his head upward as though trying to see over the sides of the maze. He turned
completely around, retraced through 1_f and proceeded through 1_t to
the choice point in alley 2. Here hesitation and visual exploration
were repeated. He went through 2_t to alley 3, hesitated and explored,

entered 3_f. Hesitation and exploration repeated. He turned around and retraced through 3_f and 2_t and entered 2_f. It is needless to describe further the animal's behavior, other than to point out that always in the early trials he hesitated for periods varying from a few seconds to a minute or more before turning to the right or left in a newly gained alley. The choice made, he moved directly and rather rapidly forward until he reached the next choice point. Once through the maze he climbed directly into the feeding pan and began searching about under water for the food.

Records for the various trials are given below. Alleys 1_f, 2_f and so on represent culs-de-sac, as will be seen in the diagram of the maze. The time the turtle spent in the starting box prior to beginning to run the maze is shown at the beginning of each record. The time spent after he began to leave the starting box and up to the time of his entering the food box is shown after the record of each trial.

1. April 5, 1930. Starting box 6 minutes. 1_f, 1_t, 2_t, 3_f, 2_t, 2_f, 2_t, 3_t, 4_t, 5_f, 5_t, F. Errors 4. Time (after leaving starting box) 15 minutes.

2. April 19, 1930. Starting box 10 minutes. 1_t, 2_f, 2_t, 3_f, 3_t, 4_t, 5_f, 5_t, F. Errors 3. Time 9 minutes.

3. April 29, 1930. Starting box 11 minutes. 1_t, 2_f, 2_t, 3_t, 4_t, 5_f, 5_t, F. Errors 2. Time 10 minutes.

4. May 6, 1930. Starting box 5 minutes. 1_t, 2_t, 3_f, 3_t, 4_t, 5_f, 5_t, F. Errors 2. Time 9 minutes.

5. May 8, 1930. Starting box 6 minutes. 1_t, 2_t, 3_t, 4_t, 5_t, F. Errors 0. Time 6 minutes.

6. May 10, 1930. Starting box 7 minutes. 1_t, 2_t, 3_t, 4_t, 5_t, F. Errors 0. Time $5\frac{1}{2}$ minutes.

7. May 12, 1930. Starting box 9 minutes. 1_t, 2_t, 3_t, 4_t, 5_t, F. Errors 0. Time $5\frac{1}{2}$ minutes.

The turtle appeared to depend largely upon visual exploration in his initial choices of the path to be followed, as shown by his prolonged looking about before entering a new alley. This is in keeping with the conclusions Yerkes[3] drew from a study of the readiness with which land-dwelling, water-dwelling and amphibious tortoises would crawl off the edge of a board 30 cm. above a black cloth net. "Visual impressions" he writes, "are of prime importance in the space perceptions of tortoises, and tactual, muscular and organic data occupy a position of secondary importance" (p. 25).

[3] Yerkes, R. M.: Space perception of tortoises. Jour. Comp. Neurol. and Psychol., 1904, ii, 15–26.

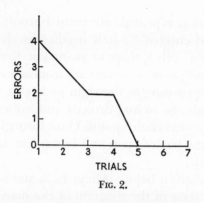

FIG. 2.

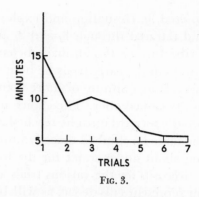

FIG. 3.

The learning, as shown by both errors and time (Figs. 2 and 3), is too consistent to be the result of chance. In my estimation, the learning of the turtle equalled the expected accomplishment of a rat in the same maze under ordinary experimental conditions. This unexpected result, with an animal as sluggish and as stupid as the turtle is reputed to be, I attribute to two factors. In the first place, the rat is usually underfed during maze experiments to insure a constant hunger drive, and the maze running trials are timed largely for the experimenter's convenience. In this brief study, the *turtle determined the spacing of the trials.* He never was starved and he was used only when he was motivated sufficiently to seek food. Secondary, where the hungry rat dashes rapidly ahead, hesitating but an instant, if at all, at choice points in the maze, the turtle paused for from one to several seconds before leaving one alley to enter the next. This deliberateness probably enabled the turtle more nearly to approach his capacity in learning than does the rat in his hurried dashing from alley to alley. On the other hand the physical sluggishness and awkwardness of the turtle may have earned for him an undeserved reputation for stupidity.

DOUBLE ALTERNATION BY RACCOONS

JOHN I. JOHNSON, JR.[1]
Marquette University

Behavioral integration in the temporal dimension has been a critical and elusive problem area (Lashley, 1951). The elusiveness is in good measure due to lack of appropriate investigative techniques. However, one method that has been available for some time is the double-alternation problem, which requires different responses to a stimulus situation which remains the same in all characteristics except for position in time. Since its formulation by Hunter (1920), the procedure has been used to investigate the presumed internal processes which differentially determine responses according to serial position in time.

Various animal forms have been *S*s of such studies, among them rats (Hunter, 1920; Hunter and Nagge, 1931), cats (Karn, 1938; Karn and Patton, 1939), dogs (Karn and Malamud, 1939), normal and brain-injured monkeys (Gellermann, 1931a, 1931c; Leary, Harlow, Settlage, and Greenwood, 1952), and humans (Bruner, Wallach, and Galanter, 1959; Gellermann, 1931b; Hunter, 1928). The earlier studies made use of Hunter's double-alternation temporal maze. Gellermann introduced an alternative procedure, wherein the *S* chose a box to open rather than a pathway to traverse. The basic problem was retained: different responses were required, in sequence, to the same stimulus situation—solution depended upon attending to internal rather than to external concurrent cues.

The ability of raccoons to solve the basic problem was first demonstrated by Hunter (1928) using the temporal maze. However, the vicissitudes of his training procedures and the small number of *S*s have precluded detailed comparison between Hunter's findings and the performances of other species tested.

Stewart and Warren (1957) reported the learning by eight cats of a double-alternation problem presented in the form of object choices

---
[1] Thanks are due to H. L. Thorgersen and to K. M. Michels for assistance in running the *S*s and for the use of the Purdue University laboratories for the conduct of this study.

in the Wisconsin General Test Apparatus. The cats had had extensive previous experience in the WGTA situation. A group of raccoons with similar experience was available, and the experiment herein reported was designed to take advantage of the opportunity for interspecies comparison. The apparatus and procedure therefore were replications of those of Stewart and Warren insofar as was possible. The only deviations from their procedure (which were necessitated by the limited time available for the study) were those noted parenthetically in the report which follows.

METHOD

Subjects and Apparatus

The Ss were seven experimentally sophisticated raccoons *Procyon lotor*. They had spent the year immediately previous serving almost continuously as Ss in studies of visual discrimination (Johnson and Michels, 1958a, 1958b), manipulatory motivation (Thackray and Michels, 1958), and tactile discrimination (Thorgersen, 1958).

A Wisconsin General Test Apparatus, described by Johnson and Michels (1958b), was used for all testing.

Procedure

In the first part of the experiment, all animals were tested on sequences of four responses. A sequence of responses was begun with the opaque screen closed, separating the caged S from the stimulus and reward materials. A peanut was placed in that one of two food wells which was designated as correct. Both food wells were then covered by the two stimulus objects, identical black wooden rectangles, $3\frac{1}{2}$ by $2\frac{1}{4}$ by $\frac{3}{4}$ in. The opaque screen was raised, and the tray bearing stimulus objects and concealed peanuts was advanced to the edge of S's cage. The S was allowed to displace only one object and to secure the reward if its choice were correct; then the opaque screen was lowered. Materials were then arranged for the next response. Time between responses was about 5 sec., and 30 sec. elapsed between the completion of one sequence and the initiation of the next. The position of reward within a sequence was always RRLL for four Ss, and LLRR for the other three. That is, in an RRLL sequence, on the first two response opportunities the reward was located under the object on the right, and on the remaining two the reward was under the object on the left.

All Ss were presented 15 four-response sequences per day (Stewart and Warren presented but 10 per day), until a criterion of 80% correct responses over 45 four-response sequences had been attained. (Stewart and Warren used as criterion 80% correct over 50 sequences.) The probability of randomly achieving 80% correct of 180 such responses is approximately that of $z = 8.06$, $p < .001$. Upon achieving the criterion, each S was immediately tested in the second part of the experiment. (Stewart and Warren continued testing after the criterion was reached, until 300 four-response sequences were completed by all Ss. This was done in order to equalize experience, so that all Ss would embark upon the second part of the experiment with a comparable degree of relevant past experience. They used, as the measure of relevant experience, the number of response opportunities. It can be argued, however, that a more appropriate measure of effectively relevant experience is the amount learned, as indicated by the achieving of the criterion, rather than the number of opportunities presented.)

In the second part of the experiment, the individual response procedure was the same but the sequence was extended from four to eight responses, e.g., RRLL-RRLL. Twelve eight-response sequences were performed per day for 8 days. (Stewart and Warren used six sequences per day for 15 days.)

Upon completion of a testing session, each S was fed its normal daily ration of rat diet. Thus, each testing was preceded by about 22 hr. without food.

RESULTS

In the first part of the experiment, with the four-response sequences, the seven raccoons attained the criterion within 90, 90, 105, 120, 150, 180, and 270 sequences, respectively. Figure 1 presents the

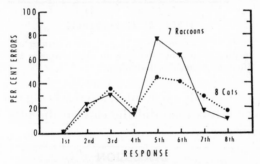

Fig. 1. Performance of cats and raccoons learning four-response sequences of double alternation.

performances of the raccoons as compared with those of cats reported by Stewart and Warren. One raccoon was consistently and markedly less successful than the rest. Two cats had similarly lagged in performance behind the other six. Their scores were reported separately by Stewart and Warren, and for consistent comparison the raccoon performances are depicted separately in like manner.

Another measure of proficiency is the percentage of sequences without error. The seven raccoons collectively achieved 5.2%, 9.0%, 30.0%, and 42.3% four-response sequences without error, respectively, on the first four blocks of 30 sequences. The corresponding achievements by the six proficient cats were approximately 5%, 7%, 11%, and 20% errorless four-response sequences.

Neither cats nor raccoons successfully mastered the eight-response sequence. Nor did either species show evidence of improvement as practice progressed. While there were some scattered errorless sequences, these never exceeded 10% of all sequences for any single raccoon. One cat was reported to have achieved 30% errorless sequences. The pattern of errors within eight-response sequences is represented in Figure 2 for cats and raccoons. The patterns are re-

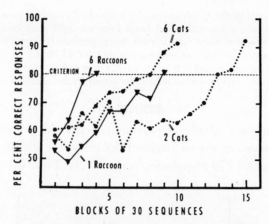

FIG. 2. Errors made by cats and raccoons according to response position in eight-response sequences of double alternation.

markably similar, the only apparent difference being that the raccoons made even more errors than did the cats on the fifth and sixth responses of a sequence.

DISCUSSION

The dogs of Karn and Malamud (1939) produced the same eight-response pattern (e.g., RRLLLLLL) as that of cats and raccoons described in Figure 2. Evidently all these animals learned, in the four-response sequence, to change to a different response on the third opportunity in a sequence. This is sufficient to obtain maximal reward in a four-response double-alternation sequence. Here the *S*s task can be considered as finding the location in the series at which the response should change, rather than abstracting a "double-alternation principle" which can be "extended" (Hunter, 1928; Stewart and Warren, 1957). And the location-finding task is simpler than the abstraction task: Hunter's anthropomorphizing "two, two" is a more difficult attainment than "change on the third." It requires a longer series, where there must be additional response changes on the fifth opportunity, and on the seventh, and so on, for the abstraction of a principle of sequential pairs to be the simpler, more economical, memorization process. While it seems evident that these dogs, cats, and raccoons did not learn a "double-alternation principle," they did accomplish a degree of abstraction in counting their responses in some fashion.

Judgments that a given species is unable to "extend the principle" (Hunter, 1928; Karn, 1938; Karn and Malamud, 1939) should await data obtained by gradually lengthening the response series, rather than immediately doubling it. That such extension more naturally follows an arithmetic than a geometric progression was implicitly acknowledged in the claim that rats, in a spatial maze, showed evidence of "extending" by running RRLLR (Hunter and Hall, 1941). Gellermann (1931c) recognized the importance of the length of the training series, and of a graded extension program. His monkeys were trained on eight-response sequences, which they successfully extended to 10-, then 12-, 14-, and finally 16-response sequences.

The relative abilities of species to learn responses according to paired temporal sequence is for the most part undetermined as yet. Gellermann's monkeys demonstrated an ability to abstract, in the human fashion, the sequence-pairs idea. But Leary et al. (1951) could not obtain successful performance on eight-response sequences from their intact monkeys. The temporal-maze performance of dogs (Karn and Malamud, 1939) and cats (Karn, 1938) was equivalent to that of the cats of Stewart and Warren. The comparison of the present experiment shows raccoon performance on the four-response sequence generally superior to that obtained from cats, although there is overlap. A superiority of the cats on the eight-response sequences could conceivably result from their opportunities to overlearn the four-response sequence during practice after achieving criterion, or to the greater distribution of practice they enjoyed.

While Gellerman obtained superior monkey performance after substituting object choice for the temporal maze, this change in methodology did not help cats (Stewart and Warren, 1957). Compared with Hunter's adventures in obtaining the first double-alternation by raccoons, the experience of the current experiment suggests that, compared with the temporal maze, the object choice method has several advantages for *E,* if not for *S.*

SUMMARY

To measure the performances of raccoons on the double-alternation problem and to compare them with those of cats, seven raccoons were tested by following the procedures used by Stewart and Warren with cats. The raccoons were required to displace one of two identical objects in order to secure a food reward. Responses were arranged in sequences of four, with rewards available in RRLL or LLRR sequence. All raccoons achieved the criterion, 80% correct responses in a group of 45 successive sequences, within 270 sequences. The raccoon performances on this problem were generally superior to those reported for cats. However, the raccoons failed to learn a sequence of eight responses, e.g., RRLLRRLL. The pattern of errors on this problem was remarkably similar to that of cats.

REFERENCES

BRUNER, J. S., WALLACH, M. A., and GALANTER, E. H. The identification of recurrent regularity. *Amer. J. Psychol.*, 1959, 72, 200–209.

GELLERMANN, L. W. The double-alternation problem: I. The behavior of monkeys in a double alternation temporal maze. *J. genet. Psychol.*, 1931, 39, 50–72. (a)

GELLERMANN, L. W. The double-alternation problem: II. The behavior of children and human adults in a double-alternation temporal maze. *J. genet. Psychol.*, 1931, 39, 197–226. (b)

GELLERMANN, L. W. The double-alternation problem: III. The behavior of monkeys in a double-alternation box-apparatus. *J. genet, Psychol.*, 1931, 39, 359–92. (c)

HUNTER, W. S. The temporal maze and kinaesthetic sensory processes in the white rat. *Psychobiology*, 1920, 2, 1–17.

HUNTER, W. S. The behavior of raccoons in a double-alternation temporal maze. *J. genet. Phychol.*, 1928, 35, 374–88.

HUNTER, W. S., and HALL, B. E. Double-alternation behavior of the white rat in a spatial maze. *J. comp. Psychol.*, 1941, 32, 253–66.

HUNTER, W. S., and NAGGE, J. W. The white rat and the double-alternation temporal maze. *J. genet. Psychol.*, 1931, 39, 303–19.

JOHNSON, J. I., and MICHELS, K. M. Discrimination of small intervals and objects by raccoons. *Anim. Behav.*, 1958, 7, 164–70. (a)

JOHNSON, J. I., and MICHELS, K. M. Learning set and objective-size effects in visual discrimination learning by raccoons. *J. comp. physiol. Psychol.*, 1958, 51, 376–79. (b)

KARN, H. W. The behavior of cats on the double-alternation problem in the temporal maze. *J. comp. Psychol.*, 1938, 26, 201–8.

KARN, H. W., and MALAMUD, H. R. The behavior of dogs on the double-alternation problem in the temporal maze. *J. comp. Psychol.*, 1939, 27, 461–66.

KARN, H. W., and PATTON, R. A. The transfer of double-alternation behavior acquired in a temporal maze. *J. comp. Psychol.*, 1939, 28, 55–61.

LASHLEY, K. S. The problem of serial order in behavior. In L. A. Jeffress (Ed.), *Cerebral mechanism in behavior. The Hixon symposium.* New York: Wiley, 1951.

LEARY, R. W., HARLOW, H. F., SETTLAGE, P. H., and GREENWOOD, D. D. Performance on double-alternation problems by normal and brain-injured monkeys. *J. comp. physiol. Psychol.*, 1952, 45, 576–84.

STEWART, C. N., and WARREN, J. M. The behavior of cats on the double-alternation problem. *J. comp. physiol. Psychol.*, 1957, 50, 26–28.

THACKRAY, R. I., and MICHELS, K. M. Externally-aroused drives in the raccoon. *Anim. Behav.*, 1958, 6, 160–163.

THORGERSEN, H. L. Studies of tactual discrimination by raccoons. Unpublished doctoral dissertation, Purdue University, 1958.

THE QUESTION OF INSIGHT AND DELAYED REACTION IN FISH

NORMAN L. MUNN
Bowdoin College

The European minnow (*Phoxinus laevis*) has discriminated tones (8) and various visual patterns (2), and it has learned such skills as jumping from the water to snatch meat (9) and entering the mouth of a bottle to obtain food (10). In addition, this minnow has learned various problems calling for response to equivalent stimuli (11). These accomplishments are within the range of those often found in lower vertebrates, and they of course provide no sound basis for attributing higher processes to fish.

Because *Phoxinus* had done so well in learning experiments, the late Paul Schiller decided to test its ability in detour (5) and delayed-reaction (7) situations. As a result of his findings he credited these fish with insight and symbolic memory. This outcome could hardly have been predicted, for such processes had not previously been evident below the mammalian level. Moreover, the brain of this minnow (1), in common with that of other fishes, seemed too simple to mediate symbolic processes. As a matter of fact, however, Schiller's findings are vitiated by his failure to observe certain controls usually considered necessary in the study of higher processes. Possible guidance from olfactory cues was not sufficiently controlled, and, in the delayed reaction studies, the correctly responding animal was also performing a right-left alternation. It was to check on such apparent shortcomings of this research, and possibly to extend it in certain directions, that the experiments reported here were undertaken.

EXPERIMENT 1

This experiment is a repetition and extension of Schiller's (6) research on detour behavior in the minnow, *P. laevis*.

METHOD

Subjects

The Ss were five minnows of a group imported from Germany and kept in a 15-gal. filtered and aerated aquarium. They ranged in over-all length from about 1½ to 2½ in.

Apparatus

The apparatus was a U-shaped device having a 4- by 6-in. glass front and 4- by 6-in. metal sides. The detour and the water in it had a depth of 6 in. A white mother-of-pearl disc ¾ in. across indicated the position of the lure. It was placed at the end of a piece of copper wire which hung over the edge of the glass so that the disc was about 2 in. above the floor of the aquarium.

Procedure

About four weeks before training began the fish were isolated in small aerated aquaria filled to a depth of 6 in. with spring water. The water temperature was held below 70° C., and it seldom fell below 60° C. This upper limit was on advice of the importer. During a training session, the aerating equipment was removed and the pumps turned off. The Ss were maintained on a diet of chopped snails and commercially available dried daphnia, shrimp, and liver meal.

Pretraining. Several times daily the white disc, with a piece of shaved-off white snail meat on its hook, was lowered into the aquarium. This procedure continued until the fish dashed at the hook as soon as it was lowered. During this procedure the Ss received no food except snail meat taken from the hook.

Training. The detour apparatus was placed on the bottom of the aquarium about 5 min. before the daily session began. Then, as the fish came into an appropriate position (appropriateness depending upon the particular detour involved), the lure was suspended on the side of the glass away from the animal. As soon as S struck at the lure through the glass, a stop watch was started. Time was taken until the fish, having detoured, reached the food. In later trials some fish did not always make contact with the glass, but darted toward it, then turned to detour. In this event, time was taken from the beginning of the turn.

Although Schiller changed the location of his detour apparatus from time to time with respect to the position of the fish, four Ss of the present experiment were trained with a fixed position. For one fish, however, the position varied from trial to trail throughout training.

RESULTS

All Ss learned to detour; thus, the results are in general agreement with those reported by Schiller (6) and do not require detailed consideration.

The performance of one fish given two daily trials with a fixed position of the apparatus is somewhat typical. The number of seconds required for consecutive detours was as follows: 274, 135, 16, 26, 16, 31, 7, 22, 13, 14, 15, 15, 22, 15, 15, 11, 22, 15, 10, 8, 10, and 14. Most of the elapsed time of the early trials was spent attempting, as it were, to get through the glass. In the course of its back-and-forth movements along the glass during the first trial the fish eventually contacted the metal wall and moved along it. Then, finding itself outside of the enclosure, it proceeded along this side, although not always in contact, until confronted by the bait. On the next trial, the time was halved. This resulted mostly from decreased persistence in direct response to the inaccessible lure. There was also less contact with the side of the apparatus. On its third trial, the fish went for the lure as before, but quickly turned and circumvented the barrier without contact with the wall. In subsequent trials the time showed only slight variation. It is interesting to note that this *S* always took a detour to the left. In order to test for possible guidance from food odors, a perfectly new disc and wire were used without bait, although, when the fish reached this, the usual lure was substituted. This control had no apparent effect on *S*'s response. Similar results were obtained with three other *S*s, although two of these exhibited more variability from trial to trial than the one already mentioned. One preferred the right, but sometimes went left. In later trials with another fish the apparatus was placed so that, instead of going out of the U to obtain food, *S* had to enter it. This reversal led to a marked initial increase in time. Within a few trials, however, there was a return to the former level of response.

In an experiment which more closely approximated Schiller's procedure, an *S* without previous training was confronted with a detour which changed from trial to trial, sometimes requiring exit from, and sometimes entrance into, the U in order to obtain the lure. Here, as one might expect, time scores were much more variable than in the experiments already cited. The initial trial required 192 sec. In the next trial, with the direction of the detour reversed, the time was 943 sec. After this, however, there was a marked, although fluctuating, decrease in time. A level was finally reached where, regardless of the altered detours from trial to trial, less than 20 sec. elapsed between placement of the lure and attainment of the goal.

DISCUSSION

Although the *S*s adapted rapidly to detour problems, their behavior failed to suggest the presence of insight. The direct approach was not entirely given up, even after many trials. As Schiller found in his later study (6), which referred to the earlier *Phoxinus* experiments and included new ones on *Gambusia,* "most of the solution time was consumed by circling in front of the visible goal" What the fish learned, apparently, was to spend less time in a direct approach to the lure. With rare exceptions, the initial direction of the detour (right or left around the wall) was maintained. Moreover, if the time taken in a direct approach is discounted, there is little if any reduction, from trial to trial, in the time of the detour *per se.*

EXPERIMENT 2

This is a repetition of a delayed-reaction experiment reported by Schiller (7). Although two delayed-reaction experiments were described, only one seemed worthy of repetition. The other has been criticized elsewhere (4, p. 120) on the ground that it involved no control of possible odor cues from the nearby food and hence provides poor evidence of delayed reaction.

METHOD

Subjects

The Ss were nine minnows from the same source and of the same range as those of Experiment 1. They were selected from a larger group on the basis of their avidity in snatching at the lure during pretraining tests.

Apparatus

A ground plan of the apparatus, a replica of that used by Schiller, is shown in Figure 1. The solid lines represent galvanized iron. Movable doors made of glass

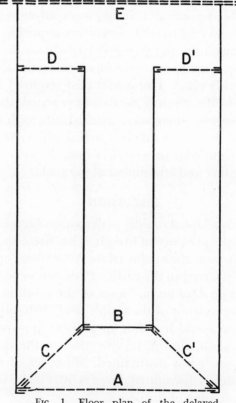

Fig. 1. Floor plan of the delayed-reaction apparatus.

are represented by broken lines. A large glass door (*A*) admitted *S* and confined it to the apparatus. Entrance into the central alley was blocked by another door (*B*). Two glass doors (*C*, *C*¹) completed the entrance chamber, and it was behind one of these that the lure was suspended. When the central door (*B*) was raised, *S* could swim toward the other end of the apparatus, which rested against the glass wall of the aquarium (*E*). The end doors (*D*, *D*¹) could be removed to provide access to the lure. If this was at *C*, for example, *D* was open and *D*¹ was closed. Overall dimensions were: width 6 in., length 12 in., depth 6 in. The central alley was 8 in. long. However, a modification of this apparatus used with some *S*s involved a central alley of only 4 in. Each alley had a width of approximately 2 in. Side windows (*C*, *C*¹) were approximately 2½ in. wide. The lure was as described for Experiment 1. The copper wire which held it was hung over the glass at *C* or *C*¹ so that the disc was about 2 in. from the floor of the apparatus.

The experiment was conducted in a small room with one window and a 300-w. overhead light. In some instances additional light came from a 150-w. bulb placed directly above the aquarium at a height of 42 in. The apparatus itself rested upon the sandy bottom of the aquarium. As in Experiment 1, the water temperature was kept below 70° and seldom fell below 60°C.

Procedure

The *S*s were isolated in small aquaria as described for Experiment 1. Conditioning to the lure was also as described there.

Pretraining. The apparatus was placed in the aquarium with all its doors removed. After *S* had become accustomed to this and had been swimming freely through the alleys, the lure was introduced at about the position it would occupy in the later tests. But, since the glass partitions (*C*, *C*¹) were removed, *S* could reach the bait without obstruction. During this pretraining, the position of the lure was alternated from right to left in accordance with a chance series. After a ready response to the lure in this free situation had been established, the delayed-reaction tests were introduced.

Training. The apparatus was placed on the floor of the aquarium, and about 5 min. before the trials began the appropriate doors were inserted. Door *A* was raised and, as *S* entered, it was closed again. The *S* now found itself confined to the entrance chamber. To some fish, this appeared disturbing, but all were adapted to it within a few days. The lure was suspended behind *C* or *C*¹ and door *D* or *D*¹ was removed. As *S* made a direct response to the lure (usually by darting at it), door *B* was removed. The *S* could now make a detour and reach the bait. At first the response was similar to that described in Experiment 1, with much time spent in a direct approach to the lure. Eventually, however, *S* swam up the central alley. Sometimes it returned to the entrance and again approached the bait. The trial terminated when the lure had been reached and the food eaten. At the end of the central alley *S* could go right or left. It was credited with a correct response only if its initial turn, upon reaching the end of the central alley, was in the direction of the lure. In this case it could swim without interruption to the latter. If the opposite turn was taken, the glass door blocked entrance to the chamber on that side, and *S* had to reverse its direction in order to reach the lure. This it was allowed to do, even though it was credited with an error on that trial. After reaching the lure, *S* was free to move around in the apparatus until it returned to the entrance chamber. If it did not do this of its own accord, it was gently guided there.

The right-left placement of the lure varied with different *S*s. In Schiller's experiment, its placement in the right or left window depended upon the response of the fish in the preceding trial. When *S* responded correctly, and only then, the lure was shifted to the other side. Thus a series of correct responses involved a right-left alternation. This was a major criticism of his procedure, for S may have been learning an alternation rather than remembering on which side the lure had been seen. Therefore, our initial procedure, carried out with three Ss, was designed to avoid solution on the basis of a right-left alternation. The lure was placed in the right or left window in accordance with a chance sequence and thus quite independently of how S had reacted in the preceding trial. However, the results obtained under these conditions suggested that it might be well to train other Ss with Schiller's alternation procedure and later, as a control, introduce a chance sequence of placements. Six Ss were thus trained in accordance with the latter procedure.

Except in the initial sessions, where few trials could be given because of the persistence of S in attempting to approach the lure directly, the usual procedure was to give 5 trials in the early forenoon and 5 more in the afternoon. Since only a minute piece of meat was received at each trial, motivation was kept at a high level for 10 trials per day. Schiller gave his fish 12 daily trials, although in three sessions of 4 trials each.

RESULTS

Three Ss trained with the longer apparatus and with a chance positioning of the lure made no progress toward solution. Although they were given, respectively, 170, 210, and 110 trials, their accuracy did not go above 7 correct responses out of 10, and even this level was not maintained. At about 100 trials, moreover, the fish began to show a great deal of so-called VTE (3) at the choice point. This was followed by position habits. The experiment was terminated because one fish could not be induced to leave the starting point except with prodding and because the others were taking an inordinately long time to respond.

At this point it seemed wise to follow Schiller's procedure more closely, as described above. It was hoped that the fish would learn to respond with a high degree of accuracy as Schiller's had done and that the influence of simple alternation could then be checked by introducing a chance positioning of the lure.

Three new Ss were presented with this problem, again using an apparatus of the same dimensions as Schiller's. They were given, respectively, 620, 270, and 280 trials under these conditions.

The first S started with an accuracy of 8 out of 10. Its accuracy ranged from 3 to 6 out of 10 for 120 trials, then went to 9 out of 10, followed by 7, 7, 8, 5, 7, 8, 6, 8, 5, 6, 8, 6, 4, 8, 7, 4, 6, and similar accuracies until, after 410 trials two successive accuracies of respectively, 8 and 9 out of 10 were achieved. It seemed that the time was near when a random placement of the lure might be introduced. However, accuracy soon deteriorated. It did not again reach 8 out of 10 until 580 trials had been given. This was followed by position habits and low scores. The fish was given further training on the shorter apparatus used in experiments to be described later, but position habits persisted. Coincident with the achievement of relatively high scores, beginning at around 150 trials, S not only showed VTE, but also erratic behavior not described in Schiller's studies. If often dashed in one direction or the other, even so violently that it hit its head against the aquarium. In addition, quick, jerky movements were at times evident. There was also, in the entrance to the central path, a picking at stray pieces of sand in a manner resembling "displacement activity" as described by ethologists. Quite frequently S swam to the choice point, then backed up until once more at the start. These reactions suggest not only that the task was a particularly difficult one, but also that conflict was present.

Similar results were obtained in the second of these fish. After accuracies ranging from 3 to 6 out of 10, this S, beginning with trial 90, achieved successive accuracies of 9 and 8, then 5, 5, 8, 5, 5, 5, 5, 8. Subsequently, however, it developed position habits, and its accuracy did not again go above 6 out of 10. It was given further training on the shorter apparatus for a total of 320 trials, but the highest accuracy achieved was 7, and this not consistent, and VTE and erratic behavior like that already described was displayed. At times S failed to take the food, although outside the apparatus it snatched at this as avidly as ever.

The third fish reacted much as the others had done. After 110 trials it achieved accuracies of 8, 7, 9, and 8 in succession, then became erratic and exhibited position habits. This S achieved one more 9 and one more 8, separated by poor performances. However, a consistently high level of accuracy was not attained. In the shorter apparatus, on which this fish was given 160 trials after 280 on the apparatus of Schiller's dimensions, there was no improvement.

These Ss had at times seemed on the verge of solution. It appeared, therefore, that new fish trained from the beginning with a shorter delay might solve the problem. Accordingly, three new Ss were trained with a central alley reduced from 8 in. to 4 in. Again, Schiller's alternation procedure was used. The fish were each given from 400 to 420 trials on this apparatus, but their performance was no better than that already described. In each S, some accuracies as high as 8 and 9 out of 10 occurred, but there was never a consistently high accuracy. All three Ss at times showed VTE, assumed position habits, and exhibited erratic behavior as the others had done.

It should be pointed out that all fish in this investigation, as in Schiller's, swam along the middle of the central alley, making no contact with the side walls; nor did they show any consistent tendency to move diagonally toward the correct side after leaving the entrance. The problem would doubtless have been simpler had they adopted one of these procedures.

DISCUSSION

The discrepancy between the present results and Schiller's is without apparent explanation. Of the six fish used by him, only four learned the problem, but these were responding with fairly consistent accuracy within from 168 to 300 trials. They were, of course, doing a right-left alternation, as mentioned earlier, but six of the above fish were also given the opportunity to respond in this fashion and failed to do so with consistent accuracy. It was therefore not possible to check the role of alternation per se. Of possible significance in this connection, however, is the fact that three fish presented with a chance positioning of the bait did more poorly than those allowed to alternate.

Presumably, although Schiller did not say so, his fish were credited with a correct response, as in these experiments, only when they made the correct turn initially. Correspondence with Mrs. Schiller leads to this presumption, although she is not certain about the criterion of correct response. This point is important because a fish will frequently turn in the wrong direction, then reverse before contacting the obstruction in the incorrect alley. This should not be regarded as a correct response because, as soon as its head gets around the side wall, the fish may see whether or not the bait is down that alley. Indeed, there is a remarkable change at this point, depending upon whether or not the lure is on that side. If it is there, S makes a precipitate dash toward it. If it is not, the fish usually turns and swims to the other alley.

In seeking other possible explanations for the discrepancy between these results and Schiller's, it occurred to E that he might have held the wire containing the lure, thus providing movement cues in the water, or possibly a shadow from his hand (these fish have a marked preference for shadows). However, it has been learned from Mrs. Schiller that her husband hung the bait over the window as E did, thus avoiding movement in the water and also the possibility of response to a shadow made by his hand.

Schiller did not mention VTE, erratic behavior, and persistent position habits such as the Ss of this experiment exhibited. Indeed, his description makes the problem appear relatively simple. Hence, although E is unable to cite them, he suspects the presence of extraneous cues in Schiller's experiment.

SUMMARY

Five minnows of the species *Phoxinus laevis* readily learned to circumvent U-shaped detours. Controls showed that the response was not influenced by possible diffusion of olfactory cues. These results support Schiller's findings on detour behavior, and also his conclusion that improvement comes from a reduced tendency to make a direct approach. There were no sudden solutions which might be taken as evidence of insightful learning.

Nine minnows were used in an attempt to verify and extend Schiller's findings on delayed reaction. Since this investigator shifted the lure to the other side after the fish made a correct detour, successful performance might involve memory of the position of the lure or it might be a right-left alternation. To check on the latter possibility, three fish were trained with a chance placement of the lure. They made no progress toward solution. Three new fish were then trained with Schiller's alternation procedure in the hope that, after the problem had been learned, the sequence of placements could be changed to determine whether or not the fish were merely alternating. These fish reached a high level of accuracy at times, but performance was so inconsistent that the desired control could not be used. Erratic behavior, VTE at the choice point, and persistent position habits all suggested that the problem was exceedingly difficult. In subsequent training, so that the task might be made easier by utilizing a shorter delay, the over-all length of the apparatus was halved. Performance did not improve under this condition, either in the three Ss just mentioned or in three trained with the shorter delay from the start. The performance of the latter was no better than that of fish trained with the longer delay; VTE, position habits, and erratic behavior were again observed.

The discrepancy between Schiller's results on delayed reaction and those reported here has not been explained. One suspects that his fish may have been aided by extraneous cues. If there were such cues, their nature is not evident. The existence of a discrepancy, however, suggests the need to reserve judgment concerning delayed reaction in fish.

REFERENCES

1. Frisch, K.v., and Stetter, H. Untersuchungen über den Sitz des Gehörsinnes bei der Elritze. *Z. vergl. Physiol.,* 1932, **17**, 686–801.
2. Meesters, A. Über die Organization des Gesichtsfeldes der Fische. *Z. Tierpsychol.,* 1940, 4, 84–149.
3. Muenzinger, K. F. Vicarious trial and error at a point of choice. I. A general

survey of its relation to learning efficiency. *J. genet. Psychol.*, 1938, **53**, 75–86.
4. MUNN, N. L. *The evolution and growth of human behavior.* Boston: Houghton Mifflin, 1955.
5. SCHILLER, P. V. Umwegversuchen an Elritzen. *Z. Tieřpsychol.*, 1942–1943, **5**, 101–30.
6. SCHILLER, P. H. Analysis of detour behavior. I. Roundabout pathways in fish. *J. comp. physiol. Psychol.*, 1949, **42**, 463–75.
7. SCHILLER, P. H. Delayed response in the minnow. *J. comp. physiol. Psychol.*, 1948, **41**, 233–38.
8. STETTER, H. Untersuchungen über den Gehörsinn der Fische, besonders von *Phoxinus laevis* L. und *Ameiurus nebulosus* Raf. *Z. vergl. Physiol.*, 1929, **9**, 339–477.
9. ZUNINI, G. Osservazioni sul salto delle sanguinerole (*Phoxinus laevis* Agas). *Arch. Sci. biol., Napoli,* 1936, **22**, 407–36.
10. ZUNINI, G. Esperimenti del giro con sanguinerole. *Contrib. psicol. sperimental. Univ. Cattol. Sacro cuore.* 1938, No. 16.
11. ZUNINI, G. Researches on fish's learning. *Arch. néerl Zool.*, 1953, Suppl. 2, **10**, 127–39. A summary in English of studies carried out by Zunini between the years 1937–1941.

LEARNING SETS IN MARMOSETS[1]

RAYMOND C. MILES[2] and DONALD R. MEYER
Ohio State University

The common marmoset, genus *Callithrix,* has perhaps more features to command the attention of the student of animal behavior than any other relative stranger to the laboratory. Although it is scarcely larger than a full-grown albino rat, this diminutive primate has a brain that is as large in proportion to its body size as any in the animal kingdom. Unlike its close relatives, however, the marmoset has claw-like nails, and in a manner more typical of lower mammals than of primates, gives birth to either twins or triplets. The possibilities that this species affords to studies of brain organization and of developmental factors are thus both striking and obvious.

From a comparative standpoint, the marmoset is in a phylogenetic position of more than passing interest. Standing as it does at the transition between major subdivisions of its order (1, 7), this most primitive of monkeys affords a reference point at which tests of behavioral capacity have unusual significance. This experiment has been designed to perform one such evaluation, to study the ability of marmosets to form discrimination learning sets.

Learning sets develop, as Harlow (3) first established through extensive studies with macaques, if the Ss are trained on successive discriminations between objects that differ in several stimulus dimensions. One can trace an orderly transition, by this method, from performances in which little evidence of learning is manifest after six trials, to those in which solutions are obtained by the animals within a single trial (9).

Harlow (5) has proposed that an evaluation of such phenomena will undoubtedly reveal systematic differences between groups of animals that all learn simple habits readily. The data for a test of this hypothesis are largely nonexistent at present, but several years ago the

[1] Supported by funds allocated by the University Advisory Committee on Research Grants.

[2] Now at the University of Wisconsin.

junior author had an opportunity to study learning-set formation in a single raccoon. This animal, which served in lieu of a badger as mascot of the local football team, had excellent use of its paws and a singular fondness for raisins. It was tested in the same apparatus that had been used in the initial work by Harlow, but extensive presentations of discrimination problems revealed very little indication of a trend toward interproblem improvement. Since raccoons have been traditionally held in relatively high esteem by comparative psychologists, the *E* concluded that this capacity is at best rudimentary in infraprimate mammals. Thus, the evidence is clearly in keeping with the contention that tests of interproblem transfer provide the most discriminative complex indices that we have for assessing behavioral evolution.

That such tests will separate, on a quantitative basis, some species within the primate order has been known from the inception of the program. Thus M. K. Harlow (cited in 3), while emphasizing similarities, found that preschool children are clearly superior to monkeys if both are studied under conditions as comparable as it is possible to make them. Whether monkeys differ as much within themselves, or at all, is the question asked by the present experiment. Unless we are willing to disregard completely the comparative anatomy, expectations are that the marmosets will be inferior to *Macaca mulatta*. Efforts have been made, despite our human tendencies to make each new study *new*, to duplicate the conditions under which the learning set phenomenon was first introduced.

METHOD

Subjects

The *Ss* were three adult common marmosets and four adolescent rhesus monkeys. The latter were maintained and tested at the Primate Laboratory, University of Wisconsin, and the data obtained were kindly furnished by Professor Harry Harlow. The marmosets were from a colony established at The Ohio State University. All the macaques and one marmoset had not been tested prior to this experiment; two marmosets had learned three discriminations of differences in hue. These variations were not deemed important, apart from the adaptation standpoint, in view of the relatively large number of problems that one must present to marmosets before any evidence of transfer is forthcoming.

Apparatus

The rhesus monkeys were studied in the form-board situation provided by the Wisconsin General Test Apparatus, which was used as a model for the smaller apparatus employed for the marmosets. The latter was a rectangular box 27 in. long, 13 in. wide, and 13 in. high. It was constructed of plywood, painted a uniform gray, and provided with an overhead light for interior illumination. Half the box served as a restraining cage, and this was separated from a test compartment by vertically arranged iron rods spaced 1 in. apart. An opaque screen, which could be raised or lowered through a cord and pulley arrangement, was installed between the cage and the compartment. The E watched the animals perform through a one-way–vision screen placed across the end of the compartment; this was of glass from the top of the box to a line halfway down and of cheesecloth beyond that level. Within the test compartment was a movable form-board tray, and carved into this tray were two 1-in. circular food wells spaced 8 in. apart. A supply of small, lightweight objects similar to those employed in prior experiments completed the marmoset equipment; there were 1,000 in all, and included were such things as aspirin tins, ladies' heels, and small jars.

Procedure

The general procedure for handling and testing rhesus monkeys have been repeatedly detailed (3, 4, 9), and were duplicated as far as possible in the work with the marmosets. The Ss were never handled by E, but were trained to enter cages for transport between their residence and the apparatus. Prior to the experiment proper, the rhesus monkeys and the naive marmoset were thoroughly adapted to their respective situations and given brief practice in displacing a neutral object that on each presentation covered one or the other food well. To make such responses, the animals reached through the bars of their restraining cages, and were reinforced by a small piece of food which they found in the underlying well. Peanuts or raisins were used in the work with macaques, while the marmosets were treated to small slivers of cooked white-of-egg or apple. Between presentations E lowered the opaque screen, retracted and arranged the tray, raised the screen in front of the monkey, and after a pause of 1 sec. returned the tray to its position in front of the bars. The same procedures were followed in setting up the problems for discrimination learning.

During the conduct of the formal tests, the marmosets were fed for 15 min. a day after each experimental session; their diet consisted of bananas, apples, oranges, and eggs, occasionally supplemented by a vitamin mixture spread on bread. Actually, the bulk of their diet was obtained in the test situation, for the daily series averaged about 120 trials. This extension beyond the session of 42 trials used in the procedure with macaques was deemed essential because of the prolonged training required to demonstrate the transfer phenomenon in the more primitive species.

The rhesus monkeys, which were being utilized as a control for still another study, encountered a series of 392 discrimination problems. In each of these problems, a pair of dissimilar stimulus objects was presented on the test tray for a total of six trials. A food reward was placed under one of these objects, and was obtained by the monkey if its choice was correct. The position of the object reinforced varied from trial to trial in counterbalanced sequences similar to those employed by Harlow (4) in his study of error factors in discrimination learning. Essentially the same conditions prevailed in tests with the marmosets, though it was soon discovered that they were often unable to move even the light objects used in their test. This was countered by assistance from E, who attached threads to the objects and withdrew them whenever they were touched by the monkey.

The rhesus monkeys learned 7 problems per day; the marmosets 14 to 20, depending upon their individual caprice. After 100 problems had been presented, however, all marmosets would work consistently for 20 problems per day. They encountered, in all, a total of 1,000 problems. The first 500 were arranged with novel test objects, and then these objects were rearranged at random for presentation in the last 500 problems.

RESULTS

The obtained data are summarized in Figure 1. The curves indicate per cent correct performances as a function of intraproblem

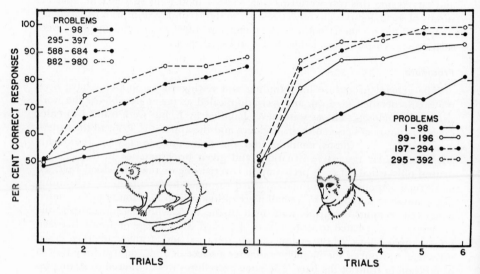

Fig. 1. Intraproblem learning curves based on selected blocks of interproblem experience.

practice. Each point is based upon the scores obtained in a given block of problems, and individual scores are combined. The first impression to be gained from these graphs is the formal similarity between the two sets of functions, one for macaques and the other for marmosets. Both show, for example, that rate of learning-set formation first accelerates and then decelerates. Both sets of curves can be interpreted in terms of a developing discontinuity between trials 1 and 2, though this point is one that must be judged primarily upon the basis of other evidence. Despite the similarities, however, the quantitative disparity between the two groups is enormous. Thus, the performances of marmosets with 500 problems behind them is scarcely better than that obtained from the naive rhesus monkey, and the rhesus macaques with prior experience of 98 problems are ahead of marmosets with 881.

Learning-set formation, in terms of trial 2 performance, is shown in Figure 2. One gains the impression from these graphs that marmosets approach an asymptote which is considerably below that for the rhesus monkeys. It would appear, in fact, that had the experiment

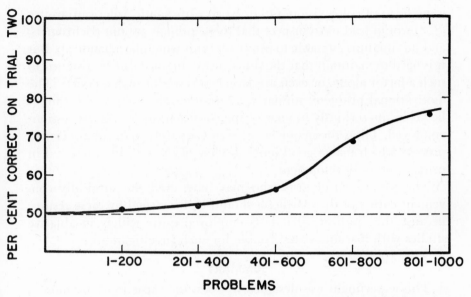

FIG. 2.   Per cent correct responses for successive problem blocks in the marmoset.

continued, a persistent difference of about 20 per cent (which is a significant fraction of the possible range of improvement with this type of problem) would have been obtained.

With regard to statistical reliability, it seems sufficient to say that the dullest macacque was at all times better than the brightest marmoset, and that within-group differences were small compared with the difference between the species.

DISCUSSION

An outcome of this kind is in keeping with our preconceptions. The familial resemblances between our two species are revealed through the formal learning parallels; the differences between them, however, are as gross as those revealed through studies of structure. Harlow's contention, accordingly, has survived a critical test. There is every indication that the method will order different primate species in a series comparable to those that have been drawn by taxonomists. This, of course, has been attempted before, but with little success apart from that encountered in studies with delayed response tasks (6).

With regard to the classical dilemma of sensory-motor comparability, it may be said that unpublished experiments have shown that marmosets are capable of fine discriminations of brightness and have some form of color vision. Other work with South American groups (2, 8) would lead us to suspect that these animals are not trichromats, and it is not unreasonable to imply that this would be a handicap. But it is hard to maintain that the differences obtained can be assigned to such a factor alone, or even are largely a result of such a deficit. The motivational problem, similarly, while undoubtedly present, cannot be taken too seriously in view of the consistent and long test sessions employed. Thus, the major factor seems squarely to be an associative process, which makes good sense in view of the well-known trend in primate brain development.

The psychoneurologists who may have eyed the surgically convenient cortex of the marmoset should be heartened by these results, because they indicate that tests employed quite widely in ablative studies with macaques are suitable for such investigations.

SUMMARY

This experiment was designed to assess the capacity of marmosets, genus *Callithrix,* to form discrimination-learning sets. Three animals were trained according to the customary procedure, and their performances compared with those obtained from four rhesus monkeys. The results showed that macaques and marmosets are qualitatively alike, but that marmosets are grossly inferior on a quantitative basis. This conclusion is in keeping with the view that tests of interproblem transfer provide discriminative indices of phylogenetic status, and that marmoset behavior can be meaningfully assessed in psychoneurological studies with the same procedures that have been developed for higher members of the primate order.

REFERENCES

1. CLARK, W. E. L. *History of the primates.* London: Adlard, 1953.
2. GRETHER, W. F. Color vision and color blindness in monkeys. *Comp. psychol. Monogr.,* 1939, **15**, No. 4, 1–38.
3. HARLOW, H. F. The formation of learning sets. *Psychol. Rev.,* 1949, **56**, 51–65.
4. HARLOW, H. F. Analysis of discrimination learning by monkeys. *J. exp. Psychol.,* 1950, **40**, 26–39.
5. HARLOW, H. F. Primate learning. In C. P. Stone (Ed.), *Comparative psychology.* New York: Prentice-Hall, 1951.
6. HARLOW, H. F., UEHLING, H., and MASLOW, A. H. Comparative behavior of primates: 1. Delayed reaction tests on primates from the lemur to the orangoutan. *J. comp. Psychol.,* 1932, **13**, 313–43.
7. HOOTON, E. *Man's poor relations.* Garden City, New York: Doubleday, 1942.
8. MALMO, R. B., and GRETHER, W. F. Further evidence of red blindness (protanopia) in cebus monkeys. *J. comp. physiol. Psychol.,* 1947, **40**, 143–48.
9. MEYER, D. R. Intraproblem-interproblem relationships in learning by monkeys. *J. comp. physiol. Psychol.,* 1951, **44**, 162–67.

CONCEPT FORMATION IN CHIMPANZEES

by

ROGER T. KELLEHER *

*Yerkes Laboratories of Primate Biology,
Orange Park, Florida*

Abstract. Animals performed with a high degree of accuracy on two concept problems. The bases of these performances, however, differed qualitatively. In one problem, successful performance was based upon responding to specific stimulus patterns. In the other problem, successful performance was based upon responding to the common element or concept.

Learning to respond to a class of stimuli on the basis of some common physical characteristic is referred to as "concept formation." Although concept formation has been demonstrated in animals (*1*), the experimental analysis of this complex behavioral process has received little attention in recent years. This report presents some results obtained with a new technique for the study of concept formation (*2*).

The two subjects were food-deprived chimpanzees. These animals had been trained to press a telephone key for food reward (reinforcement). Above the telephone key there were nine small Plexiglas windows arrayed in a 3-by-3 square. Stimulus patterns were programmed by illuminating some Plexiglas windows while leaving others dark. A sequence of 26 successive stimulus patterns, 13 positive and 13 negative, could be programmed (*3*). The positive stimulus patterns were characterized by a common element which was not present in any of the negative patterns.

During the presentation of positive stimulus patterns, a 100-response variable-ratio schedule of reinforcement was in effect—that is, the number of times that the subject had to press the key for food varied randomly from 1 to 200, with a mean of 100 (*4*). Positive stimulus patterns terminated at reinforcement. During the presentation of negative, could be programmed (*3*). The positive stimulus patterns were not reinforced. Negative stimulus patterns terminated when the animal had not pressed the telephone key for 1 minute. Experimental

---

* Present address: Smith, Kline and French Laboratories, Philadelphia, Pa.

sessions were interrupted for a 30-second "time-out" period after the termination of each stimulus pattern and ended when 50 reinforcements had been delivered (*4*). The experimental procedures were automatically programmed, and the results were automatically recorded.

Two concept problems were investigated. Initially, on each of these problems, the animals were repeatedly exposed to one sequence of stimulus patterns. When the animals' behavior showed no consistent trend, the stimulus patterns were presented in a new sequence, but none of the specific stimulus patterns was changed. After several experimental sessions on the new sequence, 6 positive and 6 negative stimulus patterns were changed. However, the concept was not changed.

Representative positive and negative stimulus patterns from each of four sequences are shown in the upper sections of Figure 1. The

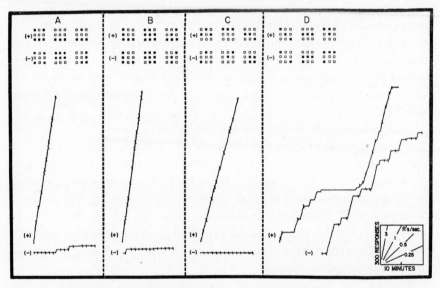

Fig. 1. Representative stimulus patterns and cumulative response curves, showing the effects of changing specific stimulus patterns without changing the concept. Sections *A* and *B* are from the first concept problem; sections *C* and *D* are from the second concept problem.

dark squares correspond to illuminated windows. Cumulative response records from each of the four sequences are shown in the lower sections of Figure 1. Responses during positive and negative stimulus patterns were recorded separately, and they are presented in the upper and lower curves, respectively. The short diagonal strokes on these curves indicate the points at which stimulus presentations terminated. The records did not run during the 30-second intervals between stimulus presentations. Coordinates and representative slopes are presented in the lower right corner of the figure.

The stimulus patterns in the upper section of Figure 1*A* exemplify the first concept problem. The illumination of the bottom row of windows was the concept. The cumulative response records in the lower section of Figure 1*A* show the performance that had developed after about 100 experimental hours on the first sequence of stimulus patterns. The animals responded at high rates during positive stimulus patterns, but they seldom responded during the negative stimulus patterns. When the stimulus patterns were presented in a new sequence, there was no disruption of this performance. When 6 positive and 6 negative stimulus patterns were changed without changing the concept, there was still no disruption of the performance. For example, the stimulus patterns shown in Figure 1*A* were changed to those shown in Figure 1*B*. Cumulative records from the first sequence following the change are shown in the lower section of Figure 1*B*.

The stimulus patterns in the upper section of Figure 1*C* exemplify the second concept problem. The illumination of three windows was the common element in positive stimulus patterns; two or four windows were illuminated in negative stimulus patterns. The cumulative response records in the lower section of Figure 1*C* show the performance that had developed after about 150 experimental hours on this sequence. As in the first concept problem, this performance was not disrupted when the stimulus patterns were presented in a new sequence. However, when 6 positive and 6 negative stimulus patterns were changed without changing the concept, performance was markedly disrupted. The changed stimulus patterns are exemplified in the upper section of Figure 1*D*; cumulative response records from the first sequence following this change are shown in the lower section of Figure 1*D*. There was excessive initial pausing in two of the positive patterns, and high rates of responding prevailed in the negative patterns that had been changed.

The animals developed clear discriminations on both concept problems. Neither discrimination was affected by changing the sequence in which the stimulus patterns were presented. However, the discriminations were differentially affected by changing specific stimulus patterns without changing the concept. Thus, the discriminations were qualitatively different. In the first concept problem, the discrimination was based upon response to the common element. In the second concept problem, the discrimination was based upon response to specific stimulus patterns—that is, the chimpanzees were responding appropriately to at least 12 specific stimulus patterns presented in successive fashion. In further studies, it would be possible to determine the maximum number of specific patterns to which these animals could respond effectively. Until such studies have been completed, investigations of complex discriminations with chimpanzees should be interpreted with caution, until the bases of the discriminations have been assessed.

With the procedure described above, concept formation was a function of the concept problem. The common element of the first concept problem (the bottom row of windows) had a specific spatial location; the common element of the second concept problem (any three windows) did not. This difference in the level of abstractness of the two problems may have been an important factor. With a different procedure, the chimpanzees could probably have been trained to respond to the common element of the second concept problem. If the stimulus patterns were changed after each sequence without changing the concept, for example, the animals would have been unable to maintain a discrimination by responding to specific patterns.

REFERENCES AND NOTES

1. P. E. Fields, *Comp. Psychol. Monograph No. 9* (1932); B. Weinstein, *Genet. Psychol. Monograph No. 31* (1945), p. 3; L. H. Hicks, *J. Comp. and Physiol. Psychol.* **49**, 212 (1956).
2. This investigation was supported in part by research grant M-1005 from the Institute of Mental Health of the National Institutes of Health, U.S. Public Health Service, and in part by the National Science Foundation. The technique presented in this report is similar to one used for studying concept formation in human beings [E. J. Green, *J. Exptl. Psychol.* **49**, 175 (1955)].
3. One negative stimulus pattern in which all windows were dark appeared in all sequences.
4. C. B. Ferster and B. F. Skinner, *Schedules of Reinforcement* (Appleton-Century-Crofts, New York, 1957).

RAPHAEL'S "IDEALESS" BEHAVIOR[1]

GREGORY RAZRAN
Queens College

Raphael, a chimpanzee, was brought to Pavlov's Leningrad (Koltushi, now Pavlovo) laboratory in 1933 at the age of six years. He died in 1942, six months after a month-long evacuation journey in subzero weather (December, 1941) from besieged Leningrad to Kazan. In the course of his eight year stay in the Pavlov laboratory, Raphael was a subject in a great variety of experiments, some just mentioned by Pavlov in the second and third volumes of his *Wednesdays* (1949a, 1949b, seven separate references) and some reported in full detail by Vatsuro (1945, 1947a, 1947b, 1948, 1955), by Shtodin (1947a, 1947b, 1947c), and by Vatsuro and Shtodin (1947). Pavlov, Vatsuro, and Shtodin are in unison in declaring that the results of the Raphael experiments establish firmly that the ape's special intelligence was wholly a function of readier and more labile conditioning and in no way a matter of some special insight or "aha" reactions à la Köhler. Some of Pavlov's remarks on Raphael's behavior are available in English in the last sections of *Selected Works* (Pavlov, 1955) and in the identical *Experimental Psychology and Other Essays* (Pavlov, 1957). However, the almost 100 pages of protocols, tables, and figures in the reports of Vatsuro's and Shtodin's experiments and the 255 pages (163–318) on Raphael in Vatsuro's 1948 book, *The Study of Higher Nervous Activity of Anthropoids* (Chimpanzee), are, as far as the writer is aware, available only in Russian.

The experiment to be presented here was singled out by the writer because it represents a special aspect of current Russian interpretation of anthropoid intelligence, namely, the view that, lacking a second-signal system (i.e., true language or true verbal conditioning), anthropoids are devoid of true ideation. ("A word is by its very nature an abstraction or generalization," said Pavlov, and "words and thoughts

[1] Research done under Grant M–2196 of the National Institute of Mental Health, National Institutes of Health, Public Health Service, United States Department of Health, Education, and Welfare.

reflect the general," said Lenin.) However, there was also a more prosaic reason for the selection of the particular experiment: Raphael's performance is very plain in accompanying Figure 1, a combina-

FIG. 1. Raphael's "idealess" behavior (Vatsuro, 1948). In the laboratory, Raphael was taught to extinguish a flame, which was barring a visible fruit in a fruit magazine, by turning on a faucet in a water jug, obtaining water in a cup, and pouring the water on the flame. At first, the jug was on a platform above the flame, but later it was placed at some distance on a separate stand. Moreover, the cup was kept inside a box which the ape could open only by inserting a stick in a hole in the top of the box. On hot summer days, Raphael was taken to a lake where he stayed on a float 5 m. away from another float, and learned quickly to cool himself by pouring over his body water which he obtained from the surrounding lake by means of a cup. Now, the fruit magazine was brought to the lake and placed on the float on which Raphael was staying, while the water jug was put on the other float. The flame barring the fruit was lit, and a long, joined bamboo pole was made available. As may be seen in the figure, Raphael finally solved the problem of obtaining the fruit in a very laborious and "idealess" way. He threw the pole over to the other float, crossed over on it, obtained the water from the jug, recrossed with the cup of water, and extinguished the flame by pouring the water on it. Because of the lack of a second-signal system, the water-in-the-cup-obtained-from-the-lake-to-cool was not "ideated"—combined or abstracted—with the water-in-the-cup-obtained-from-the-container-to-extinguish. (The flame on top of the right-hand stand of the upper left segment of the figure was drawn in from an adjacent figure in which was also shown an opening through which Raphael could see the fruit.)

tion of four Russian figures, and should be read in the sequence of upper left segment, lower left, upper right, and lower right. The experiment was first reported by Vatsuro in 1948 but was performed during one summer between 1938 and 1941 (exact summer is unfortunately not specified).

REFERENCES

PAVLOV, I. P. *Pavlov's Wednesdays.* Vol. 2. *Stenographic reports of 1933–1934.* Moscow: Akad. Nauk SSSR, 1949. Pp. 166–67, 385–89, 516–517, 574, 582–86.(a)

PAVLOV, I. P. *Pavlov's Wednesdays.* Vol. 3. *Stenographic reports of 1935–1936.* Moscow: Akad. Nauk SSSR, 1949. Pp. 16–21, 120–21.(b)

PAVLOV, I. P. *Selected works.* Moscow: Foreign Languages, 1955.

PAVLOV, I. P. *Experimental psychology and other essays.* New York: Philosophical Library, 1957.

SHTODIN, M. R. Certain forms of behavior of anthropoid apes (chimpanzee) in experimental situations. *Trud. Inst. Evolut. Fiziol. Patol. Vyssh. Nerv. Deyatel. Pavlova,* 1947, **1**, 191–98. (a)

SHTODIN, M. R. The problem of higher nervous activity of anthropoid apes (chimpanzee): I. Formation of complex motor habits. *Trud. Inst. Evolut. Fiziol. Patol. Vyssh. Nervn. Deyatel. Pavlova,* 1947, **1**, 171–81. (b)

SHTODIN, M. R. The problem of higher nervous activity of anthropoid apes (chimpanzee): II. Systematicity of behavior. *Trud. Inst. Evolut. Fiziol. Patol. Vyssh. Nerv. Deyatel. Pavlova,* 1947, **1**, 183–90. (d)

VATSURO, E. G. Comparative lability of processes of higher nervous activity in individual analyzers. *Trud. Fiziol. Lab. Pavlova,* 1945, **12**, 33–57.

VATSURO, E. G. The problem of the mechanisms of the behavior of anthropoids (chimpanzee): Communication I. *Trud. Inst. Evolut. Fiziol. Patol. Vyssh. Nerv. Deyatel. Pavlova,* 1947, **1**, 201–10. (a)

VATSURO, E. G. The problem of the mechanisms of the behavior of anthropoids (chimpanzee): Communication III. *Trud. Inst. Evolut. Fiziol. Patol. Vyssh. Nerv. Deyatel. Pavlova,* 1947, **1**, 225–38.(b)

VATSURO, E. G. *Study of higher nervous activity of anthropoids (chimpanzee).* Moscow: Medgiz, 1948.

VATSURO, E. G. *Pavlov's teachings of higher nervous activity.* (Trans. into German by Volk u. Wissen, Berlin, 1950) Moscow: UchPchGiz, 1955.

VATSURO, E. G., and SHTODIN, M. R. The problem of the mechanisms of the behavior of anthropoids (chimpanzee): Communication II. *Trud. Inst. Evolut. Fiziol. Patol. Vyssh. Nerv. Deyatel. Pavlova,* 1947, **1**, 211–24.

CHAPTER 13

NEURAL TISSUE IN RELATION TO
COMPLEXITY OF LEARNED BEHAVIOR

At the present time the state of knowledge and methods of investigation in physiology are inadequate to illuminate many behavioral problems that interest the psychologist. This is not to say that there has been a dearth of research.in these areas. The contrary is true. For example, a great deal of psycho-physiological research has been done in the area of learning, with the focus on the central nervous system. But this research is characterized by *gross* analysis at both the neural and behavioral level. Probably the most progress toward making a detailed physiological analysis has been in the area of sensory processes, as in the analysis of the visual systems. The reader is referred to Chapter 6, pp. 292–95 for a brief discussion of the names of various parts of the central nervous system.

Relationships between Behavior and Physiology

The present relationship between psychology and physiology is fairly complex and needs to be clarified. In the first place it is important to recognize that the relationship is a two-way street. The study of physiological problems is facilitated at least as much by the use of behavioral data as behavioral problems are illuminated by the use of physiological or morphological data.

Role of Behavior in Study of Physiology. The study of neural mechanisms involved in vision, for example, typically requires an acting organism. A more specific example of the dependence of physiological analysis upon psychological variables is reflected in the statement by Pribram that the delayed alternation method is a more reliable measure of frontal lobe deficit than the delayed response method (Harlow and Woolsey, 1958). Another illustration of the relationship is the temporal lobe syndrome discovered by Kluver and Bucy (1938). This unique behavioral syndrome has been frequently found in primates, including man, after bilateral temporal lobectomy.

674

It consists of: (*a*) loss of ability to recognize visual objects and inability to rely on visual cues alone; (*b*) extreme tendency to examine all objects by mouth; (*c*) extreme tendency to attend to every visual stimulus and contact it; (*d*) marked diminution of emotional response even to objects which previously evoked strong fear or excitement; (*e*) a striking increase in sexual activity, including abberrant behavior; (*f*) marked change in dietary habits, involving the eating of meat by monkeys (noncarniverous). The obvious implication of this behavioral syndrome is that it provides the physiologist with leads as to the possible function of certain structures of the brain.

Role of Physiology in the Study of Behavior. Knowledge of physiological variables frequently leads to a better identification or understanding of psychological variables (stimulus and response). If nothing else, this knowledge can lead to more appropriate theoretical statements by the psychologist. Examples of how knowledge of physiology mediates better psychological theorizing have been pointed out by Harlow (Harlow and Woolsey, 1958). For years, delayed-response has been considered a "memory test," but when normal monkeys and monkeys with prefrontal lobectomy (inferior performers) are compared, the difference between them *decreases* with *increase* in delay. Such a result would seem to indicate that the original *information-getting* variable in delayed-response learning is of more importance than the retention variable. And in the analysis of learning set the physiological data appear to indicate that different cortical centers are involved in learning set (interproblem learning) than are involved in single-problem learning. Because different cortical centers appear to be involved, the psychologist interested in understanding learning set is led to search for stimulus-response variables that are not present in the single-problem case. It is an interesting comparative point that the brain region which is presumed important for learning set is best developed in those animals which form learning sets readily. Finally, the work by Solomon and Wynne (1953) using sympathectomized dogs underlines the theoretical importance of smooth muscle response (an emotional component) in avoidance learning. Dogs without the connected sympathetic nervous system learned a hurdle-jumping avoidance response much more slowly than intact animals and extinguished much more rapidly.

The relationship between psychology and physiology is characterized by the ever-present attempt on the part of psychologists and others to demonstrate the physicalistic basis for all behavior. And as might be expected, there are many studies which show that a particular portion of the nervous system is important for or essential to some aspect of behavior, for example, the so-called localization studies. The danger here is that such correlations are often considered to "explain" behavior. Such a view of the explanation of behavior has been labeled reductionism and has its pitfalls. It frequently implies a one-to-one relation between a behavior and a structure, which is quite misleading. It also draws attention away from stimulus or environmental variables and as a consequence can hinder rather than help the psychologist in his attempts to predict and control behavior. Being able to understand the neuro-humoral processes participating in behavior is helpful, interesting in its own right, provides the ultimate backing for a physicalistic as opposed to a mentalistic view of behavior, and can lead to appreciable control of behavior as demonstrated by the brain stimulation work. However, the closed system that we are interested in definitely includes the environment with its endless variety of stimulus inputs.

Representative Studies. The study of the neural bases for behavior is exemplified by the work on split-brain animals where the corpus callosum and anterior commissure have been transected, separating the left and right hemispheres of the brain. When *inexperienced* monkeys and chimpanzees are used as subjects and the transection of the commissures is complete certain results are quite clear. There are two distinct ways of conducting such research depending upon when the surgery is performed, that is, before training *or* after training. In the type of experiment described by Ebner and Myers (1962 **) the surgery is performed first. Then the recovered animal is trained to press a bar or make a tactual discrimination *using only one hand*. The animal is next presented with the same problem using only the *other* hand. Such as animal takes just as long to learn with the second hand as it did with the first. Unoperated animals, however, learn much more quickly with the second than they did with the first. Without the commissural structures present *prior* to training, bilateral transfer of training does not occur. An interesting sidelight here is that the sectioned animals learn the initial problem just as well as unoperated animals.

In the other type of experiment, normal animals first learn the problem with one hand and *then* the commissures are sectioned. After recovery from the operation they are tested with the other hand. Under these conditions the operated animals can perform with the untrained hand just about as well as unoperated control animals. For both groups of animals some retraining may be necessary but bilateral transfer is clearly present in each group. In other words, learning with one hand establishes neural connections in both hemispheres which can function independently after callosal sectioning (Ebner and Myers, 1962 **).

MYERS, R.   Functions of the corpus callosum in interocular transfer. *Brain*, 1956, **79**, 358–63.
    Cats with the corpus callosum removed had one eye covered during discrimination training and were overtrained on the other, uncovered, eye. The trained eye was then covered and the untrained eye was tested for transfer. This eye revealed a performance decrement to near-chance level (as opposed to high-level transfer when corpus callosum was intact). Failure of interocular transfer to occur and the fact that conflicting problems were learned by the eyes without interference suggest that the two hemispheres are operating independently in visual learning and recall. These findings give clear evidence for assuming the existence of an integrative function of the corpus callosum in visual learning and transfer.

The great variety of correlations between behavior and structure is illustrated in the following set of representative studies. As pointed out in Chapter 6, the removal of the anterior hypothalamus in male rats clearly reduces but does not eliminate copulation. Complete removal of the neocortex eliminates sex behavior in male but not in female rats and rabbits. Removal of the visual cortex in rats destroys brightness discrimination, but such a discrimination can be relearned by the operated animals. Form or pattern discrimination, on the other hand, is not only disrupted by such an operation but cannot be relearned. The use of electroconvulsive shock (ECS) directly after the acquisition of a response results in the elimination of the habit, while if ECS is delayed for an hour or more there is no noticeable loss of habit. As found by Penfield and his associates (1951), the electrical innervation of a particular region of the temporal lobe in humans can result in the recovery of specific "memories" which are often trivial and seemingly inaccessible (forgotten). In summary, these data illustrate the complex ways in which neural factors participate in behavior.

DUNCAN, C. P.   The retroactive effect of electroshock on learning. *J. comp. physiol. Psychol.*, 1949, **42**, 32–44.
    Albino rats were given avoidance training which involved running from the grid compartment of a box to the "safe" compartment. The animals were divided into eight groups receiving electroshock at different intervals after the completion of avoidance training. The intervals were 20 seconds, 40 seconds, 60 seconds, 4 minutes, 15 minutes, 1 hour, 4 hours, and 14 hours. Below 1 hour, the shorter the interval the poorer the subsequent performance; the other groups did not differ *significantly* from each other or from the control group which did not receive electroshock. It was suggested that newly learned material undergoes a period of consolidation and that up to one hour after acquisition electroshock can produce forgetting.

PENNINGTON, D. F.   The effect of ECS on retention of a discrimination habit in rats subjected to anoxia. *J. comp. physiol. Psychol.*, 1958, **51**, 687–90.

Forty rats subjected to severe anoxia (experimental group) and forty controls were trained on a horizontal-vertical discrimination task. Half of the experimental group and half of the control group were subjected to ECS (30 seconds past completion of the learning trials) and two days later all groups were given a retention test. The anoxic (brain-damaged) animals were affected more by the ECS than the controls, showing little if any retention of the original response and very slow relearning. One interpretation of this deleterious effect of ECS is that the anoxic or brain-damaged animals had a longer perseveration of neural activity following learning, which overlapped more with the ECS period.

THOMPSON, R. and PRYER, R. S.   The effect of anoxia on the retention of a discrimination habit. *J. comp. physiol. Psychol.*, 1956, **49**, 297–300.

Six groups of albino rats were trained on a horizontal-vertical stripe discrimination. Five of the groups (the sixth acted as control group) were then subjected to anoxia at intervals of 30 seconds, 2 minutes, 15 minutes, 1 hour, and 4 hours, respectively, following the last criterion trial. The 30-second and 2-minute groups showed a significant deficit in retention, while the other groups did not differ significantly from the control group. These results were contrasted with those obtained when ECS was employed where retention was affected up to one hour after the last criterion trial (see C. P. Duncan, 1949 *).

Methods of Investigation

Before proceeding any further let us examine the main experimental methods in the area. The use of electrical innervation as a tool has been dealt with previously, in Chapter 9.

Extirpation Method.   The earliest method in physiological psychology was cutting out or ablating different portions of the nervous system in order to determine what effect the removal of these neural tissues would have on behavior. A variation on this method is the transection or cutting of tracts and nerves. Extirpation has been accomplished by means of a variety of surgical techniques, including electrical and chemical, and has been studied with respect to locus, amount, and even shape of the lesion. Here could be included the use of anesthetic blockade, asphyxiation, and accidental brain injuries, including ischemia (a local and temporary deficiency of blood).

A number of difficulties are associated with the extirpation method —the most serious of which is that the removal of a structure—does not necessarily tell what function the structure has when it is there. Remaining structures of the brain can assume or already perform the functions that might belong to the ablated portion of the nervous system (the principle of equipotentiality). In addition, it is very difficult to isolate a particular structure so as to be sure all of it is removed without, at the same time, including other structures. A reverse twist on the traditional ablation technique, which may circumvent these difficulties, has recently been introduced by Sperry and his co-workers (Harlow and Woolsey, 1958). The two hemispheres of the cerebrum are isolated by transecting the corpus callosum and anterior commissure, then all of the tissue of one hemisphere is removed *except* the portion which is under study. This way function can be nicely pinpointed both for sensory input and motor output. The animal is still quite intact because one hemisphere is whole.

Spreading Depression. One of the newer techniques is called spreading depression (SD) and is described in the study by Bureš *et al.* (1958 **). It is like the extirpation method but different in that the affected area is only removed *temporarily*. Thus with SD it is possible to conduct subsequent tests on an intact organism. SD is achieved by applying a piece of filter paper soaked with KCl (potassium chloride) directly to the cortex through small openings in the skull of an anaesthetized animal (a 25% KCl solution is frequently employed). Very shortly thereafter the whole cortex of the treated hemisphere is nonfunctional. This has been independently determined from depressed activity in electroencephalographic (EEG) recordings. The EEG or brain wave records taken from the brain or scalp constitute an important research tool for the neurophysiologist and the physiological psychologist. With SD only the neocortex, and not the lower brain, is affected; and in several hours cortical functioning is fully recovered. A special advantage of SD is the fact that the treated animal can be tested immediately. This eliminates interference from slowly developing compensating mechanisms as is possible in surgically decorticated animals which are not tested until they have recovered from the operation, several days later.

Other Methods. The structural characteristics of the nervous system have also been manipulated by modifying the body chemistry. This has been done by means of diet and use of drugs as illustrated in the summarized studies by Overton (1958) and Blough (1956–1957). In addition, the brain and other portions of the nervous system have recently been subjected to a variety of biochemical assays. Chemical assessments of excitation, inhibition and even learning are currently being undertaken, though it is still too early to tell where these analyses will lead. For example, the large molecule or protein-like substance, RNA, which is used to explain genetic transmission has been speculatively linked to associative changes (learning).

BLOUGH, D. S. Some effects of drugs on visual discrimination in the pigeon. *Annals N.Y. Acad. Sc.*, 1956–57, **66**, 733–39.

Five pigeons were first tested on a "conditional" discrimination task, pecking on bright or dark keys depending upon the illumination of a vertical bar. Their performance was subsequently evaluated following oral administration of chlorpromozine hydrochloride, meperidine hydrochloride, caffiene, pentobobartital sodium, and LSD, respectively. LSD produced an initial decrease in response rate but improved accuracy of responding. The administration of chlorpromazine reduced both accuracy and total response output, and the other three drugs had generally similar effects.

OVERTON, R. K.   An effect of high and low calcium diets on the maze performance of rats. *J. comp. physiol. Psychol.*, 1958, **51**, 697–700.

Rats were trained on mazes and subsequently divided into groups receiving low and high calcium diets. A retention test was administered twenty-four days later, and it was found that the performance of the rats was inverseley related to the amount of calcium in the brain, as determined by chemical analysis. This result lends tentative support to the hypothesis that calcium displacement in the brain may be a physiological concomitant of learning. Additional research is required to check out alternative interpretations.

The Evolutionary Picture

Since this is a book on comparative psychology, the remainder of the chapter is organized around evolutionary facts and principles. Of these, the principle of *encephalization* is one of the best known, though not necessarily the best established. This principle states that, as evolution proceeds, the newly developed brain (typically the cerebrum) gains control and dominance over lower centers. In actual fact, encephalization is revealed by behavior: removal of the cerebrum in the fish does not disturb its swimming behavior, but removal of the cerebrum in the monkey makes it unable to walk. Pribram (Harlow and Woolsey, 1958) has suggested a convincing qualification of the encephalization principle to the effect that the development of the brain involves more than the simple adding on of structures, such as the cerebral cortex. He points out that the evolutionary development of the brain involves differentiation of the internal core of the neural system as well as differentiation of the more external portion of the forebrain. This neurological fact serves to complicate any full-scale evaluation of the encephalization principle.

A second evolutionary principle, which has also been suggested by Pribram, denies any clear-cut ordered differences in complexity of behavior among vertebrates, as a function of greater differentiation of the brain. This is most obvious when the total repertoire of behavior is scrutinized at each level. As one climbs the scale from the fish to the primates the principle seems to be best stated as follows: the higher the phyletic level, the greater the *multiple determination* of behavior. Essentially, the same view was developed and presented in Chapters 9 and 12. What is meant is that the variety and complexity of stimuli which can be involved in learning and consummatory behavior increase steadily with phyletic level. Perhaps thinking in man represents the peak of multiple-behavioral determination, for thinking can be characterized as a chain of implicit responses which are primarily cued by the subtle kinesthetic aftereffects of each preceding "chunk" of behavior.

The *multiple determination* principle will be elaborated later when vertebrate behavior is examined in greater detail. But first it is necessary to indicate that this generalization does *not* suffice below the fish or the higher insects (*Hymenoptera*).

The Nervous System and the Behavior of Invertebrates. Though many of the specifics are still unknown, it is clear that the behavior of the lower forms has considerably less variety and plasticity than is true of the higher organisms. Among the lower organisms, degree of behavioral complexity is positively correlated with developmental level, including above all the architecture of the nervous system. In the lowest forms (hydras, jellyfish, sea anemones, corals) the nervous system is a simple, diffuse system called a nerve net. This network is *not* a continuous, unbroken affair, though it approaches this sort of structure; and behavior can in part be localized rather than diffuse by reason of the fact that the all-or-none law does not hold at this level (there is a loss in strength of transmission over distance). But the system still allows for little flexibility of action. The inefficiency of the indiscriminate network is increased by the fact that transmission of the nerve impulse can occur in either direction along a nerve fiber because of the absence of synapses as we know of them in higher forms and by the fact that impulse transmission is slow. In higher organisms the nerve fibers are larger in diameter and myelinated (ensheathed), increasing speed of nerve transmission many fold.

As one ascends the phylogenetic scale through the lower forms, the nervous system departs from a simple nerve net, and specialization of sense organs and effectors occurs. As a consequence, behavior becomes more variable and better coordinated. Coordination is achieved by the development of specific conduction pathways which make it possible for an appropriate movement to follow a particular kind of stimulation. However, no *central* control is present until the appearance of a bilaterally symmetrical nervous system. The beginnings of this structure occur in the flatworm and molluscs, where the evidence for the presence of habituation and learning has been gaining acceptance among comparative psychologists. It is interesting to note that the nerve net is never entirely lost, even when the nervous system develops into the highly centralized system of the higher vertebrates. For example, the net controls the sluggish, diffuse peristaltic movements of the mammalian intestine, in an efficient manner.

In higher invertebrates such as insects, there is a synaptic nervous system, but the small size of the organism severely limits the number of neurones present. That is, there is a definite lower limit to the size of all neurones. Because muscle action in insects is accomplished with very few neurones compared to a similar innervation in vertebrates it is possible to conclude that the nervous system of insects is quite sophisticated, in the sense of being neat and efficient.

Vertebrate Behavior and the Brain. With evolutionary development there is continued development of centralization in the nervous system. But behavioral complexity from the fish upward shows *no* consistent advance with the development of the brain. The variety and intricacy of response patterns do not remain dimensions along which species can be most meaningfully differentiated. Rather, as already referred to and as will be further discussed, vertebrate behavior is better differentiated in terms of *multiple determination* or flexibility.

According to the available evidence, phylogenetic increases in behavioral potential, regardless of how they are described, are accomplished without the introduction of new mechanisms or processes in the nervous system. The nerve unit (neurone) remains essentially the same throughout evolutionary history. Up to a point at least, the increase in number of neurones and interconnections plus the architecture of the structure as a whole appears to account for any new functions associated with the brain.

There is an interesting sidelight to the phylogenesis of the nervous system in the study of the ontogenetic aspects of neural development. Sperry and his coworkers (1958) have found that the developing nerve fibers in vertebrates establish their synaptic associations in a highly specific manner from the very beginning. The vertebrate nervous system is *not* a haphazard substrate which is functionally channeled into patterns through training or learning, as propounded by Holt (1931). The view that the nervous system is well organized and adaptively patterned from the start has been supported by a number of experiments. In these experiments the adult or developing nervous system was surgically disarranged in many different vertebrates (Weiss, 1941; Sperry, 1945). Such surgery results in *permanent,* machine-like disfunctions of behavior which *cannot* be remedied by training. For example, when the motor nerves to the extensor and flexor muscles of the frog's leg have been interchanged the frog never learns to respond appropriately. Such findings are reinforced by other data which show, for example, that severed nerve fibers regenerate according to a predetermined growth process regardless of whether the course of regeneration is advantageous to the organism. The conception that specific behavior potentials are built into the organization of the nervous system and sensory and effector systems is entirely consistent with the position we have taken throughout the book. Time and time again we have emphasized that learning is only the modification of responses which are already available to the organism.

An important corollary of the point just made is that the vertebrate nervous system is highly redundant, consisting of a large amount of overlap in neural connections. Such a state of affairs means that extensive neural lesions will not necessarily disrupt behavior. Thus the interpretation of traditional neurophysiological data is a risky undertaking. For example, if all but two, any two, dorsal sensory roots of the spinal cord of the toad are transected the toad can still walk with all four limbs moving in the proper diagonal sequence. If all the roots are cut, the toad gets no proprioceptive feedback and, of course, cannot walk (Gray and Lissman, 1946). The study by Dykman and Shurrager (1956 **) which shows conditioning in a spinal animal might also be considered a case in point. In the brain, the effect of redundancy is known as the *principle of equipotentiality* or vicarious functioning. According to this principle, when one part of the brain is missing its function can be assumed by a different part of the brain.

Complex Cues, the Brain, and Behavior.   The importance of the neocortex appears to manifest itself best in learning situations which involve complex or subtle cues. This evolutionary or comparative point is entirely consistent with the viewpoints of the preceding chapter (Chapter 12). In fact, evidence for this type of relationship has been available ever since Lashley (1929) ran both decorticated and normal rats through both simple and complex mazes. For the complex-maze, the impairment in learning and performance is roughly proportional to the *size* of the lesion (the locus and shape of the lesion are essentially irrelevant). This relation is Lashley's well-known *mass-action principle*. In a *simple* T-maze, on the other hand, rats can learn with practically no cortex at all (Thompson, 1959).

According to the encephalization principle, the principle of mass-action should hold less well for primates than for lower mammals and vertebrates. But the evidence for such an assertion is questionable.

At the human level, studies by Teuber and associates (1959) even indicate that extensive cerebral injury can result in gains rather than losses in intelligence test scores. Furthermore, the newest structures in terms of evolution, the frontal lobes, show rather nonspecific functioning as judged from cases of impairment in human beings with frontal lobe lesions. The effects of lesions on sensory functioning, on the other hand, are usually quite specific and more in accord with the encephalization principle.

But let us examine behaviors which involve more transient or subtle cues than is the case in learning a complex maze. When this is done an additional generalization seems possible. The results from studies of learning set, delayed response, delayed alternation, double alternation, so called "reasoning," and the like all seem to indicate that at this level of stimulus determination the locus and possibly even the shape of the lesion in the cortex can be a critical variable (see the article by Riopelle *et al.*, 1953 **). Apparently the less distinctive the cue, the more important specific portions of the brain become. Several studies support this view, including the selected study by Mishkin and Pribram and the summarized study by the same authors, particularly when these two studies are viewed together. As these two studies show, frontal lesions lose importance in a delayed-response situation when the cue presented prior to the delay has been made highly distinctive.

MISHKIN, M. and PRIBRAM, K. H. Analysis of the effects of frontal lesions in monkeys: III. Object alternation. *J. comp. physiol. Psychol.*, 1956, **49**, 41–45.

   Frontal lesions in monkeys interfere as much with performance on object alternation as they do with performance on spatial alternation. Thus the *spatial* aspect of typical predelay cues in delayed-response tasks is not crucial in the frontal operate's failure on delayed response. Rather, distinctiveness of the predelay cue appears to be critical.

To sum up, the evolutionary picture seems fairly consistent. The higher brain structures seem to be expressly related to how well the organism can use a variety of subtle cues. In turn, the better the animal's performance in tasks involving complex cues (learning set, delayed response, etc.), the higher the animal usually is on the phyletic scale.

ADDITIONAL SUMMARIZED STUDIES

BROMILEY, R. B. Conditioned responses in a dog after removal of neo-cortex. *J. comp. physiol. Psychol.* 1948, **41**, 102–10.

   A decorticate dog (minus neo-cortex with the remainder of its brain left largely intact) developed conditioned avoidance responses to a light as the

CS on some trials and to a sound (whistle) as the CS on other trials. Shock to the right forepaw was the US. The CR was an isolated flexion of the shocked leg. The dog was then trained to discriminate between the light and the whistle (the light became the positive CS and the response to the whistle was extinguished). *Note:* Conditioning took place even though the dog often engaged in competing activity such as whining or licking its chops, though when the competing responses were vigorous the CS had no effect.

KELLOGG, W. N., DEESE, J., PRONKO, N. H., and FEINBERG, M. An attempt to condition the chronic spinal dog. *J. exp. Psychol.*, 1947, **37**, 99–117.

Spinal transection was performed on dogs (chronic preparation) to test for spinal conditioning, using shock to the left hind foot as the CS and shock to the right hind foot as the US. The animals were conditioned prior to transection and reconditioned following the operation. After transection both a slight muscle twitch and extension of the leg to be conditioned were noted as response tendencies, but these have questionable status as conditional responses. There was no evidence of retention from preoperative conditioning to postoperative performance or from session to session postoperatively. *Note:* Although these results are not in good accord with those of Dykman and Shurrager **, it needs to be emphasized that the use of shock as both CS and US seriously complicates the interpretation of the results.

WADE, MARJORIE. Behavioral effect of prefrontal lobectomy, lobotomy, and circumsection in the monkey *Macaca Mulatta*. *J. comp. Neurol.*, 1952, **96**, 179–207.

Three groups of monkeys were independently subjected to (1) removal of the prefrontal lobes (lobectomy), (2) sectioning of the prefrontal lobes so as to separate them from the lower brain centers thus sparing cortical tissue and most cortical interconnections (lobotomy), and (3) severing or transecting the short transcortical connections between the frontal region and the adjacent cortex while leaving the projection fibers to the thalamus intact (circumsection).

Prior to the operation all monkeys were trained on latch problems, rake tests, spatial-delayed response, and a conditional discrimination where the positive and negative cues switched values with a change in the color of the background. Performance on most tasks postoperatively was initially poor but with retraining recovery was essentially complete except for delayed response. The ability to perform delayed response was equally poor for lobectomy and lobotomy conditions but unaffected by circumsection. The finding of equal deleterious effects from lobectomy and lobotomy was unexpected because it does not coincide with the data based on clinical material, which of course comes from human beings. Lobectomy is supposed to produce more impairment. Perhaps this last result is an example of the encephalization principle in operation.

The greatest amount of impairment due to circumsection was in conditional discrimination.

MULTIPLE DISCRIMINATION AND PATTERNED STRING

PERFORMANCE OF NORMAL AND

TEMPORAL-LOBECTOMIZED MONKEYS[1]

A. J. RIOPELLE, R. G. ALPER, P. N. STRONG, and H. W. ADES

Emory University

This report compares the performances of normal and brain-injured animals on two diverse types of visually guided tasks. Such comparisons seem fruitful for indicating the nature as well as the generality of performance decrements which follow cortical assault.

ANIMALS AND OPERATIONS

Two groups of rhesus monkeys served in the experiments. The Normal Group consisted of four intact animals (RF–6, RF–7, RF–8, FT–1) whereas the Temporal Group consisted of four animals that had been subjected to extensive surgical assault to the temporal lobes (RF–1, RF–3, RF–4, RF–5).

All operations were performed in two stages under complete aseptic precautions. Unilateral aspiration of the desired regions occurred in the first stage, and in the second stage, about a week or ten days later, the tissue of the contralateral side was removed in the same manner. In all cases, the surgical approach was by way of the temporal neocortex.

So far as could be ascertained at the time of operation, the greater parts of the hippocampus and the hippocampal gyrus were removed at each operation. The amygdala probably escaped serious encroachment, but exact information must await histological analysis, which is presently being performed. The results of this analysis will be reported in another paper.

The members of the Temporal Group were operated prior to having any formal discrimination training. Before the present experiment was begun, however, both groups were adapted to the test situation and were trained on a series of six discrimination problems scaled in difficulty and involving a total of more than two thousand trials. The animals were thus well tamed and accustomed to routine testing procedures.

MULTIPLE DISCRIMINATION TESTS

Procedure

The animals of both groups were trained to select the rewarded members of a series of 315 pairs of stimulus objects. The members of each pair differed from

[1] This investigation was supported in part by a research grant (MH–359) from the National Institute of Mental Health of the National Institutes of Health, Public Health Service.

each other in many respects, and the successive pairs of objects were equally diverse in nature. The two stimuli constituting a problem were presented simultaneously in a duplicate of the Wisconsin General Test Apparatus. With this device the animal confronts a gray tray bearing the two test objects. One member of the pair of stimuli was arbitrarily designated as correct, and its selection resulted in food reward for the animal. The individual test-trial procedures were identical to those used in a number of studies reported by Harlow and his associates (6). A noncorrection procedure was used throughout, and blinds were used appropriately to minimize experimental artifacts.

Each problem was presented for six trials, and six problems were administered each day. The first five problems on any day were completely new to the animals. After the fifth problem, either the first or the fourth problem on that day was reintroduced, but this time the previously unrewarded object covered the food. Thus, each day's testing consisted of five new discrimination problems and subsequently one of these reversed. A total of 315 discrimination and 63 discrimination-reversal problems was presented.

Results

Figure 1 portrays the performances of the Normal and the Tempo-

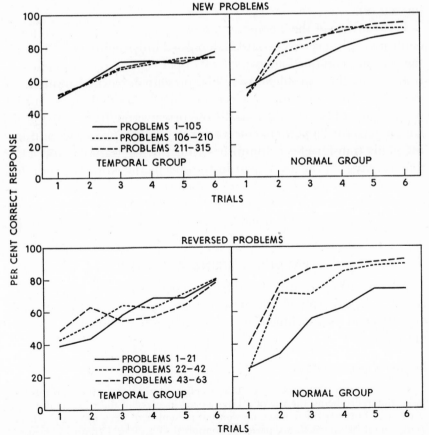

Fig. 1. Intraproblem learning of new and reversed problems at three stages of training by normal and temporal lobectomized monkeys

ral Groups on both the new and the old, reversed problems. The graphs show the average intraproblem improvements in performance at three stages of training covering 21 days of testing. The upper panels of the figure apply to the new problems and the lower panels to the old, reversed problems.

All curves show improvement in performance from the first to the sixth trial. The normal animals also show improvement in intraproblem learning from the early to the late stages of training, but no such improvement appears for the operated animals. This difference is most readily seen from the performances on the second trials of the new problems of the two groups at three stages of training. Whereas the trial 2 performance of the Normal Group increases from the first to the last training stage, the comparable score for the Temporal Group does not increase. Identical comparisons for trials 3–6 similarly show interproblem improvement for only the normal animals. Such interproblem improvement has been termed the formation of learning sets (6).

Performance of the Temporal Group on problems presented a second time with reversed reward is depressed only slightly even though these animals attained an average of 75 per cent correct responses on trial 6 when these problems were first presented. Normal animals, on the other hand, continue to select the object rewarded on the initial presentation of the problem, trial 1 performance on the reversed problems being only 25 per cent correct during the first two stages of training. This transfer effect diminishes with further training, and a detailed analysis of the decrement in transfer by the Normal Group has been presented (11). Both groups learned to solve the reversed problems. The Operated Group performed less efficiently on these reversed problems than did the Normal Group during the final stages of training.

PATTERNED STRING PROBLEMS

All animals previously described except RF–1 participated in this phase of the experiment. The test requires the ability to trace a chain visually from its attachment to a food morsel to a point within reach of the hand.

Apparatus and Procedure

The apparatus and procedures were similar to those described earlier, the major difference being the use of a large board in place of the tray. At the edge of the board nearest the monkey was located a number of screw-eyes to which the chains could be attached. Six patterns, composed of 2, 3, or 4 chains, were used.

The particular patterns were selected from the series used by Harlow and Settlage (7). The rewarded chain varied from trial to trial in a balanced order. The animal was given 25 trials per day on a particular pattern until it reached a criterion of 20 correct responses in one day, or until it had been given 150 trials.

Results

The patterns used and the percentage of correct responses on each pattern for the first day of testing are shown in Figure 2. In contrast to

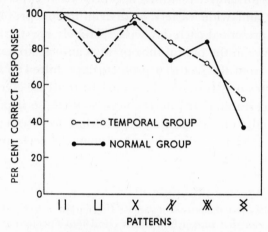

Fig. 2. Performance on patterned string problems by normal and temporal-lobectomized monkeys

the results of multiple discrimination problems, no systematic deficit can be found for the operated animals on patterned string problems. Although an adequate range of difficulty was covered by these tests, difficulty per se is relatively ineffective for differentiating the normal from the operated animals. Performance of the normal animals was superior to that of the operated animals on only half the problems. These interpretations are borne out by the analysis of variance performed on the data.[2] This analysis revealed that the only significant source of variation was due to an interaction between operation and problem. This is interpreted to mean that there is a tendency for the problems to be ordered differently with respect to difficulty for the two groups.

---

[2] Although detailed statistical analyses are not reported in this paper, they were, nevertheless, performed. Any difference claimed in this report was significant beyond the 1 per cent level of confidence. For detailed statistical analyses and tabular material order Document No. 3907 from the American Documentation Institute, Auxiliary Publications Project, Photoduplication Service, % Library of Congress, Washington 25, D.C., remitting $1.25 for 35 mm. microfilm or $1.25 for 6- by 8-in. photocopies readable without optical aid.

RATE OF PROBLEM ALTERNATION AND RETENTION

The failure of the operated animals to form learning sets despite adequate performance on patterned string problems points to the complex nature of "visual association," and attempts to identify the nature of functional loss following circumscribed insult to the central nervous system will be successfully only insofar as they can define the variables underlying performance. Learning sets arise from experience with a large number and wide variety of discrimination problems. Many problems are presented each day with relatively few trials per problem. The failure on the part of the operated animals to form learning sets may stem from the fact that problems are shifted at a rapid rate even though they may be learned if sufficient trials are given in succession. It is conceivable that interferences might arise if problems are alternated rapidly one after another, interferences strong enough to reduce proficiency. The following experiment was performed to check this hypothesis.

Procedure

It was desired to test the effects of rate of alternation rather independently of rate of learning. For that reason four normal and four operated animals (RF–3, RF–4, RF–5, FT–2, unilateral operation) were first given 25 trials in succession on each of ten object-discrimination problems of the type described earlier. After the training series, the animals were tested on these problems for 1, 2, 3, or 6 trials per problem. Every problem appeared six times on each day, the only variation being in the number of times that a particular problem appeared on successive trials. Sixty trials per day were administered for eight days, each rate of alternation occurring on two successive days. The order in which the rates were given varied from animal to animal according to a four-by-four latin square. Two identical latin squares, one for each group, were used so that the variation in performance due to differing rates of problem alternation could be isolated from the effects of differing over-all levels of performance. For each latin square three main sources of variation can be analyzed in addition to experimental errors: *Sequence, Order Confounded with Animals,* and *Rates.* The individual test-trial procedures were identical to those described above.

Results

The result of principal interest is that relating proficiency of performance to the number of successive trials occurring in a single problem presentation. Inspection of Table 1 reveals that the number of times a particular problem is presented before going on to the next problem is not a significant factor in determining performance either for the normal animals or for the operated animals. For neither group

TABLE 1
TOTAL ERRORS PER 120 TRIALS AS A FUNCTION OF TRIALS
PER PROBLEM

Group	*1* *Trial*	*2* *Trials*	*3* *Trials*	*6* *Trials*	*Sum*
Temporal	27	31	13	26	97
Normal	9	7	8	9	33

did the variance due to rate of problem alternation attain the usually required levels of significance.

The two significant sources of variation were *Sequence* and *Order-Animals*. Significant differences between individual animals are to be expected but are of little theoretical interest. The effects of *Sequence* are shown in Table 2. From this table it is seen that successively fewer

TABLE 2
TOTAL ERRORS PER 120 TRIALS AS A FUNCTION
OF CONSECUTIVE TWO-DAY TEST PERIODS

Group	Period			
	First	*Second*	*Third*	*Fourth*
Temporal	53	18	16	10
Normal	18	6	4	5

errors were made on each succeeding pair of test days. In other words, performance continued to improve throughout the eight test days.

DISCUSSION

The present results indicate that temporal-lobectomized monkeys failed to learn how to learn discrimination problems, but their performance on patterned string problems was generally as efficient as that of normal animals. Thus two diverse samples of visually guided tasks were presented, but the operated animals showed loss only on one of these. The fact that the operated animals exhibited intra-problem improvement suggests that the operated animals gain from specific experience but do not benefit from the broad experience with a variety of problems that is significant for the formation of learning sets.

Decrement in performance on patterned string problems has been shown for a variety of cortical lesions. Temporary loss was obtained by Settlage (12) in animals subjected to bilateral invasion of the occipital lobes. Corresponding loss was found by Harlow (5) in unilateral occipital-lobectomized animals. The dependence of initial postoperative performance upon the degree of intactness of the visual field is further reported in a joint publication by these authors (8). Their partially hemidecorticate monkeys showed more profound loss than was shown by monkeys subjected to bilateral invasion of the frontal regions.

Decrement in performance in such tests by temporal-lobectomized animals has been described by Klüver and Bucy (9, 10). They point out, however, that their animals responded indiscriminately to the strings, and probably did so irrespective of the particular string patterns. The animals of this experiment did not display this compulsive behavior and their proficient performances reflect responses to a well-differentiated field.

The extent to which the failure to form discrimination learning sets is specific to injury to the temporal lobes is, of course, impossible to say in advance of additional experimentation. Data are available, however, which indicate that monkeys subjected to partial hemidecortication can form effective learning sets, and do so at a rate comparable to that of normal animals, although the general level of performance is lower (6). Furthermore, these same animals form pattern-discrimination learning sets even after additional surgical removals of frontal and posterior association areas on the contralateral sides (13).

An increasing number of studies (1, 3, 4) as well as other unpublished data from this laboratory point to the importance of the integrity of the temporal lobes for certain visually guided tasks despite the physiological remoteness of these regions from the primary visual projection area (2). All these studies show differential rather than uniform loss and point to the multivariate nature of visual performance.

SUMMARY

1. The performance of normal monkeys on visually guided tasks was compared with that of temporal-lobectomized monkeys. The operated animals were able to learn specific discrimination problems but were unable to learn them rapidly even after 200 to 300 such problems. The normal monkeys progressively improved in the ability to solve such problems. The operated animals thus failed to form learning sets.

2. There was no evidence of a general loss in the ability to solve patterned string problems by the Temporal Group.

3. A further investigation designed to evaluate the extent to which rate of problem presentation affected performance on multiple discrimination problems revealed that temporal-lobectomized animals,

like normal animals, performed as well if problems, were changed after every trial as after six trials, at least if both groups of animals had 25 trials' preliminary training on each problem.

4. It was concluded that these animals were unable to benefit from extensive past experience, experience which is only indirectly related to problems engaging their activity.

REFERENCES

1. BLUM, JOSEPHINE S., CHOW, K. L., and PRIBRAM, K. H. A behavioral analysis of the organization of the pariento-temporo-occipital cortex. *J. comp. Neurol.,* 1950, **93,** 53–100.
2. BONIN, G. VON, GAROL, H. W., and McCULLOCH, W. S. The functional organization of the occipital lobe. *Biol. Sympos.,* 1942, **7,** 165–92.
3. CHOW, K. L. Effects, of partial extirpation of the posterior association cortex on visually mediated behavior in monkeys. *Comp. Psychol. Monogr.,* 1951, **20,** 187–218.
4. CHOW, K. L. Further studies on selective ablation of associative cortex in relation to visually mediated behavior. *J. comp. physiol. Psychol.,* 1952, **45,** 109–18.
5. HARLOW, H. F. Recovery of pattern discrimination in monkeys following unilateral occipital lobectomy. *J. comp. Psychol.,* 1939, **27,** 467–89.
6. HARLOW, H. F. The formation of learning sets. *Psychol. Rev.,* 1949, **56,** 51–65.
7. HARLOW, H. F., and SETTLAGE, P. H. Comparative behavior of primates: VII. Capacity of monkeys to solve patterned string problems. *J. comp. Psychol.,* 1934, **18,** 423–35.
8. HARLOW, H. F., and SETTLAGE, P. H. In J. F. Fulton (Ed.), *The frontal lobes.* Baltimore: Williams and Wilkins, 1948.
9. KLÜVER, H., and BUCY, P. C. An analysis of certain effects of bilateral temporal lobectomy in the monkey, with special reference to "Psychic Blindness." *J. Psychol.,* 1938, **5,** 33–54.
10. KLÜVER, H., and BUCY, P. C. Preliminary analysis of functions of the temporal lobes in monkeys. *A. M. A. Arch. Neurol. Psychiat.,* 1939, **42,** 979–1000.
11. RIOPELLE, A. J. Transfer suppression and learning sets. *J. comp. physiol. Psychol.,* 1953, **46,** 108–14.
12. SETTLAGE, P. H. The effect of occipital lesions on visually guided behavior in the monkey: II. Loss and recovery of function as studied by performance on patterned string tests. *J. comp. Psychol.,* 1939, **27,** 109–31.
13. WARREN, J. M., and HARLOW, H. F. Learned discrimination performance by monkeys after prolonged postoperative recovery from large cortical lesions. *J. comp. physiol. Psychol.,* 1952, **45,** 119–26.

CONDITIONED REFLEXES AND LEÃO'S SPREADING

CORTICAL DEPRESSION

J. BUREŠ, O. BUREŠOVÁ, and A. ZÁHOROVÁ
Institute of Physiology of the Czechoslovak Academy of Sciences, Prague

During the last years attention of numerous electrophysiologists has been attracted by the remarkable phenomenon of spreading depression of EEG activity, first described in 1944 by Leão. Various stimuli—electrical, mechanical, or chemical—applied directly to the cortical surface evoke local depression of spontaneous EEG activity, spreading slowly at a rate of 3 to 6 mm. per min. in all directions along the cortex. In every cortical area the depression lasts for 3 to 6 min. Complete restitution of the original EEG amplitude is attained only 10 to 20 min. after the onset of spreading depression. At the same time, cortical excitability temporarily decreases as judged by the increased threshold of the motor cortex and by a depression of evoked sensory potentials. The front of the wave of spreading depression is accompanied by a striking variation of cortical steady potential, an initial surface negativity (5–10 mv.) followed after 1 to 2 min. by a wave of prolonged positivity.

Although conditions necessary for the initiation of spreading depression have been described repeatedly, little is known so far about the physiological significance of this phenomenon in unanesthetized animals. The possibility of producing spreading depression in animals without general anesthesia was shown by Whieldon and Van Harreveld (24) in curarized rabbits, by Sloan and Jasper (21) on "cerveau isolé" in cats, and by Bureš (4) in restrained rats. The same results were obtained as in anesthetized animals. On the other hand, Clark and Ward (11), Clark, Chow, Gillaspy, and Klotz (10), and Druckman (12) did not succeed in eliciting depression of the motor responses produced by electrical stimulation of motor cortex with implanted electrodes in unanesthetized cats. Explanation was sought in the assumption of Marshall and co-workers (18) that spreading depression develops only in abnormal cortex, subjected after extensive craniotomy to effects of air, desiccation, cooling, etc. This view was rejected, however, by Van Harreveld and Stamm (23) and Ross and Magun (20), who have demonstrated that spreading depression can traverse an area of normal cortical tissue between two small trephine holes, and by Bureš (3), who has elicited spreading depression by applying direct current to the cerebral cortex of rats and mice without opening the skull at all.

Burešová (7) has shown that spreading depression elicited by local application of KCl solutions to the cerebral cortex of both hemispheres in unrestrained conscious rats leads to a severe impairment of cortical functions although subcortically integrated reflexes (postural reflexes) remained unaffected.

The purpose of the present paper is to verify these results by another technique.

METHOD

Subjects

Adult male albino rats about 120 days old at the time of the experiment were used throughout the study.

Procedure

Food conditioned reflexes (CRs). Rats in individual mesh cages were fed once per day by lowering small food pellets through an opening in the ceiling into the cage. Ten sec. before and 20 sec. after the food had been introduced, an acoustic signal (10,000 cps) was used as the conditioned stimulus (CS). There were 5- to 10-min. intervals between stimuli. The natural, food CR—reaching the food seen and smelled by the animal—was soon replaced by the artificial CR. When the tone sounded, the rat stood up under the hole in the ceiling awaiting the food pellet. Five to 10 pellets were given each day. The CR was considered as established when S attained the criterion of 90% positive responses to the CS on five successive days.

Avoidance conditioned reflexes. Rats kept in the vivarium and allowed free access to food and water were trained three times per week. The apparatus consisted of a box 40 by 40 by 40 cm. with an electrifiable grid as floor. Three wooden walls had a smooth surface, while the fourth was of wire mesh. The procedure required the rat to jump from the electrified floor to the unelectrified wire mesh and to remain there until the electrical stimulus was over. Single shocks of approximately 110 v. and a maximal amperage of 2 ma. applied to the grid by a hand-operated switch served as the unconditioned stimulus (US). The CS (noise of a buzzer) was applied 5 sec. before the US was turned on. Both CS and US remained on for a further 15 sec. Even if the rat did not escape from the electrified floor during this time, both CS and US were then terminated, and 2 to 4 min. after the last application of the CS the next trial was started. There were eight to ten trials each day. The criterion of successful establishment of the CR was 90% avoidances on five successive days. Response latencies were recorded by stop watch to the nearest 0.1 sec.

Surgery. In rats anesthetized with ether, exposure of occipital, frontal, or temporal regions of both hemispheres was achieved by trephine openings 5 mm. in diameter. As removing of dura may cause edema of brain tissue, trephine holes were made cautiously in order to avoid cutting of the dura. Skin was then replaced over the skull and fastened with one or two loose sutures. Four to 24 hr. after the operation the rats were quite normal and ready for further experiments.

Spreading-depression experiments. Only animals fully recovered from the operative procedure were used. The skin sutures were cut and trephine openings revised. Small filter papers, 2 by 2 mm. to 3 by 3 mm., soaked with saline in control experiments and with 2% or 25% KCl solution in experimental series, were cautiously applied to symmetrical cortical areas. For this, 15 to 30 sec. were necessary. Immediately thereafter the rat was replaced in its cage (in the case of food CRs) or in the testing box (in the case of avoidance CRs) and CRs established in the preoperative period were investigated.

RESULTS

As the electrophysiological phenomena of spreading depression are well reproducible, and as we did not succeed in registering EEG and slow potential changes in unrestrained rats without artifacts, changes of CRs, caused by spreading depression in one group of rats, were compared with electrophysiological changes occurring under similar conditions in another group.

Control Experiments

Both food and avoidance CRs remained unchanged when tested in various intervals after application of saline to the cortical surface. Thirteen rats were used as controls in the food-conditioning experiments and observed for 1 hr. after application of saline. The percentage of positive responses was the same as in the preoperative period.

In the avoidance experiments, each experiment was started with application of saline. Conditioned reflexes were observed for 10 to 15 min. afterward. The percentage of positive responses and even the response latencies remained almost unchanged (Table 1). The results are in good agreement with the fact that saline never elicits a spreading depression in rats if mechanical stimulation of the cortex is prevented.

Experiments with 25% KCl Applied to Parieto-occipital Regions

According to Burešová (7), there are no substantial changes in somatic URs in rats after application of 25% KCl to the cerebral cortex. Normal posture and normal motor activity are preserved. Corneal, pupillary, and other reflexes remain unchanged, and spinal flexory reflexes are even exaggerated. Cortical functions are, on the other hand, seriously impaired: Cortical postural reflexes (placing and hopping reactions) disappear after 1 to 2 min. and reappear only after several hours. Figure 1 illustrates the experiments with conditioned food and avoidance reflexes. Both methods of conditioning gave substantially similar results. One-half to 1 min. after application

TABLE 1
THE EFFECT OF APPLICATION OF SALINE ON
CONDITIONED REFLEXES

	Percentage of Positive Responses				Mean Latencies of the Avoidance Response	
	Alimentary CR		Avoidance CR			
	Per cent	n	Per cent	n	Sec.	n
One day before operation	100.0	13	92.0	18	2.29 ± 0.15	18
After local application of saline	98.5	13	87.5	18	2.55 ± 0.37	18

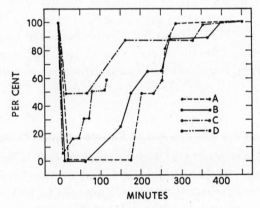

FIG. 1. Effect of spreading depression evoked by 25% KCl applied on occipital areas of both hemispheres. The ordinate indicates the percentage of alimentary (A) and avoidance (B) CRs, percentage of escape reactions (C), and EEG amplitude expressed as percentage of the initial amplitude (D). Time in minutes after the application of KCl solution appears on the abscissa. The curves represent mean values for 16 (A), 8 (B, C), and 6 (D) rats.

of 25% KCl on the parieto-occipital cortex, CRs were still present. Conditioned stimuli applied at 10-min. intervals elicit neither the food nor the avoidance CRs. Animals assumed a sitting position in a corner of the cage and seemed to be asleep. They did not respond to the CS at all. The impairment of nervous functions was sometimes so severe that in the avoidance experiments the rats were not able to escape from the electric shocks by jumping on the unelectrified wire-mesh wall. Only unconditioned jumping responses to electrical shocks were displayed; the rat was agitated and ran about the box but was completely unable to find the safe place.

When the depression was retreating, escape reactions were the first to recover. Conditioned avoidance responses reappeared later approximately at the same time as the alimentary CRs. Three to 5 hr. after application of 25% KCl the restitution of CRs was completed. Figure 2, giving mean latencies of the avoidance or escape reactions after application of 25% KCl, illustrates the slow recovery of normal cortical function.

Electrical changes of comparable duration occur in the cerebral cortex under similar conditions. Twenty-five per cent KCl causes a deep depression of EEG activity lasting for several hours. Negative slow potential waves start in the region treated with 25% KCl in regular 3- to 12-min. intervals and spread over the cortex. Their voltage slowly diminishes from the 6 to 10 mv. of the first wave to 1 to 3 mv. of the tenth or further waves. Slow potential changes cease after 1 to 2 hr., but the recovery of EEG amplitude is not fully completed after 3 to 5 hr. The relation between changes of EEG activity and CRs is evident.

Experiments with 2% KCl Applied on Parieto-occipital Cortex

After application of 2% KCl to the cerebral cortex, similar but less expressed changes in behavior were found by Burešová (7). Results of our experiments with 2% KCl are illustrated by Figure 3. The first phase of the disturbance of CRs caused by 2% KCl was almost identical with the changes occurring with 25% KCl. Stimuli were applied at 10-min. intervals. The CRs, however, were not completely abolished, and escape reactions were preserved in most rats. Normal CRs returned after 30 to 60 min.

Direct comparison of mean latencies of the avoidance or escape reaction after 2% and 25% KCl is given in Figure 2. The EEG manifestations can well account for the changes in CRs. Two per cent KCl quite reliably evokes 1 to 3 waves of spreading depression which can be easily recognized by the slow voltage variation. Reduction of EEG amplitude lasts for 15 to 30 min.

Experiments with 2% KCl Applied to the Frontal or Temporal Cortex

The purpose of these experiments was to find the relation between the localization of the focus and the changes in CRs. Avoidance CRs

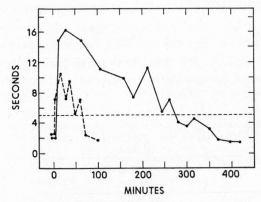

Fig. 2. Mean latencies of avoidance and escape reactions after application of 25% KCl (solid line) and 2% KCl (broken line). The measure of the ordinate is latency in seconds from the onset of the CS to the moment of jumping onto the unelectrified wire mesh. The abscissa presents time in minutes after application of KCl. Data are means from two groups of 8 rats each.

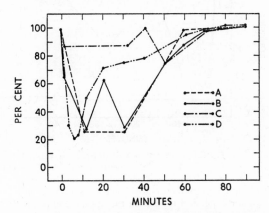

Fig. 3. Effect of spreading depression evoked by 2% KCl applied on occipital areas of both hemispheres. The same symbols as in Figure 1 are used. The curves represent mean values of 8 (A), 8 (B, C), and 6 (D) rats.

were elicited in 1- to 2-min. intervals until normal reactions returned. As in experiments with parieto-occipital foci, CRs are unchanged in the first minute after application of KCl. They disappear, however, in the second minute and reappear in the eighth to twelfth minute only. In some experiments this reappearance of CRs was immediately followed by complete recovery. During the next 20 min. the rat never failed to respond to the CS with the avoidance reaction. In other experiments this recovery was merely temporary, however, and was followed by another wave of extinction of CRs. Sometimes several waves could be detected, with a recurrence period (time elapsed from the first recovered CR through the following extinction period to the next recovered one) of 7.0 ± 0.7 min. This periodical disappearance and reappearance of CRs evidently corresponds to repeated waves of

TABLE 2
THE AVERAGE INTERVAL BETWEEN RECOVERED CONDITIONED
REFLEXES OR SLOW POTENTIAL WAVES AFTER
2% KCl

	Conditioned Reflexes	Slow Potential Waves
Min.	7.0 ± 0.7	5.2 ± 0.3
n	19	18

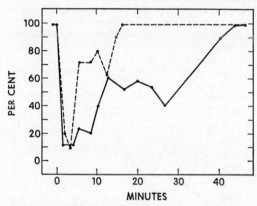

FIG. 4. Effect of spreading depression evoked by 2% KCl applied on the frontal (solid line) or the temporal (broken line) regions of both hemispheres. Percentage of avoidance CRs appears on the ordinate, and time from the application of the KCl solution appears on the abscissa. The data are means from 9 experiments with frontal and 11 experiments with temporal application of KCl.

spreading depression. The average interval between two subsequent waves of negative potential accompanying the spreading depression elicited by 2% KCl is 5.2 min. (Table 2). The average interval between periods of suppression of CRs is longer than the average interval between the slow potential waves because the recovery of CRs, when the slow potential waves are separated by short intervals, is probably very short-lasting and may thus easily escape detection. This results in greater dispersion and general shift to longer intervals. In any case, it is possible to find a very consistent relation between electrical phenomena and changes in CRs.

Average values giving percentage of positive CRs in these experiments are summarized in Figure 4. Complete recovery occurred after 15 to 30 min. in this experimental series and after 30 to 60 min. in experiments with local application of 2% KCl to occipital regions. Such a difference suggests that the site of application may be of importance, but this evidence cannot be regarded as conclusive because different intervals between CSs were used in both experiments.

DISCUSSION

Inhibition of CRs caused by local application of KCl on the cerebral cortex of both hemispheres is undoubtedly connected with the development of spreading depression. Close correlation between the time course of the electrical phenomena and of CRs (duration of changes after 2% and 25% KCl, periodicity of the slow potential waves, and recovery of CRs), as well as other arguments, speak in favor of this explanation. External inhibition caused by nociceptive stimulation of meninges would be maximal immediately after local application of KCl, but the CRs in most rats are still present during the first minute. Diffusion of KCl from the application locus is too small and too slow to explain the fact development of the extinction of CRs. Similar changes of CRs could be elicited, finally, by another stimulus evoking a spreading depression. In some cases we observe that accidental mechanical stimulation of the cortex during application of filter papers with saline caused a temporary disappearance of CRs analogous with the 2% KCl effect.

On the basis of electrophysiological data it is impossible to decide now whether spreading depression results from hyperactivity or from inactivity of cortical neurons (15, 22). Whatever the final conclusion may be on this subject, from the point of view of CRs, spreading depression means deep, reversible inhibition of all cortical functions. Well-defined electrophysiological properties of spreading depression, the possibility to elicit it from various points on the cerebral cortex and to follow its course exactly through the hemisphere may turn this remarkable phenomenon into a valuable research tool. In most laboratories engaged in the study of CRs, electrophysiological correlates of conditioning are searched for. Special methods are necessary for this purpose because well-established CRs are realized by a progressively decreasing number of neurons whose activity can scarcely be recognized in the common neuronal noise level. Spreading depression permits another approach to this problem. Behavioral changes caused by a transient, precisely localized, electrophysiological process can be studied. It is hoped that spreading depression may be used as a model of reversible decortication and that it may throw further light on problems of localization of complex functions in the cerebral cortex. From this point of view the present data are only preliminary. With the three areas of stimulation corresponding approximately to visual, acoustic, and motor regions, we have found no gross differences in latencies of the CR disturbance. One minute after application of KCl the avoidance reaction was still present; in the second minute, it disappeared. Various reasons may account for this: (*a*) It is possible that each of these three areas is of equal importance for the realization of the CR—the acoustic area as the projection area of the CS, the motor area as the projection area of the US, and the visual area as the cortical region necessary for proper orientation in the box—and the depression in any of them will cause similar changes. But this seems rather improbable, for, according to electrophysiological data during 1 min. after application of KCl, an area of some 6 to 7 mm. in diameter, almost covering the whole projection concerned, will be invaded by the depression. (*b*) It is possible that more important than the stimulation locus is the total area of the cortex depressed. In 2 to 3 min. the wave of spreading depression elicited from one of the areas used will reach the other two. Conditioned reflexes disappear, however, sooner—in the second minute, when the depressed area attains in each hemisphere a size of approximately 10 to 16 mm. in diameter. Important intracortical connections may be thus interrupted. (*c*) Depression in a large cortical area may lead to excitability changes in subcortical regions, especially in the reticular substance. Decrease in susceptibility of mice to audiogenic seizures elicited by spreading depression was recorded in our previous work (5). Barbiturate anesthesia (6) and animal hypnosis (5) were prolonged by repeated waves of spreading depression. Impairment of thermoregulation and diuresis (8, 9) is another outstanding manifestation of spreading depression. All these changes indicate severe disturbance of cortico-subcortical relations during spreading depression. Great reduction of cortical efflux directed to the reticular substance of the brain stem may decrease the latter's excitability and thus disturb the close interaction between cortical and subcortical neurones which seems to be essential in establishing CRs (1, 2, 13, 14, 17, 19). Simultaneous comparison of electrophysiological signs of spreading depression with the changes of CRs will be necessary to find the correct answer.

There are interesting differences in the duration of changes induced by spreading depression elicited by 2% KCl applied on occipital or frontal and temporal regions. As spreading depression elicited from these parts of the hemisphere are quite similar from the electrophysiological point of view, the differences must be attributable either to the site of the KCl application or to the frequency of CSs. The possibility that the arousing influence of rapidly repeated CSs can shorten the inhibition of CRs will be studied in further work.

SUMMARY

The effect of spreading cortical depression (16) on simple alimentary and avoidance conditioned reflexes (CRs) was studied in unrestrained unanesthetized rats.

Spreading depression evoked by 2% KCl applied on occipital areas of both hemispheres, exposed by trephine openings 5 mm. in diameter, results in the disappearance of alimentary and avoidance CRs for 30 to 60 min. Repeated waves of spreading depression elicited by 25% KCl similarly applied lead to an analogous effect lasting 3 to 5 hr.

Even the escape reaction is abolished in 50% of rats during the first hour after application of 25% KCl.

Close correlation between electrophysiological changes and the disturbance of CRs was found.

Spreading depression elicited by local application of 2% KCl on frontal or temporal areas of both hemispheres gave principally similar results. The shorter duration of suppression of CRs in these experiments is discussed.

Spreading depression is considered as deep but completely reversible cortical inhibition, which may be used for its well-defined electrical signs as a new approach to electrophysiological study of cortical mechanisms of conditioning.

REFERENCES

1. Artemjev, V. V., and Bezladnova, H. I. Električeskaja reakcija sluchovoj oblasti kory polušarii pri obrazovanii uslovnogo oboronitelnogo refleksa. *Trudy ins. fiziologii im. Pavlova*, 1952, **1**, 228–36.
2. Bremer, F., and Terzuolo, C. Rôle de l'écorce cérébrale dans le processus du réveil. *Arch int. physiol.*, 1952, **60**, 228–31.
3. Bureš, J. On the question of electrotonic mechanisms in the activity of the central nervous system. The production of spreading depression of EEG activity by electrotonus. *Physiol. Bohemosl.*, 1954, **3**, 272–87.
4. Bureš, J. Direct potential difference between the cerebral hemispheres during the depression of EEG activity in anaesthetised and non-anaesthetised rats. *Physiol. Bohemosl.*, 1954, **3**, 288–95.
5. Bureš, J., and Burešová, O. The influencing of reflex acoustic epilepsy and

reflex inhibition ("animal hypnosis") by spreading EEG depression. *Physiol. Bohemosl.*, 1956, **5**, 395–400.

6. BUREŠ, J., and BUREŠOVÁ, O. Zur Frage der narkotischen Wirkung der Polarisation auf das Zentralnervensystem. *Physiol. Bohemosl.*, 1956, **5**, 26–37.

7. BUREŠOVÁ, O. Vlijanie rasprostranjajuščejsja EEG depressii na bezuslovnye i naturalnye uslovnye piščevye refleksy v tečenie depressii *Physiol. Bohemosl.*, 1956, **5**, 350–58.

8. BUREŠOVÁ, O. Influencing water metabolism by protracted EEG depression. *Physiol. Bohemosl.*, 1957, **6**, 12–20.

9. BUREŠOVÁ, O. Poruchy thermoregulace a metabolismu jako důsledek dlouhotrvající EEG deprese. *Čsl. fysiol.*, 1957, **6**, 376–81.

10. CLARK, G., CHOW, K. L., GILLASPY, C. C., and KLOTZ, D. A. Stimulation of anterior limbic region in dogs. *J. Neurophysiol.*, 1949, **12**, 459–63.

11. CLARK, G., and WARD, J. W. Responses elicited from the cortex of monkeys by electrical stimulation through fixed electrodes. *Brain*, 1948, **71**, 332–42.

12. DRUCKMAN, R. A. Critique of "suppression" with additional observations in the cat. *Brain*, 1952, **75**, 226–43.

13. GALAMBOS, R. Physiological studies on the descending auditory pathway. XX International Physiological Congress (Brussels). *Abstracts of Communications*, 1956, 321.

14. GASTAUT, H., ROGER, A., and REGIS, H. Étude électroéncephalographique des différentes variétés d'inhibitions individualisées par Pavlov XX International Physiological Congress (Brussels). *Abstracts of Communications*, 1956, 327–28.

15. GRAFSTEIN, B. Mechanism of spreading cortical depression. *J. Neurophysiol.*, 1956, **19**, 154.

16. LEÃO, A. A. P. Spreading depression of activity in the cerebral cortex. *J. Neurophysiol.*, 1944, **7**, 359–90.

17. LIVANOV, M. N., and FRENKEL, G. K. Voprosulokalizacii uslovnoj svjazi v kore golovnos mozga krolika pri oboronitelnom reflekse dannym elektrofiziologičeskich issledovanii. *Sov. po probl. v.n.d.*, 1951, 30.

18. MARSHALL, W. H., and ESSIG, C. F. Relation of an exposure of cortex to spreading depression Leão. *J. Neurophysiol.*, 1951, 14, 265–73.

19. PAVLOV, I. P. *Lekcii o rabote bolšich polusass golovnogo mozga.* Moscow, 1927.

20. ROSS, J., and MAGOUN, R. Comparisons between the speed of spread of seizure discharges and spreading depression. *EEG clin. Neurophysiol.*, 1954, **6**, 518.

21. SLOAN, N., and JASPER, H. The identity of spreading depression and suppression. *EEG clin. Neurophysiol.*, 1950, **2**, 59–78.

22. VAN HARREVELD, A., and OCHS, S. Electrical vascular concomitants of spreading depression. *Amer. J. Physiol.*, 1957, **189**, 159.

23. VAN HARREVELD, A., and STAMM, J. S. On the conditions for the recording of Leão's spreading depression. *EEG clin. Neurophysiol.*, 1951, **3**, 325–28.

24. WHIELDON, J. A., and VAN HARREVELD, A. Cumulative effects of minimal cortical stimulation. *EEG clin. Neurophysiol.*, 1950, **2**, 49–57.

CORPUS CALLOSUM AND THE INTERHEMISPHERIC

TRANSMISSION OF TACTUAL LEARNING[1]

FORD F. EBNER and RONALD E. MYERS

*Department of Physiology and Division of Neurological
Medicine, Johns Hopkins University School of
Medicine, Baltimore, Maryland; and
Department of Neurophysiology,
Walter Reed Army Institute of
Research, Washington, D. C.*

The importance of the forebrain commissures to the transfer of tactual learning between the two sides of the body remains uncertain. Discordant reports have originated from different laboratories.

Bykov (3), as early as 1924, found that dogs with the corpus callosum destroyed could no longer generalize tactile conditioned responses between the two sides of the body. Instead, in such animals, closely conflicting reflexes could for the first time be established to stimulation of homologous loci of the two body halves. It is interesting to note Bykov's qualification that even in the commissure sectioned dog, strong skin stimulation could give rise to bilateral effects in learning.

Also using the technique of the conditioned reflex, Airapetyants (1) and Bianki (2) obtained results at variance with those of Bykov. Their evidence pointed instead toward an eventual restoration of bilateral conditioned signalization on touch stimulation after section of major portions of corpus callosum.

In the cat, corpus callosum destruction prevented transfer of touch discrimination learning between the forepaws, according to a report by Stamm and Sperry (14). In similar experiments with monkeys, however, corpus callosum transection interfered with transfer of training in only part of the animals (12, 13). After further investigation, Glickstein and Sperry (4) indicated that corpus callosum sectioned monkeys readily transferred "motor pattern and testing set" between the hands but cross availability of "distinctive sensory knowledge" seemed de-

[1] Supported in part by Grant B-2627 from the Public Health Service.

ficient in most cases. Still later these authors suggested that corpus callosum sectioned monkeys could transfer tactile discrimination responses between the hands only if the somatosensory area of one hemisphere had been damaged (5).

Normal chimpanzees that have learned laboriously to solve complex
latch-box problems with one hand immediately solved them with the
other. Chimpanzees with corpus callosum sectioned failed in such second hand recognition and required separate relearning through the
second hand (9).

Humans with varying expanses of the corpus callosum surgically
divided have been tested for intermanual transfer of stylus-maze learning (11). Both the commissure operated group and matched controls
failed to achieve errorless performance on first trials through the second, untrained hand. However, errorless second hand performance
was achieved significantly more rapidly by the control groups than by
the commissure damaged group though the latter group did achieve
more rapid solution working through the second hand than working
through the first. Commissure damage, according to this study, failed
to interfere completely with transfer of stylus-maze learning between
the hands in the human.

A human being with corpus callosum agenesis has been studied
for transfer of training between the hands (10). The patient was tested
with a Sequin-Goddard formboard, first through one hand and then
the other. This patient required a slightly longer time to solve the
formboard through the second hand than through the first. Normal
subjects, in contrast, required considerably less time for second hand
solving after experience through the first hand. Agenesis of the corpus
callosum seemed, in this patient, to interfere with transfer of training
between the hands. In another study a second patient with corpus
callosum agenesis exhibited excellent transfer of training between the
hands (8).

These discrepancies in findings give rise to considerable uncertainty
as to the actual role of the corpus callosum in the across-the-midline
transmission of tactual learning. The suggestion is strong indeed that
transfer of training may occur under some circumstances in corpus callosum sectioned subjects. However, if transfer occurs, the factors important in determining its presence remain unknown. Differences in
species, in complexity of tasks handled, in prior learning experiences,
and in kind and energy of stimulation all may play a role. At the same
time, inadequacies in anatomical control of lesions or in utilization

of psychological techniques applied to the problem may enter to affect in some degree the experimental outcome.

The present study seeks to examine once again the role of corpus callosum in the transfer of training between the hands and also, for the first time, between the feet of monkeys. Particular attention was paid to the strict control of factors that might influence transfer. Specifically, to avoid generalization effects animals with no prior formal training in the laboratory setting were used. Anatomical check of the lesion was carried out for each operated subject to rule out the possibility of incomplete lesions. Four or more monkeys were used in each phase of the experiment. Additionally, detailed learning curves were traced for each animal so that exact comparison of the course of learning through the separate body members was possible.

Transfer of a simple bar-pressing behavior as well as of a warm-cold and a tactual form discrimination was studied. Results have been obtained which indicate whether factors such as response complexity or sensory modality may determine the presence or the degree of transfer.

METHODS

Seventeen immature monkeys (*Macaca mulatta*) ranging in weight from 5 to 8 lb. were employed in the present investigation. These animals were completely inexperienced in formal laboratory training situations. Eight of the seventeen monkeys underwent corpus callosum and anterior commissure section prior to training, while the remaining nine monkeys served as unoperated controls.

Intraperitoneal pentobarbital was used to produce surgical anesthesia during these operative procedures. Using sterile precautions the skin of the head was incised paramedially from the region of the supraorbital ridge to the occipital crest. After retraction of muscle and fascia and elevation of the periostium, a large free bone flap lying 1 mm. to the left of the midline was removed, using a motor-mounted dental-crown saw. The bone up to the superior sagittal sinus was chipped away with bone forceps. Dura was widely opened and laid back across the midline, exposing the convexity of the left hemisphere. By gentle retraction of the hemisphere with a broad spatula inserted into the longitudinal fissure, the corpus callosum and anterior commissure were directly observed and transected, using a thin glass pipette and low vacuum suction. The transection in its entirety was carried out under visual control through an otological microscope. Afterwards, dura and bone flap were replaced and covering fascia and skin reapposed with silk sutures. Procaine penicillin (1,200,000 units) was given intramuscularly at the time of surgery. In all cases the postoperative course was uneventful.

A semiautomatic training apparatus served in teaching the monkeys discrimination tasks (Fig. 1). This apparatus was equipped with electrical control and relay circuits to activate machinery for tactful stimuli presentation. During training sessions the food-deprived animals were seated and secured in a restraining enclosure in juxtaposition to the training apparatus. In this enclosure they were visually isolated from the tactual stimuli and from the general environment. Each of the four extremities had separate access to the tactual stimuli through four sep-

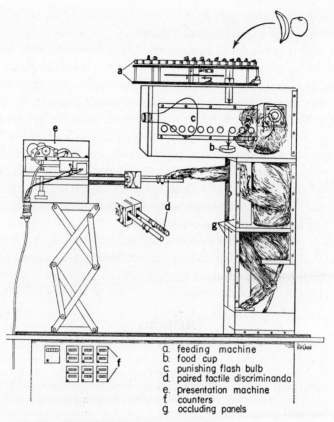

a. feeding machine
b. food cup
c. punishing flash bulb
d. paired tactile discriminanda
e. presentation machine
f. counters
g. occluding panels

FIG. 1.   Tactile training apparatus. Any three of the extremities
may be constrained in a comfortable position while the fourth is
free to manipulate and respond to the tactile stimulus objects.

arate portals. Occluding panels (Fig. 1g) were used to block three of the four
portals in different combinations. In this fashion it was possible to specify the
particular extremity the monkey could use in responding to the tactual stimuli
through any given session or series of sessions. The monkey's total experience with
a given tactual task could be limited to any one of the four extremities. The
effects of such one-extremity learning on successive performances through the remaining extremities could then be tested by simple rearrangements of the portal
occluders.

At the outset the animals were placed in the training apparatus for $\frac{1}{2}$ hour
each day for several days to familiarize them with the behavioral situation. The
animals were then taught to "bar press" or to depress a blank lever in the form
of a 1-inch-square aluminum shaft. Each bar press yielded a small banana reward
through a feeding machine (Fig. 1a). After they had learned to successfully bar
press through one extremity they were presented with the lever successively
through the other extremities. Where necessary, the animals were retaught the
response through the other extremities, including the feet.

The monkeys were then ready for training on a tactual or a warm-cold discrimination problem. The paired stimuli of each discrimination task were pre-

sented to the animals as separate objects attached to separate lever arms oriented side by side (Fig. 1*d*). The monkeys could make their choice by depressing or elevating one or the other of the stimulus objects against a moderate spring tension. Following choice, these objects were automatically retracted, indexed and represented in the same or reversed position according to a chance sequence. A correct choice delivered a food reward to the monkey in addition to causing the rapid retraction and return of the stimuli. An incorrect choice delivered no reward, retracted and withheld the stimuli for a 15-sec. delay period, extinguished the animal's dim houselight, and delivered an initial 1-sec. punishing photoflood lamp flash in his eyes. Following incorrect choices, the stimulus objects were represented in the same position until the next correct choice was made, whereupon the chance stimulus presentation sequence was resumed.

Each animal was run a total of 100 trials each day regardless of score. As learning proceeded the number of correct responses increased. Finally, after the score reached 85 or more correct trials in 100 (an arbitrary criterion of learned performance) each monkey was run an additional 5 days of 100 overtraining trials each, to stabilize performance level through the trained limb. Some of the monkeys were required to learn first through one of the hands while others were required to learn initially through one of the feet.

After the monkeys had acquired and stabilized the response through the one limb, transfer of training tests were carried out through the opposite limb. Where immediate cross recognition was not seen additional retraining trials were given through the second limb. In like manner, the animals were subsequently tested and reconditioned in the discrimination through the other two remaining limbs. Learning curves were constructed to represent the course of learning through each of the four limbs, in turn.

In the present investigation unimanual (or unipedal) learning and transfer of two separate discrimination responses was studied. The stimulus pair of one discrimination consisted of two aluminum rods $3/8$ inch in diameter and 4 inches long, one a smooth cylinder and the other a smooth cylinder containing in addition five equally spaced, right-angled, turned grooves $1/8$ inch wide (Fig. 2). The grooved rod was arbitrarily designated as the positive, rewarding stimulus of the two. This discrimination task is referred to as the groove-smooth discrimination. The stimulus pair of the second task consisted of two smooth brass cylinders, both 1 inch in diameter and rounded at the end. In surface qualities these two cylinders were identical except that one was warmed by an internal electric heater and the other was cooled by an iced core. The warmed lever was designated the positive, rewarding stimulus of the pair. This discrimination is referred to as the warm-cold discrimination.

The completeness of transection of corpus callosum and anterior commissure was verified in the animals of this study by examination of the formalin-fixed brains. In all instances it was possible to gain this verification by close inspection of gross slices of the brain alone. In addition to transection of corpus callosum and anterior commissure, concomitant division of the commissural fibers of the psalterium occurred as they underlay the splenium and corpus of the corpus callosum. Additional variable injury occurred to the septa pellucida, the columns of the fornix, and/or the anterior cingulate gyrus.

RESULTS

Bar-pressing Behavior. Both the normal and the commissure sectioned monkeys required 4–7 days of assisted training to achieve rapid and consistent bar-pressing behavior through one hand. Four addi-

Fig. 2. Tactile stimulus objects. Left pair is the groove-smooth problem in which the grooved lever was positive and rewarded. Identical brass cylinders on the right were used in the warm-cold problem in which the warmed lever was consistently rewarded.

tional days of bar pressing was then allowed through this hand. The blank bar-press lever was next presented to the animals for continuation of bar-pressing behavior through the second hand.

The normal monkeys resumed rapid and consistent bar pressing through the second hand after a very brief period of fumbling. The commissure sectioned animals, on the contrary, failed to resume bar pressing through the second hand and required separate reconditioning through this hand. Further, these operated animals required as long to relearn bar pressing through the second hand as they required to learn initially through the first hand.

The lever was next presented to the monkeys through one foot. Despite the prior experience through both hands the animals were hesitant to reach out with the foot. In the end, however, they learned to bar press through the first foot after 4–6 days of assisted practice. Following a period of overtraining through the first foot the lever was presented to the animals for performance through the second foot. Even the normal animals required initial retraining through the second foot but were bar pressing well by the end of the second day. The commissure sectioned monkeys, however, required the full 4–6 days of reconditioning through the second foot before satisfactory bar-pressing behavior ensued.

Groove-Smooth Discrimination.   Three normal monkeys were taught the groove-smooth discrimination through one hand, two (*709* and *636*) through the right hand, and the third (*579*) through the left hand. *Monkey 709* required 1,300 trials, *monkey 636,* 1,800, and *monkey 579,* 500 trials to reach the 85 correct in 100 criterion of learned response through the first hand. Following subsequent over-training, performance through the second, inexperienced hand was tested. *Monkey 709* responded correctly 91 times, *monkey 636,* 89 times, and *monkey 579,* 88 times in the first 100 trials. On the second 100 trials all three monkeys performed at a high level. The learning curves through the two hands of these monkeys may be seen in Figure 3.

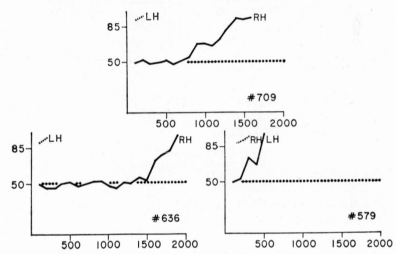

Fig. 3. Serial learning curves achieved through the two hands of three normal monkeys on the groove-smooth problem. Learning through the first hand is represented by the solid line; through the second hand by the dashed line. The second hand benefited greatly from the previous experiences through the first hand.

Two corpus callosum and anterior commissure sectioned monkeys received initial training through the right hand and two through the left hand. The first two required 1,800 (*536*) and 1,200 (*720*) trials to reach the 85 correct in 100 criterion performance while the latter two required 900 (*754*) and 600 (*664*) trials. After overtraining, transfer performance was tested through the inexperienced second hand of these animals. All performed at a chance level during the first days of testing. Further, each monkey in turn required extensive retraining through his second hand. The two animals that required 1,800 and 1,200 trials to learn through the right hand required 1,900 and 1,300 trials to relearn through the left hand. The animals that required 900 and 600 trials to learn initially through the left hand required 900 and 500 trials to relearn through the right hand. The learning curves through both hands of these four commissure sectioned animals are reproduced in Figure 4.

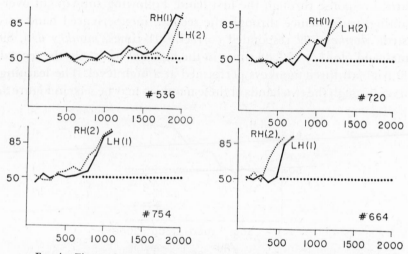

Fig. 4. First and second hand learning curves on the groove-smooth problem in four corpus callosum sectioned monkeys. Similarity of learning through the two hands is striking.

One normal monkey (*701*) was taught the groove-smooth discrimination first through the right foot. This animal required 6,800 trials for primary pedal learning. When the stimuli were subsequently presented to this animal through the other foot, however, only 500 trials were required for relearning. A second normal monkey failed to show signs of first foot learning after 5,000 trials. No further training was carried out with this animal.

Three normal monkeys with prior learning of the groove-smooth discrimination through both hands required 3,000 (*636*), 2,000 (*709*), and 3,400 (*551*) trials to learn through a first foot and 700 (*636*), 750 (*709*), and 900 (*551*) trials to relearn through the second foot. Figure 5 represents the performance of the two separate feet subsequent to both hand learning of only one of these animals (*636*).

None of the commissure sectioned animals experienced the groove-smooth discrimination primarily through a foot but two received pedal training subsequent to learning through both hands. They re-

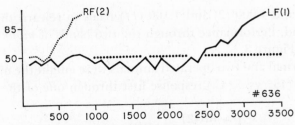

FIG. 5. Serial learning through the two feet following both hand learning on the groove-smooth discrimination. Despite the prior hand experience learning through the feet was prolonged. The saving in number of trials required for second foot learning was considerable. However, training transfer between the feet was imperfect compared to training transfer between the hands.

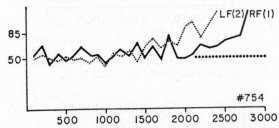

FIG. 6. Foot learning and interpedal transfer following both hand learning on the groove-smooth discrimination in a corpus callosum sectioned monkey. Forebrain commissure section interfered with transfer of training between the feet.

quired 2,800 (*754*) and 3,300 (*536*) trials for learning through the first foot and 2,300 (*754*) and 5,000 (*536*) trials for relearning through the second foot. Figure 6 illustrates the learning of the groove-smooth discrimination through the two separate feet of commissure sectioned *monkey 754.*

Warm-Cold Discrimination. Two normal monkeys received primary manual training with the warm-cold discrimination (45° vs. 3° C.). They required 800 (*526*) and 300 (*214*) trials to achieve a learned performance through the first hand while they both achieved high level performance on the first 100 trials through the second hand. Figure 7 shows curves of learning through the two hands of *monkey 526.*

Two monkeys with corpus callosum and anterior commissure sectioned received manual training, using a more subtle warm-cold discrimination (45° vs. 15° C.). With this small difference in temperature they required 1,200 (*2*) and 700 (*14*) trials to learn through the first hand and 1,000 (*2*) and 1,100 (*14*) trials to relearn through the second hand. Performance through the two hands of *monkey 14* may be seen in Figure 8.

Two normal and two operated animals were taught the more severe warm-cold (45° vs. 3° C.) response first through one of the feet. The

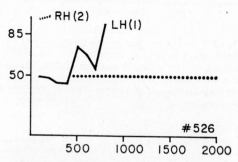

FIG. 7. Serial learning of a warm-cold discrimination through the two hands of a normal monkey. The animal exhibited immediate recognition through the untrained hand.

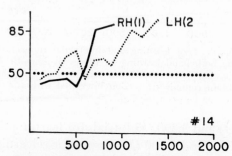

FIG. 8. Intermanual transfer of warm-cold discrimination learning in a corpus callosum sectioned monkey. As with the groove-smooth problem, there was little evidence of training transfer between the hands after commissure section.

normal monkeys required, 1,500 (*813*) and 1,200 (*633*) trials to achieve a high level response through the first foot and 300 (*813*) and 400 (*633*) trials for reinstatement of the response through the second foot. The corpus callosum sectioned monkeys required 700 (*629*) and 2,500 (*802*) trials to learn through the first foot and 900 (*629*) and 2,600 (*802*) trials to relearn through the second foot. The first of the two operated animals (*629*) was then taught the warm-cold discrimination through one of the hands. Five hundred trials were required for such manual relearning following foot learning. Subsequently this operated monkey required 700 trials for relearning the same response through the second hand. Figures 9 and 10 represent the course of learning of the warm-cold discrimination through the separate feet of normal *monkey 633* and commissure sectioned *monkey 629*.

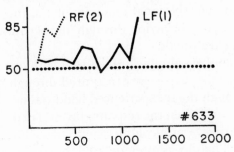

FIG. 9. Transfer of warm-cold discrimination learning between the feet of a normal monkey.

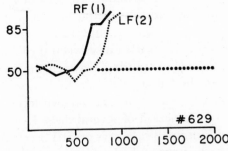

FIG. 10. Failure of interpedal transfer of training on the warm-cold discrimination after section of the corpus callosum.

DISCUSSION

Some of the animals acquired the discrimination responses initially through a foot while others learned them first through a hand. Initial learning through a foot required many more hundreds of trials than comparable learning through a hand. This held true even for the learning of the warm-cold discrimination. However, once learning had been achieved the pedally trained monkeys performed at levels through the feet comparing favorably with those of manually trained animals through the hands. It seemed clear that the animals, operated or unoperated, were capable, on a behavioral basis, of discriminating the differences between the specific tactual stimuli quite well through both the feet and the hands.

Normal monkeys that had been taught to bar press through one hand resumed bar pressing almost immediately through the second, inexperienced hand. The corpus callosum sectioned animals, in contrast, failed to resume bar-pressing behavior on presentations through the second hand but instead required separate, second hand reconditioning. Approximately equal amounts of training were required to instate bar-pressing behavior through the separate hands of the commissurotomized animals.

The normal monkeys also performed well with one hand the more purely tactual learning experiences acquired through the other hand. Recollection through the inexperienced hand was nearly complete on the first day of testing when the response investigated was the simpler, more quickly learned, warm-cold discrimination. Full recall through the inexperienced hand was often delayed, however, until the second day of testing when the response under study was the more difficult, more slowly acquired, groove-smooth discrimination. Such slight depression of performance on initial testing through the untrained hand points to some imperfection in the interhemispheric transmission of tactual learning. A similar imperfection has been described in the exchange of visual information between the hemispheres 6, 7, 8.

The degree of transfer of training between the feet stood in contrast to that between the hands in the normal animals. Performance through the second foot was at or near chance levels on first testing and it remained so for a period of several days. However, relearning through the second foot in all cases was greatly accelerated when compared to initial learning through the first foot. Thus, some transfer of training between the feet clearly obtained but was evidenced only as savings in relearning scores. Transfer of training between the feet in the normal animal is very much more hampered than is transfer of training between the hands.

Just as corpus callosum interruption halted the cross-availability of learned bar-pressing behavior between opposite extremities so did it prevent the across-the-midline transfer of more purely tactually mediated learning. This was as true of the relatively simple warm-cold differentiation as it was of the more complex groove-smooth discrimination. The degree of interruption of cross communication occurring with the transection of the commissures may be gauged from the curves characterizing learning through the opposite extremities of the operated animals (Figs. 4, 6, 8, and 10). In no instance was there indication of a significantly more rapid learning through the second hand (or foot) than that which obtained through the first. Rather, the striking feature was the close similarity of the course of learning through opposite body members following commissure section.

Consideration of the rates of learning of both the normal and the commissure sectioned monkeys revealed a wide spread within each group in the number of trials required for initial unimember learning. However, no evidence existed in the data which would indicate slower learning by the corpus callosum sectioned monkeys compared to the normal controls. In fact, the average number of trials required for initial unimanual learning of the groove-smooth discrimination by the three normal animals was 1,200 trials in contrast to an average 1,100 trials required by the four operated subjects. These data suggest that section of the forebrain commissures has little if any effect on the rate of tactual learning in the monkey.

SUMMARY

Nine normal monkeys and eight with corpus callosum and anterior commissure sectioned were studied for transfer of training between the hands and between the feet. The normal animals recognized almost immediately with one hand tasks learned with the other hand. They failed, however, in such immediate recognition on tests with a second foot but exhibited more rapid relearning through this foot than through the first foot. By contrast, animals with their commissures sectioned failed to exhibit any evidence of cross-recognition between the hands or between the feet of *1)* a simple bar-pressing behavior, *2)* a warm-cold discrimination response, and *3)* a more complex tactual form discrimination response. The concept that section of the corpus callosum depresses rates of learning through the separate body members received no support from the present study.

REFERENCES

1. AIRAPETYANTS, E. S. *Higher Nervous Activity and Internal Organ Receptors.* Moscow-Leningrad, Akad. Nauk. USSR, 1952.
2. BIANKI, V. L. Effect of partial section of the corpus callosum in dogs on the differentiation of visual, auditory and cutaneous stimuli. *Sech. Physiol. J. USSR.*, 1958, 44: 660–66.
3. BYKOV, K. Versuche an Hunden mit Durchschneiden des Corpus Callosum. *Zbl. ges. Neurol. Psychiat.*, 1924, **39**: 199.
4. GLICKSTEIN, M. and SPERRY, R. W. Intermanual transfer of somesthetic discrimination in split-brain Rhesus monkeys. *Physiologist*, 1959, 2(3): 45–46.
5. GLICKSTEIN, M. and SPERRY, R. W. Intermanual somesthetic transfer in split-brain Rhesus monkeys. *J. comp. Physiol. Psychol.*, 1960, 53: 322–27.
6. MYERS, R. E. Interhemispheric communication through corpus callosum: limitations under conditions of conflict. *J. comp. Physiol. Psychol.*, 1959, 52: 6–9.

7. MYERS, R. E.   Corpus callosum and visual gnosis, in: Fessard, Gerard, and Konorski, eds., *Brain Mechanisms and Learning.* Oxford, Blackwell Scientific Publications, 1961.
8. MYERS, R. E.   Transmission of visual information within and between the hemispheres: a behavioral study, in: *Cerebral Dominance and Interhemispheric Relations,* V. B. Mountcastle (editor). Baltimore, Johns Hopkins University Press, in press, 1962.
9. MYERS, R. E. and HENSON, C. O.   Role of corpus callosum in transfer of tactuokinesthetic learning in chimpanzee. *Arch. Neurol. Psychiat., Chicago,* 1960, 3: 404–9.
10. RUSSELL, J. R. and REITAN, R. M.   Psychological abnormalities in agenesis of the corpus callosum. *J. nerv. and ment. Dis.,* 1955, 121: 205–14.
11. SMITH, K. U.   Learning and the associative pathways of the human cerebral cortex. *Science,* 1951, 114: 117–21.
12. SPERRY, R. W.   In: Brazier, M. A. B., The Central Nervous System and Behavior. Transactions of First Conference, Feb. 23–26, 1958, Josiah Macy, Jr. Foundation, New York, 1959, pp. 386–92.
13. SPERRY, R. W.   Corpus callosum and interhemispheric transfer in the monkey (*Macaca mulatta*). *Anat. Rec.,* 1958, 131: 297.
14. STAMM, J. S. and SPERRY, R. W.   Function of corpus callosum in contralateral transfer of somesthetic discrimination in cats. *J. comp. Physiol. Psychol.,* 1957, 50: 138–43.

SUCCESSIVE AND MAINTAINED CONDITIONING

IN SPINAL CARNIVORES[1]

ROSCOE A. DYKMAN
School of Medicine, University of Arkansas

and PHIL S. SHURRAGER
Illinois Institute of Technology

The experiments reported in this paper indicate that ability to learn exists at lower levels of the central nervous system and is not limited to CNS levels above the spinal cord. Although Shurrager and collaborators described phenomena which they designated spinal conditioned responses in the semitendinosus muscles of young acute spinal dogs (11, 12, 13, 14, 15), subsequent investigators, notably Kellogg, *et al.* (1, 4, 5, 6, 7, 8) and Pinto and Bromiley (9), either failed to produce spinal conditioned responses or felt that explanations other than spinal conditioning were plausible. Two articles which appeared comparatively recently in the foreign press should also be mentioned. Russian physiologists Shamarina and Niesmieyanova (10) attempted to verify some of Shurrager's work with spinal dogs but concluded that the results obtained could be explained without using the concept of spinal conditioning. On the other hand, Franzisket (3) claims to have demonstrated conditioning in spinal frogs. He employed an ingenious technique of refrigerating the spinal frogs between training sessions, thus reducing the activity of the animals and apparently thereby enabling them to accumulate the effects of previous learning trials.

Both acute and chronic spinal preparations were used in the present study. It was undertaken to extend our knowledge of the behavior of spinal animals and to meet, in part, criticisms of previous experiments designed to test the hypothesis that spinal learning is possible.

[1] This investigation was supported in part by a research grant (RG 1578) from the U.S. Public Health Service to P. S. Shurrager.

719

METHOD

The experimental population consisted of 15 spinal kittens and one spinal puppy. Three kittens failed to give evidence of conditioning, but the puppy and 12 kittens gave positive results, which are reported below.[2]

Transection between two ligatures approximately 1 cm. apart was performed under ether anesthesia at levels ranging from fifth thoracic to first lumbar spinal roots. The procedure has been described in detail elsewhere (13). Age at transection varied from 2 days to 3 months, and days elapsing between transection and initiation of training ranged from zero to 70. The duration of training, age at transection, locus of transection, and postoperative days before the initiation of training for the 13 spinal preparations which gave positive results are summarized in Table 1. Some of the spinal animals were used in several phases of the experiments.

TABLE 1

EXPERIMENTAL POPULATION YIELDING POSITIVE SPINAL CONDITIONING RESULTS

Conditioning Type	Ani-mal *	Experi-mental Period	Age at Tran-section (Days)	Locus of Tran-section	Postop-erative Days before Training
Successive	1	5 hr.	84	T 5	0
Ipsilateral	3	4 hr.	60	T 7	0
	5	8 hr.	84	T 5	0
Contralateral	4	23 days	28	L 1	0
	8	26 days	35	T 10	0
	9	35 days	2	T 12	0
	10	7 days	7	T 11	36
	11	6 days	7	T 13	24
	12	24 days	14	L 1	9
Tail	4	10 days	—	—	26
	9	5 days	—	—	36
	12	7 days	—	—	35
Maintained	13	10 days	14	T 12	8
	12	15 days	—	—	46
Contralateral	13	15 days	—	—	28
	16	14 days	21	T 12	10
Tail	9	14 days	—	—	51
	10	13 days	—	—	48
	11	11 days	—	—	45
Control	10	3 days	—	—	70
Sensitization	12	3 days	—	—	65
	13	3 days	—	—	50
Latency	9	2 days	—	—	45
	14	3 days	21	L 1	28
Regeneration	9	20 days	77†	T 8–10	0
Kymograph	14	5 days	—	—	15
	15	10 days	4	T 13	25

* 1–15, cats; 16, dog.
† Second operation.

[2] Additional records can be found in the doctoral dissertation of R. A. Dykman, submitted to the University of Chicago in 1949 (2). The authors are indebted to Dr. N. Kleitman, Department of Physiology, University of Chicago, who sponsored the dissertation and made valuable suggestions and criticisms, and to Dr. H. C. Shurrager, of Illinois Institute of Technology.

In the conditioning experiments animals were securely fastened to a padded board by strips of gauze around the body. Hind legs were free in the air. In this position the hind legs of some spinal animals make constant stepping movements. Such animals cannot be used to demonstrate learned motor responses in the hind legs, and so they were not included in the experimental population.

The unconditioned stimulus (UCS) was an electrical shock applied to the right hind leg just above the paw and intense enough to produce strong flexion of the leg with varying degrees of extension and flexion of the opposite leg. This response to the UCS is hereafter designated UCR (unconditioned response). One electrode, a small piece of gauze moistened with saline, was attached to the paw. The ground electrode was attached to a cloth belly band moistened with saline. Leads were moistened every 3 to 5 min.

The conditioned stimulus (CS) was in most cases a light touch of a sable hair brush which remained in contact with the animal's fur from about 0.5 to 1.0 sec. This CS was chosen to check the suggestion that the spinal conditioned response resulted from electrical facilitation. Only in Control Experiment 3 was the CS an electrical shock. The area of application of the CS varied in different phases of the study.

The spinal conditioned response (CR) was a movement of the hind leg or legs in response to the CS. The criteria of conditioning were: (*a*) the CS was originally neutral, failing to elicit a response of the hind limbs before it was presented in conjunction with the UCS in the conditioning procedure; (*b*) after CS and UCS were presented together a number of times, the animal responded to the CS with a movement of the hind limbs (CR); (*c*) the CR persisted and was present when the CS was presented after a rest period; and (*d*) the CR could be extinguished by successive spaced presentations of the CS without reinforcement by the UCS.

In all experiments a series of unreinforced CS trials was conducted first to establish the neutrality of the CS. This was followed by a series of conditioning trials in which the CS was reinforced by the UCS. When conditioning resulted, a final series of unreinforced trials was continued until the CS failed to elicit a CR for ten consecutive trials. Neutrality trials in any session subsequent to the first session were also measures of both sustained extinction and spontaneous recovery.

The responses were observed by a minimum of two persons in all experiments, and the CR had to reach a magnitude at which it was unquestionably a movement of the hind limb(s) in response to the CS before it was scored a CR. Three *O*s' independent ratings were checked for reliability in one typical daily procedure on each of the 12 kittens giving positive results. The agreement among *O*s was almost perfect.

It was felt that kymograph recordings of the responses would be more conclusive than the judgment of *O*s. This was at first proposed as the method to be used in all experiments, but it was found that the necessary encumbrance of the hind legs frequently caused the CR to be absent or reduced in magnitude. Kymograph records were, however, obtained for over 200 conditioning trials with animals 14 and 15. The simultaneous independent ratings of three *O*s were checked against the kymograph records for these trials and found to agree very closely with the kymographically recorded data.

The general procedures above were followed throughout the experiments. The various phases of the study and the experimental procedures specific to the subdivisions follow. Three types of successive conditioning (ipsilateral, contralateral, and tail) and two types of maintained conditioning (contralateral and tail) were attempted.

In a successive conditioning routine the sequence of unreinforced, conditioning, and extinction trials followed each other on the same day. Trials were continued until the animals gave a CR (in a conditioning series) or failed to give it (in an extinction series) for ten successive trials in two five-trial units. For example, to meet the criterion of conditioning, the animal had to respond to the CS for trials 6 to 15 or 11 to 20, etc.

Successive ipsilateral conditioning was attempted on eight spinal animals within ½ to 2 hr. following transection, the exact time depending on their recovery from anesthesia. Three animals gave positive results. The CS was the stroke of a soft brush to the right side of the animal, lateral and proximal to the vertebrae. The brush moved along a line from about the fourth sacral vertebra to the tail. The ipsilateral conditioning series (all trials given on the day of transection) was preceded by 30 to 60 presentations of the unreinforced CS to determine the neutrality of this stimulus. Animals were then conditioned by reinforcing the CS with the UCS. A brush-shock sequence was given every 30 to 60 sec., the time interval between the brush and shock varying from 0.5 to 5.0 sec. When a CR was established, it was extinguished by presenting the CS without the UCS. The conditioning and extinction trials were alternated through several consecutive sequences.

Successive contralateral conditioning was attempted on nine animals, six of which gave positive results. Procedure differed in three respects from the ipsilateral procedure: (*a*) the CS was the stroke of a brush along a 1-in. line on the inner side of the cat's left hind leg (the leg contralateral to the UCS); (*b*) conditioning attempts were begun from zero to 36 days after transection and continued beyond the acute period; (*c*) conditioning and extinction sessions were run at the rate of one per day, each animal receiving on any one day 30 to 60 neutrality trials, a number of conditioning trials, and a number of extinction trials. Animals were subjected to daily conditioning and extinction procedures through several consecutive series. A brush-shock sequence was given every 15 to 60 seconds. The time lag between the CS and UCS varied randomly from 0.5 to 5.0 sec. In contralateral conditioning, CR's were recorded in the right leg only.

In successive tail conditioning, the experimental procedure was the same as in contralateral conditioning except that the CS was the stroke of a brush upward over a 1-in. area on the middle of the right side of the tail. When the CR was well established, the animals responded almost immediately following the first contact of the brush with the tail. Four animals were used.

In the maintained conditioning routine, neutrality conditioning, and extinction trials were spread over a number of days (i.e., several days of neutrality trials, then conditioning trials for a number of consecutive days, and finally extinction trials for a number of days). The latter procedure is typical of most conditioning work.[3]

A maintained conditioning procedure was employed with five spinal kittens and the spinal puppy. Three kittens were conditioned by the tail technique and two kittens and the puppy by the contralateral technique. The procedure consisted of five neutrality sessions, conditioning sessions until the animals reached a constant level of performance, and extinction sessions until the CR disappeared. Each session was limited to 40 trials.

In addition to the successive and maintained conditioning experiments described above, several control experiments were carried out. To avoid confusion, the procedures in these are described immediately preceding their results.

RESULTS

Although the original experimental population included 15 spinal kittens and 1 spinal puppy, the data presented in this paper are based

---

[3] Dr. Kleitman suggested the maintained conditioning routine as a more effective demonstration of conditioning than the successive conditioning routine.

entirely on the 12 kittens which did condition and the puppy (Table 1).

In establishing a spinal CR, age appeared to be a factor. Animals whose spinal cords were transected at a younger age required fewer sessions to acquire a stable CR. The actual age differences among the animals were small, since none was older than four months at the time of transection. These small absolute differences may, however, be critical, for other workers have failed to establish conditioned responses in mature animals. Animals 6 and 2, which did not condition, were transected at two and four months, respectively. While animal 5, transected at three months, conditioned in the period immediately following the operation, it did not show the maintained responses of the younger animals.

The CR in animal 13 did not extinguish to the criterion after the first successive tail extinction session. On the first experimental day, the CR of this animal did extinguish. It had recovered by the CS neutrality session the following day, and the response showed no tendency to weaken through eight days of extinction sessions. This was the only animal that did not give consistent results in the successive routines.

Three animals gave positive results in the successive ipsilateral conditioning routine. Four cycles of conditioning and extinction were completed with these animals. Persistence of the CR was tested by allowing the animals to rest from 5 to 60 min. following attainment of the conditioning criterion before beginning further trials. One hundred per cent persistence of the CR in both hind legs of all three animals was observed when conditioning trials were resumed after rest intervals following initial attainment of the criterion. Spontaneous recovery was checked by introducing rest intervals between attainment of the extinction criterion and further extinction trials. It was found to be negligible, the highest value being an average of 12 per cent in the left hind legs in the second series of spontaneous recovery checks. Zero spontaneous recovery was observed in the third and fourth series of spontaneous recovery checks and in a fifth series of neutrality trials run after the elapse of 1 hr. following the fourth series of spontaneous recovery checks.

Persistence and spontaneous recovery checks in successive contralateral and tail conditioning were similar to those in ipsilateral conditioning except that the elapsed time intervals between criterion attainment and checking for persistence or spontaneous recovery were in some cases as long as 24 hr.

Six cats gave positive results in successive contralateral conditioning, and six complete cycles of conditioning and extinction were completed. Average persistence of the CR varied from 59 per cent (session 2) to 95 per cent (sessions 5 and 6), and average spontaneous recovery from 3 per cent (sessions 1 and 2) to 14 per cent (session 5).

Successive tail conditioning was continued through four complete cycles with three animals which gave positive results. Average persistence in the first cycle was 50 per cent in the left and 65 per cent in the right hind leg, and in the fourth cycle 100 per cent in the left and 95 per cent in the right hind leg. Spontaneous recovery was zero in both hind legs in the first cycle and 5 and 7 per cent in the left and right hind legs, respectively, in the fourth cycle.

In these experiments, especially in the contralateral and tail procedures which were carried out over a number of days, the CR increased in magnitude as a function of the number of conditioning trials, progressing from a slight muscular twitch in the UCS leg to repetitive stepping in both hind legs. The ipsilateral animals progressed to a stage of giving a partial flexion of one or both hind limbs. The CR occurring in the persistence trials appeared to be identical in nearly all cases to the CR that developed during the conditioning trials. During extinction the magnitude of the response decreased as extinction proceeded.

It was found that the duration of the time interval between conditioning and persistence trials for all successive routines was not significant when the mean number of CR's given during the persistence trials presented 1 hr. after conditioning was compared with the mean number of CR's given in persistence trials conducted from 1 to 24 hr. later ($p < .40$). The spontaneous recovery of the CR analyzed in a similar manner was also independent of time ($p < .50$).

When successive conditioning data were analyzed to determine the significance of the differences between the means of the persistence of the CR after rest intervals following conditioning sessions and the means of spontaneous recovery after rest intervals following extinction sessions, the differences were found to be significant beyond the .01 level.

The mean trial at which the criterion series (i.e., ten consecutive CR's in conditioning or ten consecutive failures to respond in extinction) was begun in five consecutive sessions by the animals used in the successive ipsilateral, contralateral, and tail conditioning experiments was determined. These means are plotted in Figures 1 and 2, which show that in consecutive sessions, the animals on the average required fewer trials to reach the criteria. While means of CR's of the right leg represent data from 12 animals, means of CR's in the left leg represent

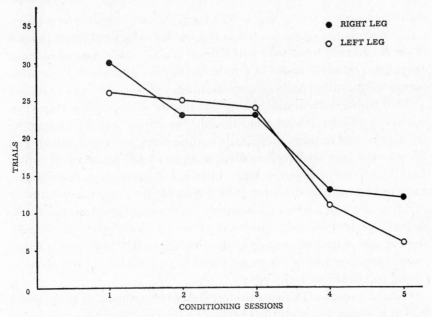

Fig. 1. Mean trial at which 12 animals initiated criterion series in five consecutive successive conditioning sessions.

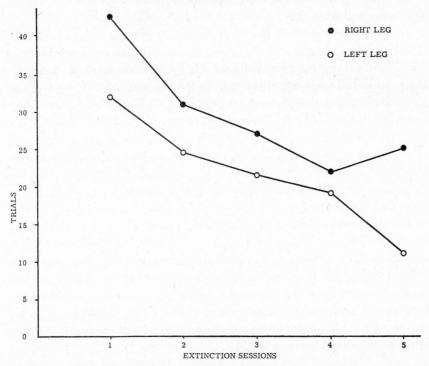

Fig. 2. Mean trial at which 12 animals initiated criterion series in five consecutive successive extinction series.

data from only 6 animals, since in contralateral conditioning no attempt was made to record CR's in the left leg. The final point in each of these curves is based on contralateral conditioning data only, since only four complete cycles of conditioning and extinction were completed in ipsilateral and tail conditioning.

Two spinal kittens and the spinal puppy gave positive results in maintained contralateral conditioning, and three spinal kittens gave positive results in maintained tail conditioning. The mean number of CR's in the first seven consecutive sessions of the maintained conditioning routines are presented in Figure 3. Each curve represents the average response of three animals. Figure 4 gives the mean number of CR's in the first seven consecutive daily extinction sessions. These figures clearly show the cumulative effects of consecutive daily conditioning and consecutive daily extinction trials. The data suggest that conditioned responses are more difficult to establish by the contralateral conditioning technique.

Control experiments were undertaken to investigate certain controversial points not specifically checked by the conditioning procedures. They were designed to answer three questions:

1. Does sensitization of the preparation by the UCS account for the appearance of the CR?

For three days animals 10, 12, and 13 were given a series of trials in which 60 UCS presentations without the CS preceded 40 contralateral and 40 tail CS presentations without the UCS. The sequence of contralateral and tail CS's was alternated so that an animal undergoing tail CS's first one day was given contralateral CS's first the next day. The combined means of "CR's" were 8 and 2 per cent, respectively, for the tail and contralateral procedures. These animals failed to develop a consistent response to the CS when it was not directly reinforced by the UCS.

2. Does possible regeneration of fibers across the transection account for CR results?

Chronic spinal kitten 9, originally transected at T12, was later ligated at T10 and T8 and a section of cord between the two ligatures removed. This eliminated a section of possibly overlapping neurones. Prior to the second operation the animal was conditioned by the tail method to a level of 100 per cent persistence. The CR established before the second operation was present and extinguishable after the transection. This agrees with results of a second transection after training reported elsewhere (14).

3. How does the latency of the UCR to the UCS compare with the latency of the CR to the CS?

Procedure was the same as in tail conditioning except that the CS was a minimal electrical stimulus applied to the tail. The output pulse of the stimulator had a constant wave form with wave rising rapidly

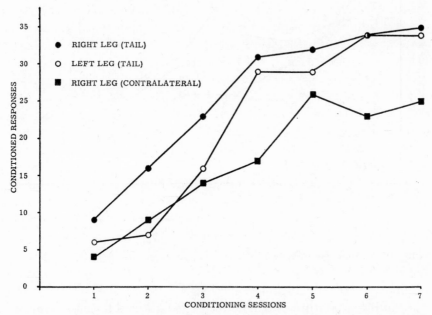

FIG. 3. Mean number of CR's in seven consecutive daily maintained conditioning sessions of 40 trials each.

to a maximum, followed by an exponential decay with a time constant of 0.3 msec. Output impedance was determined by position of 15,000-ohm variable output control. The intensity of the CS was just enough to elicit a barely observable twitch in a limited area of the tail. A motion picture of the CR established in animal 9 was made, photographing the animal and an electric timer simultaneously. Calculations were made of mean latencies in milliseconds of the CR during conditioning and extinction and of the UCR in a series of trials in which only the UCS was given. The latency of the CR was longer and more variable than that of the UCR. The (approximate) mean latency of the CR during conditioning was 96 msec., with a standard deviation of 45; during extinction it was 115, with an *SD* of 21. The mean latency of the UCR was 28 msec., with an *SD* of 3. When mean latencies of the CR for the first halves of conditioning and extinction trials were

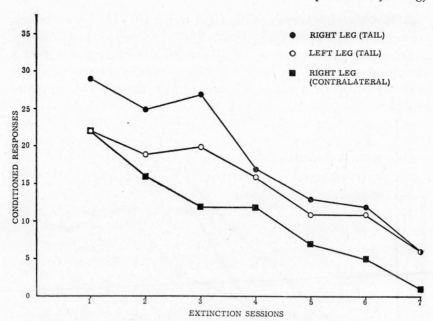

FIG. 4. Mean number of CR's in seven consecutive daily maintained extinction sessions of 40 trials each.

compared with mean latencies for the second halves of the trials, it was evident that the latency of the CR tends to decrease during conditioning and increase during extinction.

A similar procedure was carried out with animal 14, yielding results consistent with those obtained from animal 9.

Motion pictures of contralateral conditioning, using a brush stimulus, were also analyzed, latencies being calculated from CS response to CR and from UCS to UCR. It was necessary to use the minute CS response in these calculations because it was otherwise impossible to determine the moment of effectiveness of a brush stimulus. The UCR always occurred in the frame of stimulation (68 trials), while the CR occurred from one to ten frames later. These differences, although rather crudely obtained, also strongly suggest two different populations of responses (i.e., CR's and UCR's).

DISCUSSION

Several controls were used in this work to obviate an assumption of pseudoconditioning. The purpose of the CS neutrality trials was to insure that the CS was neutral to the animals at the beginning of every conditioning routine.

There may be some question as to why a brush stimulus was used for the CS, since the brush does not permit convenient quantification. The brush was used to test the hypothesis of electrical facilitation advanced by other investigators. To mention one such explanation, Pinto and Bromiley (13) suggested that the skin resistance of a spinal animal may decrease during conditioning; as a consequence, a previously indifferent electrical CS may become effective in producing a reflex movement. In effect, the CS becomes a UCS. Since in these experiments spinal conditioned responses were established to mechanical conditioned stimuli, it would appear that spinal conditioning phenomena cannot be dismissed as artifacts resulting from electrical facilitation.

The spontaneous recovery trials showed that the CR had no significant tendency to recover following extinction. Since the differences between the incidence of CR's following rest periods after conditioning (persistence) and the incidence of CR's following rest periods after extinction (spontaneous recovery) are significant at the .01 level, the different procedures of conditioning and extinction evidently effected some relatively permanent modification in the CNS. Rest intervals were in some cases as long as 24 hr.

When animals were conditioned over a number of days in the maintained conditioning routine, the CR frequency increased from one day to the next (Fig. 3). Extinction reversed the cumulative changes observed during conditioning (Fig. 4). This indicates that spinal animals acquire conditioned responses under procedures that are similar to those used in establishing salivary, cardiac, respiratory, and motor conditioned responses in intact animals and that the spinal conditioned response develops and disappears in a manner comparable to the conditioned response in the normal animal. The daily improvement of the spinal animals during maintained conditioning, as well as the significant differences in the incidence of CR's during trials checking persistence and spontaneous recovery, support the hypothesis that spinal conditioning depends on something other than temporary changes in the state of excitation of the spinal cord.

SUMMARY

It is difficult to summarize the data presented in this paper in concise form. Experimental population varied in terms of age of transection, locus of transection, time intervening between transection and training, and number of spinal animals in different phases of the study. Experimental procedures also varied widely. Under these diverse conditions phenomena were observed which meet the generally accepted criteria of conditioning. Whether these phenomena should be designated "spinal conditioned responses" or more cautiously, "responses which can be interpreted within a conditioning paradigm" is perhaps a moot question. If we accept as adequate to identify a conditioned response in the spinal animal those criteria which are accepted as adequate to identify it in the normal animal, we can conclude that results of the experiments here reported and analysis of the data indicate that:

1. Both acute and chronic spinal carnivores acquire motor conditioned responses.

2. Rapidity of conditioning and extinction is a function of the number of trials. In each reconditioning the animals require fewer trials to acquire stable conditioned responses. The same is true of extinction. In each succeeding extinction fewer trials are required to extinguish the conditioned response.

3. Within the time limits of these experiments, spinal conditioned response persistence and spontaneous recovery are not related to the duration of rest periods following successful conditioning or extinction.

4. The spinal conditioned response is not an artifact resulting from lowered skin resistance.

5. The latency of the spinal conditioned response is greater and more variable than the latency of the reflex produced by direct electrical stimulation.

REFERENCES

1. DEESE, J., and KELLOGG, W. N. Some new data on the nature of 'spinal conditioning.' *J. comp. physiol. Psychol.*, 1949, 42, 157–60.
2. DYKMAN, R. A. Experiments in spinal conditioning. Unpublished doctor's dissertation, Univer. of Chicago, 1949.
3. FRANZISKET, L. Gewohnheits Bilding und Bedigte Reflexe bei Rückenmarks Fröschen. *Z. f. vergl. Physiol.*, 1951, 33, 142–78.
4. KELLOGG, W. N. A search for the spinal conditioned response. *Amer. Psychologist*, 1946, 1, 274–75.
5. KELLOGG, W. N. Is 'spinal conditioning' conditioning? Reply to 'a comment.' *J. exp. Psychol.*, 1947, 37, 263–265.
6. KELLOGG, W. N., DEESE, J., and PRONKO, N. H. On the behavior of the lumbospinal dog. *J. exp. Psychol.*, 1946, 36, 503–11.
7. KELLOGG, W. N., DEESE, J., PRONKO, N. H., and FEINBERG, M. An attempt to condition the *chronic* spinal dog. *J. exp. Psychol.*, 1947, 37, 99–117.
8. KELLOGG, W. N., PRONKO, N. H., and DEESE, J. Spinal conditioning in dogs. *Science*, 1946, 103, 49–50.
9. PINTO, T., and BROMILEY, R. A search for 'spinal conditioning' and for evidence that it can become a reflex. *J. exp. Psychol.*, 1950, 40, 121–30.

10. SHAMARINA, N. M., and NIESMIEYANOVA, T. N. Operedyelke reflycktornykh reaktzi spinnovo mozga v oosloviakh experimenta. *Russian J. Physiol.*, 1953, 39, 601–9.

11. SHURRAGER, P. S. A comment on 'an attempt to condition the *chronic* spinal dog.' *J. exp. Psychol.*, 1947, 37, 261–63.

12. SHURRAGER, P. S. Conditioning in the spinal dog. Unpublished doctor's dissertation, Univer. of Illinois, 1939.

13. SHURRAGER, P. S., and CULLER, E. Conditioning in the spinal dog. *J. exp. Psychol.*, 1940, 26, 133–59.

14. SHURRAGER, P. S. and DYKMAN, R. A. Walking, spinal carnivores. *J. comp. physiol. Psychol.*, 1951, 44, 252–62.

15. SHURRAGER, P. S., and SHURRAGER, H. C. Comment on "a search for 'spinal conditioning' and for evidence that it can become a reflex." *J. exp. Psychol.*, 1950, 40, 135–37.

ANALYSIS OF THE EFFECTS OF FRONTAL LESIONS

IN MONKEY: II. VARIATIONS OF DELAYED RESPONSE[1]

MORTIMER MISHKIN[2] and KARL H. PRIBAM
Department of Neurophysiology, Institute of Living,
Hartford, Connecticut

The initial study of this series (5) tested the hypothesis that frontal operates fail both delayed alternation and delayed response because they have difficulty with the left-right response choice which these tasks require. Specifically, after the delay period of either task, the monkey is confronted with two containers which are distinguishable only by their positions—one cup appears on the left, the other on the right. In delayed alternation, for example, the correct mode of response is simply to alternate between the two cups; yet the performance of frontal operates rarely rises above chance. In the earlier study, therefore, frontal operates' performance on traditional left-right alternation was compared with their performance on two variants of alternation. In one variant, monkeys were trained to displace, alternately, two cups arranged one above the other—an up-down alternation; in the other, they were trained to alternate between displacing and not displacing a single centered cup (i.e., displace the cup on one trial, leave it alone on the next, displace it on the third trial, and so on)—a "go–no-go" alternation. Results on the up-down problem, which showed that frontal operates perform this task as poorly as they perform the traditional left-right alternation, disproved the original hypothesis.

On the "go–no-go" problem, however, the same operates achieved a performance level of nearly 90 per cent correct. The first of the present experiments was undertaken to determine whether similar improvement would result in frontal operates' *delayed-response* performance, if delayed response were varied from the traditional "left-

[1] This study was supported in part by a grant from Contract DA-49-007-MD-401 of the Army. The authors wish to thank Drs. Margaret A. Varley, L. Weiskrantz, and W. A. Wilson, Jr., for suggestions on preparing the manuscript.
[2] Now at the National Institute of Mental Health, Bethesda, Maryland.

right" task to a "go–no-go" task. Positive results would permit an analysis, using additional delayed-response variations, aimed at isolating the factors responsible for the frontal operates' improved performance. The second experiment proceeds with this analysis.

METHOD

Subjects

Eight immature macaques were used throughout this study: Four (LF 2, 3, 5, and 11) had bilateral anterolateral frontal ablations, and four (IT 4, 15, 26, and 37) had bilateral inferotemporal ablations. All but one (IT 37) had served as *S*s in the earlier experiment (5). The data for the present experiment were gathered in the interval four months to nine months after operation. Anatomical data on the four frontal and four temporal control operates may be found in references 5 and 9, respectively.

Apparatus

The apparatus consisted of an enclosure divided into two sections—an unlit chamber for the animal cage and an illuminated section for the testing tray, to which either one or two cups were attached. A sliding plywood panel was lowered between the two sections to hide the cups from the animal during the delay period. A one-way-vision screen concealed *E* when the sliding panel was raised.

EXPERIMENT I

All animals were trained on classical delayed response and on the variation. Each task was presented by both the direct method of cueing, in which the animal is shown the correct cup being baited with food, and by the indirect method, in which the animal is shown an object signaling the baited cup.

Traditional, direct method. For the traditional procedure the sliding panel was raised, a peanut was held for an instant over the left or the right cup (these were 12 in. apart and beyond the animal's reach), the peanut was dropped into it, and the cup covered with a lid. The panel was lowered for 5 sec., the tray pushed forward, and the panel raised again to permit the animal to respond. If the animal displaced the lid of the baited cup, it obtained the reward.

Variation, direct method. The variation on delayed response, analogous to the variation on delayed alternation used in the previous study, was presented in the following way: The sliding panel was raised, a peanut was held for an instant over a *single centered cup* (placed beyond the animal's reach), dropped into the cup, and covered with the lid. The panel was lowered for 5 sec., the cup pushed forward, and the panel was raised to permit response. This was a "go" trial; i.e., if the animal displaced the lid it found the reward. On a "no-go" trial, the panel was raised, *E* displayed an empty hand, and closed the lid of the empty cup. The panel was lowered for 5-sec. delay, the tray was pushed forward, and the panel was raised again. If it displaced the lid *on this trial, S* found the cup was empty. This "no-go" trial was scored correct only if the animal did not manipulate the lid in the 5 sec. permitted for response.

The "go" and "no-go" trials were presented in a predetermined, balanced order, as were the "left" and "right" trials in the traditional procedure. Fifty trials a day, with delayed self-correction for errors, were presented for 500 trials on each task, unless the animal attained the criterion of 90 correct in 100 trials before this training limit was reached. Two animals from each operate group received the traditional procedure first, and two received the varation first. In both tests the intratrial delays were 5 sec., with the panel interposed, and 5 sec. was permitted for response.

After completing these two tasks, all animals were given further training on the variation presented by the direct method with longer intratrial delays. Each animal received 30 trials a day (with delayed self-correction for errors) for three days. Within each daily session an equal number of 5-, 10-, and 15-sec. delays were presented in a predetermined, balanced order; at each delay, half the presentations were "go" trials and half were "no-go" trials.

Traditional, indirect method. For traditional delayed response presented by the indirect method, the stimulus object employed for half the animals was a round gray ash tray and for the other half, a square, colored tobacco tin. In the predelay period, the object appeared on top of one of the two covered cups, indicating which one contained the reward.

Variation, indirect method. For the variant procedure both objects were used with each animal. When one object (the same as that used in the traditional procedure) appeared on top of the single centered cup, it indicated that the cup *did* contain food and that the correct response was "go"; the other object indicated that the cup did *not* contain food, and that the correct response was "no go." [3]

In both tests, the object was always removed during the 5-sec. delay period. The two tests were again balanced for order, and in all other respects the training procedures were identical to those used with the direct method of baiting.

Results

The results, shown in Table 1, are the same for both the direct and indirect methods of baiting. On traditional delayed response, all control operates attained the 90 per cent criterion in less than 250 trials; all frontal operates received 500 trials and still performed at a

TABLE 1

RESULTS, EXPERIMENT I

(Scores are number of trials, including criterion run, required to attain the criterion of 90 per cent correct in 100 consecutive trials. A score of 500 trials denotes failure to reach criterion, and is accompanied by the per cent correct achieved in the final 100 trials on that task.)

	Traditional		Cue and Response Variation	
Subjects	Direct	Indirect	Direct	Indirect
LF 2	500 (53)	500 (58)	120	100
LF 3	500 (56)	500 (63)	160	140
LF 5	500 (56)	500 (53)	250	210
LF 11	500 (49)	500 (58)	210	250
IT 4	100	100	140	100
IT 15	160	100	110	110
IT 26	250	180	130	100
IT 37	100	100	160	160

[3] All the animals had been trained previously in "go-no-go" *visual discrimination* (9) using the same two discriminanda.

chance level. On the variation procedures, however, all operates, frontals as well as controls, achieved criterion in less than 250 trials. The controls averaged somewhat fewer trials than the frontals on the delayed response variations, but there was considerable overlap between the learning scores of the two groups.

The average percentage correct for the three delay periods on the variation presented by the direct method (in the order 5, 10, and 15 sec.) were as follows: Temporal operates—92, 92, and 88; frontal operates—90, 81, and 79. The frontal animals thus showed a somewhat greater decrease in accuracy with increasing delays, yet they continued to perform well above chance at the longest delay interval. It is of interest to note that on the variation, 95 per cent of the total errors of *both* groups were made on "no-go" trials.

EXPERIMENT II

The delayed-response variation which the frontal operates learned differed in two major respects from classical delayed response, which they failed to learn. Not only was the response choice varied from the traditional "go left–go right" to "go–no go," but the predelay cues were varied from the traditional "bait left–bait right" to "bait–no bait." The differences may be paraphrased this way: Instead of choosing *where* to go on the basis of *where* the cue had been presented, the animal must now choose *whether* to go on the basis of *which* cue had been presented. The following experiment was designed to answer which of these two variations, the change in the cue or the change in response choice, was more effective in eliciting successful performance by the anterofrontal operates.

TABLE 2
Cue-Response Variations for Experiments I and II

	Response Where (2 Cups)	Whether (1 Cup)
Cue		
Where (1 cue)	Classical	Response varied
Which (2 cues)	Cue varied	Cue and response varied

Table 2 presents a two-by-two classification, indicating the cue-response combinations which define classical (upper left) and variant (lower right) delayed response as used in the first experiment, together with the two new variations presented in the present experiment. Specifically, the traditional cueing by "bait left–bait right" was combined with the variant response choice, "go–no go" (upper right in the table); also the variant cueing by "bait–no bait" was combined with the traditional response choice, "go left–go right (lower left). As before, the tasks were presented first by the direct method of baiting and then by the indirect method.

Procedure

Response varied, direct method. A peanut was held about 10 in. to the left *or* to the right of a single, centered, closed cup. For half the animals (two from each group) bait on the left indicated that, following delay, the correct response was "go," whereas bait on the right indicated that, following delay, the correct response was "no go" (i.e., the single cup was empty). The other animals were trained with these cue-response relationships re*v*ersed.

Cue varied, direct method. A peanut *or* an empty hand was displayed between two closed cups. For half the animals, bait indicated that, after delay, the correct response was "go left," whereas an empty hand indicated that the correct response was "go right." The other animals were trained with these relationships reversed.

Response varied, indirect method. The stimulus object, either a tobacco tin or an ash tray, was the same as that used in the first experiment. The object (tobacco tin for four animals, and ash tray for the four others) was placed approximately 10 in. to the left *or* to the right of a singel, centered, closed cup. For half the animals, an object on the left indicated that, following delay, the correct response was "go," whereas the same object on the right indicated that, following delay, the correct response was "no go." For the other animals these cue-response relationships were reversed.

Cue varied, indirect method. This task was presented first by the following method: The tobacco tin *or* ash tray was placed in a central position, halfway between two closed cups; for half the animals the tobacco tin indicated that, after delay, the correct response was "go left," whereas the ash tray indicated that, after delay, the correct response was "go right." The other animals were trained with these relationships reversed. None of the animals showed any indication of learning this task after 200 trials, and it was apparent from observing their behavior that they were not reacting to the centrally placed stimulus. The procedure was therefore modified after 200 trials (these 200 trials were not included in the final scores) by placing the tobacco tin or the ash tray *on* the left cup for four animals and *on* the right for the other four. For the animals that were presented with the stimuli on the left cup, the ash tray indicated that the correct response was "go left," whereas the tobacco tin indicated that the correct response was "go right." For the animals that were presented with the objects on the right cup, the tobacco in indicated that the correct response was "go right," whereas the ash tray indicated that the correct response was "go left."

The two problems presented by the direct method were balanced for order, as were the two problems presented by the indirect method, and in all other respects the training methods were identical to those used in the first experiment.

Results

The animals' learning scores and final performance on each task are shown in Table 3. In general, this series of four problems was more difficult than were the problems presented in the first experiment. Indeed, on the response-varied task with indirect baiting, no control or frontal operate attained criterion within the limits of training. However, on the response-varied task with direct baiting, three temporal operates eventually achieved 90 per cent (and the fourth, 83 per cent) correct performance, whereas none of the frontal operates met this criterion. The scores of the frontal animals *are* nearly comparable to those of the controls for those tasks in which only the cue was varied. With indirect baiting, three of the four frontal animals learned the cue-varied delayed response, and in ap-

TABLE 3

RESULTS, EXPERIMENT II

(Scores are number of trials, including criterion run, required to attain the criterion of 90 per cent correct in 100 consecutive trials. A score of 500 trials denotes failure to reach the criterion, and is accompanied by the per cent correct achieved in the final 100 trials in that task.)

	Response Varied		Cue Varied	
Subjects	Direct	Indirect	Direct	Indirect
LF 2	500 (75)	500 (65)	250	330
LF 3	500 (52)	500 (48)	500 (74)	450
LF 5	500 (50)	500 (53)	500 (74)	500 (49)
LF 11	500 (53)	500 (50)	250	100
IT 4	450	500 (54)	140	130
IT 15	500 (83)	500 (48)	290	100
IT 26	420	500 (54)	500 (75)	470
IT 37	430	500 (50)	500 (72)	210

proximately the same number of trials as the four controls. With direct baiting, the frontal operates again performed at approximately the same level as controls, though only two animals from each group attained the 90 per cent criterion, the others achieving a performance level of approximately 75 per cent correct.

DISCUSSION

The surprisingly small number of trials taken by frontal operates to reach criterion performance on the cue-and-response variation of *delayed response,* supports the finding of successful performance on a variation of *delayed alternation* used in the earlier study (5). This striking achievement of frontal operates in a delay situation differs from that obtained with experimental manipulations which have been attempted in the past, in that criterion performance was quickly established in all operates. Elimination of interference factors during delay (4), use of predelay reinforcement (1), and injection of barbiturates (6, 8) have not consistently improved performance to a control level;

and in most instances, the improvement that did occur appeared only after lengthy training. In the cue-and-response–varied problem described in the present study, all frontal operates attained a level of 90 per cent correct in less than 250 trials, and they continued to perform well above chance with relatively long intratrial delays.

Results of the subsequent experimental analysis of this task suggest that the rapid learning by the frontal animals was due largely to the change from a positional to a nonpositional cue. That is, the frontals performed nearly as well as controls whenever a single cue presented in one of two places was replaced by one of two cues presented in a single place. This analysis of the frontal operates' performance is not conclusive, however, because of the difficulty of the tasks in Experiment 2 and because of the extensive training provided previously on similar tasks. Nevertheless, the results suggest that varying the predelay cue is relatively more effective than varying the response choice for eliciting correct delayed response in frontal operates.

These findings are important in connection with various hypotheses advanced to account for the impairment produced by anterofrontal lesions. For example, this impairment has been characterized recently as a "loss of act inhibition" (10). The facility with which frontal operates learned to avoid the food-cup completely in certain of the "go–no-go" procedures seems to contradict this hypothesis. Explanations relating specifically to frontal operates' performance on delayed response have ascribed the deficit to failure in one-trial learning, i.e., failure when competing response tendencies are established on successive trials (3, 7), to increased retroactive inhibition (4), or simply to a "defect of recent memory" (2). Yet, the present results indicate that frontal animals perform successfully tasks which are indistinguishable from the traditional tasks in terms of the conditionality and delay features on which the conceptions of impairment in one-trial learning and recent memory are based.

The present studies were not undertaken as a specific test of any of these hypotheses, and the evidence of successful performance on a variant of delayed response does not refute them. However, the fact that frontal operates show little or no impairment in the performance of a delayed-response task when it is altered simply by varying the predelay cues suggests that the (predelay) stimulus parameter is as important as are the parameters of conditionality and of delay for an adequate conceptualization of the impaired behavior resulting from frontal lesions.

SUMMARY

The performance of four frontal and four temporal control operates was compared on a series of eight delayed-response tasks. These tasks included traditional delayed response and three variations, each presented by both the direct and indirect methods of baiting. The variations of delayed response employed (*a*) nonpositional instead of positional predelay cues; (*b*) a "go–no go" instead of a left-right response choice, and (*c*) both cue and response variations combined. The results demonstrated that frontal operates perform nearly as well as control animals whenever traditional predelay cues are replaced by nonpositional cues, irrespective of the response choice, or whether direct or indirect baiting is employed. These findings suggest that frontal operates' impairment on traditional delayed-response–type problems is related, not only to the delay, but to some aspect of the predelay cue as well.

REFERENCES

1. FINAN, J. L. Delayed response with pre-delay reinforcement in monkeys after removal of the frontal lobes. *Amer. J. Psychol.*, 1942, **55**, 202–14.
2. JACOBSEN, C. F., WOLFE, J. B., and JACKSON, T. A. An experimental analysis of the functions of the frontal association areas in primates. *J. nerv. ment. Dis.*, 1935, **82**, 1–14.
3. LASHLEY, K. S. The mechanism of vision: XVIII. Effects of destroying the visual "associative areas" of the monkey. *Genet. Psychol. Monogr.*, 1948, **37**, 107–66.
4. MALMO, R. B. Interference factors in delayed response in monkey after removal of frontal lobes. *J. Neurophysiol.*, 1942, **5**, 295–308.
5. MISHKIN, M., and PRIBRAM, K. H. Analysis of the effects of frontal lesions in monkeys: I. Variations of delayed alternation. *J. comp. physiol. Psychol,* in press.
6. MISHKIN, M., ROSVOLD, H. E., and PRIBRAM, K. H. Effects of Nembutal in baboons with frontal lesions. *J. Neurophysiol.*, 1953, **16**, 155–59.
7. NISSEN, H. W., RIESEN, A. H., and NOWLIS, V. Delayed response and discrimination learning by chimpanzees. *J. comp. Psychol.*, 1938, **26**, 361–86.
8. PRIBRAM, K. H. Some physical and pharmacological factors affecting delayed response performance of baboons following frontal lobotomy. *J. Neurophysiol.*, 1950, **13**, 373–82.
9. PRIBRAM, K. H., and MISHKIN, M. Simultaneous and successive visual discrimination by monkeys with inferotemporal lesions. *J. comp. physiol. Psychol.*, 1955, **48**, 198–202.
10. STANLEY, W. C. and JAYNES, J. The function of the frontal cortex. *Psychol. Rev.*, 1949, **56**, 18–32.

REFERENCES

ADAMS, G.   On the negative and positive phototropism of the earthworm *Allolobophora foetida* as determined by light of different intensities. *Amer J. Physiol,* 1903, **9**, 26–34. Ch. 4.

ADAMSON, J.   *Born Free,* 1960, Collins and Harrill, London, Eng. Ch. 7.

ADELMAN, H. M. and MAATSCH, J. L.   Resistance to extinction as a function of the type of response elicited by frustration. *J. Exp. Psychol.,* 1955, **50**, 61–65. Ch. 11.

ALLEE, W. C.   *Animal Aggregations: A Study in General Sociology,* 1931, University Chicago Press, Chicago, Ill. Ch. 8.

ALLEE, W. C.   *The Social Life of Animals,* rev. ed., 1951, Beacon Press, Boston, Mass. Ch. 8.

ALLEE, W. C., COLLIAS, N., and LUTHERMAN, C. Z.   Modification of the social order among flocks of hens by injection of testosterone propionate. *Physiol. Zool.,* 1939, **12**, 412–20. Ch. 8.

ALLEE, W. C. and FOREMAN, D.   Effects of an androgen on dominance and subordinance in six common breeds of *Gallus gallus. Physiol. Zool,* 1955, **28**, 89–115. Ch. 6.

AMSEL, A. and MALTZMAN, I.   The effect upon generalized drive strength on emotionality as inferred from the level of the consummatory response. *J. Exp. Psychol.,* 1950, **40**, 563–69. Ch. 9.

ANASTASI, ANNE.   *Psychological Testing,* 2nd ed., 1961, Macmillan, New York, N.Y. Ch. 2.

ANDERSON, A. L.   The sensitivity of the legs of common butterflies to sugars. *J. Exp. Zool.,* **63**, 235–59. Ch. 3.

ANDERSON, J. W.   The production of ultrasonic sounds by laboratory rats and other animals. *Science,* 1954, **119**, 808–9. Ch. 3.

ANDREW, R. J.   The origin and evolution of the calls and facial expressions of the primates. *Behav.,* 1963, **20**, 1–109. Ch. 2.

ARMSTRONG, E. A.   *Bird Display,* 1942, Cambridge University Press, Cambridge, Eng. Ch. 5.

ARMSTRONG, E. A.   *Bird Display and Behaviour,* 1942, Cambridge University Press, Cambridge, Eng. Ch. 1.

ARMSTRONG, E. A.   The ecology of distraction display. *Brit. J. Anim. Behav.,* 1954, **2**, 121–35. Ch. 5.

ARMSTRONG, E. A.   *The Wren,* 1955, Collins, London, Eng. Ch. 1.

ARMUS, H. L.   Effect of magnitude of reinforcement on acquisition and extinction of a running response. *J. Exp. Psychol.,* 1959, **58**, 61–63. Ch. 11.

BACON, H. R.; WARREN, J. M.; and SCHEIN, M. W. Non-spatial reversal learning in chickens. *Animal Behavior,* **10,** 1962, 239–43. Ch. 12.

BAERENDS, G. P. Frontpflanzungarsrhalten und Grientierung der Grabruespe *Ammophila compestos. Jur. Tijdchr. Entomol.,* 1941, **84,** 68–275. Ch. 12.

BAERENDS, G. P. Specializations in organs and movements with a releasing function. In *Symposium of the Society for Experimental Biology,* Vol. IV, *Physiological Mechanisms in Animal Behaviour,* 1950, Cambridge University Press, Cambridge, Eng. Ch. 5.

BAERENDS, G. P.; BROUWER, R.; and WATERBOLK, H. T. On the ethology ol *Lebistees reticulatus* (Peters) 1. Analysis of the male courtship pattern. *Behav.,* 1955, **8,** 249–335. Ch. 5.

BARNES, G. W. Conditioned stimulus intensity and temporal factors in spaced-trial classical conditioning *J. Exp. Psychol.,* 1956, **51,** 192–98. Ch. 10.

BASTOCK, M. A. A gene mutation which changes a behavior pattern. *Evolution,* 1957, **10,** 421–39. Ch. 2.

BEACH, F. A. Analysis of the stimuli adequate to elicit mating behavior in sexually inexperienced rats. *J. Comp. Psychol.,* 1942, **33,** 163–207. Ch. 5.

BEACH, F. A. *Hormones and Behavior,* 1948, Hoeber, New York, N.Y. Ch. 6.

BEACH, F. A. The snark was a boojum. *Amer. Psychologist,* 1950, **5,** 115–24. Ch. 1.

BEACH, F. A. Evolutionary aspects of psychoendocrinology. In *Behavior and Evolution,* 1958 (eds. Roe, Ann and Simpson, G. G.), Yale University Press, New Haven, Conn. Ch. 6.

BEACH, F. A. Neural and chemical regulation of behavior. In *Biological and Biochemical Bases of Behavior,* 1958 (eds. Harlow, H. F. and Woolsey, C. N.), University of Wisconsin Press, Madison, Wis. Ch. 6.

BEACH, F. A.; CONOVITZ, M. W.; STEINBERG, F.; and GOLDSTEIN, A. C. Experimental inhibition and restoration of mating behavior in male rats. *J. Genet. Psychol.,* 1956, **89,** 165–81. Ch. 6.

BEACH, F. A.; GOLDSTEIN, A. C.; and JACOBY, G. A., JR. Effects of electroconvulsive shock on sexual behavior in male rats. *J. Comp. Physiol. Psychol.,* 1955, **48,** 173–79. Ch. 6.

BEACH, F. A. and JAYNES, J. Effects of early experience upon the behavior of animals. *Psychol. Bull.,* 1954, **51,** 239–63. Ch. 7.

BEACH, F. A., and LEVINSON. Effects of androgen on the *glans penis* and mating behavior of castrated male rats. *J. Exp. Zool.,* 1950, **114,** 159–68. Ch. 6.

BEACH, F. A. and ZITRIN, A. Induction of mating in male cats. *Ann. N.Y. Acad. Sci.,* 1945, **46,** 42–44. Ch. 6.

BEAMAN, ELIZABETH A. The effect of the male hormone on the aggressive behavior of mice. *Physiol. Zool.,* 1947, 373–405, **20.** Ch. 6.

BEAUCHAMP, R. S. A. Rate of movement and rheotaxis in *planaria alpina; J. Exp. Biol.,* 1937, **14,** 104–16. Ch. 4.

BEHREND, E. R. and BITTERMAN, M. E. Avoidance-conditioning in the goldfish: Exploratory studies of the CS–US interval. *Amer. J. Psychol.,* 1962, **75,** 18–34. Ch. 10.

BEHREND, E. R. and BITTERMAN, M. E. Sidman avoidance in the fish. *J. Exp. Anal. Behav.,* 1963, **6,** 47–52. Ch. 11.

BENJAMIN, L. S. The effect of frustration on the nonnutritive sucking of infant rhesus monkey. *J. Comp. Physiol. Psychol.,* 1961, **54,** 700–703. Ch. 9.

BERG, I. A. Development of behavior: The micturition pattern in the dog. *J. Exp. Psychol.,* 1944, **34**, 343–68. Ch. 6.

BERKSON, G. Food motivation and delayed response in gibbons. *J. Comp. Physiol. Psychol.,* 1962, **55**, 1040–43. Ch. 12.

BERNSTEIN, I. S. The utilization of visual cues in dimension-abstracted oddity by primates. *J. Comp. Physiol. Psychol.,* 1961, **54**, 243–47. Ch. 12.

BEST, J. B. The photosensitization of *Paramecium aurelia* by temperature shock. *J. Exp. Zool.,* 1954, **126**, 87–100. Ch. 11.

BEST, J. B. and RUBINSTEIN, I. Maze learning and associated behavior in planaria. *J. Comp. Physiol. Psychol.,* 1962, **55**, 560–66. Ch. 11.

BINDRA, D. *Motivation: A Systematic Reinterpretation,* 1959, Ronald Press, New York, N.Y. Ch. 6.

BIRCH, D. A motivational interpretation of extinction. In Jones, M. R. (ed.) *Nebraska Symposium on Motivation,* 1961. Ch. 11.

BIRCH, H. G. and CLARK, G. Hormonal modification of social behavior: IV. The mechanism of estrogeninduced dominance in chimpanzees. *J. Comp. Physiol.* 1950, **43**, 181–93. Ch. 6.

BITTERMAN, M. E. Toward a comparative psychology of learning. *Amer. Psychologist,* 1960, **15**, 704–12. Ch. 1.

BITTERMAN, M. E. and WODINSKY, J. Simultaneous and successive discrimination, *Psychol. Rev,* 1953, **60**, 371–76. Ch. 11.

BLOUGH, DONALD S. Some effects of drugs on visual discrimination in the pigeon. *Annals N.Y. Acad. Sc.* 1956–57, **66**, 733–39. Ch. 13.

BOLLES, R. C. The readiness to eat and drink: The effect of deprivation conditions. *J. Comp. Physiol. Psychol.,* 1962, **55**, 230–34. Ch. 9.

BOLWIG, NIELS. A study of the behavior of the Chacma Baboon. *Behav.,* 1959, **14**, 136–63. Ch. 5.

BOVARD, E. W. The effects of early handling on viability of the albino rat. *Psychol. Rev.,* 1958, **65**, 257–71. Ch. 7.

BOVBJERG, R. V. Some factors affecting aggressive behavior in crayfish. *Physiol. Zool.,* 1956, **29**, 127–36. Ch. 6.

BOYCOTT, B. B. and YOUNG, J. Z. Reversal of learned responses in *Octopus vulgaris. Anim. Behav.,* 1959, **6**, 45–52.

BRADDOCK, J. C. The effect of residence on the dominance in fish, *Platypoecilus maculatus. Physiol. Zool.,* 1949, **22**, 151–69. Ch. 8.

BRADY, J. V. The Paleocortex and Behavior Motivation. (eds. Harlow, H. F. and Woolsey, C. N.) *Biological and Biochemical Bases of Behavior,* 1958, University of Wisconsin Press, Madison, Wis. Ch. 6.

BRELAND, K. and BRELAND, MARION. The misbehavior of organisms. *Amer. Psychologist,* 1961, **16**, 681–84. Ch. 1.

BRIDGMAN, C. S. and SMITH, K. U. The absolute threshold of vision in cat and man with observations on its relation to the optic cortex. *Amer. J. Physiol.,* 1942, **136**, 463–66. Ch. 13.

BROADHURST, P. L. Analysis of maternal effects in the inheritance of behavior. *Anim. Behav.,* 1961, **9**, 129–41. Ch. 2.

BRODY, E. G. Genetic basis of spontaneous activity in the albino rat. *Comp. Psychol. Mono.,* 1941, **17**, 1–23. Ch. 2.

BROMILEY, R. B. Conditioned responses in a dog after removal of neocortex. *J. Comp. Physiol. Psychol.,* 1948, **41**, 102–10. Ch. 13.

BROWN, F. A. Living clocks. *Science,* 1959, **130**, 1533–44. Ch. 3.

BROWN, H. W. and GEISELHART, R.   Age differences in the acquisition and extinction of the conditioned eyelid response. *J. Exp. Psychol.*, 1959, 57, 386–88. Ch. 10.

BRUN, R.   *General Theory of Neurons*, 1951, International Universities Press, New York, N.Y. Ch. 6.

BUEXEKOM, G. V.   Some experiments on the optical orientation in *Philanthus triangulum. Behav.*, 1948, 1, 195–225. Ch. 4.

BULLOCK, D. H. and BITTERMAN, M. E.   Habit reversal in the pigeon, *J. Comp. Physiol. Psychol.*, 1962, 55, 958–62. Ch. 12.

BUREŠ, J.; BUREŠOVÁ, O.; and ZÁHOROVÁ, A.   Conditioned reflexes and Leao's spreading cortical depression. *J. Comp. Physiol. Psychol.*, 1958, 51, 263–68. Ch. 13.

BUTLER, R. A.   Discrimination learning by Rhesus monkeys to visual-exploration motivation. *J. Comp. Physiol. Psychol.*, 1953, 46, 95–98. Ch. 11.

BYKOV, K. M.   *The cerebral cortex and the internal organs.* Translated and edited by W. H. Gantt. Chemical Publishing Co., New York, 1957.

CALHOUN, J. B.   "Behavioral Sink." (ed. Bliss, E. L.) *Roots of Behavior*, 1962, Hayser, New York, N.Y. Ch. 8.

CALHOUN, J. B.   The ecology and sociology of the Norway rat., 1962, U.S. Dept. of Health, Education and Welfare, Bethesda, Md.

CAMPBELL, B. A. and KRAELING, D.   Response strength as a function of drive level during training. *J. Comp. Physiol. Psychol.*, 1954, 47, 101–3. Ch. 11.

CAPRETTA, P. J.   An experimental modification of food preference in chickens. *J. Comp. Physiol. Psychol.*, 1961, 54, 238-42. Ch. 9.

CARPENTER, C. R.   A field study of the behavior and social relations of howler monkeys, *Alouatta palliata. Comp. Psychol. Monogr.*, 1934, 10, #2, 168 pg. Ch. 8.

CARR, R. M. and WILLIAMS, C. D.   Exploratory behavior of three strains of rats. *J. Comp. Physiol. Psychol.*, 1957, 50, 621–23. Ch. 2.

CARTHY, J. D.   *An Introduction to the Behaviours of Invertebrates,* 1958, Allen and Unwin, London, Eng. Ch. 4.

CASPARI, E.   Genetic basis of behavior. In *Behavior and Evolution,* 1958 (eds. Roe, Anne and Simpson, G. G.), Yale University Press, New Haven, Conn. Ch. 2.

CHAMBERS, R. M. and FULLER, J. L.   Conditioning of skin temperature changes in dogs. *J. Comp. Physiol. Psychol.*, 1958, 51, 223–26. Ch. 10.

CHANCE, M. R. A. and MEAD, A. D.   Competition between feeding and investigation in the rat. *Behav.*, 1955, 8, 174–81. Ch. 9.

CHEN, S. C.   Social modification of the activity of ants in nest building. *Physiol. Zool.*, 1938, 10, 420–36. Ch. 9.

CLARK, E.; ARONSON, L. R.; and GORDON, M.   Mating behavior patterns in two sympatric species of Xphophorin fishes: Their inheritance and significance in sexual isolation. *Bull. Am. Mus. Nat. Hist.*, 1954, 103, 135–226. Ch. 2.

CLARK, F. C.   The effect of deprivation and frequency of reinforcement on variable-interval responding. *J. Exper. Anal. Behav.*, 1958, 1, 221–28. Ch. 11.

CLARK, G.   Prepubertal castration in the male chimpanzee with some effects of replacement therapy. *Growth*, 1945, 9, 327–39. Ch. 6.

CLARK, R. B.   Habituation of the polychaete *Nereis* to sudden stimuli. 1. General properties of the habituation process. *Anim. Behav.*, 1960, 8, 82–91. Ch. 4.

CLIFFORD, L. T.   Experimental extinction following different amounts of continuously rewarded training and latent extinction. Unpublished doctoral dissortation, University of Michigan, Ann Arbor, Mich., 1963. Ch. 11.

COLBERT, E. H.   Morphology and behavior. In *Behavior and Evolution,* 1958 (eds. Roe, Anne and Simpson, G. G.), Yale University Press, New Haven, Conn. Ch. 2.

COLLIAS, E. C. and COLLIAS, N. E.   The response of chicks of the Franklin's gull to parental bill color. *Auk,* 1957, 74, 371–75. Ch. 5.

COLLIAS, N. E.   Hormones and behaviors with special reference to birds and the mechanisms of hormone action. *Symposium on Steroid Hormones* (ed. Gordon, E. S.) 1950, University of Wisconsin Press, Madison, Wis. Ch. 6.

COLLIAS, N. E.   Problems and principles of animal sociology. *Comparative Psychology,* 3rd ed., 1951 (ed. Stone, C. P.), Prentice–Hall, Englewood Cliffs, N.J. Ch. 8.

COLLIAS, N. E.   The development of social behavior in birds. *Auk,* 1952, 127–59. Ch. 8.

COLLIAS, N. E.   An ecological and functional classification of animal sounds. In *Animal Sounds and Communication,* 1960 (eds. Lanyon, W. and Tavolga, W. N.), *AIBS Symposium Publication,* Vol. 7. Ch. 5.

COTT, H. B.   *Adaptive Coloration in Animals,* 1940, Methuen, London, Eng. Ch. 5.

COTTON, J. W.   Running time as function of amount of food deprivation. *J. Exp. Psychol.,* 1953, 46, 188–98. Ch. 11.

CRAGG, J. B. and COLE, P.   Laboratory studies on the chemosensory reactions of blowflies. *Ann. Appl. Biol.,* 1956, 44, 478–91. Ch. 3.

CRANE, J.   Crabs of the genus *Uca* from the West Coast of Central America. *Zoologica,* 1941, 26, 145–208. Ch. 4.

CRANE, J.   Comparative biology of salticid spiders of Rancho Grande, Venezuela. IV. An analysis of display. *Zoologica,* 1949, 34, 159–214. Ch. 4.

CRAWFORD, M. P.   The social psychology of vertebrates. *Psychol. Bull.,* 1939, 407–46. Ch. 8.

CROWCROFT, P.   Notes on the behavior of shrews. *Behav.,* 1955, 8, 63–80. Ch. 5.

CROZIER, W. J.   The geotropic response in *Asterina. J. Gen. Physiol.,* 1935, 18, 729–38. Ch. 4.

CROZIER, W. J. and NAVEZ, A. E.   The geotropic orientation of gastropods. *J. Gen. Physiol.,* 1930, 3, 3–37. Ch. 4.

CRUZE, W. W.   Maturation and learning in chicks. *J. Comp. Psychol.,* 1935, 19, 371–409. Ch. 11.

DAANJE, A.   On locomotory movements in birds and the intention movements derived from them. *Behav.,* 1951, 48–98. Ch. 2.

DARBY, C. L. and RIOPELLE, A. J.   Observational Learning of Monkey. *J. Comp. Physiol. Psychol.,* 1959, 52, 94–98. Ch. 12.

DARLING, F. F.   *A Herd of Red Deer,* 1937, Claredon, Press, Oxford, Eng. Ch. 8.

DARWIN, C.   *The Expression of the Emotions in Man and Animals,* 1920, D. Appleton Co., New York, N.Y. Ch. 1.

DAVENPORT, D.; CAMOUGIS, G.; and HICKOK, J. F.   Analyses of the behavior of commensals in host-factor. A hesioned polychaste and a pinnotherid crab. *Anim. Behav.,* 1960, 8, 209–18. Ch. 4.

DAVIS, D. E.   The phylogeny of social nesting habits in the Crotophaginae. *Quart. Rev. Biol.,* 1942, 17, 115–34. Ch. 2.

DAVIS, D. E.   Territorial rank in starlings. *Anim. Behav.,* 1959, 7, 214–21. Ch. 8.

DAVIS, R. H.   The effect of spacing units on simultaneous vs. successive discrimination. *J. Comp. Physiol. Psychol.,* 1957, 50, 207–10. Ch. 11.

DENENBERG, V. H. and KARAS, G. G.   Effects of differential handling upon weight gain and mortality in the rat and mouse. *Science,* 1959, **130,** 629–30. Ch. 7.

DENNISTON, R. H.   Escape and avoidance learning as a function of emotionality level in the Wyoming Ground Squirrel, *Citellus richardsonii elegons. Anim. Behav.,* 1959, **7,** 241–43. Ch. 7.

DENNY, M. R.   Learning through stimulus satiation. *J. Exp. Psychol,* 1957, **54,** 62–64. Ch. 12.

DENNY, M. R.   One bar-press per day: Acquisition and extinction. *J. Exper. Anal. Behav.,* 1959, **2,** 81–85. Ch. 11.

DENNY, M. R. and ADELMAN, H. M.   Elicitation theory: I An analysis of two typical learning situations. *Psychol. Rev.,* 1955, **62,** 290–96. Ch. 1, 10, 11.

DENNY, M. R. and KING, G. F.   Differential response learning on the basis of differential size of reward. *J. Genet. Psychol,* 1955, **87,** 317–20. Ch. 11.

DENNY, M. R.; KOONS, P. B.; and MASON, J. E.   Extinction of avoidance as a function of the escape situation. *J. Comp. Physiol. Psychol.,* 1959, **52,** 212–14. Ch. 10, 11.

DENNY, M. R. and WEISMAN, R. G.   Avoidance behavior as a function of the length of nonshock confinement. *J. Comp. Physiol. Psychol.* (In press) Ch. 11.

DENNY, M. R.; WELLS, R. H.; and MAATSCH, J. L.   Resistance to extinction as a function of the discrimination habit established during fixed-ratio reinforcement. *J. Exp. Psychol.,* 1957, **53,** 451–56. Ch. 11.

DETHIER, V. G. and STELLAR, E.   *Animal Behavior,* 1961, Prentice–Hall, Englewood Cliffs, N.J. Ch. 1.

DEWS, P. B.   Some observations on an operant in the octopus. *J. Exp. Anal. Behav.,* 1959, **2,** 57–64. Ch. 11.

DOLLEY, W. L. and GOLDEN, L. H.   The effect of temperature and age on the temperature at which reversal in reaction to light in *Eristalis tenax* occurs. *Biol. Bull.,* 1947, **92,** 178–86. Ch. 4.

DOMM, C. V. and VAN DYKE, H. B.   Precocious development of sexual characters in the fowl by daily injections of hebin 1. The male. *Proc. Soc. Exp. Biol. Med.,* 1932, **30,** 349–50. Ch. 6.

DONNER, K. G.   The visual acuity of some passerine birds. *Acta Zool. Fennica,* 1951, **66,** 1–40. Ch. 3.

DUNCAN, C. P.   The retroactive effect of electroshock on learning. *J. Comp. Physiol. Psychol.,* 1949, **42,** 32–44. Ch. 13.

DYKMAN, R. A. and SHURRAGER, M. S.   Successive and maintained conditioning in spinal carnivores. *J. Comp. Physiol. Psychol.,* 1956, **49,** 27–35. Ch. 13.

EBNER, F. F. and MYERS, R. E.   Corpus Callosum and the interhemispheric transmission of tactual learning. *J. Neurophysiol,* 1962, **25,** 380–91, Ch. 13.

EBNER, F. F. and MYERS, R. E.   Direct and transcallosal induction of touch memories in the monkey. *Science,* 1962, **3536,** 51–52. Ch. 13.

EISMAN, E.   An investigation of the parameters defining drive (D). *J. Exp. Psychology,* 1956, **52,** 85–89. Ch. 11.

EISNER, ERICA.   The relationship of hormones to the reproductive behavior of birds, referring especially to parental behavior: A review. *Anim. Behav.,* 1960, **8,** 155–80. Ch. 6.

ELLIOT, O. and KING, J. A.   Effect of early food deprivation upon later consummatory behavior in puppies. *Psychol. Rep.,* 1960, **6,** 391–400. Ch. 9.

ETTLINGER, G.   Cross-modal transfer of training in monkeys. *Behav.,* 1960, **16,** 56–65. Ch. 12.

EVANS, H. E.   An ethological study of the digger wasp, *Bembecimus neglectus*, with a review of the ethology of the genus. *Behav.,* 1955, **7**, 287–304. Ch. 4.

EVANS, S. M.   The effect of brain extirpation on learning and retention in neroid polychaetes. *Anim. Behav.,* 1963, **11**, 172–78. Ch. 13.

FERSTER, C. B. and SKINNER, B. F.   *Schedules of Reinforcement,* Appleton-Century-Crofts, New York, 1957. Ch. 11.

FESTINGER, L.   Development of differential appetite in the rat. *Psychol. Bull.,* 1942, **39**, 441–42. Ch. 11.

FINCH, G.   Delayed matching-from-sample and non-spatial delayed response in chimpanzees. *J. Comp. Psychol.,* 1942, **34**, 315–19. Ch. 12.

FINK, H. K.   *Mind and Performance,* 1954, Vantage Press, New York, N.Y. Ch. 1.

FISCHER, G. J. and KITCHENER, S. L.   Comparative learning in young gorillas and orangutans. *Anim. Behav.* (In press) Ch. 12.

FISHER, A. E. and HALE, E. B.   Stimulus determinants of sexual behavior and aggressive behavior in male domestic fowl. *Behav.,* 1957, **60**, 309–23. Ch. 5.

FRAENKEL, G. S. and GUNN, D. D.   *The Orientation of Animals,* 1961, Dover, N.Y. Ch. 4.

FREE, J. B.   The defense of bumblebees colonies. *Behav.,* 1958, **12**, 233–42. Ch. 8.

FREE, J. B.   The stimuli releasing the stinging response of honey bees. *Anim. Behav.,* 1961, **9**, 193–97. Ch. 4.

FRENCH, J. W.   Trial and error learning in paramecium. *J. Exp. Psychol.,* 1940, **26**, 609–13. Ch. 11.

FRINGS, H. and FRINGS, M.   The production of stocks of albino mice with predictable susceptibilities to audiogenic seizures. *Behav.,* 1953, **5**, 305–19. Ch. 2.

FRISCH, K. v.   Uherden Geschmackssinn der bienen: eine beitragage vor vergleichenden physiologie des geschamachs. *Z. Verl. Physiol.,* 1934, **21**, 11–156. Ch. 9.

FRISCH, K. v.   "Language" and orientation of bees. *Proc. Amer. Phil. Soc.,* 1956, **100**, 515–19. Ch. 3.

FULLER, J. L.   Hereditary differences in trainability of purebred dogs. *J. Genet. Psychol.,* 1955, **87**, 229–38. Ch. 2.

FURCHTGOTT, E.; MURPHEE, R. L.; PAGE, H. B.; and DEES, J. W.   Mating activity in fetally irradiated male swine and rats. *Psychol. Rep.,* 1959, **5**, 545–48. Ch. 6.

GANZ, L. and REISEN, A. H.   Stimulus generalization to hue in the dark reared Macaque. *J. Comp. Physiol. Psychol.,* 1962, **55**, 92–99. Ch. 7.

GARDNER, L. P. and NISSEN, H. W.   Simple discrimination behavior of young chimpanzees: Comparisons with human aments and domestic animals. *J. Genet. Psychol.,* 1948, **72**, 145–64. Ch. 11.

GARTH, T. R. and MITCHELL, M. P.   The learning curve of a land snail. *J. Comp. Psychol.,* 1926, **6**, 103–13. Ch. 11.

GELBER, BEATRICE.   Investigation of the behavior of *paramecium aurelia*: I. Modification of behavior after training with reinforcement. *J. Comp. Physiol. Psychol.,* 1952, **45**, 58–65. Ch. 11.

GERALL, A. A.   Effect of interruption of copulation on male guinea pig sexual behavior. *Psychol. Rep.,* 1958, **4**, 215–21. Ch. 9.

GERALL, A. A.; SAMPSON, P. B.; and BOSLOV, G. L.   Classical conditioning of human pupillary dilation. *J. Exp. Psychol.,* 1957, **54**, 467–74. Ch. 10.

GIBSON, E. J. and WALKER, R. D. The effects of prolonged exposure to visually presented patterns on learning to discriminate them. *J. Comp. Physiol. Psychol.,* 1956, **49**, 239–42. Ch. 7.

GOETACH, W. *The Ants,* 1957. University of Michigan Press, Ann Arbor, Mich. Ch. 6.

GORBMAN, A. and BERN, H. A. *A Textbook of Comparative Endocrinology,* 1962, Wiley, New York, N.Y. Ch. 6.

GORMEZANO, I.; SCHNIEDERMAN, N.; DEAN, E.; and FUENTES, I. Nictitating Membrane: Classical conditioning and extinction in the Albino Rabbit. *Science,* 1962, **138**, Nu3536, 33–34. Ch. 10.

GRAY, J. and LISSMAN, H. W. Further observations on the effect of deafferentation on the locomotory activity of amphibian limbs. *J. Exp. Biol.,* 1946, **23**, 121–32. Ch. 13.

GRAZIANO, A. M. A gestalt versus a stimulus-response analysis of reasoning in the rat. Unpublished MA thesis, Michigan State University, East Lansing, Mich., 1956. Ch. 13.

GREGERSON, M. I. Studies on the regulation of water intake of dogs as registered continuously by a protometer. *Amer. J. Physiol.,* 1932, **102**, 344–49. Ch. 9.

GRICE, G. R. The relation of secondary reinforcements to delayed reward in visual discrimination learning. *J. Exp. Psychol.,* 1948, **38**, 1–16. Ch. 11.

GRICE, G. R. An experimental test of the expectation theory of learning. *J. Comp. Physiol. Psychol.,* 1948, **41**, 137–43. Ch. 12.

GRIFFIN, D. R. Bird Sonar. *Scien. Amer.,* 1954, **190**, 79–83. Ch. 3.

GRIFFIN, D. R. More about Bat "Radar." *Scien. Amer.,* 1958, **199**, No. 1, 40–44. Ch. 3.

GRIFFIN, D. R.; WEBSTER, F. A.; and MICHAEL, C. N. The echolocation of flying insects by bats. *Anim. Behav.,* 1960, **8**, 141–54. Ch. 3.

GRIFFITHS, W. J., JR. Effect of isolation on treadmill running in the albino rat. *Psychol. Rep.,* 1961, **8**, 243–50. Ch. 7.

GROSCH, D. S. Experimental studies of the mating reactions of the male Habrobracon. *J. Comp. Physiol. Psychol.,* 1948, **41**, 188–95. Ch. 4.

GROSCH, D. S. Olfactometer experiment with male braconids. *Ann. Ent. Soc. Amer.,* 1950, **43**, 334–42. Ch. 4.

GROSS, C. G. Effect of deprivation on delayed response and delayed alternation performance by normal and brain operated monkeys. *J. Comp. Physiol. Psychol.,* 1963, **56**, 48–51. Ch. 12.

GROSSLIGHT, J. H. and RADLOW, R. Patterning effect of the nonreinforcement-reinforcement sequence in discrimination situation. *J. Comp. Physiol. Psychol.,* 1956, **49**, 542–46. Ch. 11.

GUHL, A. M. Social behavior of the domestic fowl. *Tech. Bull. 73,* Ag. Exp. Sta., Kansas State College, Pittsburg, Kansas. Ch. 8.

GUNN, D. L. The humidity reactions of the woodlouse, *Porcellio scaber. J. Exp. Biol.,* 1937, 14, 178–86. Ch. 4.

GUNN, D. L. Temperature and humidity relations of the cockroach. Temperature preference. *Z. Vergl. Physiol.,* 1944, **20**, 617–25. Ch. 4.

GUTTMAN, N. and KALISH, H. I. Discriminability and stimulus generalization. *J. Exp. Psychol.,* 1956, **51**, 79–88. Ch. 11.

HAFEZ, E. S. E. *The Behavior of Domestic Animals,* 1962, Bailliere, Tindall, Cox, London, Eng. Ch. 1, 3.

HAFEZ, E. S. E.; WILLIAMS, M. and WIERZBOWSKI, S. The behavior of horses. In *The Behavior of Domestic Animals,* 1962, (ed. Hafez, E. S. E.) Bailliere, Tindall, Cox, London, Eng. Ch. 3.

HAILMAN, J. P. Pecking of laughing gull chicks at models of the parental head. *Auk,* 1962, **79,** 89–98. Ch. 5.

HALAS, E. S.; JAMES, R. L.; and STONE, L. A. Types of responses elicited in planaria by light. *J. Comp. Physiol. Psychol.,* 1961, **54,** 303–5. Ch. 10.

HALE, E. B. Effects of forebrain lesions on the aggressive behavior of the green sunfish, *Lepomis cyanellus. Physiol. Zool.,* 1956, **29,** 107–27. Ch. 6.

HALL, C. S. Emotional behavior in the rat. I. Defecation and urination as measures of individual differences in emotionality. *J. Comp. Psychol.,* 1934, **18,** 385–403. Ch. 2.

HALL, C. S. The inheritance of emotionality. *Amer. Scientist,* 1938, **26,** 17–27. Ch. 2.

HALL, C. S. The genetics of behavior. In *Handbook of Experimental Psychology,* 1951 (ed. Stevens, S. S.), Wiley, New York, N.Y. Ch. 2.

HAMILTON, G. V. A study of trial and error reactions in mammals. *J. Anim. Behav.,* 1911, **1,** 33–66. Ch. 12.

HAMILTON, W. F. and COLEMAN, J. B. Trichromatic vision in the pigeon as illustrated by the spectral line discrimination curve. *J. Comp. Psychol.,* 1933, **15,** 183–91. Ch. 3.

HANSON, H. M. Discrimination training effect on stimulus generalization gradient for spectral stimuli. *Science,* 1957, **125,** 888–89. Ch. 11.

HARALSON, J. V. The effects of drive level on performance and extinction of a learned response in rats and fish. *J. Comp. Physiol. Psychol.,* 1958, **51,** 732–36. Ch. 11.

HARDY, A. C. and BAINBRIDGE, R. Effects of pressure on the behavior of decapod larvae. *Nature,* 1951, **167,** 354–55. Ch. 4.

HARKER, JANET E. Diurnal rhythms in the animal kingdom. *Biol. Rev.,* 1958, **33,** 1–52. Ch. 6.

HARLOW, H. F. Forward conditioning, backward conditioning and pseudo-conditioning in the goldfish. *J. Genet. Psychol.,* 1939, **55,** 49–58. Ch. 10.

HARLOW, H. F. The formation of learning sets. *Psychol. Rev.* 1949, **56,** 51–65. Ch. 12.

HARLOW, H. F. The nature of love. *Amer. Psychologist,* 1958, **13,** 673–85. Ch. 8.

HARLOW, H. F. Development of affection in primates. *Roots of Behavior,* 1962 (ed. Bliss, E. L.), Harper, New York, N.Y. Ch. 7.

HARLOW, H. F. and WOOLSEY, C. N. *Biological and Biochemical Bases of Behavior,* 1958, Univ. of Wisconsin Press, Madison, Wis. Ch. 6, 13.

HARTLEY, P. H. T. An experimental analysis of interspecific recognition. In *Symposium of the Society for Experimental Biology,* Vol. IV. *Physiological Mechanisms in Animal Behaviour,* 1950, Cambridge, Eng. Ch. 5.

HASKELL, P. T. Stridulation and associated behavior in certain Orthoptera. 2. Stridulation of females and their behavior with males. *Anim. Behav.,* 1958, **6,** 27–42. Ch. 4.

HASKELL, P. T. Stridulation and associated behaviours in certain Orthoptera. 3. The influence of the gonads. *Anim. Behav.,* 1960, **8,** 76–81. Ch. 6.

HASLER, A. D. and LARSEN, J. A. The homing Salmon. *Sc. America,* 1955, **201,** 3–6. Ch. 3.

HAYES, C. *The Ape in Our House,* Harper, New York, 1951. Ch. 7, 12.

HAYES, K. and HAYES, C. The intellectual development of a home-raised chimpanzee. *Proc. Amer. Phil. Soc.,* 1951, **95**, 105–9. Ch. 7.

HEARST, E. Delayed alternation in the pigeon. *J. Exp. Anal. Behav.,* 1962, **5**, 225–28. Ch. 12.

HEBB, D. O. *The Organization of Behavior,* 1949, Wiley, New York, N.Y. Ch. 7.

HEBB, D. O. Drives and the C.N.S. (conceptual nervous system). *Psychol. Rev.,* 1955, **62**, 243–54. Ch. 7.

HERSHEY, L.; MOORE, A. V. and RICHMOND, J. B. Effect of post partum separation of mother and kid on material care in the domestic goat. *Science,* 1958, **128**, 1342 (Nov. 28). Ch. 9.

HESS, E. Effects of meprobamate on imprinting in waterfowl. *Ann. N.Y. Acad. Sci.,* 1957, **67**, 724–33. Ch. 7.

HESS, E. Imprinting. *Science,* 1959, **130**, 133–40. Ch. 7.

HESS, E. H. Space perception in the chick. *Sci. Amer.,* 1956, **195**, 71–80. Ch. 11.

HESS, E. H. Ethology: An approach toward the complete analysis of behavior. In *New Directions in Psychology.,* 1962 (eds. Brown, R., Galanter, E., Hess, E. H., and Mandler, G.), Holt, Rinehart and Winston, New York, N.Y. Ch. 1.

HESS, W. N. Reactions to light in the earthworm, *Lumbricus terrestris. J. Morphol. & Physiol.,* 1924, **39**, 515–42. Ch. 3, 4.

HILGARD, E. R. and MARQUIS, D. G. Acquisition, extinction and retention of conditioned lid responses to light in dogs. *J. Comp. Psychol.,* 1935, **19**, 29–58. Ch. 10.

HILL, W. F.; COTTON, J. W.; and CLAYTON, K. N. Effect of rewarded and non-rewarded incorrect trials on T-maze learning. *J. Comp. Physiol. Psychol.,* 1963, **56**, 489–96. Ch. 12.

HILL, W. F. and SPEAR, N. E. Resistance to extinction as a joint function of reward magnitude and the spacing of extinction trials. *J. Exp. Psychol.,* 1962, **64**, 636–39. Ch. 11.

HINDE, R. A. The conflict between drives in the courtship and copulation of the chaffinch (*Fringella coelebs*). *Behav.,* 1953, **5**, 1–31. Ch. 9.

HINDE, R. A. Factors governing the changes in strength of a partially inborn response as shown by the mobbing behaviors of the chaffinch (*Fringella coelebs*). *Proc. Roy. Soc. B.,* 1954, **142**, 306–58. Ch. 5.

HINDE, R. A. The behavior of certain cardueline F_1 inter-species hybrids. *Behav.,* 1956, **9**, 201–13. Ch. 2.

HINDE, R. A. Some recent trends in ethology. In *Psychology: A Study of a Science.* Vol. II, 1959 (ed. Koch, S.), McGraw-Hill, New York, N.Y. Ch. 1, 5.

HINDE, R. A. Some factors influencing sexual and aggressive behavior in male chaffinches. *Bird Study,* 1959, **6**, 112–22. Ch. 8.

HINDE, R. A. Unitary drives. *Anim. Behav.,* 1959, **7**, 130–41. Ch. 5.

HINDE, R. A. Behavior. *Biology and Comparative Physiology of Birds.* Vol. II, 1961 (ed. Marshall, A. J.), Academic Press, New York, N.Y. Ch. 8.

HINDE, R. A.; THORPE, W. H.; and VINCE, M. A. The following response of young moorhens and coots. *Behav.,* 1956, **9**, 214–42. Ch. 7.

HINDE, R. A. and TINBERGEN, N. The comparative study of species-specific behavior. In *Behavior and Evolution* (eds. Roe, Ann and Simpson, G. G.), 1958, Yale University Press, New Haven, Conn. Ch. 5.

HIRSCH, J. Recent developments in behavior genetics and differential psychology. *Dis. Nerv. Syst., Mono. Suppl.,* 1958, **19**, 1–8. Ch. 2.

HIRSCH, J. Studies of experimental behavior genetics: II, Individual differences in geotaxis as a function of chromosome variations in synthesized *Drosophila* populations. *J. Comp. Physiol. Psychol.,* 1959, **52**, 304–8. Ch. 2.

HIRSCH, J. and BOUDREAU, J. C. Studies in experimental behavior genetics 1. Heritability of phototaxis in *Drosophila melanogaster. J. Comp. Physiol. Psychol.,* 1958, **51**, 647–51. Ch. 2.

HODGSON, E. S. Electrophysiological studies of anthropod chemoreception, II. Responses of labellor chemoreceptors of the blowfly to stimulation by carbohydrates. *J. Insect. Physiol.,* 1957, **1**, 240–47. Ch. 3.

HOLLIS, J. H. Habituatory response decrement in pupae of *Tenebrio molitor. Anim. Behav.,* 1963, **11**, 161–63. Ch. 4.

HOLST, E. V. and SAINT PAUL, U. V. On the functional organisation of drives. *Anim. Behav.,* 1963, **11**, 1–20.

HOLT, E. B. *Animal Drive and the Learning Process,* Holt, New York, 1931. Ch. 13.

HONZIK, C. H. Delayed reaction in rats. *Univ. Calif. Publ. Psychol.,* 1931, **4**, 307–18.

HOUSE, BETTY J. and ZEAMAN, D. Position discrimination and reversals in low-grade retardates. *J. Comp. Physiol. Psychol.,* 1958, **51**, 614–18.

HOVERY, H. B. Associative hysteresis in flatworms. *Physiol. Zool.,* 1929, **2**, 323–33. Ch. 10.

HOWARD, R. S. The occurrence of fighting behavior in the grain beetle, *Tenebrio molitor* with possible formation of a dominance hierarchy. *Ecology,* 1955, **36**, 281–85. Ch. 8.

HUMPHREYS, L. G. The effect of random alternation of reinforcement on the acquisition and extinction of conditioned eyelid reactions. *J. Exp. Psychol.,* 1939, **25**, 141–58. Ch. 11.

HUMPHRIES, A. A., JR. Observations on the mating behavior of normal and pituitary implanted *Triturus viridescens. Physiol. Zool.,* 1955, **28**, 73–79. Ch. 6.

HUNT, F. L. Establishment of conditioned responses in chick embryos. *J. Comp. Physiol. Psychol.,* 1949, **42**, 107–17. Ch. 10.

HUNTER, W. S. The delayed reaction in animals and children. *Behav. Monogr.,* 1912, **2**, No. 1, 1–85. Ch. 12.

HUNTER, W. S. A kinaesthetically controlled maze habit in the rat. *Science,* 1940, **91**, 267–69. Ch. 12.

ISON, J. R. Experimental extinction as a function of number of reinforcements. *J. Exp. Psychol.,* 1962, **64**, 314–17. Ch. 11.

JAMES, H. Flicker: An unconditioned stimulus for imprinting. *Can. J. Psychol.,* 1959, **13**, 59–67. Ch. 7.

JAMES, H. Social inhibition of the domestic chicks response to visual flicker. *Anim. Behav.,* 1960, **8**, 223–24. Ch. 7.

JAMES, W. T. Social organization among dogs of different temperaments, Terriers and Beagles reared together. *J. Comp. Physiol. Psychol.,* 1951, **44**, 71–77. Ch. 8.

JAMES, W. T. Social facilitation of eating behavior in puppies after satiation. *J. Comp. Physiol. Psychol.,* 1953, **46**, 427–28. Ch. 9.

JAMES, W. T. The development of social facilitation of eating in puppies. *J. Genet. Psychol.,* 1960, **96**, 123–27. Ch. 9.

JANDER, R. and WATERMAN, T. H.   Sensory discrimination between polarized light and light intensity patterns by anthropods. *J. Cellular & Comp. Physiol.,* 1960, **56**, 137–60. Ch. 3.

JAYNES, I.   Imprinting: the interaction of learned and innate behavior: I Development and generalization. *J. Comp. Physiol. Psychol.* 1956, **49**, 201–6. Ch. 7.

JENKINS, D. W.   Territory as a result of despotism and social organization in geese. *Auk,* 1947, **61**, 30–47. Ch. 8.

JENNINGS, H. S.   *Behavior of the Lower Organisms,* 1923, Columbia University Press, New York, N.Y. Ch. 4.

JENSEN, D. D.   Experiments on learning in paramecium. *Science,* 1957, **125**, 191–92. Ch. 11.

JENSEN, P. K.   The effects of blinds and frequency in latent learning. Unpublished doctoral dissertation, Michigan State University, East Lansing, Mich., 1957. Ch. 12.

JOHNSON, J. I.   Double alternation by raccoons. *J. Comp. Physiol. Psychol.,* 1961, **54**, 248–51. Ch. 12.

KAHN, M. W.   The effect of socially learned aggression or submission on the mating behavior of C57 Mice. *J. Genet. Psychol.,* 1961, **98**, 211–17. Ch. 9.

KALMUS, H.   The discrimination by the nose of the dog of individual human odours and in particular the odours of twins. *Brit. J. Anim. Behav.,* 1955, **5**, 25–31. Ch. 3.

KANTOR, J. R.   *The Scientific Evolution of Psychology,* Vol. I, 1963, Principia Press, Chicago, Ill. Ch. 1.

KATZ, M. S. and DETERLINE, W. A.   Apparent learning in the paramecium. *J. Comp. Physiol. Psychol.,* 1958, **51**, 243–48. Ch. 11.

KAUFMAN, M. E. and PETERSON, W. M.   Acquisition of a learning set by normal and mentally retarded children. *J. Comp. Physiol. Psychol.,* 1958, **51**, 619–21. Ch. 12.

KEENLEYSIDE, M. H.   Some aspects of the schooling behavior of fish. *Behav.,* 1955, **8**, 183–248. Ch. 8.

KELLEHER, R. T.   Concept formation in chimpanzees. *Science,* 1958, **128**, 777–78. Ch. 12.

KELLOGG, W. N.   Echo ranging in the porpoise. *Science,* 1958, **128**, 982–88. Ch. 3.

KELLOGG, W. N.   Galvanotropism as an avoidance response. *J. Comp. Physiol. Psychol.,* 1958, **51**, 652–57. Ch. 10.

KELLOGG, W. N.   Auditory scanning in the dolphin. *Psychol. Record,* 1960, **10**, 25–27. Ch. 3.

KELLOGG, W. N.; DEESE, J.; PRONKO, N. H.; and FEINBERG, M.   An attempt to condition the chronic spinal dog. *J. Exp. Psychol.,* 1947, **37**, 99–117. Ch. 13.

KELLOGG, W. N. and SPANOVICK, P.   Respiratory changes during the conditioning of fish. *J. Comp. Physiol. Psychol.,* 1953, **46**, 124–28. Ch. 10.

KENDEIGH, S. C.; WEST, G. C.; and COX, G. W.   Annual stimulus for spring migration in birds. *Anim. Behav.,* 1960, **8**, 180–85. Ch. 6.

KIMBLE, G. A.   *Hilgard and Marquis' Conditioning and Learning,* Century-Croft, New York, 1961. Ch. 11.

KING, J. A.   Parameters relevant to determining the effect of early experience upon the adult behavior of animals. *Psychol. Bull.,* 1958, **55**, 46–58. Ch. 7.

KING, J. A.   Swimming and reaction to electric shock in two subspecies of deermice (*Peromyscus maniculatus*) during development. *Anim. Behav.,* 1961, **9**, 142–50. Ch. 2, 7.

KING, J. A. and ELEFTHERIOU, B. E.   Effects of early handling upon adult behavior in two subspecies of deermice, *Peromyscus maniculatus. J. Comp. Physiol. Psychol.,* 1959, 52, 82–88. Ch. 7.

KING, J. A. and MAVROMATIS, A.   The effect of a conflict situation on learning ability of two strains of inbred mice. *J. Comp. Physiol. Psychol.,* 1956, 49, 465–68. Ch. 2.

KING, J. A. and WEISMAN, R. G.   Discriminated bar pressing with sand reinforcement. *Anim. Behav.* (In press) Ch. 11.

KIRBY, R. H.   Acquisition, extinction, and retention of an avoidance response in rats as a function of age. *J. Comp. Physiol. Psychol.,* 1963, 56, 158–66. Ch. 11.

KLING, J. W.; HOROWITZ, L.; and DELHAGER, J. E.   Light as a positive reinforcer for rat responding. *Psychol. Rep.,* 1956, 2, 337–40. Ch. 11.

KLOPFER, P. H.   Influence of social interactions on learning rates in birds. *Science,* 1958, 128, 903. Ch. 11.

KLUVER, H. and BUCY, P. C.   An analysis of certain effects of bilateral temporal lobectomy in the rhesus monkey, with special reference to "psychic blindness." *J. Psychol.,* 1938, 5, 33–54. Ch. 13.

KNAPP, R. K.   The acquisition and extinction of instrumental avoidance as a function of the escape situation. Unpublished doctoral dissertation, Michigan State University, East Lansing, Mich., 1960. Ch. 11.

KOEHLER, O.   Sinnephysiologieder Susswrasseyslanarien. *Z. Vergl. Physiol.,* 1932, 16, 606–756. Ch. 4.

KUNZE, G.   Einige versuche aber Attennengeschackssinn der Honigbiene *Zool. Jb., Abt. Allg. Zool. Physiol,* 1933, 52, 465–512. Ch. 9.

KUO, ZING YANG.   Studies on the basic factors in animal fighting: V. Inter-species coexistence in fish. *J. Genet. Psychol.,* 1960, 97, 181–94. Ch. 8.

KUO, ZING YANG.   Studies on the basic factors in animal fighting: VII. Inter-species coexistence in mammals. *J. Genet. Psychol.,* 1960, 97, 211–25. Ch. 7.

LACK, D.   *The Life of the Robin,* 1943, H. F. and G. Witherby, London, Eng. Ch. 5, 8.

LARSSON, K.   The effect of restraint upon copulatory behavior in the rat. *Anim. Behavior.,* 1959, I, 23–25. Ch. 9.

LASHLEY, K. S.   *Brain mechanisms and intelligence,* University of Chicago Press, Chicago, 1929. Ch. 13.

LECKART, B. T.   Satiation learning: One trial per day. Unpublished M.A. thesis, Michigan State University, East Lansing, Mich., 1963. Ch. 13.

LEES, A. D.   The sensory physiology of the sheep tick, *Ixodersricinus. J. Exp. Biol.,* 1948, 25, 145–207. Ch. 6, 9.

LEHRMAN, D. S.   Induction of broodiness by participation in courtship and nest-building in the Ring Dove (*Streptopella risoria*). *J. Comp. Physiol. Psychol.,* 1958, 51, 32–37. Ch. 6.

LEHRMAN, D. S.   Effect of female sex hormones on incubation behavior in the Ring Dove. *J. Comp. Physiol. Psychol.* 1958, 51, 142–45. Ch. 6.

LERNER, I. M.   *Population Genetics and Animal Improvement,* 1950, Cambridge Univ. Press, Cambridge, Eng. Ch. 2.

LEVINE, S. Psychophysiological effects of infantile stimulation. *Roots of Behavior,* 1962 (ed. Bliss, E. L.), Harper, New York, N.Y. Ch. 7.

LILLY, J. C. and MILLER, A. M. Operant conditioning of the bottlenose Dolphin with electrical stimulation of the brain. *J. Comp. Physiol. Psychol.,* 1962, **55,** 73–79. Ch. 11.

LORENZ, K. The human companion in the bird's world. *Auk,* 1937, **54,** 245–73. Ch. 7.

LORENZ, K. The comparative method in studying innate behaviour patterns. In Symposium of the Society for Experimental Biology, Vol. IV, *Physiological Mechanisms in Animal Behaviour,* 1950, Cambridge University Press, Cambridge, Eng. Ch. 1, 5, 7.

LORENZ, K. and TINBERGEN, N. Taxis and instinctive action in the egg-retrieving behavior of the graylag goose. In *Instinctive Behavior,* 1951 (ed. Schiller, C. H.), International Universities Press, New York, N.Y. Ch. 5.

LORENZ, K. *King Solomon's Ring,* 1952, Methuen, London, Eng. Ch. 5, 7.

LORENZ, K. The nature of instinct. In *Instinctive Behavior,* 1957 (ed. Schiller, Claire E.), International Universities Press, New York, N.Y. Ch. 2.

MAATSCH, J. L. Learning and fixation after a single shock trial. *J. Comp. Physiol. Psychol.,* 1959, **52,** 408–10. Ch. 10, 11.

MACCASLIN, E. F. Successive and simultaneous discrimination as a function of stimulus similarity. *Amer. J. Psychol.,* 1954, **67,** 308–14. Ch. 11.

MACDONALD, A. The effect of adaptation of the unconditioned stimulus upon the formation of conditioned avoidance responses. *J. Exp. Psychol.,* 1946, **36,** 1–12. Ch. 10.

MACDUFF, M. M. The effect on retention of varying degrees of motivation during learning in rats. *J. Comp. Psychol.,* 1946, **39,** 207–40. Ch. 11.

MCGAUGH, J. L.; WESTBROOK, W.; and BURT, G. Strain differences in the facilitative effects of 5–7 diphenyl–1–3–diazadamantan–6–ol (1757 I.S.) on maze learning. *J. Comp. Physiol. Psychol.,* 1961, **54,** 502–5. Ch. 2.

MCGILL, T. E. Sexual behavior in three inbred strains of mice. *Behav.,* 1962, **19,** 341–50. Ch. 2.

MCMICHAEL, R. E. The effects of preweaning shock and gentling on later resistance to stress. *J. Comp. Physiol. Psychol.,* 1961, **54,** 416–21. Ch. 7.

MCNAMARA, H. J.; LONG, J. B.; and WIKE, E. L. Learning without response under two conditions of external cues. *J. Comp. Physiol. Psychol.,* 1956, **49,** 477–80. Ch. 12.

MCNIVEN, M. A. Social releaser mechanisms in birds. *Psychol. Rec.,* 1960, **10,** 259–65. Ch. 5.

MARLER, P. Studies of fighting in chaffinches (4) Appetitive and consummatory behavior. *Brit. J. Anim. Behav.,* 1957, **5,** 29–37. Ch. 5.

MARLER, P. Developments in the study of animal communication. *Darwin's Biological Works: Some Aspects Reconsidered,* 1959 (ed. Bell, P. R.), Cambridge University Press, Cambridge, Eng. Ch. 7.

MARTINS, T. and VALLE, J. R. Hormonal regulation of the micturition behavior of dogs. *J. Comp. Physiol. Psychol.* 1948, **41,** 301-11. Ch. 6.

Marx, M. H. Infantile deprivation and adult behavior in the rat: retention of increased rate of eating. *J. Comp. Physiol. Psychol.,* 1952, 45, 43–49. Ch. 9.

Mason, W. A. The effect of special restriction on the behavior of rhesus monkeys. I. Free social behavior. *J. Comp. Physiol. Psychol.,* 1961, 98, 211–17. Ch. 9.

Mason, W. A. and Harlow, H. F. Formation of conditioned responses in infant monkeys. *J. Comp. Physiol. Psychol.,* 1958, 51, 68–70. Ch. 10.

Mason, W. A. and Harlow, H. F. Performance of infant rhesus monkeys on a spatial discrimination problem. *J. Comp. Physiol. Psychol.,* 1958, 51, 71–74. Ch. 11.

Mast, S. O. *Light and the Behavior of Organisms,* 1911, Wiley, New York, N. Y. Ch. 4.

Mast, S. O. Photic orientation in insects with special reference to the drone fly, *Eristalis tenax* and the robber fly, *Erax rufibaris. J. Exp. Zool.,* 1923, 38, 109–205. Ch. 4.

Mast, S. O. Factors involved in the process of orientation of lower organisms in light. *Biol. Rev.,* 1938, 13, 186–224. Ch. 4.

Mateer, F. *Child Behavior,* Boston, The Corham Press, 1918. Ch. 10.

Mayr, E. *Systematics and the Origin of Species,* 1942, Columbia University Press, New York, N.Y.

Melzack, R. Effects of early perceptual restriction on simple visual discrimination. *Science,* 1962, 137, 978–79. Ch. 7.

Melzack, R. and Scott, T. H. The effect of early experience on response to pain. *J. Comp. Physiol. Psychol.,* 1957, 50, 155–61. Ch. 7.

Menzel, E. W., Jr.; Davenport, R. K., Jr.; and Rogers, C. M. Some aspects of behavior toward novelty in young chimpanzees. *J. Comp. Physiol. Psychol.,* 1961, 54, 16–20. Ch. 5.

Miles, R. C. Learning set in the marmoset. *J. Comp. Physiol. Psychol.,* 1956, 49, 219–22. Ch. 12.

Miles, R. C. Color vision in the marmoset. *J. Comp. Physiol. Psychol.,* 1958, 51, 152–54. Ch. 3.

Miller, H. M. Variability of behavior of larval trematodes. *Science,* 1928, 68, 117–18. Ch. 4.

Miller, N. E.; Bailey, C. J.; and Stevenson, J. A. Decreased "hunger" but increased food intake resulting from hypothalamic lesions. *Science,* 1950, 112, 256–59. Ch. 9.

Miller, N. E. and Dollard, J. *Social Learning and Imitation,* 1941, Yale University Press, New Haven, Conn. Ch. 8, 12.

Miller, R. E. and Murphy, J. V. Social interactions of rhesus monkeys: I. Food-getting dominance as a dependent variable. *J. Soc. Psychol.,* 1956, 44, 249–55. Ch. 8.

Mishkin, M. and Pribram, K. H. Analysis of the effect of frontal lesions in monkeys: II. Variations of delayed response. *J. Comp. Physiol. Psychol.,* 1956, 49, 36–40. Ch. 13.

Mishkin, M. and Pribram, K. H. Analysis of the effects of frontal lesions in monkeys: III. Object alternations. *J. Comp. Physiol. Psychol.,* 1956, 48, 41–45. Ch. 13.

MOLL, R. P.   The effect of drive level on acquisition of the consummatory response. *J. Comp. Physiol. Psychol.*, 1959, 52, 116–19. Ch. 9.

MOLTZ, H.   Imprinting: empirical basis and theoretical significance. *Psychol. Bull.*, 1960, 57, 291–314. Ch. 7.

MORGAN, C. L.   *Introduction to Comparative Psychology*, 1894, Methuen, London, Eng. Ch. 1.

MORGAN, C. L.   *Animal Behaviour*, 2nd ed., 1908, Longmans, Green, New York, N.Y. Ch. 1.

MOWRER, O. H. and JONES, H. M.   Habit strength as a function of the pattern of reinforcement. *J. Exp. Psychol.*, 1945, 35, 293–311. Ch. 11.

MUNN, N. L.   The question of insight and delayed reaction in fish. *J. Comp. Physiol. Psychol.*, 1958, 51, 92–97. Ch. 12.

MURPHY, J. V. and MILLER, R. E.   The effect of spatial contiguity of cue and reward in the object-quality learning of rhesus monkeys. *J. Comp. Physiol. Psychol.*, 1955, 48, 221–24. Ch. 12.

MYERS, A. K.   Alcohol choice in wistar and G–4 rats as a function of environmental temperature and alcohol concentration. *J. Comp. Physiol. Psychol.*, 1962, 55, 606–9. Ch. 9.

MYERS, R.   Functions of the corpus callosum in interocular transfer. *Brain*, 1956, 79, 358–63. Ch. 13.

NICE, M. M.   Studies in the life history of the song sparrow II. The behavior of the song sparrow and other passerines. *Trans. Linnean Soc. of New York*, 1943, 6, 1–329. Ch. 8.

NISSEN, H. W.   Social behavior in primates, Ch. 13 in Stone, C. P. *Comparative Psychology*, 3rd ed., Prentice-Hall, New York, 1951.

NISSEN, H. W.   Analysis of a complex conditional reaction in chimpanzees. *J. Comp. Psychol.* 1951, 44, 9–16. Ch. 12.

NISSEN, H. W.; CHOW, K. L.; and SEMMES, J.   Effects of restricted opportunity for tactual kinesthetic, and manipulative experience on the behavior of a chimpanzee. *Amer. J. Psychol.*, 1951, 64, 485. Ch. 7.

NOBLE, G. K.   The effect of forebrain lesions on the sexual and fighting behavior of *Betta Splendens* and other fishes. *Anat. Rec. Suppl.*, 1941, 79, 49. Ch. 6, 8.

NOBLE, G. K. and BORNE, N.   The effect of sex hormones on the social hierarchy of *Xiphorphorus helleri*. *Anat. Rec.*, 1940, 78, supp. 147. Ch. 8.

NOBLE, G. K. and GREENBERG, B.   Testosterone propionate, a bisexual hormone in the American Chameleon. *Proc. Soc. Exp. Biol. Med.*, 1940, 44, 460–62. Ch. 6.

NOBLE, G. K. and KUMPF, K. F.   The sexual behavior and secondary sex characteristics of a gonadectomized fish. *Anat. Rec.*, 1936, 67, 113. Ch. 6.

NOBLE, M. and ADAMS, C. K.   Conditioning in pigs as a function of the interval between CS and US. *J. Comp. Physiol. Psychol.*, 1963, 56, 215–19. Ch. 10.

NORTH, A. J. and STIMMEL, D. T.   Extinction of an instrumental response following a large number of reinforcements. *Psychol. Rep.*, 1960, 6, 227–34. Ch. 11.

NOWLISS, V.   The relation of degree of hunger to competition interactions in chimpanzees. *J. Comp. Psychol.*, 1941, 32, 91–115. Ch. 8.

O'CONNELL, C. P.   Use of the fish school for conditioned response experiments. *Anim. Behav.*, 1960, 8, 225–27. Ch. 10.

O'KELLEY, L. I. and HEYER, A. W.   Studies in motivation and retention. V. The influence of need duration on retention of a mate habit. *Comp. Psychol. Monogr.*, 1951, 20, 287–301. Ch. 11.

OLDS, JAMES. Effects of hunger and male sex hormone on self-stimulation of the brain. *J. Comp. Physiol. Psychol.*, 1958, 51, 320–24. Ch. 9.

OPFINGER, E. Uber die Orientierung des Biene an der Futterquelle. *Z. Vergl. Physiol.*, 1931, 15, 431–87. Ch. 11.

OVERTON, R. K. An effect of high and low calcium diets on the maze performance of rats. *J. Comp. Physiol. Psychol.*, 1958, 51, 697–700. Ch. 13.

PADILLA, S. G. Further studies on the delayed pecking of chicks. *J. Comp. Psychol.*, 1935, 20, 413–43. Ch. 11.

PANCHENKOVA, E. F. The ontogenetic development of conditioning in the white rat. *Zh. Vssh. Noru. Deiat*, 1956, 6, 312–18. Ch. 10.

PASCAL, G. R.; STOLUROW, L. M.; ZABARENKO, R. N.; and CHAMBERS, K. S. The delayed reaction in mental defectives. *Amer. J. Ment. Defic.*, 1951, 56, 152–60. Ch. 12.

PASTORE, N. Discrimination learning in the canary. *J. Comp. Physiol. Psychol.*, 1954, 47, 389–90. Ch. 12.

PAULSEN, H. Morphological and ethological notes on a hybrid between a domestic duck and a domestic goose. *Behav.*, 1951, 3, 99–104. Ch. 2.

PAVLIK, W. B. and REYNOLDS, W. F. Effects of deprivation schedule and reward magnitude on acquisition and extinction performance. *J. Comp. Physiol. Psychol.*, 1963, 56, 452–55. Ch. 11.

PAVLOV, I. P. Conditioned reflexes. (Translated by G. V. Anrep.) Oxford Univ. Press, 1927, London, Eng. Ch. 10.

PENFIELD, W. Memory mechanism, A.M.A. *Arch. Neurol. Psychiat.*, 1952, 67, 178–98. Ch. 13.

PENNINGTON, D. F. The effect of ECS on retention of a discrimination habit in rats subjected to anoxia. *J. Comp. Physiol. Psych.*, 1958, 51, 687–90. Ch. 13.

PEREBOOM, A. C. and CRAWFORD, B. B. Instrumental and competing behavior as a function of trials and reward magnitude. *J. Exp. Psychol.*, 1958, 56, 82–85. Ch. 11.

PERKINS, C. C. The relations of secondary reward to gradients of reinforcement. *J. Exp. Psychol.*, 1947, 37, 377–92. Ch. 12.

PETERSEN, N. Control of behavior by presentation of an imprinted stimulus. *Science*, 1960, 132, 1395. Ch. 11.

PHILLIPS, R. E. and McKINNEY, F. The role of testosterone in the displays of some ducks. *Anim. Behav.*, 1962, 10, 244–46. Ch. 6.

PHOENIX, C. H.; GOY, R. W.; GERALL, A. A.; and YOUNG, W. C. Organizing action of prenatally administered testosterone proprionate on the tissue mediating mating behavior in the female guinea pig. *Endocrinology*, 1959, 65, 369–82. Ch. 6.

PREMACK, K. Reversibility of the reinforcement relation. *Science*, 1962, 136, 255–57. Ch. 11.

PRIBRAM, K. Comparative neurology and the evolution of behavior, in Roe, A. and Simpson, G. G., *Behavior and Evolution*, 1958, Yale University Press, New Haven, Conn. Ch. 13.

PRIBRAM, K. Neocortical function in behavior, in Harlow, H. F. and Woolsey, C. N., *Biological and Biochemical Bases of Behavior*, 1958, University of Wisconsin, Madison, Wis.

PROSSER, C. L. Comparative neurophysiology. In *Evolution of Nervous Control*,

1959 (ed. Bass, A. D.), Publication #52 of Amer. Assoc. Advanc. Sci., Washington, D.C. Ch. 1.

PUBOLS, B. A. "Incentive magnitude, learning and performance in animals." *Psych. Bull.,* 1960, **57,** 89–115. Ch. 11.

RAMSAY, A. O. and HESS, E. H. A laboratory approach to the study of imprinting. *Wilson Bull.,* 1954, **66,** 196–206. Ch. 7.

RAO, R. T. Visual response of mosquitos artificially rendered flightless. *J. Exp. Biol.,* 1947, 24, 64–78. Ch. 4.

RATNER, S. C. The effects of learning to be submissive on status in the peck order of domestic fowl. *Anim. Behav.,* 1961, 9, 34–37. Ch. 8.

RATNER, S. C. Conditioning of decerebrate worms, *Lumbricus terrestris. J. Comp. Physiol. Psychol.,* 1962, 55, 174–77. Ch. 10.

RATNER, S. C. and MILLER, K. R. Classical conditioning in earthworms, *Lumbricus terrestris. J. Comp. Physiol. Psychol.,* 1959, 52, 102–5. Ch. 16.

RATNER, S. C. and RINGER, R. K. An activity cage and recorder for domestic fowl. *Anim. Behav.,* 1959, 7, 245–47. Ch. 2.

RATNER, S. C. and THOMPSON, R. W. Immobility reactions (fear) of domestic fowl as function of age and prior experience. *Anim. Behav.,* 1960, 8, 186–91. Ch. 5, 7.

RAZRAN, G. Conditioned responses in children—a behavioral and quantitative critical review of experimental studies. *Arch. Psychol.,* 1933, 148. Ch. 10.

RAZRAN, G. The dominance contiguity theory of the acquisition of classical conditioning. *Psychol. Bull.,* 1957, 54, 1–46. Ch. 10.

RAZRAN, G. Recent Soviet phyletic comparisons of classical and of operant conditions: Experimental designs. *J. Comp. Physiol. Psychol.,* 1961, 54, 357–65. Ch. 10.

RAZRAN, G. Raphael's "Idealess" behavior. *J. Comp. Physiol. Psychol.,* 1961, 54, 366–67. Ch. 12.

REYNOLDS, A. E. The normal seasonal reproductive cycle in the male *Eumeces faciatus* together with some observations on the effects of castration and hormone administration. *J. Morphol.,* 1943, 72, 331–77. Ch. 6.

RICHTER, C. P. Total self-regulatory functions in animals and human beings. *Harvey Lectures,* 1942–43, 38, 63–103. Ch. 6.

RIEGERT, P. W. The humidity reactions of grasshoppers. Humidity reactions of *Melanaphus Liabittanus* (say) and *Cammula ellucida* (Scudd). *Canad. Entomalogist,* 1959, 91, 35–40. Ch. 4.

RIESEN, A. H. Stimulation as a requirement for growth and function in behavioral development. *Functions of Varied Experience,* 1961 (eds. Fiske, D. W. and Maddi, S. R.), Dorsey Press, Homewood, Ill. Ch. 7.

RILEY, D. A. and ROSENZWEIG, M. R. Echolocation in rats. *J. Comp. Physiol. Psychol.,* 1957, 50, 323–28. Ch. 3.

RIOPELLE, A. J.; ALPER, R. C.; STRONG, P. N.; and ADES, H. W. Multiple discrimination and patterned string performance of normal and temporal-lobectomized monkeys. *J. Comp. Physiol. Psychol.,* 1953, 46, 145–49. Ch. 13.

ROE, A. and SIMPSON, G. (eds.) *Behavior and Evolution,* 1958, Yale University Press, New Haven, Conn. Ch. 13.

ROEDER, K. D.   An experimental analysis of the sexual behavior of the Praying Mantis. *Biol. Bull.,* 1935, **69**, 203–20. Ch. 6.

ROGERS, C. G.   *Textbook of Comparative Physiology,* 1938, McGraw-Hill, New York, N.Y. Ch. 1.

ROMANES, G. J.   *Animal Intelligence,* 1912, D. Appleton, New York, N.Y. Ch. 1.

ROSENBLATT, J. S. and ARONSON, L. R.   The influence of experience on the behavioral effects of androgen in prepuberally castrated male cats. *Anim. Behav.,* 1958, 171–82. Ch. 6.

ROSS, W. D.   *The Student's Oxford Aristotle, Vol. III. Psychology,* 1942, Oxford University Press, London, Eng.

ROTH, L. M.   An experimental laboratory study of the sexual behavior of *Aedes aegypti. Amer. Midl. Nat.,* 1948, **40**, 265–352. Ch. 3.

ROTH, L. M. and WILLIS, E. R.   A study of cockroach behavior. *Amer. Midland Nat.,* 1952, **47**, 66–129. Ch. 4.

ROTHENBUHLER, W. C.   Genetics of a behavior difference in honeybees. *Proc. Intern. Cong. Genet.,* 10th meeting, 1958, **2**, 242. Ch. 2.

SANDERS, F. K.   Second-order olfactory and visual learning in the optic tectum of goldfish. *J. Exp. Biol.,* 1940, **17**, 416–34. Ch. 10.

SANDERSON, G. C.   Growth and behavior of a litter of captive long tailed weasels. *J. Mammol,* 1949, **30**, 412–15. Ch. 5.

SANDFORD, R. N.   The effects of absinence from feed upon imaginal processes: a preliminary experiment. *J. Psychol.,* 1936, **2**, 129–36. Ch. 9.

SCHALLER, G. B. and EMLEN, J. T.   The development of visual discrimination patterns in the crouching reactions of nestling Grackles. *Auk,* 1961, **78**, 125–37. Ch. 7.

SCHEIR, M. W., and FOHRMAN, M. H.   Social dominance relationships in a herd of dairy cattle. *Brit. J. Anim. Behav.,* 1955, **3**, 45–55. Ch. 8.

SCHILLER, P. A.   Innate motor action as a basis of learning. (ed. Schiller, C. H.), in *Instinctive Behavior,* 1957, International Universities Press, New York, N.Y. Ch. 5, 12.

SCHLOSBERG, H.   A study of the conditioned patellar reflex. *J. Exp. Psychol.,* 1928, **11**, 468–94. Ch. 10.

SCHLOSBERG, H.   Conditioned responses in the white rat. *J. Genet. Psychol.,* 1934, **45**, 303–35. Ch. 10.

SCHLOSBERG, H. and KATZ, A.   Double alternation lever-pressing in the white rat. *Amer. J. Psychol.,* 1943, **56**, 274–82. Ch. 12.

SCHMIDT, R. S.   The evolution of nest building behavior in *Apicotermes. Evolution,* 1955, **9**, 157–81. Ch. 2.

SCHNEIRLA, T. C.   Learning and orientation in ants. *Comp. Psychol. Monogr.* 1929, **6**, pp. 143. Ch. 12.

SCHREIVER, L. and KLING, A.   Behavioral changes following rhinencephalic injury in cats. *J. neurophysiol.,* 1953, **16**, 643–59. Ch. 6.

SCOTT, J. P.   *Aggression,* 1958, University of Chicago Press, Chicago, Ill. Ch. 2.

SCOTT, J. P.   *Animal Behavior,* 1958, University of Chicago Press, Chicago, Ill. Ch. 8.

SCOTT, J. P. and CHARLES, M. S.   Genetic differences in the behavior of dogs: Case of magnification by thresholds and by habit formation. *J. Genet. Psychol.,* 1954, **84**, 175–88. Ch. 2.

SCOTT, J. P. and FREDRICKSON, E.   The causes of fighting in mice and rats. *Physical Zool.,* 1951, **24,** 273–309. Ch. 8.

SCOTT, J. P. and MARSTON, M. U.   Critical periods affecting the development of normal and maladjustive social behavior in puppies. *J. Genet. Psychol.,* 1950, **77,** 25–60. Ch. 7.

SEARLES, L. V.   The organization of hereditary maze brightness and maze dullness. *Genet. Psychol. Mono.,* 1949, **39,** 279–375. Ch. 2.

SEIDMAN, E.   Relative ability of newt and terrapin to reverse a direction habit. *J. Comp. Physiol. Psychol.,* 1949, **42,** 320–27. Ch. 12.

SELYE, H.   The general adaptation syndrome and the diseases of adaptation. *J. Clin. Endocrin.,* 1946, **6,** 117–230. Ch. 6.

SHAW, E.   The development of schooling behavior in fishes. *Physiol. Zool.,* 1960, **33,** 79–86. Ch. 8.

SHEPARD, J. F.   An unexpected cue in maze learning. *Psychol. Bull.,* 1929, **26,** 164–65. Ch. 12.

SHEPARD, J. F.   More learning. *Psychol. Bull.,* 1931, **28,** 240–41. Ch. 12.

SHEPARD, J. F.   Selection in maze learning. *Psychol. Bull.,* 1938, **35,** 637–38. Ch. 12.

SHEPARD, J. F. and BREED, F. S.   Maturation and use in the development of an instinct. *J. Animal Behav.,* 1913, **3,** 274–85. Ch. 11.

SHEPP, B. E.   Some cue properties of anticipated rewards in discrimination learning of retardates. *J. Comp. Physiol. Psychol.,* 1962, **55,** 856–59. Ch. 11.

SIEGEL, P. S.   Food intake in the rat in relation to the dark-light cycle. *J. Comp. Physiol. Psychol.,* 1961, **54,** 294–301. Ch. 9.

SIEGEL, P. S. and TALANTIS, BILLIE S.   Water intake as a function of privation interval when food is withheld. *J. Comp. Physiol. Psychol.,* 1950, **43,** 62–65. Ch. 9.

SIMPSON, G. G.   *Principles of Animal Taxonomy,* 1961, Columbia University Press, New York, N.Y. Ch. 2.

SINGH, S. D.   Conditioned emotional response in the rat: I. Constitutional and situational determinants. *J. Comp. Physiol. Psychol.,* 1959, **52,** 574–78. Ch. 10.

SKINNER, B. F.   *The Behavior of Organisms,* Appleton Century, New York, 1938. Ch. 11.

SMALL, W. S.   Experimental study of the mental processes of the rat. II. *Amer. J. Psychol.,* 1901, **12,** 206–39. Ch. 11.

SMITH, F. E. and BAYLOR, E. R.   Bees, daphnia and polarized light. *Ecology,* 1960, **41,** 360–63. Ch. 3.

SMITH, M. P.   The stimulus-trace gradient in visual discrimination learning. *J. Comp. Physiol. Psychol.,* 1951, **44,** 154–61. Ch. 11.

SMITH, M.; POOL, R.; and WEINBERG, H.   The role of bulk in the control of eating. *J. Comp. Physiol. Psychol.,* 1962, **55,** 115–20. Ch. 9.

SMITH, W. I.; KRAWCZUN, A. J.; WISEHAUPT, N. J.; and ROSS, S.   Hoarding behavior of adrenalectomized hamsters. *J. Comp. Physiol. Psychol,* 1954, **47,** 154–56. Ch. 6.

SNYDER, L. H. and DAVID, P. R.   *The Principles of Heredity,* 5th ed, 1957, Heath, Boston, Mass. Ch. 2.

SOLOMON, R. L. and WYNNE, L. C.   Traumatic avoidance learning: acquisition in normal dogs. *Psychol. Monogr.,* 1953, **67,** No. 4. Ch. 13.

SPELT, D. K.   The conditioning of the human fetus in utero. *J. Exp. Psychol.*, 1948, **38**, 338–46. Ch. 10.

SPENCE, K. W.; HAGGARD, D. F.; and ROSS, L. E.   Intrasubject conditioning as a function of the intensity of the unconditioned stimulus. *Science*, 1958, **128**, 774–75. Ch. 10.

SPERRY, R. W.   The problem of central nervous reorganization after nerve regeneration and muscle transposition. *Quart. Rev. Biol.*, 1945, **20**, 311–69. Ch. 13.

SPERRY, R. W.   On the neural basis of the conditioned response. *Brit. J. Anim. Behav.*, 1955, 3, 41–44. Ch. 10.

SPERRY, R. W.   Physiological plasticity and brain circuit theory, in Harlow, H. F. and Woolsey, C. N., *Biological and biochemical bases of behavior*. University of Wisconsin Press, Madison, Wis., 1958. Ch. 13.

SPRAGG, S. D. S.   Anticipation as a factor in maze errors. *J. Comp. Psychol.*, 1933, 15, 313–29. Ch. 12.

SRB, A. M. and OWEN, R. D.   *General Genetics*, 1952, Freeman, San Francisco, Cal. Ch. 2.

STAMM, J. S.   Genetics of hoarding: II. Hoarding behavior of hybrid and back-crossed strains of rats. *J. Comp. Physiol. Psychol.* 1956, 49, 349–52. Ch. 2.

STEIN, D. G.   The effects of spacing of training and extirpation of cerebral ganglia on the unconditioned responses of earthworms. 1962. Unpublished MA thesis, Department of psychology, Michigan State University, East Lansing, Mich. Ch. 4.

STERRITT, G. M.   Inhibition and facilitation of eating by electric shock. *J. Comp. Physiol. Psychol.*, 1962, **55**, 226–29. Ch. 9.

STEVENSON, H. W. and SWARTZ, J. D.   Learning set in children as a function of intellectual level. *J. Comp. Physiol. Psychol.*, 1958, **51**, 755–57. Ch. 12.

STOKES, A. W.   The comparative ethology of Great, Blue, Marsh and Coal Tits at a winter feeding station. *Behav.*, 1962, **19**, 208–18. Ch. 2.

SUTHERLAND, N. S.; MACKINTOSH, N. J.; and MACKINTOSH, J.   Simultaneous discrimination training of *Octopus* and transfer of discrimination along a continuum. *J. Comp. Physiol. Psychol.*, 1963, **56**, 150–56. Ch. 11.

TAVOLGA, W. N.   The effect of gonadectomy and hypophysectomy on the prespawning behavior of the males of the gobiid fish, *Bathygobius soporator. Physiol. Zool.*, 1955, **28**, 218–33. Ch. 6.

TAYLOR, J. A.   Level of conditioning and intensity of the adapting stimulus. *J. Exp. Psychol.*, 1956, **51**, 127–30. Ch. 10.

TEST, F. H.   Social aggressiveness in an amphibian. *Science*, 1954, **120**, 140–41. Ch. 5.

TEUBER, H. L.   Some alterations in behavior after cerebral lesions in man, in *Evolution of Nevous Control*, pp. 157–94, Washington, D.C., Amer. Assn. for the Advancement of Science, 1959. Ch. 13.

THOMPSON, E. L.   An analysis of the learning process in the snail, *Physa gyrina* say. *Behav. Monogr.*, 1917, 3, 97. Ch. 10.

THOMPSON, R.   Successive reversal of a position habit in an invertebrate. *Science*, 1957, **126**, 163–64. Ch. 12.

THOMPSON, R.   Transient memory in albino rats. *Science*, 1959, **129**, 842–43. Ch. 12.

THOMPSON, R.   Learning in rats with extensive neocortical damage. *Science*, 1959, **129**, #3357, 1223–24. Ch. 13.

THOMPSON, R. and McCONNELL, J.   Classical conditioning in the Planarian *Dugesia dorotocephala*. *J. Comp. Physiol. Psychol.*, 1955, 48, 65–68. Ch. 10.

THOMPSON, R. and PRYER, R. S.   The effect of anoxia on the retention of a discrimination habit. *J. Comp. Physiol. Phychol.*, 1956, 49, 297–300. Ch. 13.

THOMPSON, W. D. and SONTAG, L. W.   Behavioral effects in the offspring of rats subjected to audiogenic seizures during the gestation period. *J. Comp. Physiol.*, 1956, 49, 454–56. Ch. 7.

THOMPSON, W. R.   The inheritance of behavior: Behavioral differences of 15 mouse strains. *Can. J. Psychol.*, 1953, 7, 145–55. Ch. 2.

THOMPSON, W. R. and HERON, W.   The effects of restricting early experience on the problem solving capacity of dogs. *Can. J. Psychol.*, 1954, 8, 17-31. Ch. 7.

THOMPSON, W. R. and SCHAEFER, T.   Early environmental stimulation. *Functions of Varied Experience*, 1961 (eds. Fiske, D. W. and Maddi, S. R.), Dorsey Press, Homewood, Ill. Ch. 7.

THORNDIKE, E. L.   Animal intelligence: experimental study of the associative processes in animals. *Psychol. Rev. Monogr. Suppl.*, 1898, 2, No. 4. Ch. 11.

THORPE, W. H.   *Learning and Instinct in Animals,* 1956, Methuen, London, Eng. Ch. 4, 6, 7.

THORPE, W. H.   Problems common to animals and men. *Current Problems in Animal Behavior,* 1961, Cambridge University Press, Cambridge, Eng. Ch. 7.

THORSON, G.   Reproduction and larval ecology of marine bottom invertebrates. *Biol. Rev.*, 1950, 25, 1–45. Ch. 9.

TINBERGEN, N.   *The Study of Instinct,* 1951, Clarendon Press, Oxford, Eng. Ch. 5, 8.

TINBERGEN, N.   *Social Behavior in Animals,* 1953, Methuen, London, Eng. Ch. 8.

TINBERGEN, N.   *Curious Naturalists,* 1958, Country Life Ltd., London, Eng. Ch. 1, 5.

TINBERGEN, N.   Comparative studies of the behaviors of gulls (Laridae): A progress report. *Behav.*, 1959, 15, 1–70. Ch. 5.

TINKLEPAUGH, O. L.   Maze learning of a turtle. *J. Comp. Psychol.*, 1932, 13, 201–6. Ch. 12.

TINKLEPAUGH, O. L.   Multiple delayed reaction with chimpanzees and monkeys. *J. Comp. Psychol.*, 1932, 13, 197–236. Ch. 12.

TOLMAN, E. C. and HANZIK, C. H.   "Insight" in rats. *Univ. of Calif. Publ. Psychol.*, 1930, 4, 215–32. Ch. 12.

ULLYOT, P.   The behavior of *Dendrocoelum lacteum. J. Exp. Biol.* 1936, 13, 253–64. Ch. 4.

VALENSTEIN, E. S.; RISS, W.; and YOUNG, W. C.   Sex drive in genetically heterogenous and highly inbred strains of male guinea pigs. *J. Comp. Physiol. Psychol.*, 1955, 48, 397–403. Ch. 2.

VANDEVENTER, J. H. and RATNER, S. C.   Variables affecting the frequency of response of planaria to light. *J. Comp. Physiol. Psychol.*, 1964, 57, 407–11. Ch. 4.

VERPLANCK, W. S. and HAYES, J. R.   Eating and drinking as a function of maintenance schedule. *J. Comp. Physiol. Psychol.*, 1953, 46, 327–33. Ch. 9.

VINCE, M. A.   "String pulling" in birds. (2) Difference related to age in greenfinches and canaries. *Anim. Behav.*, 1958, 6, 53–59. Ch. 10.

VOWLES, D. M.   The foraging of ants. *Brit. J. Anim. Behav.*, 1955, 3, 1–13. Ch. 4.

VOWLES, D. M.   Neural mechanisms in insect behavior. *Current Problems in Animal Behavior.*, 1961 (eds. Thorpe, W. H. and Zangwell, O. L.), Cambridge University Press, Cambridge, Eng. Ch. 6.

WADE, M.   Behavioral effect of prefrontal lobotomy, lobectomy, and circumsection in the monkey *Macaca mulatta. J. Comp. Neurol.*, 1952, 96, 179–207. Ch. 13.

WALLIS, D. I.   Behaviour patterns of the ant, *Formica fusca. Animal Behav.*, 10, 105–11. Ch. 8.

WARDEN, C. J. and HAMILTON, E. L.   The effect of variations in length of maze pattern upon the rate of fixation in the white rat. *J. Genet. Psychol.*, 1929, 36, 229–37. Ch. 12.

WARDEN, C. J.; JENKINS, T. N.; and WARNER, L. H.   *Comparative Psychology: Plants and Invertebrates.* Vol. II, 1941, Ronald Press, New York. Ch. 8.

WARDEN, C. J. and REISS, B. F.   Relative difficulty of mazes of different lengths for chicks. *J. Psychol.*, 1941, 11, 411–19. Ch. 12.

WARREN, J. M.   Effect of geometrical regularity on visual form discrimination by monkeys. *J. Comp. Physiol. Psychol.*, 1953, 46, 237–40. Ch. 12.

WARREN, P. R. and HINDE, R. A.   The effect of estrogen and progesterone on the nest-building of domestic canaries. *Anim. Behav.*, 1959, 7, 209–13. Ch. 6.

WATSON, J. B.   Kinaesthetic and organic sensations: their role in the reactions of the white rat to the mate. *Psychol. Monogr.*, 1907, 8, pp. 100. Ch. 11.

WEINSTEIN, B.   Matching-from-sample by rhesus monkeys and by children. *J. Comp. Psychol.*, 1941, 31, 3–48. Ch. 12.

WEINSTEIN, B.   The evolution of intelligent behavior in rhesus monkeys. *Genet. Psychol. Monogr.*, 1945, 31, 3–48. Ch. 12.

WEINSTOCK, S.   Acquisition and extinction of a partially reinforced running response at a 24-hour interval. *J. Exp. Psychol.*, 1958, 56, 151–58. Ch. 11.

WEISE, P. and BITTERMAN, M. E.   Response selection in discriminative learning. *Psychol. Rev.*, 1951, 58, 185–95. Ch. 11.

WEISS, P. A.   Self-differentation of the basis patterns of coordination. *Comp. Psychol. Monogr.*, 1941, 17, 1–96, Ch. 13.

WEISS-FOGH, T.   An aerodynamic sense organ in locusts. *Nature*, 1949, 164, 873–74. Ch. 4.

WELKER, W. I.   An analysis of exploratory and play behavior in animals, in Fiske, D. W. and Maddi, S. R. *Functions of Varied Experience*, Dorsey Press, 1961, Homewood, Ill. Ch. 9.

WELLS, M. J. and WELLS, J.   The effects of lesions to the vertical and optic lobes on tactile discrimination in *Octopus. J. Exp. Biol.*, 1957, 34, 378–93. Ch. 13.

WIEPKEMA, P. R.   An ethological analysis of the reproductive behavior of the bitterling (*Rodeus amurus*, Block). *Behav.*, 1961, 16, 103–99. Ch. 5.

WIGGLESWORTH, V. S. and GILLETT, J. D.   The function of the antennae of *Rhodnius prolixus* and the mechanism to orientation to the host. *J. Exp. Biol.*, 1934, 11, 120–39. Ch. 4.

WILSON, E. O.   Chemical communication among workers of the fire ant, *Solenopsis saevissima* (Fr. Smith). 3: The experimental induction of social responses. *Anim. Behav.*, 1962, 10, 159–64. Ch. 4, 8.

WILSON, M. O.   Symbolic behavior in the white rat: 1. Relation of amount of interpolated activity to adequacy of the delayed response. *J. Comp. Physiol. Psychol.*, 1, 29–49. Ch. 11.

WITSCHI, E.   Sex and secondary sexual characteristics. Vol. 2, 1961, (ed. Marshall, A. S.), *Biology and Comparative Physiology of Birds,* Academic Press, New York, N.Y. Ch. 6.

WODINSKY, J. and BITTERMAN, M. E.   Solution of oddity problems by the rat. *Amer. J. Psychol.,* 1953, 66, 137–40. Ch. 12.

WODINSKY, J. and BITTERMAN, M. E.   Partial reinforcement in the fish. *Amer. J. Psychol.,* 1959, 72, 184–99. Ch. 11.

WOLFE, J. B. and SPRAGG, S. D. S.   Some experimental tests of "reasoning" in white rats. *J. Comp. Physiol. Psychol.,* 1934, 18, 455–69. Ch. 12.

WOOD–GUSH, D. G. M.   The courtship of the Brown Leghorn cock. *Brit. J. Anim. Behav.,* 1954, 2, 95–102. Ch. 5.

WOOD–GUSH, D. G. M. and OSBORNE, R.   A study of differences in the sex drive of cockerels. *Brit. J. Anim. Behav.,* 1956, 4, 102–10. Ch. 2.

WOODS, P. J.   Behavior in a novel situation as influenced by the immediate preceding environment. *J. Exp. Anal. Behav.,* 1962, 5, 185–90. Ch. 5.

YOUNG, F. A.   Studies of pupillary conditioning. *J. Exp. Psychol.,* 1958, 55, 97–110. Ch. 11.

YOUNG, P. T. and ASDOURIAN, D.   Relative acceptability of sodium chloride and sucrose solutions. *J. Comp. Physiol. Psychol.* 1957, 50, 499–503. Ch. 9.

YOUNG, W. C.   Internal secretions and behavior. *Comparative Psychology,* 3rd ed., 1951 (ed. Stone, C. P.), Prentice-Hall, Englewood Cliffs, N.J. Ch. 6.

ZEAMAN, D.   Response latency as a function of the amount of reinforcement. *J. Exp. Psychol,* 1949, 39, 466–83. Ch. 11.

ZIMBARDO, P. G. and MONTGOMERY, K. C.   The relative strength of consummatory responses in hunger, thirst, and exploratory drive. *J. Comp. Physiol. Psychol.,* 1957, 50, 504–08. Ch. 9.

INDEX

A

Acquisition, one bar-press per day, 587–93
Activity
  affected by early experience, 414–15
  measurement, 30
Adaptation
  of termite nests, 87–90
  of US, 526
Adrenal hormones and hoarding, 292
Affectional behavior, 361, 435
Aggressive behaviour of birds, 449–50
Aggressiveness
  and genetics, 29
  measurement, 29
Altered stimulation
  general effects, 367
  and later behavior, 354–55
  and learning, 404–7
Ameno-taxis, 170
Amphibians, reproduction, 283
Analogy in evolution, 33
Androgen effects
  on cats, 286
  on dogs, 289
Animal behavior
  comparative analysis, 3–4
  reasons for study, 1–6
Anoxia, 678
Ant
  chemical communication, 425
  chemical stimuli, 175
  digging behavior, 486
  stimuli for social responses, 175
  types of social behavior, 423
Appetitive acts in instincts, 218–20
Appetitive behavior, 480
Aristotle, 11
Arousal theory and innate behavior, 278
Audiogenic seizures, 21
  and early experience, 359
Audition, phylogenetic comparisons, 100–2
Avoidance learning, 567, 578

B

Bats
  detection and capture of insects, 138–62
  echolocation, 101–2, 138–62

Bees
  care of larva, 22
  defense of hive, 432
  orientation to light, 171
  response to chemical stimuli, 174
  stimuli releasing stinging, 190–97
Behavioral sink, 434
Bilateral effects in learning, 705–17
Birds, 229
  aggressive behavior, 449–50
  calls and their functions, 447–48
  comparisons for nest building, 337
  development of fear, 360
  development of song, 363
  distraction display, 229
  dominance hierarchy, 428
  early experience and fear, 360
  evolution of nesting, 93–94
  genetics and behavior, 24, 29
  intention movements, 52–74
  locomotion
    hopping, 54–56
    walking, 56–59
  mating, 489
  mobbing, 229
  reaction to predator, 230
  reproduction, 284–85
    hormones, 284
    secondary sex characteristics, 284
  territorial behavior, 445–57
Bitterling fish
  mating, 222
  reproductive behavior, 243–60
Bittern, freezing, 62–63
Blinds, complex maze, 630–32
Blodgett, latent learning, 629
Bloodsucker, response to temperature, 168
Brain
  of invertebrates, 294
    anatomy of, 294
  self-stimulation, 296, 481–82
    instrumental learning, 505–10
    method, 506–7
    rats, 506–10
  of vertebrates
    anatomy of, 293–94
    relation to behavior, 682–84

Buxton-Haney, latent learning, 629

C

Canaries, nest building, 330–38
Canon of parsimony, 13–14
Care of the body surface and evolution, 35
Care of young, 226
  activities, 226
  weaning, 227
Cats
  double alternation, 647–48
  reproduction, 286
  visual acuity, 104–5
Cattle, dominance hierarchy, 427
Cerebral injury, 678, 684
Chaffinch, 220
  mobbing, 229
Chaining, 529, 620
Chance similarity in evolution, 33
Chemical effects on behavior, 679–80
Chemical gradient, as a stimulus, 169
  for ants, 175
Chemical senses, phylogenetic comparisons,
  106–7
Chemical stimulus
  bee sting, 193–94
  commensal behavior, 198–215
  marine animals, 199–215
  wasp mating, 183–84
  worms, 202–5
Chemokinesis
  of crab, 208–10
  worms, 202–5
Chemotaxis
  of crab, 210–11
  worms, 205
Chickens
  dominance hierarchy, 438–44
  early experience and fear, 358
  effect of pituitary, 288
  imprinting, 361
  responses in mating, 224
  stimuli for mating, 224
  vocalization, 435
Chimpanzees
  concept formation, 667–71
  fighting and hormones, 291
  growth, 287
  "insight," 671–73
  novel stimuli, 231
Circle-blinds, 630–31
Circumsection, 685
Circus movements, 169
Cognitive map, 629
Color as a stimulus for bee sting, 190–91
Color vision, 100
  marmoset, 112–15
  phylogenetic comparisons, 105–6
Commensal behavior, 198–215

Communication
  ants, 175, 425
  baboons, 266–71
  bees, 129–37
  birds, 435, 447–48
  locust, 299–308
  primates, 36
Comparative psychology, 1–16
  definition, 1
  history, 11–15
  methods for research, 6
  objectives and criticisms, 4–6
Competing responses, 511–18, 573, 577
Complex behavior, 619–73
  role of neural tissue, 674–739
Complex maze, 619–23, 642
  learning, 632
Concept formation, 636–37
  chimpanzees, 667–71
Conditional discrimination, 679–80, 685
Conditioned reinforcer (S^r), 569
Conditioned response (CR), 523–30
  spinal, 719–30
Conditioned stimulus (CS), 523–30
  brush stimulus, 721, 728–29
Conditioning
  analysis of social behavior of birds, 442–
    43
  backward, 525, 531, 534–43
  classical, 523–65
  decorticate and spinal dog, 684–85
  differential, 568
  earthworms, 544–50
  goldfish, 534–43
  higher order, 528–29
  human fetus in utero, 523
  infant monkeys, 555–60
  intensity of US, 561–65
  mentally retarded, 533
  method to identify stimuli, 99
  methodology, 524–26
  nictitating membrane, 551–54
  one trial, 528
  ontogenetic limits, 532–33
  phylogenetic limits, 531–32
  rabbit, 551–54
  relation to instrumental learning, 528–
    29
  simultaneous, 525
  spinal carnivores, 719–30
  stimulus factors, 526–27
  temporal conditions, 527–28
  trace, 525
Conflict of motives, 489
  between feeding and exploration, 511–18
Consummatory behavior, 218–20, 479–523,
  572
  characteristics, 479
  examples, 479

Consummatory behavior—*Cont.*
  incentive, 485
  measurement, 480–81
  nonnutritive sucking, 499–505
  other variables, 487
  phylogenetic considerations, 487–89
  prior learning, 483–85
  stimulus situation, 486
  variables affecting, 481–87
Contact as stimulus, 173
Contiguity, S–R, 576
Converegence in evolution, 33
Cooperative behavior, 433–36
  and learning, 435–36
Copulation of rats, 484, 490–93
  measurement, 490–93
Corpora pedunculata, 295
Corpus callosum and learning, 705–17
Counter-conditioning, 575
Courtship, 225
  of hybrid birds, 79
Crab
  commensal behavior, 198–215
  display, 94
Crayfish, dominance hierarchy and variables affecting, 430–31
Critical period
  acceptance between goat and kid, 519
  ducks, 395–96
  and imprinting, 356–66
Crustacean larvae and behavior, 177–79
Cuckoo
  behavior and evolution, 35–36
  nesting and young, 226
Cue complexity
  delayed response, 738
  stimulus context, 619, 635–36
Cue utilization, 621–23, 633, 636
Cues, complex, 619–39, 684
  phylogenetic and ontogenetic comparisons, 638
Cycles, feeding and drinking, 487
Cyclical behaviors, 107

D

Darwin, Charles, 13
Defensive distance, 229–30
Delayed alternation, 624, 674, 684, 732
Delayed response, 623–26, 684, 685
  dogs, 376–79
  fish, 651–60
  operated monkeys, 732–39
  primates, 625
    language, 625
    multiple, 625
Deprivation conditions and instrumental learning, 577–78
Detection, stimuli, 99
Detour behavior

Detour behavior—*Cont.*
  dogs, 375–76
  fish, 651–60
Discrimination, olfaction in the dog, 116–18
Discrimination hypothesis, 575
Discrimination learning, 567–71, 633
  method to identify stimuli, 99, 112–15
  simultaneous, 568–69
  split-brain monkeys, 705–17
  successive, 568–69
  supernormal stimulation, 385–91
Discriminative stimulus (cue), 568–72
Displacement responses, 221–23
Display
  distraction, 228–29
  flights, 69–70
  gull, 225
Dog
  development of micturition, 289, 339–50
  dominance hierarchies, 429
  early experience and problem solving, 369–84
  effects of early experience, 356
    learning, 359
    perception, 356
  effects of water deprivation, 482
  genetic differences in behavior, 20
  olfactory discrimination, 116–28
  social facilitation, 489
    eating, 494–98
Domestic fowl
  copulation, 25
  walking, 56–58
Dominance hierarchy
  baboons, 263–66
  birds, 438–44
  comparisons among species, 427–28
  consequences of, 427
  grain beetle, 470–78
  individual differences, 430
  kinds, 427–28
  measurement, 427
  variables affecting, 428–31, 478
Double alternation, 626–27, 684
  cats, 647–48
  raccoons, 645–50
Dove, nesting behavior, 288
Drosophila and genetics, 44–51
Dualism, 12
Duck
  effects of hormones, 285
  hybrid with goose, 75
  imprinting, 361
  walking, 58–59

E

Early experience
  behavior of mice, 410–21

Early experience—*Cont.*
  comparisons with species of mice, 418–20
  effects on
    bird song, 363
    learning, 359–60
    perception, 355–57
    schooling of fish, 463–64
    temperament, 357–59
  genetic factors, 27
  interaction with genetic factors, 410–21
  learning in squirrels, 404–7
  methods for study, 351–55
  social behavior, 360–63
  theories of effects, 363–66
Echolocation, 101–2
  bat, 138–62
  porpoise, 108–11
EEG, 679, 701, 702
Electric shock
  effect on consummatory behavior, 487–89
  as stimulus, 172
Electrical innervation, "memories," 677
Electro-convulsive shock, 677–78
  rats, 298
Emotionality
  effect on consummatory behavior, 487
  measurement, 28
Encephalization, 680, 683–84, 685
Eosinophil, method of measurement, 412
Equipotentiality, 678, 683
Ethological theory, 10–11
  basic concepts, 11
Ethology, 216–17, 567
Euglena, response to light, 172
Evolution, 87
  adaptation, 87–90
  behavior homologies, 34–35
  behavior of related species, 35–36
  complex behavior, 30–36, 92–94, 683–84
  convergence in nest building, 90–91
  mass-action principle, 683
  methods of study, 33–36
  nest building behavior, 81–97
  structures, 34
Evolutionary development, 31
Expectancy, 573–76
Exploratory behavior, 482
  rats, 20
Extinction
  experimental, 583–93, 723–25
  mentally retarded, 533
  one bar-press per day, 587–93
  rabbit, 551–54
  resistance to, 574–76
  theory of, 575
Extirpation method, 678–79

F

Fear and learning by squirrels, 406–7
Feedback, 98, 101
Feeding
  baboons, 271
  gull chicks, 233–42
Field research, 217
Fighting, 426–33
  baboons, 267–71
  birds, 220
  change by leaving, 484
  effect of
    early experience, 362
    hormones, 290
  insects, 470–78
  neural factors, 296
Fish
  castration method, 312–14
  dominance hierarchies, 428–29
  mating, 224
  neural factors and fighting, 296
  reproductive behavior, 243–60, 283–84, 324–26
  schooling, 433, 458–69
  territorial behavior, 433
Fixed action pattern (FAP), 218
  definition, 11
Fixed-interval reinforcement (FI), 570–71
Fixed-radio reinforcement (FR), 569–71
Flexibility, 682–84
Floor-cue, 622–23
Fly
  orientation, 168
  response to light and vibration, 169, 173
Food deprivation, 482
  effect on exploration, 517
Food preference in chickens, 484
Frontal lesions, 684–85
  delayed response in monkeys, 732–39
Frustration, 484, 573–76
  definition, 499
  effect on
    consummatory behavior, 484–85
    sucking of monkey, 499–505

G

Gellerman series, 113, 115
Generalization-decrement, 575
Genetics
  behavior, 17–30
  hoarding, 37–43
  phototaxis, 44–51
Geo-taxis, 21, 170
"Go–no-go" problem, 732–39
Goldfish conditioning, 534–43
Gonadal hormones
  behavior of fish, 309–29
  effect on nest building, 330–38
  micturition, 339–50

Gonadal hormones—*Cont.*
  reproduction of locust, 299–308
  reproductive behavior of
    invertebrates, 282–83
    vertebrates, 283–87
Goose
  defense of territory, 432
  hybrid with duck, 75
Grasshopper
  response to humidity, 166
  song and mating, 174
Grooming of baboons, 274–75
Group behavior, 433–36
Guinea pig
  copulation, 25
  reproduction, 286
Gull
  display as stimulus, 225–26
  feeding of chicks, 227
  pecking, 233–42
  response to chicks and eggs, 231

H

Habituation
  definition, 172
  hypothesis, 575
  instincts, 231
Hawke, Sarah, 582
Hayeses (Hayes, Cathy, and Hayes, Keith), 637
Head butting of fish, 251
Head down posture of fish, 248
Heritability, measurement, 44–49
Hexagon-maze, 630–31
Hierarchical organization and innate behavior, 278–79
Hoarding
  distribution of scores, 40
  effects of hormones, 292
  factors affecting, 41
  and genetics, 37–43
Homologous similarities in evolution, 31
Homoplastic similarities
  in evolution, 31
  type, 31–33
Hormones
  chimpanzees, 286
  dominance hierarchies, 428
  effect on
    consummatory behavior, 486
    self-stimulation of brain, 506–10
  innate behavior, 279–80
  instincts, 174
  leading to change in structures, 277
  methods of study, 280–82
  reproductive behavior, 282–89
Host-factor in symbiosis, 198, 212–13
Hull, Clark L., 575
Humidity as a stimulus, 165–66

Hunger, effect on
  dominance hierarchies, 430
  self-stimulation of brain, 506–10
Hybrids
  behavior, 24
  between duck and goose, 76–77
  sexual behavior, 77–78
Hypophysis; *see* Pituitary

I

Imitation, 637–38
Immobility reactions, 229
Imprinting, 360–63, 392–403
  comparisons among birds, 401
  critical age, 360–61
  ducks, 392–403
  effects of drugs, 361
    early experience, 360–63
  field studies, 400
  later effects on behavior, 361
  measurement, 393
  social facilitation, 396–97
Incentive, 482
  comsummatory behavior, 485
  delayed response, 623, 624
  magnitude of, 572–73
  phylogenetic consideration, 485
  specific response, 573–75, 577
Infant monkeys, conditioning 555–60
Innate behavior
  definition, 163
  effects of internal factors, 277–98
  invertebrates, 163–215
  modification of 230–32
  relation to learned responses, 164
  vertebrates, 216–32
Insight, 627–29
  fish, 651–60
Instinct
  components, 218–23
  definition, 173–74
  invertebrates, 163, 174–76
  nest building of termites, 86
  theory, 222–23
Instrumental learning, 566–618
  ontogenetic limitations, 581–82
  paramecium, 611–18
  phylogenetic comparisons, 580–81
Intelligence tests for dogs;
    see Problem solving
Intention movement
  definition, 59–60
  exaggeration, 64–65
  loss of coordination, 66–68
  ritualized, 64–72
  shifting thresholds, 65–66
Intermittent reinforcement, 574–76
Intertrial interval, 527–28

Invertebrates
  behavior and genetics, 21–23
  dominance hierarchy in insects, 470–78
  hormones and reproduction, 282–83
  innate behavior, 163–215
  mating responses and stimuli in
      insects, 180–89
Ischemia, 678

K

Kinesis, 163, 164–67
  modification, 171–73
Kinesthetic cue or stimulus, 98, 621–22,
  626–27
Klinokinesis, 165–66, 203, 208, 214
Klino-taxis, 167–69

L

Lapwing, locomotion, 61
Leading of fish, 253
Learned behavior as modification
  of innate, 164, 523
Learning
  delayed response, 623–25
  effect on dominance hierarchy, 438–44
  effects of
      early experience, 359–60
      groups of animals, 435–36
      social facilitation, 435–36
  genetic factors, 25–27
  latent, 628, 629–32
  via stimulus satiation, 632
Learning set, 632–35, 637, 684, 690
  marmoset, 661–66
  operated monkeys, 686–93
  rhesus monkey, 663–65
Lice, 165
Light as a stimulus, 168, 173
Lobectomy, 685
Lobotomy, 685
Locust, response to wind, 170
Lordosis in guinea pigs, 286

M

Magnet, effect on movement, 67–69
Magpie, locomotion, 60
Marmoset
  color vision, 112–15
  learning set, 661–66
Maternal behavior, 27
  effect of separation of
      mother and kid, 520–21
  goats, 519–22
  measurement of, 520
Mating behavior
  of Drosophila, 22
  of wasps, 180–89
Maze
  multiple-Y, 630–31
  open-field for dogs, 379

Maze learning, 602–10, 619–23
  backward order, 619–20
  complex, 629–32
  turtle, 640–44
Mice
  audiogenic seizures, 21
  effects of early experience and
      handling, 357, 410–21
  fighting, 484
      and hormones, 290
  genetics and behavior, 29
  learning and conflict, 25
  sexual behavior, 24
Micturition
  dogs, 339–50
  and hormones, 289
Mimicry in evolution, 33
Mobbing, 228–29
Monkey
  dominance hierarchy, 427
  nonnutritive sucking, 499–505
  social behavior, 425
Moorhen
  begging movements, 70–71
  locomotion, 68
Morgan, C. L., 13
Mosquito, response to light, 171
Motivation, 479–523
Movement as stimulus for bee sting, 195
Multiple discrimination (learning set)
  in operated monkeys, 686–93
Mussel, in reproduction of fish, 247–60

N

Neo-cortex and reproduction of
  vertebrates, 297
Nervous system
  innate behaviors of vertebrates, 295–97
  invertebrates, 681–82
  ontogeny of, 682–83
  phylogeny of, 681–84
  redundancy of, 683
Nest building
  effect of hormones, 330–38
  evolution, 35
  measurement, 330–31
  termites, 81–97
Nesting, 226
  activities, 226
  care of the young, 226–28
  cuckoos, 36
  shrew, 220
Neural tissue, complexity of
  behavior, 674–738
Nonreinforcement, 574–76
Novel stimuli, 231–32
  suppressing exploration, 511–18

O

Octopus, operant behavior, 594–602
Oddity learning, 635–36
Odor, stimulus for bee sting, 192–93
Olfaction, phylogenetic comparisons, 106–7
Ommatidium, 103
Operant behavior, 566–67
  octopus, 594–602
Operant conditioning, 566–67, 569–71
  response rate, 566
Optokinetic responses, 99
Orientation of invertebrates, 163–74
Orthokinesis, 165–66
Owl, locomotion, 61–62

P

Paramecium, instrumental learning, 611–18
Parent-young relations, 434–35
Passerine birds, 69–70
  begging movements, 70–72
  visual acuity, 104–5
Patterned string performance in lobectomized monkeys, 686–93
Peck order; *see* Dominance hierarchy
Perception, effects of early experience, 355–57
Philosophical parallelism, 31
Phototaxis, 44–51
Phylogeny based on behavior, 92–94
  bird nest, 93
  caddis fly cases, 94
  crab display, 94
  spider webs, 93
  termite nests, 93
Physiological psychology, 674–739
Pigeon
  color vision, 106
  display flight, 69
  evolution, 30
  walking, 57
Pituitary
  behavior of fish, 309–29
  removal method, 314
  reproduction, 287–89
Planaria
  response to light, 167, 173
  response to pressure, 166
Plasticity of behavior, 488–89
Polarized light, 103
  bees, 132–35
Porpoise, auditory scanning and echolocation, 101–2, 108–11
Position habits, 656, 658, 659
Predator
  effect of defensive distance, 221–30
  leading to
    distraction display, 229

Predator—*Cont.*
  leading to—*Cont.*
    escape, 228
    mobbing, 229
    reaction to protective colors, 228
Pressure as stimulus, 166, 177–79, 206
Primate
  development of affection, 361
  effects of early experience on perception, 356
  evolution of communication, 36
Problem solving, 627–29
  effects of early experience, 369–84
  measures for dogs, 373–78
Prolactin, effects on birds, 288
Pseudoconditioning, 526–27, 534–43, 728
Psychology and its relation to physiology, 674–77

Q

Quivering of fish, 253

R

Rabbit, conditioning, 551–54
Raccoons, double alternation, 645–50
Radiation and innate behavior, 298
Rat
  activity and genetic factors, 27
  analysis of actions, 490–96
  behavior of groups, 434
  copulation, 490–93
  different strains, 37
  ECS and reproduction, 298
  effect of
    early experience on learning, 385–91
    early handling, 357, 358, 359
    novel stimuli, 232
    restraint, 490–91
  emotionality and genetics, 28
  exploration and feeding, 511–18
  genetic factors in learning, 26
  hoarding, 37–43
  maternal behavior, 28
  maze-bright and maze-dull, 26
  obese, 487
  reproduction, 298
  self-stimulation of brain, 506–10
  stimuli for mating, 225
  wildness and genetics, 28
Reasoning, 627–29, 684
Reductionism, physiological, 676
Reinforcement, 572
  delay of, 576
  differential, 568
  magnitude of, 583–86
  nature of, 576–77
  number of, 573–74
  partial, 574–76
  schedules, 569–71
Releaser; *see* Sign stimulus

Reproduction; *see also* Sexual behavior
  baboons, 271–74
  bird pairing, 452–55
  effects of
    genetics on courting responses of
      males, 24
    hormones, 282–89
    fish, 244–46, 310–12
    locust, 299–308
    relation to pituitary, 287–89
    stimuli eliciting in fish, 317
    vertebrates, 223–26
Response class as a learning variable, 579
Response involvement
  conditioning, 530
  delayed response, 624
Response-produced stimulus, 98, 619,
  626–27
Response unit, hypothesis, 575
Restricted environment; *see* Subnormal
  stimulation
Reversal learning, octopus, 638
Reward, magnitude of, 572–73
Rheo-taxis, 170
  crab, 211
  worm, 205–6
RNA, 679
Robin, 219
Romanes, G. J., 14
Round dance, 130–32

S

S^D, 568–72
S^Δ, 568–72
"Safe" region, avoidance learning, 578
Salamanders and hormones, 287
Scent glands of wasp, 182
Schooling behavior of fish, 433, 458–69
  current stimuli, 463
  development, 460–62
  effect of visual stimuli, 462–63, 467
  measurement, 458–60
Secondary reinforcer (S^r), 569
Selective breeding
  backbreeding, 18
  crossbreeding, 18
  genetics of behavior, 18–19
  for phototaxis, 47–49
Sensory structures, 98–160
Serial position effect, 620
Sex skin of primates, 291
Sexual behavior; *see also* Reproduction
  hybrid birds, 77–78
  monkeys, 487
Shrew, 220
Shuttlebox learning, 578–79
Sign stimulus, 225
  definition, 11
  instinctive behavior, 219–22

Sign stimulus—*Cont.*
  mating, 225–26
  social behavior, 425–26
Simple-alternation, 626–27
Skinner, B. F., 566
Skoto-taxis, 171
Smoke, stimulus for bee sting, 192
Snail
  instrumental learning, 602–10
  response to gravity, 170, 173
Social behavior
  ants, 423
  baboon, 263–66
  functional approach, 423–24
  methods for study, 424–25
  monkeys, 425
  S–R approach, 424
  theories, 422–25, 436–37
Social facilitation
  of eating, 484, 494–98
  as secondary reinforcement, 494, 497
Social order; *see* Dominance hierarchy
Social signal; *see* Social stimuli
Social stimuli, 425–26
Sparrow display, 70
Spawning behavior, 309–29
Species-specific, 163
  as innate, 11
Spider, salticid, 175
  stimuli for prey catching and mating, 175
Spinal conditioned responses, 719–30
Split-brain animals, 676–77, 705–17
Spontaneous recovery, 589–90, 723–24, 729
Spreading depression (SD), 679
  and avoidance conditioning, 694–704
Squirrels, learning and early experience,
  404–7
Stickleback fish, mating, 225
Stimulus
  definition, 98
  effects
    on dominance hierarchies, 429–31
    of intensity on kinesis, 164–67
    on orienting responses, 172–73
  generalization, 567–68, 570–71
    effects of early experience, 356
  methods for identification, 99–100
  multiple determination, 680–81, 682–84
  relation to instinctive behavior, 174
Stimulus control, 571–72
Stimulus-response theory, 7–10
  definitions of response, 9
  definitions of stimulus, 8
Stimulus satiation, in maze learning,
  630–32
Stinging response of bees, 190–97
Stomach loading, 486
Strain comparisons and genetics of
  behavior, 19–20

Stridulation of locusts, 299–308
Subnormal stimulation, 352–53, 367, 369–84
Successive reversal learning, 634–35
Supernormal sign stimuli, 221
Supernormal stimulation, 352, 367, 385–91
Symbiosis, 198
Symbolic behavior, 619, 623, 625, 627–29
  chimpanzee, 671–73

T

Tactual learning, interhemispheric transmission, 705–17
Taxis, 163, 167–74, 297
Taxonomy, 30
Telo-taxis, 167, 171
Temperament, 27–30, 357–59
Temperature
  control, 89–90
  effect on consummatory behavior, 486
  as a stimulus, 168
Temporal lobe syndrome (Kluver and Bucy), 674–75, 692
Temporal maze, 626
Termites, 81–97
Territorial behavior, 310–12, 431–33, 445–57
Testosterone, effects of, 77–78, 285–87
Texture as stimulus for bee sting, 194
Thigmo-taxis, 173
Thinking, 681
Tolman, "cognitive map," 629
Tranquilizer, effect on dominance hierarchy, 440
Transfer of training, cross modal, 638–39
Transient memory, rats, 639
Tropo-taxis, 167–71
Turtle, maze learning, 640–44

U

Uexküll, Jakob v., 98

Unconditioned response (UR or UCR), 523–30
Unconditioned stimulus (US or UCS), 523–30
Unit-alike maze, 621–22
Unit characters and genetics of behavior, 20–21
  pleiotropic effects, 20

V

Vacuum responses, 221–22
Variable-interval schedule (VI), 570–71
Variable-ratio schedule (VR), 570–71
Vision, phylogenetic comparisons, 102–6
Visual cues, 621
Visual form discrimination, monkeys, 639
VTE (vicarious trial and error), 656–59

W

Wagging dance, 130–32
Wagtail, walking, 58
Warning calls, 228
Wasp
  mating, 180–89
  reaction of old and starved males, 185
  response to chemical stimuli, 169
  stimuli for mating, 175
Water deprivation, effects, 482, 484
Weasel, development of behavior, 227
Wisconsin General Test Apparatus, 662–63, 687
Worm
  commensal behavior, 198–215
  conditioning, 544–50
  freeliving marine, 202
  habituation, 172
  meal, 172
  polychaete, 201–8
  response to chemical gradient, 169
  response to light, 168, 172

This Book has been set on the Linotype in 11 point Baskerville, leaded 2 points and 9 point Baskerville, leaded 1 point. Chapter numbers are 12 point Tempo Medium caps with 18 point Tempo Medium figures. Chapter titles are in 18 pt Tempo Medium caps. The size of the type page is 27 by 46½ picas.